CONTEN

C000129305

Editor
Guy Thomas
guy.thomas@mytimemedia.com

Consultant Editor
Richard West

Art Director
Alexandra Bourdelon

Advertisement Manager
Jay Jones
jay.jones@mytimemedia.com

Advertisement Production
Alexandra Bourdelon

Publishers
MyTimeMedia Ltd,
Suite 25,
Eden House,
Enterprise Way,
Edenbridge,
Kent TN8 6HF.

Copyright MyTimeMedia Ltd.
Published in 2019

mytimemedia
print & digital media publishers

This guide is produced by
the team which brings you
Stamp Magazine

www.stampmagazine.co.uk

PURPOSE OF THIS BOOK

The objective of this guide is to give collectors accurate market values of Great Britain stamps: the selling prices of most dealers, as opposed to the inflated prices quoted by some catalogues. The publisher of *British Stamp Market Values* is not a dealer and is not affiliated to any dealer.

HOW TO USE THIS BOOK

The prices we quote and the abbreviations we use

This guide offers independent price information about all Great Britain stamps issued from 1840 to date, based on the selling prices of most dealers. The publisher of *British Stamp Market Values* is not affiliated to any dealer.

ABBREVIATIONS
The following abbreviations are used:
Des: designer
Perf: perforation
Wmk: watermark

GENERAL NOTES
■ Used prices quoted are for fine examples with full perforations or reasonable margins as applicable, and with either a light duplex cancellation (pre–1880) or a clear steel datestamp (post–1880).

■ Unused prices assume stamps are se–tenant where applicable.

■ As modern GB special issues are usually sold only in sets, prices of individual stamps might not be quoted.

EXPERTS WE CONSULTED OVER PRICING

RUSHSTAMPS
PO Box 1, Lyndhurst, Hampshire SO43 7PP
Rushstamps, run by Allan Grant, offers a wide range of material primarily from Great Britain.

BB STAMPS
PO Box 6267, Newbury, Berkshire, RG14 9NZ
Run by Brian Bayford, BB Stamps deals in GB stamps from Queen Victoria to Wildings.

MARK BLOXHAM
PO Box 204, Morpeth NE61 9AA
Mark Bloxham is a specialist in classic British stamps at the top end of the market.

DAUWALDERS
42 Fisherton Street, Salisbury, Wiltshire SP2 7RB
Run by Paul Dauwalder, this firm has been a leading GB and Commonwealth dealer since 1958.

DON STADDON
Stamp Magazine reporter
Don Staddon is one of the leading authorities on Machin definitives.

SIMON HEELEY
Modern GB expert
Simon Heeley is a specialist dealer in self–adhesive Machins and Post & Go stamps.

IAN HARVEY
Member of the RPSL Expert Committee
Ian Harvey is a specialist collector of booklets from Edward VII to Elizabeth II.

RICHARD WEST
Stamp Magazine editor–at–large
Richard West is a Past President of the National Philatelic Society.

STAMP PRINTERS

A quick guide to who printed what, and when

A relatively small number of security printers has dominated the production of British stamps since 1840. Here are their details.

PERKINS BACON 1840–1879
American inventor Jacob Perkins developed intaglio printing, and his son-in-law Joshua Bacon joined him in business in London.
First issue: 1840 1d black
Last issue: 1870–79 1½d rose-red

SOMERSET HOUSE 1847–1926
The Stamp Office at Somerset House in London had been printing revenue stamps since 1694, and was familiar with embossing technique required for the first high-value postage stamps.
First issue: 1847–54 1/– green
Last issue: 1924–26 definitive series

DE LA RUE 1855 to date
Guernseyman Thomas De La Rue came to prominence by offering surface-printing, which was ideal for stamps requiring perforation.
First issue: 1855–57 4d carmine

HARRISON & SONS 1911–1998
After initially printing by typography, this firm became synonymous with the photogravure technique from 1934 and remained the dominant printer of British stamps for many years. It was taken over by De La Rue in 1997.
First issue: 1911–13 definitive series
Last issue: 1998 The Queen's Beasts set

WATERLOW & SONS 1913–1955
There were two different Waterlow firms until 1920, after a family feud. The business was taken over by De La Rue in 1960.
First issue: 1913 'Seahorses' high-value series
Last issue: 1955 'Castles' high-value series

BRADBURY WILKINSON 1918–1973
A producer of colonial stamps since 1875, this company was owned by the American Banknote Company from 1903 and was acquired by De La Rue in 1986.
First issue: 1918–19 'Seahorses' high-value series
Last issue: 1973 Parliamentary Conference set

ENSCHEDÉ 1979 to date
The Dutch company founded in 1703 became a back-up for Harrisons because of its capability of printing by photogravure.
First issue: 1979 8p red definitive

WADDINGTONS 1980–1981
This firm produced stamps under its own name only briefly, before acquiring House of Questa.
First issue: 1980 4p greenish-blue definitive
Last issue: 1981 4p and 20p definitives

HOUSE OF QUESTA 1980–2003
Initially independent, the company was owned by Waddingtons from 1984, MDC from 1996 and De La Rue from 2002.
First issue: 1980 75p grey definitive
Last issue: 2003 Extreme Endeavours set

WALSALL/ISP 1989 to date
The company initially promoted itself as an expert in self-adhesive printing, but has also printed gummed issues by litho and gravure. It was fully rebranded as International Security Printers in 2014.
First issue: 1989 14p and 19p definitives (booklet)

CARTOR/ISP 2005 to date
The French company known for litho production and special printing techniques has been owned by Walsall (now ISP) since 2004.
First issue: 2004 customised Smilers sheets

GUIDE TO WATERMARKS

Identify the watermarks referred to in the price listings

Small crown	Large crown	Half penny	VR
Emblems	Small garter	Medium garter	Large garter
Spray of rose	Maltese cross	Large anchor	Small anchor
Orb	Imperial crown	Simple royal cypher GVR	Multiple royal cypher GVR
Single crown & script GVR	Multiple crowns/block GVR	Large crown & script GVR	Multiple crowns & E8R
Multiple crowns & GVIR	Single crown & GVIR	Tudor crown & E2R	St Edward's crown & E2R
Multiple St Edward's crown	Loops		

Watermarked paper was used to print most British stamps from 1840 until the later 1960s, as a security measure to make forgery difficult

To think *Dealers* told us it wouldn't work

Hi,

That's me Promoting Philately with Alan Titchmarsh on UK National TV

It all started with the two-legged stool; I remember the conversation why we wanted to start a Stamp Auction like NO other...

It was 1999. We had a good stamp business. I'd started by supplying stamps on approval. In fact, just like Victor Kiam of Remington Razors fame, I bought the stamp 'Approvals' Company called Omniphil that sent me stamps on approval when I was in my teens, but that's another story...

After a few years I decided that a 'one-legged' stamp approvals business, should stand on two feet(!), so I added a 'Buy One, Take One Free' off-paper world mixtures department which soon became a big success thanks to a loyal following of collectors who loved sorting through unsorted mixtures, and still do.

Meanwhile buying stamp collections at auction had created a pleasant problem. We had accumulated better stamps which we felt were too valuable to be sent to clients on approval through the mail. Determining how best to handle these my wife and I came to the conclusion that just like a stool, a good stamp business should not stand on two feet alone... so we decided to add a third leg to our stamp business ...

... *Yes*, a stamp auction, which (you may have already guessed) had to be unlike any other by including the best features of other auctions, whilst

eliminating the worst features such as 'caveat emptor' (buyer beware) and buyer's premiums which instinctively, we reasoned not to be in the best interests of collectors. We wrote to existing stamp auctions for their latest catalogues which we thoroughly analysed. And soon, we named our new stamp auction - Universal Philatelic Auctions and christened it UPA.

But Could We *Solve* the Stamp Trade's *BIGGEST* Problem...?

It was common knowledge in the trade that the trade's biggest problem was not what sold – **but what didn't sell.** That's the reason why you see the same overpriced stamps year in, year out with some dealers and auctions. Nowadays dealers and auctions are more sophisticated – for example they may sell on eBay as well as conventionally – but twenty years ago auctions would parcel up their unsold auction lots and sell them/swop them with other auctions, in order to 're-fresh' each other's stock, thereby offering 'NEW' stock to (hopefully) new collector clients. Other auctions would go to

ACCEPT YOUR **1st** £ **55** GBP FREE TRIAL OFFER

Making My New Auction Work

'We canvassed trade opinion – Dealers told us it wouldn't work!'

the lengths of re-describing their old unsold auction lots in order to disguise them. Just imagine, for a moment ... the Importance of Selling Your Unsold Lots – unless you are unscrupulous, your unsold lots represent your profit tied up in <u>stale</u> stock, not cash!

The 'break-through' took a fair bit of 'head-scratching' – but would it work...?

Twenty years later the answer seems simple, but it didn't feel simple then. The future health of our new UPA 'baby' depended upon getting it right. We had to break through moribund stamp industry practices which were obviously sticking a plaster on the 'unsolds' wound, whilst not facing up to the fact that if it wasn't selling it simply wasn't worth the price being asked...

...and therein lies the 'clue'. As soon as we thought of the solution, it seemed so simple that we questioned would it work? Why had no other auction – ***even to this very day*** not thought of, or deployed **a structured Reducing Estimate (and Reserve) Price System** each time an unsold lot was re-offered, and instead of trying to hide what wouldn't sell – we'd make a virtue out of a reduced price lot

and tell collectors that (sin of sins) the lot hadn't previously sold (which we call **US** for unsold once, **US2** for unsold twice etc).

We canvassed trade opinion – dealers told us it wouldn't work... BUT, sometimes, just some times ...when you're told something won't work that's the time to do it, isn't it?

650 different bidders in our 1st UPA auction almost 20 years ago

2,002 different bidders in my latest 73rd UPA auction, from 47 different Countries

And did it work? In our first auction in year 2000 we had 650 different bidders. You're going to find this hard to believe – but today, almost 20 years later – hardly another stamp auction has 650 different bidders, let alone 2,002, and why is that? Because no other international philatelic auction is prepared to offer you:

Go to the Back Cover

If you share our interest or are considering collecting GB Used Abroad you will benefit from our list which also includes rare items

PHONE, WRITE OR EMAIL TODAY...

QUEEN VICTORIA

For this reign prices are given for lightly mounted unused (left) and fine used (right). The exception is for the 1840–1841 issues, where fine used prices are subdivided into stamps with four margins (centre) and three margins (right).

Take care when buying unmounted mint because there are known cases of regumming.

LINE–ENGRAVED ISSUES

1d black

■ **1840, May 6. Penny Black**
Engraved by Charles and Frederick Heath. Printed in recess by Perkins, Bacon. Wmk: Small Crown. Imperforate. Letters in lower corners only.

1d black	£11,000	£250	78.00
1d intense black	£15,000	£275	90.00
1d grey black	£14,000	£275	90.00
Plate 1a	£14,000	£300	90.00
Plate 1b	£11,000	£225	80.00
Plate 2	£11,000	£225	80.00
Plate 3	£14,000	£250	85.00
Plate 4	£11,000	£225	80.00
Plate 5	£11,000	£225	80.00
Plate 6	£11,000	£225	80.00
Plate 7	£12,000	£275	90.00
Plate 8	£14,000	£300	95.00
Plate 9	£14,000	£350	£125
Plate 10	£24,000	£600	£175
Plate 11	£16,000	£4,000	£750
Wmk inverted	£32,000	£2,200	£600
Bleute paper	£15,000	£500	£150
Red Maltese cross cancel	–	£250	90.00
Black Maltese cross cancel	–	£225	78.00
Blue Maltese cross cancel	–	£8,000	£2,000
Magenta Maltese cross cancel	–	£2,200	£400
Ruby Maltese cross cancel	–	£750	£225
Violet Maltese cross cancel	–	£12,000	£3,000
Number in cross (1–12)	–	£10,000	£3,000
Penny Post cancel only	–	£2,600	£600
Town datestamp only	–	£2,750	£600
1844 cancel	–	£1,000	£200

2d blue

■ **1840, May 8. Twopenny Blue**
Engraved by Charles and Frederick Heath. Printed in recess by Perkins, Bacon. Wmk: Small Crown. Imperforate. Letters in lower corners only.

2d blue	£32,000	£550	£140
2d deep full blue	£36,000	£650	£170
2d pale blue	£36,000	£600	£150
Plate 1	£30,000	£550	£140
Plate 2	£40,000	£650	£170
Wmk Inverted	£60,000	£5,000	£2,800
Red Maltese cross cancel (Plate 1)	–	£600	£150
Red Maltese cross cancel (Plate 2)	–	£1,100	£225
Black Maltese cross cancel	–	£550	£140
Blue Maltese cross cancel	–	£6,000	£1,250
Magenta Maltese cross cancel	–	£4,000	£850
Ruby Maltese cross cancel	–	£2,000	£500
Number in cross (1–12)	–	£11,000	£3,000
Penny Post cancel only	–	£5,000	£1,200
Town datestamp only	–	£3,750	£800
1844 cancel	–	£1,250	£250

1d red

■ **1841, February 10. Penny Red**
Engraved by Charles and Frederick Heath. Printed in recess by Perkins, Bacon. Wmk: Small Crown. Imperforate. Letters in lower corners only.

1d red brown	£300	10.00	3.00
1d deep red brown	£550	15.00	4.00
1d orange brown	£1,200	£120	12.00
1d lake red	£3,500	£550	£100

Plate 1b	£18,000	£300	40.00
Plate 2	£19,000	£225	25.00
Plate 5	£6,000	£175	20.00
Plate 8	£8,000	90.00	20.00
Plate 9	£4,000	90.00	20.00
Plate 10	£2,000	90.00	20.00
Plate 11	£4,000	75.00	15.00
Wmk inverted	£4,000	£325	£150
Lavender paper	£1,000	£150	40.00
Red Maltese cross cancellation	–	£3,850	£875
Black Maltese cross cancellation	–	40.00	6.00
Blue Maltese cross cancellation	–	£375	75.00
Green Maltese cross cancellation	–	£8,000	£1,000
Violet Maltese cross cancellation	–	£9,000	£1,500
Number in cross (1–12)	–	£110	30.00
Penny Post cancellation only	–	£700	£125
Black town datestamp only	–	£300	95.00
Blue town datestamp only	–	£1,200	£275
Green town datestamp only	–	£2,750	£650
Black 1844 cancellation	–	9.00	3.00
Blue 1844 cancellation	–	£125	25.00
Green 1844 cancellation	–	£1,250	£250
Red 1844 cancellation	–	£12,000	£3,000
Violet 1844 cancellation	–	£2,500	£600
B blank error	–	£40,000	£18,000

2d blue

■ 1841, March 13. Twopenny Blue

Engraved by Charles and Frederick Heath. Printed in recess by Perkins, Bacon. Wmk: Small Crown. Imperforate. Letters in lower corners only. Horizontal white lines added to design.

2d blue	£3,000	50.00	12.00
2d pale blue	£3,200	55.00	12.00
2d deep full blue	£4,000	70.00	15.00
2d violet (lavender paper)	£22,000	£950	£175
Plate 3	£3,000	60.00	12.00
Plate 4	£3,500	50.00	12.00
Wmk inverted	£7,500	£450	£125
Black Maltese cross cancel	–	£150	22.50
Blue Maltese cross cancel	–	£3,000	£400
Number in cross (1–12)	–	£500	£120
Black town datestamp only	–	£1,000	£275
Blue town datestamp only	–	£4,000	£700
Black 1844 cancel	–	50.00	12.00
Blue 1844 cancel	–	£500	£100
Green 1844 cancel	–	£3,500	£750
Red 1844 cancel	–	£17,500	£3,500

1d rose-red   2d blue

■ 1854
Designs as above. Wmk: Small Crown. Perf: 16.

1d red-brown (February 1854)	£250	12.00
2d blue (March 1, 1854)	£2,200	60.00

■ 1855
Designs as above. Wmk: Small Crown. Perf: 14.

1d red-brown (January 1855)	£450	45.00
2d blue (March 4, 1855)	£7,000	£160

■ 1855
Designs as above. Wmk: Large Crown. Perf: 16.

1d red-brown (May 15, 1855)	£900	65.00
2d blue (July 20, 1855)	£10,000	£230

■ 1855
Designs as above. Wmk: Large Crown. Perf: 14.

1d red-brown (August 18, 1855)	£160	8.00
2d blue (July 20, 1855)	£1,600	30.00

1d rose-red   2d blue

■ 1858–1879
Designs as above. Wmk: Large Crown. Perf: 14. Letters in all four corners. Plate number included in design.

1d rose-red (April 1, 1864)

Plate 71	40.00	2.00
Plate 72	40.00	2.50
Plate 73	40.00	2.00
Plate 74	40.00	1.50
Plate 76	40.00	1.50
Plate 77	–	–
Plate 78	45.00	1.50
Plate 79	25.00	1.50
Plate 80	30.00	1.50
Plate 81	35.00	1.50

Plate 82	£110	2.75	Plate 144	75.00	16.00
Plate 83	£160	6.00	Plate 145	23.00	1.75
Plate 84	40.00	1.60	Plate 146	25.00	4.50
Plate 85	27.00	1.60	Plate 147	30.00	2.00
Plate 86	35.00	2.75	Plate 148	25.00	2.00
Plate 87	22.00	1.50	Plate 149	25.00	4.50
Plate 88	£200	7.00	Plate 150	15.00	1.50
Plate 89	30.00	1.50	Plate 151	40.00	7.50
Plate 90	25.00	1.50	Plate 152	40.00	4.00
Plate 91	35.00	4.50	Plate 153	90.00	7.00
Plate 92	21.00	1.50	Plate 154	30.00	1.50
Plate 93	30.00	1.50	Plate 155	30.00	1.75
Plate 94	28.00	4.00	Plate 156	35.00	1.50
Plate 95	25.00	1.50	Plate 157	30.00	1.50
Plate 96	28.00	1.50	Plate 158	23.00	1.50
Plate 97	25.00	2.50	Plate 159	23.00	1.50
Plate 98	30.00	4.50	Plate 160	23.00	1.50
Plate 99	35.00	4.00	Plate 161	40.00	5.00
Plate 100	40.00	1.50	Plate 162	30.00	5.00
Plate 101	40.00	7.50	Plate 163	30.00	2.00
Plate 102	28.00	1.50	Plate 164	30.00	2.00
Plate 103	30.00	2.75	Plate 165	35.00	1.50
Plate 104	£100	4.00	Plate 166	35.00	4.50
Plate 105	£120	5.50	Plate 167	35.00	1.50
Plate 106	35.00	1.50	Plate 168	30.00	6.00
Plate 107	45.00	5.00	Plate 169	30.00	6.00
Plate 108	70.00	1.75	Plate 170	21.00	1.50
Plate 109	65.00	2.50	Plate 171	15.00	1.50
Plate 110	40.00	7.50	Plate 172	23.00	1.50
Plate 111	36.00	1.75	Plate 173	48.00	6.50
Plate 112	50.00	1.70	Plate 174	23.00	1.50
Plate 113	30.00	9.00	Plate 175	40.00	2.50
Plate 114	£240	9.00	Plate 176	40.00	1.75
Plate 115	85.00	1.75	Plate 177	32.00	1.50
Plate 116	60.00	7.50	Plate 178	40.00	2.50
Plate 117	28.00	1.50	Plate 179	30.00	1.75
Plate 118	30.00	1.50	Plate 180	40.00	4.00
Plate 119	28.00	1.50	Plate 181	36.00	1.50
Plate 120	15.00	1.50	Plate 182	75.00	4.00
Plate 121	25.00	8.00	Plate 183	35.00	2.00
Plate 122	15.00	1.50	Plate 184	23.00	1.75
Plate 123	25.00	1.50	Plate 185	30.00	2.00
Plate 124	22.00	1.50	Plate 186	35.00	1.75
Plate 125	25.00	1.50	Plate 187	30.00	1.50
Plate 127	35.00	1.75	Plate 188	50.00	7.50
Plate 129	25.00	6.50	Plate 189	50.00	5.50
Plate 130	35.00	1.75	Plate 190	30.00	4.50
Plate 131	45.00	12.00	Plate 191	23.00	5.50
Plate 132	£200	18.00	Plate 192	30.00	1.50
Plate 133	£105	7.50	Plate 193	23.00	1.50
Plate 134	18.00	1.50	Plate 194	30.00	6.50
Plate 135	70.00	22.00	Plate 195	30.00	6.50
Plate 136	65.00	17.00	Plate 196	30.00	4.00
Plate 137	22.00	1.75	Plate 197	35.00	7.00
Plate 138	15.00	1.50	Plate 198	32.00	4.50
Plate 139	40.00	12.50	Plate 199	35.00	4.50
Plate 140	16.00	1.50	Plate 200	40.00	2.00
Plate 141	£100	7.00	Plate 201	23.00	4.00
Plate 142	50.00	22.00	Plate 202	40.00	6.50
Plate 143	40.00	12.00	Plate 203	23.00	13.00

Plate 204	35.00	1.75
Plate 205	35.00	2.25
Plate 206	35.00	7.00
Plate 207	40.00	7.00
Plate 208	35.00	12.50
Plate 209	30.00	8.00
Plate 210	45.00	10.00
Plate 211	50.00	18.00
Plate 212	40.00	10.00
Plate 213	40.00	10.00
Plate 214	45.00	15.00
Plate 215	45.00	15.00
Plate 216	50.00	15.00
Plate 217	50.00	6.00
Plate 218	45.00	7.00
Plate 219	£100	58.00
Plate 220	32.00	6.00
Plate 221	50.00	15.00
Plate 222	60.00	30.00
Plate 223	75.00	50.00
Plate 224	£110	45.00
Plate 225	£2,900	£650
2d blue (July 1858)		
Plate 7	£1,200	40.00
Plate 8	£1,200	25.00
Plate 9	£250	8.00
Plate 12	£1,800	£100
Plate 13	£260	15.00
Plate 14	£340	16.00
Plate 15	£320	16.00

½d rose-red (October 1, 1870)		
Plate 1	£180	50.00
Plate 3	£120	25.00
Plate 4	£100	18.00
Plate 5	75.00	10.00
Plate 6	80.00	10.00
Plate 8	£225	60.00
Plate 9	£5,000	£600
Plate 10	85.00	10.00
Plate 11	80.00	10.00
Plate 12	80.00	10.00
Plate 13	80.00	10.00
Plate 14	80.00	10.00
Plate 15	£115	24.00
Plate 19	£140	28.00
Plate 20	£200	50.00
1½d rose-red (October 1, 1870)		
Plate 1	£450	48.00
Plate 3	£275	32.00

EMBOSSED ISSUES

6d lilac

10d brown

1/– green

½d rose-red

1½d rose-red

■ 1870–1879
Printed in recess by Perkins, Bacon. Wmk: Half Penny extending over three stamps (½d) or Large Crown (1½d). Perf: 14. Letters in all four corners. Plate number included in design, except plate 1 of the 1½d value.

■ 1847–1854. High values
Die engraved at the Royal Mint by William Wyon. Printed using the embossed process at Somerset House. Wmk: VR (6d), or unwatermarked (10d, 1/–). Imperforate.

6d lilac (March 1, 1854)	£17,000	£525
10d brown (November 6, 1848)	£8,500	£775
1/– green (September 11, 1847)	£20,000	£550

(*These stamps are priced cut square; examples cut to shape are worth considerably less.)

NORTHERN STAMPS

SURFACE-PRINTED ISSUES

Most issues from 1862-64 to 1880-83 have the plate number incorporated into their design. Many can be found with wing margins, where the vertical gutters between panes were perforated by way of a single row of holes down the centre.

4d carmine

■ 1855-1857
Surface-printed by De La Rue. Wmk: Small Garter (1855), Medium Garter (1856) or Large Garter (1857). Perf: 14. No corner letters.

4d carmine (July 31, 1855)	£8,000	£275
4d carmine (February 25, 1856)	£9,000	£325
4d rose (January, 1857)	£1,600	55.00

6d lilac

1/– green

■ 1856
Surface-printed by De La Rue. Wmk: Emblems. Perf: 14. No corner letters

6d lilac (October 21, 1856)	£775	68.00
1/– green (November 1, 1856)	£2,200	£160

3d carmine   4d red

6d lilac   9d bistre

1/– green

■ 1862-1864
Surface-printed by De La Rue. Wmk: Large Garter (4d), Emblems (3d, 6d, 9d, 1/–). Perf: 14. Small corner letters.

3d carmine (May 1, 1862)	£1,800	£225
4d red (January 15, 1862)	£875	55.00
6d lilac (December 1, 1862)	£1,600	50.00
9d bistre (January 15, 1862)	£4,000	£280
1/– green (December 1, 1862)	£2,200	£150

3d carmine

4d vermilion

6d lilac (without hyphen)

2/- blue

6d lilac (with hyphen)

9d bistre

10d brown

1/- green

▪ 1865–1867

Surface-printed by De La Rue. Wmk: Large Garter (4d) or Emblems (3d, 6d, 9d, 10d, 1/-). Perf: 14. Large corner letters.

3d carmine (March 1, 1865)

Plate 4	£1,000	£125

4d vermilion (July 4, 1865)

Plate 7	£500	65.00
Plate 8	£400	40.00
Plate 9	£400	40.00
Plate 10	£475	85.00
Plate 11	£400	40.00
Plate 12	£400	40.00
Plate 13	£400	40.00
Plate 14	£440	60.00

6d lilac (April 1, 1865)

Plate 5	£650	55.00
Plate 6	£2,200	£100

9d bistre (December 1, 1865)

Plate 4	£4,000	£360

10d brown (November 11, 1867)

Plate 1	–	£55,000

1/- green (February 1, 1865)

Plate 4	£2,000	£125

(*Mint examples of the 9d exist from a perforated imprimatur sheet from plate 5.)

▪ 1867–1880

Surface-printed by De La Rue. Perf: 14. Wmk: Spray of Rose. Designs as above except 6d and 2/-.

3d red (July 12, 1867)

Plate 4	£1,100	£125
Plate 5	£375	35.00
Plate 6	£400	35.00
Plate 7	£500	35.00
Plate 8	£400	35.00
Plate 9	£400	35.00
Plate 10	£550	75.00

6d lilac (June 21, 1867)

Plate 6, with hyphen	£1,400	55.00
Plate 8, without hyphen	£600	55.00
Plate 9, without hyphen	£500	55.00
Plate 10, without hyphen	–	£32,000

9d bistre (October 3, 1867)

Plate 4	£1,300	£200

10d brown (July 1, 1867)

Plate 1	£1,900	£225
Plate 2	£50,000	£16,000

1/- green (July 13, 1867)

Plate 4	£675	40.00
Plate 5	£500	25.00
Plate 6	£700	25.00
Plate 7	£750	45.00

2/- blue (July 1, 1867)

Plate 1	£2,100	£140

2/- brown (February 27, 1880)

Plate 1	£27,000	£4,000

6d grey

▪ 1872–1873

Surface-printed by De La Rue. Perf: 14. Wmk: Spray of Rose.

6d brown (April 12, 1872)

Plate 11	£450	35.00
Plate 12	£2,400	£160

6d grey (April 24, 1873)

Plate 12	£1,100	£130

5/– red

10/– grey–green

2½d mauve

3d red

£1 brown

4d green

6d buff

£5 orange

8d orange

1/– green

3d on 3d lilac

6d on 6d lilac

■ 1867–1883. High values
Surface–printed by De La Rue.

Wmk: Maltese Cross. Perf: 15
5/– red (July 1, 1867)

Plate 1	£4,500	£450
Plate 2	£7,000	£550
10/– grey–green (September 26, 1878)		
Plate 1	£45,000	£2,500
£1 brown (September 26, 1878)		
Plate 1	£70,000	£4,000

Wmk: Large Anchor. Perf: 14
5/– red (November 25, 1882)

Plate 4	£25,000	£1,950
10/– grey–green (February, 1883)		
Plate 1	£100,000	£4,000
£1 brown (December, 1882)		
Plate 1	£120,000	£6,500
£5 orange (March 21, 1882)		
Plate 1	£12,000	£4,500

■ 1873–1883
Surface–printed by De La Rue. Perf: 14.

Wmk: Small Anchor
2½d mauve (July 1, 1875)

Plate 1	£385	55.00
Plate 2	£385	55.00
Plate 3	£600	80.00

Wmk: Orb
2½d mauve (May 16, 1876)

Plate 3	£750	75.00
Plate 4	£350	35.00
Plate 5	£350	35.00

Plate 6	£350	35.00
Plate 7	£350	35.00
Plate 8	£350	35.00
Plate 9	£350	35.00
Plate 10	£375	40.00
Plate 11	£350	35.00
Plate 12	£350	35.00
Plate 13	£350	35.00
Plate 14	£350	35.00
Plate 15	£350	35.00
Plate 16	£350	35.00
Plate 17	£1,050	£190

2½d blue (February 5, 1880)

Plate 17	£325	40.00
Plate 18	£350	22.50
Plate 19	£325	22.50
Plate 20	£350	22.50

Wmk: Spray of Rose
3d red (July 5, 1873)

Plate 11	£300	30.00
Plate 12	£325	30.00
Plate 14	£375	30.00
Plate 15	£300	30.00
Plate 16	£300	30.00
Plate 17	£325	30.00
Plate 18	£325	30.00
Plate 19	£300	30.00
Plate 20	£300	55.00

6d buff (March 15, 1873)

Plate 13	–	£22,000

6d grey (March 31, 1874)

Plate 13	£300	40.00
Plate 14	£300	40.00
Plate 15	£300	40.00
Plate 16	£300	40.00
Plate 17	£525	90.00

1/– green (September 1, 1873)

Plate 8	£700	80.00
Plate 9	£700	80.00
Plate 10	£700	90.00
Plate 11	£700	80.00
Plate 12	£475	65.00
Plate 13	£475	65.00
Plate 14	–	£28,000

1/– brown (October 14, 1880)

Plate 13	£4,000	£400

Wmk: Large Garter
4d vermilion (March 1, 1876)

Plate 15	£2,000	£300
Plate 16	–	£24,000

4d green (March 12, 1877)

Plate 15	£825	£180
Plate 16	£775	£170
Plate 17	–	£14,000

4d brown (August 15, 1880)

Plate 17	£2,250	£325

8d orange (September 11, 1876)

Plate 1	£900	£175

Wmk: Imperial Crown
2½d blue (March 23, 1881)

Plate 21	£350	18.00
Plate 22	£325	18.00
Plate 23	£325	14.00

3d red (February 1881)

Plate 20	£500	90.00
Plate 21	£380	55.00

3d (in red) **on 3d** lilac (January 1, 1883)

Plate 21	£400	80.00

4d brown (December 9, 1880)

Plate 17	£300	38.00
Plate 18	£300	38.00

6d grey (January 1, 1881)

Plate 17	£350	45.00
Plate 18	£310	45.00

6d (in red) **on 6d** lilac (January 1, 1883)

Plate 18	£425	80.00

1/– brown (May 29, 1881)

Plate 13	£525	90.00
Plate 14	£425	90.00

½d green

1d Venetian red

1½d Venetian red

2d red

5d indigo

■ 1880–1881

Surface–printed by De La Rue. Perf: 14. Wmk: Imperial Crown.

½d green (October 14, 1880)	35.00	6.00
1d Venetian red (January 1, 1880)	18.00	3.00
1½d Venetian red (October 14, 1880)	£140	30.00
2d red (December 8, 1880)	£180	60.00
5d indigo (March 15, 1881)	£600	65.00

1d lilac

■ 1881–1901
Surface-printed by De La Rue. Perf: 14. Wmk: Imperial Crown.

Die I. 14 white dots in each corner
1d lilac (July 12, 1881)   £200   15.00

Die II. 16 white dots in each corner
1d lilac (December 12, 1881)   1.75   0.75

2/6 lilac   5/– red

10/– blue

£1 green

■ 1883–1891. High values
Surface-printed by De La Rue. Perf: 14.

Wmk: Large Anchor

2/6 lilac (July 2, 1883)	£350	70.00
5/– red (April 1, 1884)	£700	£110
10/– blue (April 1, 1884)	£1,800	£300

Wmk: Imperial Crown

£1 brown (April 1, 1884)	£26,000	£2,500
£1 green (January 27, 1891)	£3,000	£700

Wmk: Orb

£1 brown (February 1, 1888)	£55,000	£4,000

½d blue   1½d lilac, 5d green

3d lilac, 1/– green   4d green

6d green, 2d lilac   9d green, 2½d lilac

■ 1883–84. 'Lilac & Green' series
Surface-printed by De La Rue. Perf: 14. Wmk: Imperial Crown (sideways on 2d, 2½d, 6d, 9d).

½d blue (April 1, 1884)	14.00	3.50
1½d lilac (April 1, 1884)	80.00	23.00
2d lilac (April 1, 1884)	£140	40.00
2½d lilac (April 1, 1884)	57.50	5.00
3d lilac (April 1, 1884)	£135	38.00
4d green (April 1, 1884)	£325	£100
5d green (April 1, 1884)	£325	£100
6d green (April 1, 1884)	£300	£110
9d green (August 1, 1883)	£725	£300
1/– green (April 1, 1884)	£775	£150

Insured, cover to cover

H W Wood Limited is the preferred insurance broker for many stamp collectors and dealers. We provide a range of flexible insurance plans that we consider are sure to offer you the coverage you need. Contact us today to discuss your philatelic insurance needs.

Telephone: +44 (0)20 7398 9000 Email:london@hwint.com
Visit us online at www.hwiuk.com

½d orange

1½d purple and green

6d purple on red

9d violet and blue

2d green and red

2½d purple on blue

10d purple and red

1/– green

3d purple on yellow

4d green and brown

4½d green and red

5d purple and blue

■ 1887–92. 'Jubilee' series

Surface-printed by De La Rue. Perf: 14. Wmk: Imperial Crown.

Wmk upright

½d orange (January 1, 1887)	1.20	0.50
½d green (April 17, 1900)	1.40	0.60
1½d purple and green (January 1, 1887)	10.00	2.00
2d green and red (January 1, 1887)	18.00	8.00
2½d purple, blue paper (January 1, 1887)	14.00	0.75
3d purple, yellow paper (January 1, 1887)	18.00	1.50
4d green and brown (January 1, 1887)	22.00	7.00
4½d green and red (September 15, 1892)	7.00	25.00
5d purple and blue (January 1, 1887)	26.00	5.00
6d purple, red paper (January 1, 1887)	20.00	5.00
9d violet and blue (January 1, 1887)	45.00	25.00
10d purple and red (January 1, 1887)	40.00	24.00
1/– green (January 1, 1887)	£150	40.00
1/– green and red (July 11, 1900)	45.00	70.00
Set	£400	£200

Wmk inverted

½d orange	60.00	60.00
½d green	60.00	60.00
1½d purple and green	£1,400	£400
2d green and red	£1,400	£400
2½d purple, blue paper	£3,500	£1,200
4d green and brown	£1,400	£500
5d purple and blue	£15,000	£1,200
6d purple, red paper	£8,000	£1,500
9d violet and blue	£8,000	£1,800
10d purple and red	£8,000	£2,700
1/– green	£1,600	£800
1/– green and red	£1,700	£900

KING EDWARD VII

For this reign, most stamps are priced in three columns: unmounted mint (left), mounted mint (centre) and fine used (right). However, booklet panes are priced for mounted mint only.

De La Rue printings are generally cleaner, with good centring and neat perforations. Harrison and Somerset House printings are coarser, with poor centring and ragged perfs.

A vast range of shades exists, the details of these being beyond the scope of this publication.

6d purple

7d grey

½d yellow–green

1d scarlet

9d purple and blue

10d purple and red

1½d purple and green

2d green and red

1/– green and red

2/6 lilac

2½d blue

3d purple on yellow

5/– red

10/– blue

4d orange

5d purple and blue

£1 green

■ 1902–10

Surface–printed by De La Rue. Wmk: Imperial Crown (½d to 1/–), Large Anchor (2/6, 5/–, 10/–), Three Imperial Crowns (£1). Perf: 14.

½d blue–green (Jan 1, 1902)	2.00	1.00	0.70
½d yellow–green (Nov 26, 1904)	2.00	1.00	0.70
Wmk inverted	20.00	12.00	12.00
1d scarlet (Jan 1, 1902)	1.75	1.00	0.50
Wmk inverted	7.00	5.00	6.00
1½d purple and green (Jan 1, 1902)	60.00	30.00	10.00
on chalky paper	60.00	30.00	10.00
2d green and red (Mar 25, 1902)	70.00	30.00	10.00
on chalky paper	60.00	28.00	12.00
2½d blue (Jan 1, 1902)	25.00	12.00	3.00
3d purple on yellow (Jan 1, 1902)	70.00	30.00	7.00
on chalky paper	60.00	30.00	10.00
4d green and brown (Jan 1, 1902)	95.00	40.00	18.00
on chalky paper	65.00	30.00	15.00
4d orange (Nov 1, 1909)	32.00	15.00	10.00
5d purple and blue (May 14, 1902)	90.00	40.00	15.00
on chalky paper	85.00	45.00	15.00
Wmk inverted	£6,500	£4,000	£3,000
6d purple (Jan 1, 1902)	60.00	28.00	14.00
on chalky paper	60.00	30.00	14.00
7d grey (May 4, 1910)	10.00	7.00	16.00
9d purple and blue (Jan 1, 1902)	£170	70.00	40.00
on chalky paper	£155	60.00	40.00
10d purple and red (Jul 3, 1902)	£210	60.00	40.00
on chalky paper	£175	55.00	40.00
1/– green and red (Mar 24, 1902)	£165	60.00	20.00
on chalky paper	£165	60.00	24.00
2/6 lilac (Apr 5, 1902)	£450	£200	75.00
on chalky paper	£450	£300	90.00
Wmk inverted	£7,500	£4,000	£2,500
5/– red (Apr 5, 1902)	£700	£280	£120
10/– blue (Apr 5, 1902)	£1,800	£525	£350
£1 green (Jun 16, 1902)	£2,800	£1,200	£600

Booklet panes		Wmk Upright	Inverted
Pane of five ½d with label showing St Andrew's Cross		£500	£500
Pane of six ½d		55.00	90.00
Pane of six 1d		40.00	70.00

2d Tyrian plum

■ 1910

Surface–printed by De La Rue. Wmk: Imperial Crown. Perf: 14. Prepared for use but not issued. One example is known used.

2d Tyrian plum	£115,000	–

■ 1911–13

Designs as 1902–10 series.

Surface–printed by Harrison. Wmk: Imperial Crown. Perf: 14

½d yellow–green (May 3, 1911)	3.50	2.00	1.30
Wmk inverted	60.00	40.00	40.00
1d red (May 3, 1911)	10.00	6.00	8.00
Wmk inverted	60.00	40.00	40.00
2½d blue (Jul 10, 1911)	£100	45.00	18.00
Wmk inverted	£1,800	£1,000	£1,000
3d purple (Sep 12, 1911)			
on yellow paper	£140	80.00	£140
4d orange (Jul 13, 1911)	£130	60.00	45.00

Booklet panes		Wmk Upright	Inverted
Pane of five ½d with label showing St Andrew's Cross		£1,100	£1,100
Pane of six ½d		80.00	£110
Pane of six 1d		70.00	90.00

Surface–printed by Somerset House. Wmk: Imperial Crown (½d to 1/–), Large Anchor (2/6, 5/–, 10/–), or Three Imperial Crowns (£1). Perf: 14

1½d purple and green (Jul 13, 1911)	50.00	25.00	12.00
2d green and red (Mar 11, 1912)	46.00	24.00	11.00
5d purple and blue (Aug 7, 1911)	50.00	28.00	11.00
6d purple (Oct 31, 1911)	50.00	26.00	14.00
chalky paper	50.00	28.00	60.00
7d grey (Aug 1, 1912)	20.00	12.00	15.00
9d purple and blue (Jul 24, 1911)	£105	65.00	40.00
10d purple and red (Oct 9, 1911)	£140	75.00	45.00
1/– green and red (Jul 17, 1911)	£115	58.00	25.00
Wmk inverted	£250	£150	–
2/6 purple (Sep 27, 1911)	£450	£190	85.00
5/– red (Feb 29, 1912)	£700	£280	£120
10/– blue (Jan 14, 1912)	£1,800	£600	£400
£1 green (Sep 3, 1911)	£2,800	£1,200	£700

Surface–printed by Harrison. Wmk: Imperial Crown. Perf: 15x14

½d green (Oct 30, 1911)	50.00	30.00	30.00
1d red (Oct 5, 1911)	32.00	16.00	8.50
2½d blue (Oct 14, 1911)	45.00	21.00	7.00
3d purple on yellow (Sep 22, 1911)	55.00	30.00	13.00
4d orange (Nov 22, 1911)	48.00	26.00	10.00

KING GEORGE V

For this reign, the stamps are priced in three columns: unmounted mint (left), mounted unused (centre) and fine used (right).

Stamps are found in a wide range of shades, details of which are beyond the scope of this guide.

½d green   1d red

■ 1911–1912
Des: Bertram Mackennal and G. W. Eve. Portrait based on photograph by W. and D. Downey. Die engraved by J. A. C. Harrison. Printed in typography by Harrison. Perf: 15x14.

Wmk: Imperial Crown. Issued in sheets and booklets

½d green (Jun 22, 1911)	7.50	3.50	2.00
Wmk inverted	15.00	7.50	3.50
1d red (Jun 22, 1911)	6.50	3.00	1.50
Wmk inverted	12.50	7.00	3.00

(*These stamps also exist with Wmk sideways and printed in error with perf: 14.)

Booklet panes	Wmk Upright	Inverted
Pane of six ½d	80.00	£120
Pane of six 1d	75.00	£110

Wmk: Simple Royal Cypher GVR. Issued only in booklets

½d green (Sep 28, 1912)	80.00	30.00	28.00
Wmk inverted	80.00	30.00	28.00
1d green (Sep 28, 1912)	35.00	16.00	18.00
Wmk inverted	35.00	16.00	18.00

Booklet panes	Wmk Upright	Inverted
Pane of six ½d	£550	£550
Pane of six 1d	£250	£240

■ 1912
Designs as above, except that the King's hair is lighter on the ½d and the lion is shaded on the 1d. Printed in typography by Harrison. Perf: 15x14.

Wmk: Imperial Crown

½d green (Jan 1, 1912)	8.50	4.50	1.00
Wmk inverted	£1,400	£800	£500
1d red (Jan 1, 1912)	5.00	2.00	0.80
Wmk inverted	£450	£350	£250

Wmk: Simple Royal Cypher GVR

½d green (Aug 1912)	8.00	4.00	1.25
Wmk inverted	£500	£300	£200
1d red (Aug 1912)	7.00	3.50	1.00
Wmk inverted	22.00	14.00	12.00

Wmk: Multiple Royal Cypher GVR

½d green (Oct 1912)	12.00	7.00	9.00
Wmk inverted	15.00	12.00	12.50
Wmk sideways	–	–	£3,250
1d red (Sep 1912)	15.00	9.00	4.50
Wmk inverted	20.00	15.00	16.00
Wmk sideways	£220	£150	£160

½d green, 1½d brown   1d red, 2½d blue

2d orange, 3d violet, 4d green   5d brown, 6d purple, 7d green, 8d black

9d black, 9d green, 10d blue, 1/- brown

■ 1912–1924
Des: Bertram Mackennal and G. W. Eve. Die engraved by J. A. C. Harrison. Printed in typography by Harrison (all values except 6d) and Somerset House (all values except 1d). Perf: 15x14.

Wmk: Simple Royal Cypher GVR
i) Wmk upright

½d green (Jan 16, 1913)	1.00	0.40	0.40
Wmk inverted	4.00	2.25	1.10
1d red (Oct 8, 1912)	1.00	0.40	0.40
Wmk inverted	4.00	2.25	0.90
1½d brown (Oct 15, 1912)	3.50	2.00	0.80
Wmk inverted	8.00	4.00	1.60
2d orange (Aug 20, 1912)	3.50	1.75	0.60
Wmk inverted	20.00	10.00	8.50
2½d blue (Oct 18, 1912)	16.00	8.00	2.25
Wmk inverted	£110	75.00	75.00
3d violet (Oct 9, 1912)	8.00	3.75	1.00
Wmk inverted	£160	95.00	95.00
4d green (Jan 15, 1913)	16.00	7.00	1.50
Wmk inverted	40.00	25.00	25.00
5d brown (Jun 30, 1913)	20.00	8.00	4.00
Wmk inverted	£1,100	£700	£700
6d purple (Aug 1, 1913)			
chalky paper	18.00	8.00	2.00
Wmk inverted	85.00	50.00	50.00
7d green (Aug 1, 1913)	28.00	11.00	7.50
Wmk inverted	80.00	50.00	50.00
8d black (Aug 1, 1913)			
yellow paper	42.00	20.00	11.00
Wmk inverted	£180	£110	£110
9d black (Jun 30, 1913)	20.00	10.00	3.75
Wmk inverted	£200	£125	£125
9d green (Sep 1922)	£200	75.00	24.00
Wmk inverted	£1,200	£800	£750
10d blue (Aug 1, 1913)	32.00	15.00	18.00
Wmk inverted	£3,750	£2,500	£1,800
1/– brown (Aug 1, 1913)	28.00	13.00	1.80
Wmk inverted	£300	£250	£200

Booklet panes	Wmk Upright	Inverted
Pane of six ½d	35.00	45.00
Pane of six 1d	35.00	45.00
Pane of six 1½d	60.00	75.00
Pane of four 1½d with two advert labels	£750	£750
Pane of six 2d	80.00	£130

Wmk: Multiple Royal Cypher GVR.

½d green (Aug 1913)	£160	£100	95.00
Wmk inverted	£800	£450	£450
1d red (Aug 1913)	£350	£225	£180
Wmk inverted	£1,500	£1,000	£1,000

■ **1924–1926**
Designs as above, but printed by typography by Waterlow (all values except 6d), Harrison (all values) or Somerset House (1½d, 6d), Wmk: Multiple Crowns and block GVR.

½d green (Feb 1924)	0.60	0.30	0.20
Wmk inverted	5.00	2.50	1.00
Wmk sideways	11.00	5.50	4.50
1d red (Feb 1924)	0.85	0.35	0.20
Wmk inverted	5.00	2.50	1.25
Wmk sideways	26.00	15.00	16.00
1½d brown (Feb 1924)	0.90	0.40	0.20
Wmk inverted	2.50	1.25	1.00

Wmk sideways	14.00	7.00	4.50
2d orange (Sep 1924)	2.00	0.85	0.70
Wmk inverted	60.00	40.00	40.00
Wmk sideways	£175	60.00	65.00
2½d blue (Oct 1924)	7.50	4.00	1.10
Wmk inverted	125.00	70.00	50.00
3d violet (Oct 1924)	11.00	5.00	1.00
Wmk inverted	125.00	70.00	50.00
4d green (Nov 1924)	18.00	7.00	1.40
Wmk inverted	£200	£110	75.00
5d brown (Nov 1924)	30.00	12.00	2.00
Wmk inverted	£140	95.00	80.00
6d purple (Sep 1924)	3.80	1.50	0.50
chalky paper	15.00	9.00	1.75
ordinary paper, Wmk inverted	£120	70.00	60.00
chalky paper, Wmk inverted	80.00	60.00	40.00
9d green (Dec 1924)	20.00	7.00	2.50
Wmk inverted	£120	75.00	70.00
10d blue (Nov 1924)	65.00	28.00	22.00
Wmk inverted	£3,500	£2,200	£1,600
1/– brown (Oct 1924)	35.00	16.00	1.40
Wmk inverted	£550	£400	£260

Booklet panes		Wmk Upright	Inverted
Pane of six ½d		35.00	45.00
Pane of six 1d		35.00	45.00
Pane of six 1½d		60.00	75.00
Pane of four 1½d with two advert labels		£125	£125

(*A wide range of advertising labels exists.)

2/6 brown

■ **1913–1934. High values. 'Seahorses'**
Des: Bertram Mackennal. Dies engraved by J.A.C. Harrison. Wmk: Simple Royal Cypher GVR. Perf: 11x12

Printed in recess by Waterlow. White gum. 22mm high

2/6 brown (Jun 30, 1913)	£600	£175	£100
5/– red (Jun 30, 1913)	£1,000	£325	£175
10/– blue (Aug 1, 1913)	£1,900	£700	£300
£1 green (Aug 1, 1913)	£4,000	£2,250	£1,100

Printed in recess by De La Rue. Yellowish gum. 22mm high

2/6 brown (Oct 1915)	£500	£200	£100
5/– red (Sep 1915)	£900	£280	£190
10/– blue (Dec 1915)	£3,500	£2,000	£600

Printed in recess by Bradbury Wilkinson. White gum.
22.5mm–23mm high

2/6 brown (Dec 1918)	£225	75.00	32.00
5/– red (Jan 1919)	£325	£150	45.00
10/– blue (Jan 1919)	£600	£300	£100

Printed in recess by Waterlow. Die re–engraved so that
the background to the portrait consists of horizontal and
diagonal lines.

2/6 brown (Oct 16, 1934)	£130	60.00	12.00
5/– red (Oct 16, 1934)	£350	£120	45.00
10/– blue (Oct 16, 1934)	£500	£300	50.00

1½d brown

2½d blue

1d red, 1½d brown
(1924 issue)

1d red, 1½d brown
(1925 issue)

£1 black

■ 1924–1925. British Empire Exhibition

Des: H. Nelson. Printed in recess by Waterlow. Wmk: Multiple
Crowns and block GVR. Perf: 14.

Set (April 23, 1924)	18.00	8.00	8.00
Set (May 9, 1925)	45.00	30.00	30.00
First day cover (1924)	–	–	£375
First day cover (1925)	–	–	£1,700

■ 1929, May 10. Postal Union Congress

Des: J. Farleigh (½d, 2½d), E. Linzell (1d, 1½d), H. Nelson (£1).
Printed in typography by Waterlow (½d to 2½d) or in recess by
Bradbury, Wilkinson (£1). Wmk: Multiple Crowns and block GVR
(½d to 2½d), or Large Crown and script GVR (£1).
Perf: 15x14 (½d to 2½d), or 12 (£1).

½d green	1.50	0.50	0.45
Wmk inverted	20.00	11.00	8.00
Wmk sideways	70.00	25.00	25.00
1d red	2.50	1.50	1.00
Wmk inverted	25.00	13.00	14.00
Wmk sideways	90.00	60.00	60.00
1½d brown	2.00	1.25	0.80
Wmk inverted	12.00	6.00	4.50
Wmk sideways	65.00	20.00	20.00
2½d blue	16.00	7.00	5.00
Wmk inverted	£3,500	£2,000	£1,000
Set	20.00	9.00	6.75
First day cover	–	–	£450
£1 black	£1,000	£550	£550
First day cover	–	–	£12,000

Booklet panes		*Wmk Upright*	*Inverted*
Pane of six ½d		40.00	£120
Pane of six 1d		45.00	£200
Pane of six 1½d		30.00	90.00
Pane of four 1½d with two advert labels		£250	£280

½d green

1d red

½d green, 1½d brown

1d red, 2½d blue

2d orange, 3d violet, 4d green

5d brown

9d deep green, 10d blue, 1/– brown

5d brown (Feb 17, 1936)	9.00	5.00	2.50
9d deep green (Dec 2, 1935)	16.00	7.00	2.25
10d blue (Feb 24, 1936)	25.00	11.00	9.00
1/– brown (Feb 24, 1936)	32.00	12.00	0.75

Booklet panes	Wmk Upright	Inverted
Pane of six ½d	60.00	£100
Pane of six 1d	60.00	£150
Pane of six 1½d	20.00	25.00
Pane of four 1½d with two advert labels	75.00	75.00

½d green, 1d red, 1½d brown, 2½d blue

1935, May 7. Silver Jubilee

Des: B. Freedman. Printed in photogravure by Harrison. Wmk: Multiple Crowns and block GVR. Perf: 15x14.

½d green	0.80	0.40	0.30
Wmk inverted	11.00	6.00	6.00
1d red	1.40	0.70	0.70
Wmk inverted	11.00	6.00	6.00
1½d brown	1.25	0.50	0.40
Wmk inverted	2.00	1.00	0.90
2½d blue	3.00	2.00	4.00
2½d Prussian blue	£17,000	£13,000	£15,000
Set (excluding Prussian blue)	6.00	3.25	4.75
First day cover	–	–	80.00
Pictorial cover	–	–	£800

Booklet panes	Wmk Upright	Inverted
Pane of four ½d	30.00	60.00
Pane of four 1d	30.00	60.00
Pane of four 1½d	15.00	20.00

1934–1936

Designs as 1912–24 and 1924–26 issues, but with dark shading behind the portrait. Printed in photogravure by Harrison. Wmk: Multiple Crowns and block GVR. Perf: 15x14.

½d green (Nov 19, 1934)	0.25	0.10	0.15
Wmk inverted	15.00	7.00	3.00
Wmk sideways	9.00	6.00	3.00
1d red–brown (Sep 24, 1934)	0.25	0.20	0.15
Wmk inverted	15.00	7.00	2.50
Wmk sideways	22.00	11.00	14.00
1½d brown (Aug 20, 1934)	0.20	0.15	0.10
Wmk inverted	2.50	1.25	0.60
Wmk sideways	10.00	6.00	2.50
2d orange (Jan 19, 1935)	0.60	0.35	0.40
Wmk sideways	£175	70.00	65.00
2½d blue (Mar 18, 1935)	1.40	0.90	0.75
3d violet (Mar 18, 1935)	1.80	1.00	0.75
4d grey–green (Dec 2, 1935)	2.50	1.40	0.75

 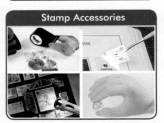

KING EDWARD VIII

For this reign stamps are priced in two columns: unmounted mint (left) and fine used (right). The exception is booklet panes, which are priced only for unmounted mint with good perforations.

½d, 1d, 1½d, 2½d

■ **1936. Accession**
Des: H. Brown, adapted by Harrison. Portrait by H. Cecil. Printed in photogravure by Harrison. Wmk: Multiple Crown and E8R. Perf: 15x14.

½d green (September, 1, 1936)	0.10	0.10
Wmk inverted	6.00	2.50
1d red (September 14, 1936)	0.20	0.20
Wmk inverted	5.00	2.25
1½d brown (September 1, 1936)	0.20	0.10
Wmk inverted	0.75	0.80
2½d blue (September 1, 1936)	0.20	0.30
Set	0.50	0.50

Booklet panes	Wmk Upright	Inverted
Pane of six ½d	15.00	42.00
Pane of six 1d	15.00	42.00
Pane of two 1½d	10.00	10.00
Pane of four 1½d with two advert labels	£110	£100
Pane of six 1½d	8.00	14.00

KING GEORGE VI

For this reign, prices are priced in two columns: unmounted mint (left) and fine used (right). The exception is booklet panes, which are priced only for unmounted mint with good perforations.

■ **1937, May 13. Coronation**

Des: E. Dulac. Printed in photogravure by Harrison. Wmk: Multiple Crown and GVIR. Perf: 15x14.

1½d	0.25	0.15
First day cover	–	3.00
Pictorial cover	–	20.00

½d, 1d, 1½d, 2d, 2½d, 3d

4d, 5d, 6d

7d, 8d, 9d, 10d, 11d, 1/-

■ **1937–51. Definitives**

Des: E. Dulac and E. Gill (½d to 6d), E. Dulac (7d to 1/-). Printed in photogravure by Harrison. Wmk: Multiple Crown and GVIR. Perf: 15x14.

Original colours

½d green (May 10, 1937)	0.15	0.10
Wmk inverted	7.00	0.50
Wmk sideways	0.25	0.30
1d red (May 10, 1937)	0.15	0.10
Wmk inverted	30.00	2.50
Wmk sideways	15.00	5.00
1½d red-brown (July 30, 1937)	0.15	0.15
Wmk inverted	9.00	1.00
Wmk sideways	1.00	0.50
2d orange (January 31, 1938)	0.50	0.35
Wmk inverted	36.00	2.50
Wmk sideways	36.00	20.00
2½d blue (May 10, 1937)	0.25	1.00
Wmk inverted	32.00	3.00
Wmk sideways	50.00	25.00
3d violet (January 31, 1938)	1.50	0.60
4d green (November 21, 1938)	1.75	0.20
5d brown (November 21, 1938)	2.00	0.30
6d purple (January 30, 1939)	1.00	0.15
7d emerald (February 27, 1939)	3.50	0.50
8d carmine (February 27, 1939)	5.00	0.50
9d deep green (May 1, 1939)	4.00	0.50
10d blue (May 1, 1939)	3.00	0.50
11d brown-purple (December 29, 1947)	1.75	1.00
1/- brown (May 1, 1939)	4.00	0.15
Set	24.00	4.00

Booklet panes	Wmk Upright	Inverted
Pane of two **½d**	60.00	60.00
Pane of six **½d**	30.00	60.00
Pane of two **1d**	60.00	60.00
Pane of six **1d**	30.00	£170
Pane of two **1½d**	20.00	30.00
Pane of four **1½d** with two advert labels (*)	£120	£120
Pane of six **1½d**	30.00	60.00
Pane of six **2d**	£120	£300
Pane of six **2½d**	£120	£250
		Wmk Sideways
Pane of four **½d**	–	70.00
Pane of four **1d**	–	£110

(*15 different combinations of advertising labels exist. Prices quoted are for the cheapest; scarcer panes can fetch up to twice as much.)

Paler colours

½d pale green (September 1, 1941)	0.15	0.10
Wmk inverted	3.00	0.40
1d pale red (August 11, 1941)	0.20	0.10
Wmk sideways	3.00	3.00
1½d pale red-brown (September 28, 1942)	0.50	0.35
2d pale orange (October 6, 1941)	0.50	0.25
Wmk inverted	3.00	0.40
Wmk sideways	10.00	8.00
2½d pale blue (July 21, 1941)	0.15	0.10

Wmk inverted	1.00	0.50
Wmk sideways	7.00	6.00
3d pale violet (November 3, 1941)	1.00	0.25
Set	1.50	1.00

Booklet panes	*Wmk Upright*	*Inverted*
Pane of two ½d	9.00	–
Pane of six ½d	20.00	30.00
Pane of two **1d**	25.00	–
Pane of two 1½d	9.00	–
Pane of six **2d**	20.00	30.00
Pane of six 2½d pale blue	10.00	15.00

Changed colours

½d orange (May 3, 1951)	0.10	0.20
Wmk inverted	0.20	0.30
1d blue (May 3, 1951)	0.10	0.10
Wmk inverted	2.25	1.00
Wmk sideways	0.20	0.40
1½d green (May 3, 1951)	0.25	0.20
Wmk inverted	2.75	2.00
Wmk sideways	1.25	1.50
2d red-brown (May 3, 1951)	0.25	0.25
Wmk inverted	4.00	3.50
Wmk sideways	0.75	0.75
2½d red (May 3, 1951)	0.15	0.15
Wmk inverted	1.00	0.50
Wmk sideways	0.60	0.85
4d blue (October 2, 1950)	1.00	0.65
Set	1.50	1.10

Booklet panes	*Wmk Upright*	*Inverted*
Pane of two ½d	10.00	–
Pane of four ½d	10.00	10.00
Pane of six ½d	6.00	6.00
Pane of two **1d**	10.00	–
Pane of three **1d** with three labels reading 'MINIMUM INLAND PRINTED PAPER RATE 1½d'	25.00	25.00
Pane of three **1d** with three labels reading 'SHORTHAND IN ONE WEEK'	35.00	35.00
Pane of four **1d**	10.00	20.00
Pane of six **1d**	20.00	25.00
Pane of two 1½d	10.00	–
Pane of four 1½d	10.00	15.00
Pane of six 1½d	20.00	25.00
Pane of six **2d**	20.00	60.00
Pane of six 2½d	6.00	8.00

2/6, 5/–

10/-, £1

1939–1948. High values

Des: E. Dulac (2/6, 5/–), G. R. Bellew (10/–, £1). Printed in recess by Waterlow. Wmk: Single Crown and GVIR. Perf: 14.

2/6 brown (September 4, 1939)	70.00	5.00
2/6 green (March 9, 1942)	9.00	0.50
5/– red (August 21, 1939)	18.00	1.25
10/– dark blue (October 30, 1939)	£220	17.00
10/– ultramarine (November 30, 1942)	30.00	3.50
£1 brown (October 1, 1948)	18.00	12.00
Set	£280	40.00

½d green, 1d red,
1½d brown,
2d orange,
2½d blue, 3d violet

1940, May 6. Centenary of the First Adhesive Postage Stamps

Des: H. L. Palmer. Printed in photogravure by Harrison. Wmk: Multiple Crown and GVIR. Perf: 14½ x 14.

Set	4.00	3.50
First day cover	–	7.50
Pictorial cover	–	35.00

Farming, homes, industry, transport (2½d)
Dove of peace (3d)

1946, June 11. Victory

Des: H. L. Palmer (2½d), Reynolds Stone (3d). Printed in photogravure by Harrison. Wmk: Multiple Crown and GVIR. Perf: 15x14.

Set	0.20	0.25
First day cover	–	9.00
Pictorial cover	–	55.00

2½d

£1

■ 1948, April 26. Royal Silver Wedding

Des: G.T. Knipe (2½d) and Joan Hassall (£1), from photographs by Dorothy Wilding. Printed in photogravure by Harrison. Wmk: Multiple Crown and GVIR. Perf: 15x14 (2½d), 14 x 15 (£1).

Set	27.00	25.00
First day cover	–	50.00
Pictorial cover	–	£425

■ 1948, May 10. Liberation of the Channel Islands

Although this set was also placed on sale at eight post offices in Great Britain, it is listed under Regional Issues.

Globe surrounded by a laurel wreath (2½d)
Globe with Olympic rings (3d)
Olympic rings (6d)
Victory and Olympic rings (1/–)

■ 1948, July 29. Olympic Games

Des: P. Metcalfe (2½d), A. Games (3d), S. Scott (6d) and E. Dulac (1/–). Printed in photogravure by Harrison. Wmk: Multiple Crown and GVIR. Perf: 15x14.

Set	7.00	1.20
First day cover	–	8.00
Pictorial cover	–	35.00

Two hemispheres (2½d)
UPU monument (3d)
Globe and compass (6d)
Globe and posthorn (1/–)

■ 1949, October 10. 75th Anniversary of the Universal Postal Union

Des: Mary Adshead (2½d), P. Metcalfe (3d). H. Fleury (6d), G. R. Bellew (1/–). Printed in photogravure by Harrison. Wmk: Multiple Crown and GVIR. Perf: 15x14.

Set	1.50	1.25
First day cover	–	9.50
Pictorial cover	–	47.00

H.M.S. Victory (2/6)
White Cliffs of Dover (5/–)
St. George and the Dragon (10/–)
Royal Coat of Arms (£1)

■ 1951, May 3. High values

Des: Mary Adshead (2/6, 5/–), P. Metcalfe (10/–, £1). Printed in recess by Waterlow. Wmk: Single Crown and GVIR. Perf: 11x12.

Set	65.00	15.00

Commerce and prosperity (2½d)
Festival symbol (4d)

■ 1951, May 3. Festival of Britain

Des: E. Dulac (2½d), A. Games (4d). Printed in photogravure by Harrison. Wmk: Multiple Crown and GVIR. Perf: 15x14.

Set	0.35	0.40
First day cover	–	3.00
Pictorial cover	–	17.00

Are You THINKING of SELLING?

This is

HOW THE STAMP TRADE WORKS

**Philatelic Expert Lets You into his *Selling Secrets* so you can benefit from a
totally different (and New) Selling Experience**

by Andrew McGavin

1 **If You want to learn** how the stamp trade works, please read on… When I was 15, I did. I wondered if there was some secret source of supply? So, I bought my 1st stamp mixture, (wholesale I thought), broke

it into 50 smaller units, advertised it in Stamp Magazine 'Classifieds', and waited for the orders to roll in… I'm still waiting, 48 years later !…

Wrong Offer ✗ **Wrong Price** ✗
Wrong Place ✗

(naïve seller ✔ = 😊 me but I was only 15 at the time!)

2 **Three years later,** attending my first public stamp auctions I wondered how some bidders seemed to buy everything, paying the highest price? It didn't occur to me that they were probably Auction Bidding Agents, paid by absent (dealer) bidders to represent them. I wondered why two collectors sitting side by side muttered to each other **"he's a dealer"** as if that justified him paying the highest price…

…but did it really? What was the real reason? How could a Dealer pay a higher price than a Collector? It doesn't make sense, does it? Collectors are customers. Customers usually pay the highest price, unless… for a Collector, this was…

Wrong Presentation ✗ **Wrong Place** ✗
therefore Wrong Price ✗

3 **Fast-forward 48 years later** to a British Empire collection, lot #1 in an International Stamp Auction – Estimated at £3,000, but we were the highest bidder at £21,000 – **YES** – some 7×higher. Including Buyer's Premium in the extraordinary sum of £4,788 we actually paid GBP£25,788= upon a £3,000 estimate… **however**, we broke it down into sets, singles, mini-collections etc. We made a profit. Some might say it found its price. Others may say:

Wrong Estimate ✗ **Wrong Presentation** ✗
Wrong Structure ✗ **Wrong Protection of Price** ✗

– *Lucky for the seller that 2 well-healed bidders saw the potential value that day* or it could have been given away… the seller

could easily have lost out couldn't he? or she?

So, by un-peeling the layers of obfuscation, hopefully we can all agree:

The Secret is Simple –

Plus the 3 Philatelic 'P's –

Presentation ✔ **Place** ✔ and **Price** ✔

4 **Understanding the problem…** I always remember the car trade had their own little 'bible' – Glass's Guide. I've no idea, I've not even looked - in this internet-dominated world, it may even have disappeared. Well, there's an insider Stamp Trade publication for Stamp Dealers called "The Philatelic Exporter". There's nothing that special about it – and you won't learn much or find massively reduced prices by subscribing – **BUT** – it is a forum, a paper focal point, a last 'bastion' in this on-line transparent world that we inhabit… whereby dealers (and auctioneers) can try and communicate with each other. I publish my own articles there…

Recently I discussed the outcome of my 10 years' simple research, asking dealers and auctioneers **'what is your biggest problem?'**

To a man, (why are we almost all men), they replied – **"my biggest problem is stock, if I can get more of the right stock I can sell it easily"**

Strange that, nobody ever asked me the same question back – because my answer would have been entirely different (and I don't treat it as a problem) – **I seek to satisfy collectors**

This is the reason why my company has such massive advertising. This is the reason why we spend up to 8% of turnover – up to £200,000 per annum in marketing costs. (Most dealers don't even sell £200K per annum).

ANDREW PROMOTING PHILATELY ON THE ALAN TITCHMARSH SHOW ITV

REQUEST Your 'Tips of The Trade' FREE copy ❱

TIPS OF THE TRADE
Your Expert Guide to Stamp Collecting

Universal Philatelic Auctions present

£55 OFF

www.upastampauctions.co.uk • info@upastampauctions.co.uk

continued on page **247** ❱

QUEEN ELIZABETH II PRE–DECIMALS

In this section, prices are priced in two columns: unmounted mint (left) and fine used (right). The exception is booklet panes, which are priced only for unmounted mint with good perforations.

Except where otherwise stated, all the stamps have the same technical details: Printed in photogravure by Harrison. Perf: 15x14 (definitives), 15x14 (special issues with a horizontal design) or 14x15 (special issues with a vertical design).

½d, 1d, 1½d, 2d

2½d, 3d

4d, 4½d

5d, 6d, 7d

8d, 9d, 10d, 11d

1/–, 1/6

1/3

■ 1952–1967. Wilding definitives

Des: Miss E. Marx (½d, 1d, 1½d, 2d). M.C. Farrar–Bell (2½d, 3d, 4d, 4½d), G. Knipe (5d, 6d, 7d), Miss M. Adshead (8d, 9d, 10d, 11d), E. Dulac (1/–, 1/3, 1/6): portrait by Dorothy Wilding Studios. On the 2½d value the top line of the diadem was initially broken (Type I), but this was later corrected (Type II).

Wmk: Multiple Tudor Crown and E2R

½d orange (August 31, 1953)	0.10	0.10
Wmk inverted	0.15	0.40
1d blue (August 31, 1953)	0.15	0.10
Wmk inverted	4.50	2.50
1½d green (December 5, 1952)	0.10	0.10
Wmk inverted	0.35	0.30
Wmk sideways	0.35	0.30
2d deep brown (August 31, 1953)	0.20	0.15
Wmk inverted	20.00	12.00
Wmk sideways	0.75	0.50
2½d carmine (type 1) (December 5, 1952)	0.15	0.10
Wmk inverted (type 2)	0.40	0.30
Wmk sideways (type 1)	3.50	4.00
3d violet (January 18, 1954)	1.00	0.20
4d blue (November 2, 1953)	1.00	0.70
5d brown (July 6, 1953)	4.00	2.50
6d purple (January 18, 1954)	3.00	0.75
7d pale green (January 18, 1954)	8.00	2.00
8d magenta (July 6, 1953)	5.00	0.75
9d myrtle–green (February 8, 1954)	14.00	1.50
10d blue (February 8, 1954)	12.00	1.50
11d brown–red (February 8, 1954)	30.00	10.00
1/– bistre (July 6, 1953)	1.00	0.50
1/3 deep green (November 2, 1953)	3.00	1.50
1/6 grey–blue (November 2, 1953)	12.00	1.25
Set	70.00	20.00
Set Wmk inverted	18.00	14.00
Set Wmk sideways	4.50	4.50
First day covers (set of 6)	–	£140
Pictorial cover	–	£600

Booklet panes	*Wmk Upright*	*Inverted*
Pane of two ½d	2.00	–
Pane of four ½d	4.00	4.00
Pane of six ½d	2.00	4.00
Pane of two **1d**	2.00	–
Pane of four **1d**	3.00	25.00
Pane of three **1d** with three labels reading: MINIMUM INLAND PRINTED PAPER RATE **1½d**	£300	£300
Pane of three **1d** with three labels reading: PLEASE POST EARLY IN THE DAY	40.00	40.00
Pane of three **1d** with three labels reading: PACK YOUR PARCELS SECURELY/ ADDRESS YOUR LETTERS CORRECTLY/ POST EARLY IN THE DAY	40.00	40.00
Pane of six **1d**	8.00	30.00
Pane of two **1½d**	2.00	–
Pane of four **1½d**	4.00	4.00
Pane of six **1½d**	2.00	4.00
Pane of six **2d**	27.00	£160
Pane of six **2½d**	3.50	3.50

Wmk: St. Edward's Crown and E2R

½d orange (August 1955)	0.15	0.10
Wmk inverted	0.20	0.20
1d blue (September 19, 1955)	0.20	0.10
Wmk inverted	0.50	0.50

1½d green (August 1955)	0.15	0.10
Wmk inverted	0.30	0.20
Wmk sideways	0.20	0.25
2d deep brown (September 6, 1955)	0.25	0.30
Wmk inverted	7.00	5.00
Wmk sideways	0.50	0.50
2d brown (October 17, 1956)	0.25	0.10
Wmk inverted	5.00	4.00
Wmk sideways	5.00	3.00
2½d carmine (type 1) (September 28, 1955)	0.25	0.15
Wmk inverted	0.75	1.00
Wmk sideways	0.75	1.00
2½d carmine (type 2) (September 1955)	0.30	0.60
Wmk inverted	0.30	0.30
3d violet (July 17, 1956)	0.25	0.20
Wmk inverted	1.75	1.50
Wmk sideways	12.00	7.50
4d blue (November 14, 1955)	1.50	2.00
5d brown (September 21, 1955)	5.00	3.00
6d purple (December 20, 1955)	3.50	1.00
6d deep purple (May 8, 1958)	3.00	1.00
7d pale green (April 23, 1956)	30.00	7.00
8d magenta (December 21, 1955)	4.00	1.25
9d myrtle–green (December 15, 1955)	12.00	2.00
10d blue (September 22, 1955)	10.00	2.00
11d brown–red (October 28, 1955)	0.50	1.25
1/– bistre (November 3, 1955)	6.50	0.50
1/3 deep green (March 27, 1956)	14.00	1.00
1/6 grey–blue (March 27, 1956)	20.00	0.75
Set	100.00	25.00
Set (Wmk inverted)	14.00	7.00
Set (Wmk sideways)	14.00	9.00

Booklet panes	*Wmk Upright*	*Inverted*
Pane of two ½d	3.00	–
Pane of four ½d	4.00	4.00
Pane of six ½d	2.00	3.50
Pane of two **1d**	3.50	–
Pane of three **1d** with three labels reading:		
PACK YOUR PARCELS SECURELY/		
ADDRESS YOUR LETTERS CORRECTLY/		
POST EARLY IN THE DAY	30.00	35.00
Pane of four **1d**	4.00	4.00
Pane of six **1d**	2.50	3.00
Pane of two **1½d**	3.50	–
Pane of four **1½d**	4.00	4.00
Pane of six **1½d**	2.00	2.00
Pane of six **2d** deep brown	13.00	65.00
Pane of six **2d** brown	8.00	22.50
Pane of six **2½d**	3.00	3.00
Pane of four **3d**	10.00	15.00
Pane of six **3d**	6.00	20.00

Wmk: Multiple St. Edward's Crown

½d orange (November 25, 1958)	0.10	0.10
chalky paper (July 15, 1963)	2.00	2.50
Wmk inverted	0.30	0.10
chalky paper and Wmk inverted	1.50	2.00
Wmk sideways	0.25	0.15

1d blue (November 1958)	0.10	0.10
Wmk inverted	0.20	0.20
Wmk sideways	0.60	0.35
1½d green (December 1958)	0.15	0.15
Wmk inverted	1.00	0.40
Wmk sideways	4.50	3.50
2d brown (December 4, 1958)	0.10	0.10
Wmk inverted	75.00	40.00
Wmk sideways	0.50	0.40
2½d carmine (type 1) (October 4, 1961)	0.10	0.40
Wmk sideways	0.20	0.25
2½d carmine (type 2) (November 1958)	0.35	0.20
chalky paper (July 15, 1963)	0.30	0.25
Wmk inverted	3.50	0.90
chalky paper & Wmk inverted	0.30	0.25
Wmk sideways	0.40	0.50
3d violet (November 1958)	0.15	0.10
Wmk inverted	0.25	0.20
Wmk sideways	0.25	0.15
4d blue (October 29, 1958)	0.50	0.25
4d deep blue (April 28, 1965)	0.20	0.12
Wmk inverted	0.35	0.20
Wmk sideways	0.35	0.15
4½d red–brown (February 9, 1959)	0.12	0.12
5d brown (November 10, 1958)	0.20	0.10
6d deep purple (December 23, 1958)	0.25	0.10
7d pale green (November 26, 1958)	0.50	0.20
8d magenta (February 24, 1960)	0.35	0.10
9d myrtle–green (March 24, 1959)	0.35	0.20
10d blue (November 18, 1958)	0.75	0.25
1/– bistre (October 30, 1958)	0.35	0.25
1/3 deep green (June 17, 1959)	0.35	0.15
1/6 grey–blue (December 16, 1958)	3.00	0.15
Set	5.00	1.50
Set (Wmk inverted)	80.00	42.00
Set (Wmk sideways)	5.50	4.00

Booklet panes	*Wmk Upright*	*Inverted*
Pane of three ½d and one 2½d (chalky paper)	8.00	8.00
Pane of four ½d	2.50	2.50
Pane of six ½d	1.25	2.00
Pane of four **1d**	2.50	2.50
Pane of six **1d**	1.50	2.50
Pane of four **1½d**	2.50	2.50
Pane of six **1½d**	5.00	6.00
Pane of six **2d**	40.00	£500
Pane of four **2½d** (chalky paper)	1.00	1.00
Pane of six **2½d**	3.00	15.00
Pane of four **3d**	2.00	2.00
Pane of six **3d**	1.50	1.50
Pane of six **4d** deep blue	1.50	1.50

	Wmk Sideways
Pane of two ½d se-tenant with two 2½d (type 2)	1.00
Pane of four ½d	2.00
Pane of two **1d** se-tenant with two **3d** to left	5.00
Pane of two **1d** se-tenant with two **3d** to right	5.00
Pane of four **1d**	3.00
Pane of four **1½d**	25.00
Pane of four **3d**	2.00
Pane of four **4d**	2.00

■ Wilding definitives, graphite-lined issue

Designs as above, but with black graphite lines on the back. All values have two vertical lines, except for the 2d which has just one line, on the right as viewed from the back.

Wmk: St. Edward's Crown and E2R upright

¹/₂d orange (November 19, 1957)	0.20	0.20
1d blue (November 19, 1957)	0.20	0.20
1¹/₂d green (November 19, 1957)	1.25	0.50
2d brown (November 19, 1957)	1.00	1.25
2¹/₂d carmine (type 2) (November 19, 1957)	4.50	3.50
3d violet (November 19, 1957)	0.75	0.50
Set	6.75	5.50
First day cover	–	75.00

Wmk: Multiple St. Edward's Crown

¹/₂d orange (June 15, 1959)	5.00	5.00
Wmk inverted	1.00	1.25
1d blue (December 18, 1958)	1.00	1.00
Wmk inverted	1.00	0.75
1¹/₂d green (August 4, 1959)	60.00	50.00
Wmk inverted	20.00	20.00
2d brown (December 4, 1958)	4.75	2.50
2¹/₂d carmine (type 2) (June 9, 1959)	6.00	6.00
Wmk inverted	35.00	30.00
3d violet (November 24, 1958)	0.60	0.45
Wmk inverted	0.55	0.40
4d blue (April 29, 1959)	3.25	3.25
4¹/₂d red-brown (June 3, 1959)	3.50	2.25
Set	70.00	55.00
Set (Wmk inverted)	60.00	50.00

Booklet panes	Wmk Upright	Inverted
Pane of six ¹/₂d	20.00	12.00
Pane of six 1d	7.50	7.00
Pane of six 1¹/₂d	£500	£125
Pane of six 2¹/₂d	30.00	£300
Pane of six 3d	4.00	4.00

■ Wilding definitives, phosphor-graphite issue

Designs as above, but with phosphor bands on the front in addition to the graphite lines on the back. All values have two bands, except for the 2d which has just one band to the left.

Wmk: St. Edward's Crown and E2R upright

¹/₂d orange (November 18, 1959)	3.00	3.00
1d blue (November 18, 1959)	9.00	9.00
1¹/₂d green (November 18, 1959)	2.50	3.00
2d brown (November 18, 1959)	£100	£100

Wmk: Multiple St. Edwards Crown

2d brown (November 18, 1959)	4.00	3.00

2¹/₂d carmine (type 2) (November 18, 1959)	10.00	10.00
3d violet (November 18, 1959)	14.00	7.50
4d blue (November 18, 1959)	8.00	5.00
4¹/₂d red-brown (November 18, 1959)	25.00	20.00
Set	50.00	40.00
First day cover	–	75.00

■ Wilding definitives, phosphor issue

Designs as above, but without graphite lines. All values have two phosphor bands, except where stated. Released on June 22, 1960 except where stated. Wmk: Multiple St. Edward's Crown.

¹/₂d orange	0.15	0.15
Wmk inverted	1.00	1.00
Wmk sideways	5.00	7.50
1d blue	0.10	0.10
Wmk inverted	0.35	0.30
Wmk sideways	0.40	0.50
1¹/₂d green	0.12	0.20
Wmk inverted	20.00	18.00
Wmk sideways	12.00	10.00
2d brown (one band)	14.00	12.00
2d brown (October 4, 1961)	0.20	0.10
Wmk sideways	0.30	0.25
2¹/₂d carmine (type 2)	0.20	0.20
Wmk inverted	£160	£140
2¹/₂d carmine (type 2, one band)	1.50	0.50
Wmk inverted	35.00	30.00
2¹/₂d carmine (type 1, one band)	40.00	35.00
3d violet	0.50	0.35
Wmk inverted	0.80	0.50
Wmk sideways	1.25	0.55
3d violet (April 29, 1965) (one band at left)	0.30	0.40
Wmk inverted	60.00	60.00
Wmk sideways	4.00	4.00
3d violet (one band at right)	0.30	0.40
Wmk inverted	6.00	6.50
Wmk sideways	4.00	4.00
se-tenant pair	0.60	1.50
se-tenant pair with Wmk inverted	65.00	65.00
se-tenant pair with Wmk sideways	8.00	10.00
3d violet (December 8, 1966) (one band)	0.25	0.25
Wmk inverted	3.00	3.50
Wmk sideways	0.40	0.50
4d blue	2.75	3.25
4d deep blue (April 28, 1965)	0.15	0.25
Wmk inverted	0.25	0.20
Wmk sideways	0.35	0.25
4¹/₂d red-brown (September 13, 1961)	0.15	0.25
5d brown (June 9, 1967)	0.20	0.25
6d deep purple (June 27, 1960)	0.20	–
7d pale green (February 15, 1967)	0.20	0.25
8d magenta (June 28, 1967)	0.20	0.25
9d myrtle green (December 29, 1966)	0.50	0.25
10d blue (December 30, 1966)	0.50	0.40
1/– bistre (June 28, 1967)	0.40	0.20
1/3 deep green	1.00	1.00
1/6 grey-blue (December 12, 1966)	2.00	2.00
Set	4.50	5.00
Set (Wmk inverted)	£180	£170
Set (Wmk sideways)	15.00	18.00

Booklet panes	Wmk Upright	Inverted
Pane of six ½d	3.00	4.00
Pane of six 1d	2.00	2.00
Pane of six 1½d	8.00	£120
Pane of six 2½d (type 2, two bands)	80.00	£1,100
Pane of six 2½d (type 2, one band)	22.00	£220
Pane of six 3d (two bands)	5.00	5.00
Pane of six 3d (one band at left or right)	20.00	£130
Pane of six 3d (one centre band)	4.00	15.00
Pane of six 4d	2.00	3.00
		Wmk sideways
Pane of four ½d		35.00
Pane of two 1d, two 3d (two bands)	–	3.00
Pane of two 1d, two 3d (one band, left)	–	11.00
Pane of two 1d, two 3d (one band, right)	–	11.00
Pane of four 1d	–	5.00
Pane of four 1½d	–	50.00
Pane of four 3d (two bands)	–	5.00
Pane of four 4d	–	1.00

Crowns and orb (2½d)
Rose, daffodil, thistle and shamrock (4d)
Coronation robe (1/3)
Crowns and cypher (1/6)

■ 1953, June 3. Coronation

Des: E.G. Fuller (2½d), M. Goaman (4d), E. Dulac (1/3), M. C. Farrar–Bell (1/6). Wmk: Tudor Crown and E2R.

Set	10.00	4.50
First day cover	–	30.00

(*The 1/3 design was reissued with a face value of £1 in the 2000 Her Majesty's Stamps miniature sheet and the 2003 A Perfect Coronation prestige stamp book.)

Carrickfergus Castle (2/6)
Caernarvon Castle (5/–)
Edinburgh Castle (10/–)
Windsor Castle (£1)

■ 1955–1968. Castle high value definitives

Des: L. Lamb. Printed in recess. Perf: 11x12.

Wmk: St. Edward's Crown and E2R. Printed by Waterlow

2/6 brown (September 23, 1955)	14.00	2.00
5/– carmine (September 23, 1955)	30.00	3.00

10/– blue (September 1, 1955)	60.00	10.00
£1 black (September 1, 1955)	85.00	20.00
Set	£160	30.00
First day cover	–	£300
Pictorial cover	–	£850

Wmk: St. Edward's Crown and E2R. Printed by De La Rue

2/6 (July 17, 1958)	25.00	3.50
5/– (April 30, 1958)	50.00	8.00
10/– (April 25, 1958)	£150	14.00
£1 (April 28, 1958)	£200	30.00
Set	£425	47.00

(*The top perforation tooth of each side of stamps from the De La Rue printing is narrower than on the Waterlow printing.)

Wmk: Multiple St. Edward's Crown. Printed by De La Rue

2/6 (July 22, 1959)	12.00	0.50
5/– (June 15, 1959)	50.00	1.00
10/– (July 21, 1959)	40.00	2.75
£1 (June 23, 1959)	80.00	12.00
Set	£150	15.00

Wmk: Multiple St. Edward's Crown. Printed by Bradbury Wilkinson

2/6 (July 1, 1963)	0.50	0.15
5/– (September 3, 1963)	2.00	0.40
10/– (October 16, 1963)	3.50	2.50
£1 (November 14, 1963)	9.50	3.00
Set	13.50	7.00

(*The Queen's diadem is more detailed on the Bradbury Wilkinson printing than on the De La Rue printing.)

Wmk: Multiple St. Edward's Crown. Printed by Bradbury Wilkinson on chalky paper

2/6 (May 30, 1968)	0.50	0.75

No Wmk. Printed by Bradbury Wilkinson

2/6 (July 1, 1968)	0.30	0.40
5/– (April 10, 1968)	1.50	0.75
10/– (April 10, 1968)	6.00	4.00
£1 (December 4, 1967)	7.00	4.50
Set	10.50	10.50

Scouting badge (2½d)
Flying swallows (4d)
Globe within compass (1/3)

■ 1957, August 1. World Scout Jubilee Jamboree

Des: Mary Adshead (2½d), P. Keely (4d), W. H. Brown (1/3). Wmk: St Edward's Crown and E2R.

Set	3.75	2.75
First day cover	–	22.00

(*These stamps were also issued in coils.)

Wilding design with added inscription (4d)

■ 1957, September 12. Inter–Parliamentary Union Conference

Des: F. Langfield. Wmk: Multiple St. Edward's Crown and E2R.

4d	0.50	0.50
First day cover	–	82.00

Welsh dragon (3d)
Games emblem (6d)
Welsh dragon (1/3)

■ 1958, July 18. British Empire & Commonwealth Games

Des: Reynolds Stone (3d), W.H. Brown (6d), Pat Keely (1/3).
Wmk: Multiple St. Edward's Crown and E2R.

Set	1.25	1.00
First day cover	–	60.00

1660 postboy (3d)
1660 posthorn (1/3)

■ 1960, July 7. 300th Anniversary of General Letter Office

Des: Reynolds Stone (3d), Faith Jaques (1/3). Wmk: Multiple St.
Edward's Crown.

Set	2.00	2.00
First day cover	–	35.00

Europa emblem (6d, 1/6)

■ 1960, September 19. First Anniversary of CEPT

Des: P. Rahikainen and Reynolds Stone. Wmk: Multiple St.
Edward's Crown.

Set	6.25	2.75
First day cover	–	27.00

Thrift plant (2½d)
Squirrel and tree (3d)
Thrift plant (1/6)

■ 1961, August 28. Post Office Savings Bank Centenary

Des: P. Gauld (2½d), M. Goaman (3d, 1/6). Wmk: Multiple St.
Edward's Crown.

Printed on a Timson machine

Set	1.25	1.25
First day cover	–	38.00

Printed on a Thrissell machine (2½d, 3d only)

Pair	2.00	2.00

(*The portrait on the 2½d is greyer from the Thrissell machine,
and that on the 3d is much clearer on the Timson printing.)

CEPT emblem (2d)
Doves and emblem (4d)
Doves and emblem (10d)

■ 1961, September 18. CEPT Conference

Des: M. Goaman and T. Kurperschoek. Wmk: Multiple St.
Edward's Crown.

Set	0.25	0.30
First day cover	–	4.00

Roof of Westminster Hall (6d)
Palace of Westminster (1/3)

1961, September 23. Commonwealth Parliamentary Conference

Des: Faith Jaques. Wmk: Multiple St. Edward's Crown.

Set	1.25	1.25
First day cover	–	20.00

Boxes bearing arrows (2½d)
Arrows over the British Isles (3d)
Joining arrows (1/3)

1962, November 14. National Productivity Year

Des: D. Gentleman. Wmk: Multiple St. Edward's Crown, inverted on 2½d and 3d values.
Non–phosphor issue

Set	1.25	1.15
First day cover	–	25.00
Phosphor issue (one band on 2½d, three bands on 3d, 1/3)		
Set	13.00	10.00
First day cover	–	£100

Ears of wheat (2½d)
Three children (1/3)

1963, March 21. Freedom From Hunger

Des: M. Goaman. Wmk: Multiple St. Edward's Crown, inverted on both values.
Non–phosphor issue

Set	1.25	1.25
First day cover	–	16.00
Phosphor issue (one band on 2½d, three bands on 1/3)		
Set	14.00	10.00
First day cover	–	32.00

Centenary of the 1863 Paris Postal Conference (6d)

1963, May 7. Paris Postal Conference Centenary

Des: Reynolds Stone. Wmk: Multiple St. Edward's Crown, inverted.
Non–phosphor issue

6d	0.20	0.25
First day cover	–	8.00
Phosphor issue (three bands)		
6d	3.75	3.00
First day cover	–	30.00

Bee on flowers (3d)
Selection of wildlife (4½d)

1963, May 16. National Nature Week

Des: S. Scott (3d), M. Goaman (4½d). Wmk: Multiple St. Edward's Crown.
Non–phosphor issue

Set	0.20	0.20
First day cover	–	12.00
Phosphor issue (three bands)		
Set	1.75	1.75
First day cover	–	34.00

Helicopter over lifeboat (2½d)
Lifeboat (4d)
Lifeboatmen (1/6)

1963, May 31. International Lifeboat Conference

Des: D. Gentlemen. Wmk: Multiple St. Edward's Crown.
Non–phosphor issue

Set	1.75	1.50
First day cover	–	17.00
Phosphor issue (one band on 2½d, three bands on 4d, 1/6)		
Set	21.00	19.00
First day cover	–	37.00

Red Cross (3d, 1/3, 1/6 with different borders)

■ 1963, August 15. Red Cross Centenary Congress
Des: H. Bartram. Wmk: Multiple St. Edward's Crown.
Non-phosphor issue

Set	2.75	2.75
First day cover	–	20.00

Phosphor issue (three bands)

Set	32.00	26.00
First day cover	–	60.00

Cable over globe (1/6)

■ 1963, December 3. Opening of Compac Cable
Des: P. Gauld. Wmk: Multiple St. Edward's Crown.
Non-phosphor issue

1/6	1.25	1.25
First day cover	–	15.00

Phosphor issue (three bands)

1/6	8.00	8.00
First day cover	–	35.00

A Midsummer Night's Dream: Puck and Bottom (3d)
Twelfth Night: Feste (6d)
Romeo and Juliet (1/3)
King Henry V (1/6)
Hamlet (2/6)

■ 1964, April 23. Shakespeare Festival
Des: D. Gentleman (3d to 1/6); C. and R. Ironside (2/6). Printed in recess by Bradbury, Wilkinson (2/6). Perf: 11x12 (2/6). Wmk: Multiple St. Edward's Crown.
Non-phosphor issue

Set	2.25	2.50
First day cover	–	5.50

Phosphor issue (three bands on 3d, 6d, 1/3, 1/6)

Set	6.00	6.00
First day cover	–	10.00

Flats, Richmond Park (2½d)
Shipbuilding, Belfast (4d)
Forest Park, Snowdonia (8d)
Nuclear Reactor, Dounreay (1/6)

■ 1964, July 1. International Geographical Congress
Des: D. Bailey. Wmk: Multiple St. Edward's Crown.
Non-phosphor issue

Set	2.00	2.25
First day cover	–	11.00

Phosphor issue (one band on 2½d, three bands on 4d, 8d, 1/6)

Set	13.00	10.00
First day cover	–	20.00

Spring gentian (3d)
Dog rose (6d)
Honeysuckle (9d)
Fringed water lily (1/3)

■ 1964, August 5. International Botanical Congress
Des: M. and S. Goaman. Wmk: Multiple St. Edward's Crown.
Non-phosphor issue

Set	2.25	2.50
First day cover	–	12.00

Phosphor issue (three bands)

Set	13.00	11.00
First day cover	–	22.00

Forth Road Bridge (3d)
Forth Road Bridge and Foth Bridge (6d)

■ 1964, September 4. Opening of the Forth Road Bridge
Des: A. Restall. Wmk: Multiple St. Edward's Crown.
Non-phosphor issue

Set	0.30	0.30
First day cover	–	3.50

Phosphor issue (three bands)

Set	2.75	2.75
First day cover	–	10.00

Sir Winston Churchill (4d, 1/3 with different designs)

■ **1965, July 8. Churchill Commemoration**
Des: D. Gentleman and R. Dease. Wmk: Multiple St. Edward's Crown.
Non–phosphor issue

Set	0.60	0.60
First day cover	–	5.00

Phosphor issue (three bands)

Set	1.25	1.50
First day cover	–	5.00

Printed on a Timson machine

4d	1.25	1.25

(*The Timson printing shows more detail on the Churchill portrait.)

Seal of Simon de Montfort (6d)
Parliament buildings (2/6)

■ **1965, July 19. 700th Anniversary of Simon de Montfort's Parliament**
Des: S.R. Black (6d), Professor R. Guyatt (2/6). Wmk: Multiple St. Edward's Crown.
Non–phosphor issue

Set	0.65	0.65
First day cover	–	8.00

Phosphor issue (three bands on 6d only)

6d	0.50	0.60
First day cover	–	15.00

Salvation Army band (3d)
Three Salvation Army members (1/6)

■ **1965, August 9. Centenary of Salvation Army**
Des: M.C. Farrar–Bell (3d), G. Trenaman (1/6). Wmk: Multiple St. Edward's Crown.
Non–phosphor issue

Set	0.60	0.60
First day cover	–	11.00

Phosphor issue (one band on 3d, three bands on 1/6)

Set	1.35	1.50
First day cover	–	22.00

Carbolic spray (4d)
Joseph Lister (1/–)

■ **1965, September 1. Centenary of Joseph Lister's Discovery of Antiseptic Surgery**
Des: P. Gauld (4d), F. Ariss (1/–). Wmk: Multiple St. Edward's Crown.
Non–phosphor issue

Set	0.50	0.75
First day cover	–	6.00

Phosphor issue (three bands)

Set	1.50	1.75
First day cover	–	10.00

Trinidad carnival dancers (6d)
Canadian folk dancers (1/6)

■ **1965, September 1. Commonwealth Arts Festival**
Des: D. Gentleman and Rosalind Dease. Wmk: Multiple St. Edward's Crown.
Non–phosphor issue

Set	0.60	0.60
First day cover	–	7.50

Phosphor issue (three bands)

Set	1.70	1.75
First day cover	–	15.00

Spitfires (4d)
Pilot in Hurricane (4d)
Overlapping wings (4d)
Spitfires attacking Heinkel bomber (4d)
Spitfire attacking Stuka bomber (4d)
Tail wing of Dornier bomber (4d)
Anti-aircraft artillery (9d)
St Paul's Cathedral (1/3)

■ **1965, September 13. 25th Anniversary of the Battle of Britain**
Des: D. Gentleman and R. Dease (4d, 1/3), A. Restall (9d). Wmk:
Multiple St. Edward's Crown. Six 4d values se-tenant.
Non-phosphor issue

Set	6.00	6.00
First day cover	–	12.00

Phosphor issue (three bands)

Set	6.00	6.00
First day cover	–	16.00

Post Office Tower and Georgian buildings (3d)
Post Office Tower and Nash Terrace (1/3)

■ **1965, October 8. Opening of the Post Office Tower**
Des: C. Abbott. Wmk: Multiple St. Edward's Crown.
Non-phosphor issue

Set	0.30	0.35
First day cover	–	3.50

Phosphor issue (one band on 3d, three bands on 1/3)

Set	0.40	0.50
First day cover	–	5.00

UN emblem (3d)
ICY emblem (1/6)

■ **1965, October 25. 20th Anniversary of United Nations and
International Co–Operation Year**
Des: J. Matthews. Wmk: Multiple St. Edward's Crown.
Non-phosphor issue

Set	0.50	0.60
First day cover	–	5.50

Phosphor issue (one band on 3d, three bands on 1/6)

Set	1.25	1.25
First day cover	–	10.00

Telecommunications (9d)
Radio waves (1/6)

■ **1965, November 15. International Telecommunication Union
Centenary**
Des: A. Restall. Wmk: Multiple St. Edward's Crown.
Non-phosphor issue

Set	0.75	0.75
First day cover	–	8.50

Phosphor issue (three bands)

Set	2.50	3.00
First day cover	–	14.00

Robert Burns portrait by Skirving (4d)
Robert Burns portrait by Nasmyth (1/3)

■ **1966, January 25. Robert Burns**
Des: G.F. Huntly. Wmk: Multiple St. Edward's Crown.
Non-phosphor issue

Set	0.35	0.40
First day cover	–	1.50

Phosphor issue (three bands)

Set	1.25	1.25
First day cover	–	4.00

Exterior of Westminster Abbey (3d)
Fan vaulting of Westminster Abbey (2/6)

■ **1966, February 28. 900th Anniversary of Westminster Abbey**
Des: Sheila Robinson (3d), Bradbury Wilkinson (2/6). Printed in
recess by Bradbury Wilkinson (2/6). Wmk: Multiple St. Edward's
Crown. Perf: 11 x 12 (2/6).
Non–phosphor issue

Set	0.50	0.50
First day cover	–	3.25
Phosphor issue (one band on 3d only)		
3d	0.20	0.20
First day cover	–	9.00

Sussex Downs (4d)
Antrim, Northern Ireland (6d)
Harlech Castle (1/3)
The Cairngorms (1/6)

■ **1966, May 2. Landscapes**
Des: L. Rosoman. Wmk: Multiple St. Edward's Crown.
Non–phosphor issue

Set	0.50	0.50
First day cover	–	3.50
Phosphor issue (three bands)		
Set	0.60	0.60
First day cover	–	5.00

Two footballers (4d)
Four footballers (6d)
Goalkeeper catching ball (1/3)

■ **1966, June 1. World Cup**
Des: D. Gentleman (4d), W. Kempster (6d), D. Caplan (1/3). Wmk:
Multiple St. Edward's Crown.
Non–phosphor issue

Set	0.40	0.40
First day cover	–	10.00
Phosphor issue (two bands on 4d, three bands on 6d, 1/3)		
Set	0.25	0.25
First day cover	–	12.00

Black–headed gull (4d)
Blue tit (4d)
Robin (4d)
Blackbird (4d)

■ **1966, August 8. British Birds**
Des: J. Norris Wood. Wmk: Multiple St. Edward's Crown. All four
values in se–tenant blocks.
Non–phosphor issue

Set (in se–tenant block of four)	0.50	0.60
First day cover	–	4.00
Phosphor issue (three bands)		
Set (in se–tenant block of four)	0.40	0.40
First day cover	–	4.50

Two footballers and 'England Winners' (4d)

■ **1966, August 18. England's World Cup Victory**
As June 1 issue, with additional inscription 'ENGLAND WINNERS'.
Non–phosphor only.

4d	0.10	0.10
First day cover	–	7.50

Jodrell Bank radiotelescope (4d)
Jaguar 'E' type and Mini cars (6d)
SR N6 hovercraft (1/3)
Windscale nuclear reactor (1/6)

■ **1966, September 19. British Technology**
Des: D. and A. Gillespie (4d, 6d), A. Restall (1/3, 1/6). Wmk:
Multiple St. Edward's Crown.
Non–phosphor issue

Set	0.40	0.40
First day cover	–	1.50

Phosphor issue (three bands)

Set	0.45	0.50
First day cover	–	3.00

Scenes from the Bayeux Tapestry (4d, 4d, 4d, 4d, 4d, 4d)
Norman ship (6d)
Norman cavalry attacking English infantry (1/3)

■ **1966, October 14. 900th Anniversary of the Battle of Hastings**
Des: D. Gentleman. Wmk: Multiple St. Edward's Crown, sideways
on 1/3 value. Six 4d values se–tenant.
Non–phosphor issue

Set	1.00	1.50
First day cover	–	2.50

Phosphor issue (three bands on 4d, 6d, four bands on 1/3)

Set	1.00	1.50
First day cover	–	3.75

King of the Orient (3d)
Snowman (1/6)

■ **1966, December 1. Christmas**
Des: Miss T. Shemza (3d), J. Berry (1/6), both aged six. Wmk:
Multiple St. Edward's Crown, upright on both values.
Non–phosphor issue

Set	0.20	0.25
First day cover	–	1.00

Phosphor issue (one band on 3d, two bands on 1/6)

Set	0.20	0.30
First day cover	–	1.00

(*The phosphor 3d can be found with the band at left or right).

Loading freight on a ship (9d)
Loading freight on an aeroplane (1/6)

■ **1967, February 20. European Free Trade Association**
Des: C. Abbott. Wmk: Multiple St. Edward's Crown.
Non–phosphor issue

Set	0.15	0.20
First day cover	–	6.00

Phosphor issue (three bands)

Set	0.20	0.25
First day cover	–	6.00

Hawthorn and bramble (4d)
Bindweed and viper's bugloss (4d)
Ox–eye daisy, coltsfoot and buttercup (4d)
Bluebell, red campion and wood anemone (4d)
Dog violet (9d)
Primrose (1/9)

■ **1967, April 24. British Wild Flowers**
Des: W. Keble Martin (4d), Mary Grierson (9d, 1/9). Wmk:
Multiple St. Edward's Crown. Four 4d values se–tenant.
Non–phosphor issue

Set	0.75	0.80
First day cover	–	2.25

Phosphor issue (three bands)

Set	0.40	0.50
First day cover	–	7.50

'Master Lambton' by Sir Thomas Lawrence (4d)
'Mares and Foals in a Landscape' by George Stubbs (9d)
'Children Coming Out of School' by L. S. Lowry (1/6)

■ **1967, July 10. British Paintings**
Des: S. Rose. No Wmk. Two phosphor bands.

Set	0.20	0.30
First day cover	–	1.50

■ **1967, July 24. Sir Francis Chichester's Single–Handed Voyage Around the World**
Des: M. and S. Goaman. No Wmk. Three phosphor bands.

1/9	0.10	0.10
First day cover	–	0.70

Radar screen (4d)
Penicillin mould (1/–)
Jet engine (1/6)
Television equipment (1/9)

■ **1967, September 19. British Discovery & Invention**
Des: C. Abbott (4d, 1/–), Negus and Sharland (1/6, 1/9). Wmk: Multiple St. Edward's Crown. Three phosphor bands on the 4d.

Set	0.25	0.30
First day cover	–	1.00

'The Adoration of the Shepherds' by the School of Seville (3d)
'Madonna and Child' by Bartolomé Murillo (4d)
'The Adoration of the Shepherds' by Louis Le Nain (1/6)

■ **1967, October 18–November 27. Christmas**
No Wmk. 3d has one central phosphor band. 3d released on November 27, 4d on October 18, 1/6 on November 27.

Set	0.15	0.20
First day cover	–	3.00

Tarr Steps (4d)
Aberfeldy Bridge (9d)
Menai Bridge (1/6)
M4 Viaduct (1/9)

■ **1968, April 29. British Bridges**
Des: J. Matthews (4d, 1/9), A. Restall (9d), L. Rosoman (1/6). No Wmk. Two phosphor bands.

Set	0.25	0.35
First day cover	–	1.00

Trades Union Congress (4d)
Votes for Women: Emmeline Pankhurst statue (9d)
Royal Air Force: Sopwith Camel and modern fighters (1/–)
James Cook's first voyage: signature and H.M.S. Endeavour (1/9)

■ **1968, May 29. Anniversaries**
Des: D. Gentleman (4d), C. Abbott (others). No Wmk.

Set	0.25	0.35
First day cover	–	2.25

'Queen Elizabeth 1' by an unknown artist (4d)
'Pinkie' by Sir Thomas Lawrence (1/–)
'Ruins of St. Mary le Port' by John Piper (1/6)
'The Hay Wain' by John Constable (1/9)

■ 1968, August 12. British Paintings
No Wmk.

Set	0.25	0.30
First day cover	–	0.50

Boy and girl with rocking horse (4d)
Girl with doll's house (9d)
Boy with train set (1/6)

■ 1968, November 25. Christmas
Des: Rosalind Dease. No Wmk.
Printed on a Rembrandt machine

Set	0.20	0.25
First day cover	–	1.25

Printed on a Thrissell machine (4d only)

4d	0.15	0.20

(*The Thrissell printing can be distinguished by the boy's pullover having a more mottled appearance.)

RMS Queen Elizabeth 2

Queen Elizabeth 2 (5d)
Elizabethan galleon (9d)
East Indiaman (9d)
Cutty Sark (9d)
S.S. Great Britain (1/–)
R.M.S. Mauretania (1/–)

■ 1969, January 15. British Ships
Des: D. Gentleman. No Wmk. Three 9d values in se-tenant strip.
Two 1/- values in se-tenant pair.

Set	0.75	1.20
First day cover	–	1.75

Concorde over Great Britain and France (4d)
Silhouettes of Concorde (9d)
Nose and tail of Concorde (1/6)

■ 1969, March 3. First Flight of Concorde
Des: Michael and Sylvia Goaman (4d), D. Gentleman (9d, 1/6).
No Wmk.

Set	0.25	0.25
First day cover	–	4.00

First transatlantic flight: Vickers Vimy, Alcock & Brown (5d)
Europa/CEPT: emblems (9d)
International Labour Organisation: hand holding wrench (1/–)
NATO: flags of member countries (1/6)
First England–Australia Flight: Vickers Vimy, route on globe (1/9)

■ 1969, April 2. Anniversaries
Des: P. Sharland (5d, 1/–, 1/6), Michael and Sylvia Goaman (9d, 1/9). No Wmk.

Set	0.25	0.40
First day cover	–	1.25

Durham Cathedral (5d)
York Minster (5d)
St Giles' Cathedral, Edinburgh (5d)
Canterbury Cathedral (5d)
St Paul's Cathedral (9d)
Liverpool Metropolitan Cathedral (1/6)

■ **1969, May 28. British Cathedrals**
Des: P. Gauld. No Wmk. Four 5d values se-tenant.

Set	0.65	0.85
First day cover	–	1.25

The King's Gate, Caernarfon Castle (5d)
The Eagle Tower, Caernarfon Castle (5d)
Queen Eleanor's Gate, Caernarfon Castle (5d)
Celtic cross, Margam Abbey (9d)
Charles, Prince of Wales (1/-)

■ **1969, July 1. Investiture of the Prince of Wales**
Des: D. Gentleman. No Wmk. Three 5d values se-tenant.

Set	0.40	0.50
First day cover	–	1.00

Mahatma Gandhi and flag of India (1/6)

■ **1969, August 13. Gandhi Centenary Year**
Des: Biman Mullick.

1/6	0.30	0.40
First day cover	–	3.50

National Giro symbol (5d)
Telephone dials (9d)
Pulse code modulation (1/-)
Automatic sorting (1/6)

■ **1969, October 1. Post Office Technology**
Des: D. Gentleman. Printed in litho by De La Rue. No Wmk.
Perf: 13½x14.

Set	0.35	0.45
First day cover	–	0.75

Herald angel (4d)
Three shepherds (5d)
Three kings (1/6)

■ **1969, November 26. Christmas**
Des: F. Wegner. No Wmk.

Set	0.25	0.25
First day cover	–	0.50

Fife harling (5d)
Cotswold limestone (9d)
Welsh stucco (1/-)
Ulster thatch (1/6)

■ **1970, February 11. Rural Architecture**
Des: D. Gentleman (5d, 9d), Sheila Robinson (1/-, 1/6). No Wmk.

Set	0.40	0.50
First day cover	–	0.75

Declaration of Arbroath: signing ceremony (5d)
Florence Nightingale: attending patients (9d)
International Co-operative Alliance: signing ceremony (1/–)
Sailing of the Mayflower: pilgrims and ship (1/6)
Royal Astronomical Society: Sir William Herschel, Francis Baily,
Sir John Herschel and telescope (1/9)

■ 1970, April 1. Anniversaries
Des: F. Wegner (5d, 9d, 1/6), Marjorie Seynor (1/–, 1/9).
No Wmk.

Set	0.50	0.50
First day cover	–	1.00

Mr Pickwick and Sam (5d)
Mr and Mrs Micawber (5d)
David Copperfield and Betsey Trotwood (5d)
Oliver Twist (5d)
Grasmere (1/6)

■ 1970, June 3. Literary Anniversaries
Des: Rosalind Dease. No Wmk. Four 5d values se–tenant.

Set	0.50	0.75
First day cover	–	1.00

Runners (5d)
Swimmers (1/6)
Cyclists (1/9)

■ 1970, July 15. British Commonwealth Games
Des: A. Restall. Printed in litho by De La Rue. No Wmk. Perf:
13½x14.

Set	0.40	0.40
First day cover	–	0.75

1840 line–engraved Penny Black (5d)
1847 embossed 1/– green (9d)
1855 surface–printed 4d carmine (1/6)

■ 1970, September 18. Philympia 1970 International Stamp Exhibition
Des: D. Gentleman. No Wmk.

Set	0.40	0.40
First day cover	–	0.75

Angel appearing to shepherds (4d)
Mary, Joseph and Jesus (5d)
Wise men bringing gifts (1/6)

■ 1970, November 25. Christmas
Des: Sally Stiff, based on the De Lisle Psalter. No Wmk.

Set	0.25	0.30
First day cover	–	0.75

PRE-DECIMAL MACHIN DEFINITIVES

In this section, prices are given for unmounted mint (left) and fine used (right). Exceptions are made where used prices are not applicable, for example booklet panes and gum varieties.

The Machin head of Queen Elizabeth II is so-called because it is based on a photograph of a sculpture by Arnold Machin. All designs in the series are similar, but small differences can be found in the head itself and in its setting in the design.

There are also varieties in the number and positioning of phosphor bands.

4d sepia

■ 1967–1969. Machin definitives
Des: A. Machin. Printed in photogravure by Harrisons. No wmk. Head A with two phosphor bands except where stated.

Gum Arabic

3d violet (August 8, 1967) (one band)	0.15	–
4d sepia (June 5, 1967)	0.15	–
head B	£2,000	–
4d red (one centre band)	1.00	–
9d green (August 8, 1967)	0.20	–
1/– pale violet (June 5, 1967)	0.20	–
1/– deep violet	1.00	–
1/6 green, deep blue (August 8, 1967)	0.30	–
1/9 orange, black (June 5, 1967)	0.35	–
First day cover (4d, 1/–, 1/9)	–	1.25
First day cover (3d, 9d, 1/6)	–	1.25

Coil stamps (August 27, 1969)

1d olive (head B, one band)	0.75	–

2d brown (head B, one band)	0.15	0.15
3d violet (head B, one band)	0.15	–
4d red (head B, one band)	0.15	–
Se-tenant coil of two 2d, one 1d, one 3d and one 4d	0.60	0.75

Booklet panes of six

Six 4d sepia	8.00	–
Six 4d red	£125	–

PVA gum

½d orange (February 5, 1968)	0.10	0.10
1d olive (February 5, 1968)	0.10	0.10
head B	0.10	0.10
head B (one centre band)	0.50	0.50
2d brown (February 5, 1968)	0.10	0.10
setting 2	0.10	0.30
3d violet (one centre band)	1.00	1.00
head B (one centre band)	3.00	2.00
3d violet	0.15	0.10
head B	0.50	0.10
4d sepia (shades)	0.15	0.10
head B	0.35	0.10
4d sepia (one centre band)	0.30	0.20
head B (one centre band)	0.10	0.10
4d red (January 6, 1969) (one centre band)	0.15	0.20
head B (one centre band)	0.10	0.10
head B (one band at left)	0.80	0.80
head B (one band at right)	0.90	0.90
5d blue (July 1, 1968)	0.20	0.30
head B	0.20	0.20
head B (two bands on 'all over' phosphor)	£275	–
6d purple (February 5, 1968)	0.20	0.20
head B	9.00	7.50
7d green (July 1, 1968) (head 2)	0.20	0.30
8d red (July 1, 1968)	0.20	0.25
8d light–blue (January 6, 1969) (head 2)	0.30	0.25
9d green	0.20	0.20
10d brown (July 1, 1968)	0.20	0.30
1/– deep violet	0.20	0.20
1/6 green, deep blue	0.30	0.20
phosphor–coated paper	0.50	0.45
1/9 orange, black	2.50	0.30
Set (one of each value)	4.80	4.80
First day cover (½d, 1d, 2d, 6d)	–	1.00
First day cover (5d, 7d, 8d red, 10d)	–	1.00
First day cover (4d red, 8d light blue)	–	2.50

Booklet panes of four

Four 4d sepia (head B, two bands)	1.50	–
Four 4d sepia (head B, one centre band)	1.50	–
Four 4d red (head B, one centre band)	1.50	–
Two 1d left of two 3d (head B, two bands)	4.00	–
Two 1d right of two 3d (head B, two bands)	3.00	–
Two 4d sepia (head B, one centre band), with two labels reading '£4,315 FOR YOU AT AGE 55' and 'SEE OTHER PAGES'	1.00	–
Two 4d red (head B, one centre band), with two labels reading '£4,315 FOR YOU AT AGE 55' and 'SEE OTHER PAGES'	1.00	–

Booklet panes of six

Six **1d** olive (head B, two bands)	1.50	–
Six **3d** violet (head A, centre band)	5.00	–
Six **4d** sepia (head A, two bands)	5.00	–
Six **4d** sepia (head A, one centre band)	1.50	–
Six **4d** red (head A, one centre band)	1.25	–
Six **4d** red (head B, one centre band)	1.25	–
Six **5d** blue (head B, two bands)	1.25	–
Four **1d** olive (one centre band) with two **4d** sepia (head B, one centre band)	5.00	–
Four **1d** olive (two bands) with two **4d** red (head B, one left band)	3.50	–

Booklet panes of 15 (all head B)

Six **1d** olive (two bands) with three **4d** red (one band at left), three **4d** red (one band at right) and three **5d** blue, with recipe label	6.00	–
Fifteen **4d** red (one centre band), with 'Stuffed Cucumber' label	1.25	–
Fifteen **4d** red (one centre band), with 'Method' label	1.25	–
Fifteen **5d** blue (two bands), with recipe label	1.25	–

(*These panes come from the £1 Stamps For Cooks booklet and can be found with just four holes in the binding margin, where stapled together, or with a larger number of equally spaced holes, where stitched.)

5/– brown–red

■ **1969, March 5. High values**
Des: A. Machin. Printed in recess by Bradbury Wilkinson. Perf: 12.

2/6 brown	0.25	0.20
5/– brown–red	1.00	0.50
10/– deep blue	3.00	4.00
£1 black	2.50	2.50
Set	5.50	5.00
First day cover	–	6.00

DECIMAL MACHIN DEFINITIVES

In this section, prices are given for unmounted mint (left) and fine used (right). Exceptions are made where used prices are not applicable, for example in the case of booklet panes and gum varieties.

All stamps have fluorescent-coated paper unless otherwise stated.

Gum

Gummed stamps can be found with three different gums. Gum Arabic is either colourless or yellow in appearance and is very shiny. Polyvinyl alcohol gum (PVA) is colourless but has a matt appearance. Polyvinyl alcohol with dextrin gum (PVAD) is also matt, but has a blueish or greenish tinge.

Self-adhesive definitives have become increasingly common since 1993.

Phosphor

Phosphor at first was applied in the form of vertical bands. When you hold a stamp up to the light and look along the surface, the paper itself appears shiny while the bands have a dull appearance.

Most stamps have two phosphor bands, on the two vertical edges; others have just one, which can be central or down the left or right vertical edge.

The width of the bands can vary, as can the size of the printing screen used to apply them, but these differences are beyond the scope of this publication.

Booklet panes, where stamps of the 2nd class rate (requiring a single phosphor band) have been printed se-tenant with other stamps (requiring two phosphor bands), have been found with the phosphor printed as bars rather than bands. Whereas bands extend across the perforations to the next stamp, these bars stop at the edge of the stamp design.

The term 'all over phosphor' is used where the phosphor was printed over the entire surface of the stamp, rather than in the form of bands. In some cases it was printed onto the paper before the stamp design was printed; in other cases it was printed afterwards.

The term 'no phosphor' is often applied to stamps with the phosphor omitted in error; such errors are outside the scope of this publication. However, the 50p and 75p values have been printed without phosphor in the normal course of events.

Paper

At first, from February 1971, these stamps were printed on what is now called 'original coated paper' (OCP), which gives a dull violet reaction when the front of the stamp is viewed under ultra-violet light.

This was gradually replaced from August 1971 by 'fluorescent coated paper' (FCP) which gives a bright reaction under ultra-violet light, and then from August 1979 by 'phosphor-coated paper' (PCP), which adds the after-glow of phosphor and makes the stamp appear uniformly shiny.

Note that stamps with phosphor omitted in error also have a uniformly shiny surface, so those with phosphor-coated paper can only be positively identified by their reaction under ultra-violet light.

The appearance of stamps with phosphor-coated paper can vary considerably due to variations in their drying time after printing. The abbreviation 'PCPI' is used to denote a dull appearance, and 'PCPII' a highly glazed appearance.

Some stamps with phosphor-coated paper have been found with the fluorescent brightener omitted. These still give a phosphor afterglow, but the paper gives a dull violet reaction similar to that found with original coated paper.

Attempts to standardise the paper produced what is known as 'advanced coated paper' (ACP), in use from March 1983. The visual difference between ACP and PCPI is minimal, but the former gives a brighter reaction under ultra-violet light.

Value and portrait

Minor changes can be noted in the position of the denomination of value in relation to the Queen's portrait, and the position of the portrait in relation to the base of the stamp.

Booklet panes

At first booklets were held together by stitching, so that a number of small holes can be found in the binding margin on the left hand side of panes. Later, the panes were stuck into booklet covers by the binding margins; in many such cases, panes can be found with the binding margin to the left or to the right.

In the case of stitched booklets, the booklet panes are recorded separately. Where the panes are stuck into the covers, most collectors prefer these as complete booklets, so the separate panes are not recorded.

Many of the early decimal booklet panes included non-postal labels se-tenant with the stamps in the pane, adjacent to the binding margin. At first these panes were perforated between the labels and the margin, but later they were not.

In 1987, as an experiment to counter complaints about the poor guillotining of panes, some booklet panes were produced with stamps with either the left or right-hand edge imperforate.

Coils

There are two different types of coils or rolls from which stamps may be found.

Where the source of a stamp is listed as 'coils', this refers to coils of the same value, usually 1st class or 2nd class, joined either horizontally or vertically. These were usually produced for use by businesses.

Where the source is listed as 'se-tenant coils', this refers to coils containing a mixture of values joined as a strip, These were usually produced for sale through vending machines.

Cartons

In an experiment staged in Scotland in 1976-78, 1st class and 2nd class definitives (including country definitives) were sold in cartons from vending machines. Sold at 30p or 60p, they contained either 6½p and 8½p, or 7p and 9p stamps.

LOW VALUES WITHOUT ELLIPTICAL PERFORATIONS, 1971–96

Des. A. Machin. Printed in photogravure by Harrisons except where stated. No Wmk. Perf: 15x14, except where stated.

▪ ½p turquoise, February 15, 1971
gum Arabic, two phosphor bands, OCP	se-tenant coils	0.30	–
gum Arabic, two phosphor bands, OCP with silicone	se-tenant coils	30.00	–
gum Arabic, two phosphor bands, FCP	sheets	0.10	–
gum Arabic, two phosphor bands, FCP with silicone	se-tenant coils	0.40	–
PVA gum, two phosphor bands, OCP	sheets, se-tenant coils, booklets	0.20	–
PVA gum, two phosphor bands, FCP	sheets, booklets	0.20	–
PVA gum, one phosphor band (left)	prestige booklets	35.00	15.00
PVAD gum, two phosphor bands	sheets, se-tenant coils, booklets	0.10	0.15
PVAD gum, one phosphor band (centre)	se-tenant coils, booklets	0.20	0.15
PVAD gum, PCPI	sheets, se-tenant coils	0.10	0.10
PVAD gum, PCPII	sheets	0.15	0.15
PVAD gum, PCP, fluorescent brightener omitted (poor gum)	se-tenant coils	£125	30.00
PVAD gum, PCP, fluorescent brightener omitted (good gum)	se-tenant coils	£950	–

▪ 1p purple, February 15, 1971
gum Arabic, two phosphor bands, OCP	se-tenant coils	0.40	–
gum Arabic, two phosphor bands, OCP with silicone	se-tenant coils	30.00	–
gum Arabic, two phosphor bands, FCP	coils	0.60	–
gum Arabic, two phosphor bands, FCP with silicone	se-tenant coils	0.60	–
PVA gum, two phosphor bands, OCP	sheets	0.10	–
PVA gum, two phosphor bands, FCP	sheets, booklets	1.25	–
PVAD gum, two phosphor bands (value lower)	booklets	0.40	0.30
PVAD gum, two phosphor bands (value intermediate)	se-tenant coils, booklets	0.40	0.35
PVAD gum, two phosphor bands (value higher)	sheets, se-tenant coils	0.20	0.30
PVAD gum, one centre phosphor band (portrait higher)	se-tenant coils	0.10	0.15
PVAD gum, one centre phosphor band (portrait lower)	se-tenant coils, booklets	0.40	0.30
PVAD gum, all-over phosphor	sheets	0.20	0.20
PVAD gum, PCPI (portrait higher)	sheets	0.10	0.10
PVAD gum, PCPI (portrait lower)	sheets, se-tenant coils	0.20	0.15
PVAD gum, PCPII	sheets	0.30	0.25
PVAD gum, ACP	sheets	0.30	0.25
PVAD gum, one phosphor band (left)	booklets	0.60	0.60
PVAD gum, one phosphor band (right)	prestige booklets	3.00	3.00

▪ 1½p black, February 15, 1971
PVA gum, two phosphor bands, OCP	sheets, booklets	0.10	0.10
PVA gum, two phosphor bands, FCP	sheets, booklets	0.50	0.50
PVAD gum, two phosphor bands	sheets, booklets	0.20	0.30

■ 2p green, February 15, 1971

gum Arabic, two phosphor bands, OCP	se–tenant coils	2.00	–
gum Arabic, two phosphor bands, OCP with silicone	se–tenant coils	£120	–
gum Arabic, two phosphor bands, FCP with silicone	se–tenant coils	2.00	–
PVA gum, two phosphor bands, OCP	sheets, booklets	0.20	–
PVA gum, two phosphor bands, FCP	sheets, booklets	1.50	–
PVAD gum, two phosphor bands (portrait higher)	sheets, se–tenant coils, booklets	0.20	0.20
PVAD gum, two phosphor bands (portrait lower)	booklets	0.40	0.40
PVAD gum, all over phosphor	sheets	0.20	0.15
PVAD gum, PCPI	sheets	0.10	0.10
PVAD gum, PCPII	sheets	0.20	0.15
PVAD gum, PCP (litho by Questa, perf 13½x14)	sheets	0.15	0.15
PVAD gum, PCP (litho by Questa, perf 15x14)	sheets	0.20	0.20
PVAD gum, ACP (litho by Questa, perf 15x14)	sheets	0.30	0.40

■ 2p deep green, February 23, 1988

PVAD gum, PCP	sheets, booklets	0.20	0.20
PVAD gum, PCP, litho by Walsall	booklets	0.60	0.60

■ 2½p pink, February 15, 1971

gum arabic, one centre phosphor band	sheets, coils	0.50	–
PVA gum, one centre phosphor band, OCP	sheets, coils, booklets	0.20	0.20
PVA gum, one centre phosphor band, FCP	sheets, booklets	0.40	0.40
PVA gum, one phosphor band (left), OCP	booklets	5.00	1.50
PVA gum, one phosphor band (left), FCP	booklets, prestige booklets	1.00	1.00
PVA gum, one phosphor band (right)	prestige booklets	1.00	1.00
PVAD gum, two phosphor bands	sheets	0.20	0.20
PVAD gum, one phosphor band (centre)	sheets	0.10	0.10

■ 2½p rose, January 14, 1981

PVAD gum, PCPI	sheets, se–tenant coils	0.20	0.20
PVAD gum, PCPII	sheets	0.15	0.20
PVAD gum, PCP, fluorescent brightener omitted	se–tenant coils	30.00	30.00
PVAD gum, two phosphor bands	booklets	0.25	0.25

■ 3p blue, February 15, 1971

gum Arabic, two phosphor bands, OCP	coils	40.00	–
gum Arabic, two phosphor bands, FCP	sheets, coils	0.75	–
gum arabic, one phosphor band (centre)	sheets	0.40	–
PVA gum, two phosphor bands, OCP	sheets, coils, booklets	0.15	0.15
PVA gum, two phosphor bands, FCP	sheets, booklets	0.15	0.15
PVA gum, two phosphor bands, PCP	(only two examples known)	£1,200	–
PVA gum, one phosphor band (centre)	sheets, booklets	0.10	–
PVAD gum, one phosphor band (centre)	sheets, coils, booklets	0.15	0.20

■ 3p pink, October 22, 1980

PVAD gum, PCPI	sheets, se–tenant coils	0.20	0.20
PVAD gum, PCPII	sheets, se–tenant coils	1.00	1.00
PVAD gum, PCP, fluorescent brightener omitted	se–tenant coils	5.00	4.00
PVAD gum, ACP	sheets, prestige booklets	1.50	1.50
PVAD gum, two phosphor bands	booklets, prestige booklets	0.15	0.20

■ 3½p olive green, February 15, 1971

PVA gum, two phosphor bands, OCP	sheets	0.10	0.20
PVA gum, two phosphor bands, FCP	sheets, booklets	1.00	–
PVAD gum, two phosphor bands, OCP	sheets	£120	50.00
PVAD gum, two phosphor bands, FCP	sheets, coils, booklets	0.50	0.25
PVAD gum, one phosphor band (centre)	sheets, coils, booklets	0.10	0.10

■ 3½p light red–brown, March 30, 1983

PVA gum, two phosphor bands, PCPI	sheets	0.30	0.30

PVA gum, two phosphor bands, ACP	sheets, prestige booklets	1.10	0.60
PVAD gum, one phosphor band (centre)	booklets	1.50	1.50

■ 4p bistre, February 15, 1971

gum arabic, two phosphor bands	sheets	0.50	–
PVA gum, two phosphor bands, OCP	sheets	0.30	0.20
PVA gum, two phosphor bands, FCP	sheets	3.50	–
PVAD gum, two phosphor bands	sheets	0.10	0.20

■ 4p greenish–blue, January 30, 1980

PVA gum, two phosphor bands (litho by Waddingtons)	sheets	0.20	0.15
PVAD gum, PCP (litho by Waddingtons)	sheets	0.30	0.20
PVAD gum, PCP (litho by Questa, perf 15x14)	sheets	0.40	0.40
PVAD gum, two phosphor bands	booklets	0.60	0.60
PVAD gum, PCPI	se-tenant coils	0.20	0.20
PVAD gum, PCP, fluorescent brightener omitted (perfect gum)	se-tenant coils	£370	35.00
PVAD gum, PCPI (value higher)	se-tenant coils	0.35	0.20
PVAD gum, one phosphor band (centre)	booklets	0.65	0.65
PVAD gum, one phosphor band (left)	prestige booklets	3.75	3.75
PVAD gum, one phosphor band (right)	prestige booklets	4.00	4.00

■ 4p bright blue, July 26, 1988

PVAD gum, PCP (litho by Questa)	sheets	0.30	0.30
PVAD gum, PCP	sheets, coils	0.20	0.25

■ 4½p grey–blue, October 24, 1973

PVAD gum, two phosphor bands	sheets, coils, booklets	0.10	0.10
PVAD gum, all–over phosphor, two phosphor bands	sheets	0.65	–

■ 5p violet, February 15, 1971

PVA gum, two phosphor bands, OCP	sheets	0.15	0.20
PVA gum, two phosphor bands, FCP	sheets	2.50	–
PVAD gum, two phosphor bands	sheets	0.10	0.10
PVAD gum, PCPI	sheets	0.20	0.20
PVAD gum, PCPI (value higher)	sheets	0.50	0.35
PVAD gum, PCP (litho by Questa)	sheets	0.30	0.20
PVA gum, PCP (litho by Questa)	sheets	0.40	0.40

(*This stamp also appears in the 2017 Machin Definitive Golden Anniversary miniature sheet, printed by ISP. Price 0.50 mint or used.)

■ 5p red–brown, January 27, 1982

PVAD gum, PCP (litho by Questa, perf 13½x14)	sheets	0.25	0.20
PVAD gum, PCP (litho by Questa, perf 15x14)	sheets	0.50	0.40
PVAD gum, ACP (litho by Questa, perf 15x14)	sheets	0.45	0.40
PVAD gum, one phosphor band (centre)	booklets	1.00	1.00

■ 5½p deep purple, October 24, 1973

PVAD gum, two phosphor bands	sheets	0.10	0.10
PVAD gum, one phosphor band (centre)	sheets	0.10	0.10

■ 6p light green, February 15, 1971

gum arabic, two phosphor bands	sheets	1.10	–
PVA gum, two phosphor bands, OCP	sheets, se-tenant coils	0.30	–
PVA gum, two phosphor bands, FCP	sheets	25.00	–
PVAD gum, two phosphor bands	sheets, se-tenant coils, booklets	0.20	0.20

■ 6p olive, September 10, 1991

PVAD gum, PCP	sheets	0.20	0.20

■ 6½p green–blue, September 7, 1974

PVA gum, two phosphor bands	sheets	30.00	–
PVAD gum, two phosphor bands	sheets	0.20	0.20

PVAD gum, one phosphor band (centre) (portrait higher)	sheets	0.20	0.20
PVAD gum, one phosphor band (centre) (portrait lower)	sheets, coils, booklets	0.20	0.25
PVAD gum, one phosphor band (left)	booklets	0.50	0.30
E) PVAD gum, one phosphor band (right)	booklets	0.50	0.30

■ 7p red–brown, January 15, 1975

PVAD gum, two phosphor bands	sheets	0.30	0.30
PVAD gum, one phosphor band (centre) (portrait higher)	sheets, coils	0.20	0.20
PVAD gum, one phosphor band (centre) (portrait lower)	sheets, coils, se–tenant coils, booklets	0.30	0.30
PVAD gum, one phosphor band (left)	booklets	0.30	0.30
PVAD gum, one phosphor band (right)	booklets	0.40	0.50

■ 7p brick–red, October 29, 1985

PVAD gum, PCP	sheets	1.00	0.90

■ 7½p brown, February 15, 1971

PVA gum, two phosphor bands, OCP	sheets	0.50	0.40
PVA gum, two phosphor bands, FCP	sheets	3.00	–
PVAD gum, two phosphor bands	sheets	0.20	0.20

■ 8p red, October 24, 1973

PVAD gum, two phosphor bands	sheets	0.20	0.20
PVAD gum, one phosphor band (centre) (portrait higher, value lower)	sheets	0.35	0.25
PVAD gum, one phosphor band (centre) (portrait lower, value higher)	sheets, coils, booklets	0.50	0.30
PVAD gum, one phosphor band (centre) (printed by Enschedé)	sheets	0.35	0.25
PVAD gum, one phosphor band (left)	booklets	0.35	0.30
PVAD gum, one phosphor band (right)	booklets	0.35	0.30

■ 8½p lime green, September 24, 1975

PVAD gum, two phosphor bands (value higher)	sheets, coils, booklets	0.20	0.25
PVAD gum, two phosphor bands (value lower)	booklets	0.45	0.35
PVAD gum, PCP	sheets	0.40	0.20

■ 9p orange and black, February 15, 1971

PVA gum, two phosphor bands, OCP	sheets	0.30	0.30
PVA gum, two phosphor bands, FCP	sheets	2.50	–
PVAD gum, two phosphor bands	sheets	1.00	0.90

■ 9p violet, February 25, 1976

PVAD gum, two phosphor bands	sheets, coils, booklets	0.20	0.20

■ 9½p purple, February 25, 1976

PVAD gum, two phosphor bands	sheets	0.30	0.30

■ 10p yellow and orange, August 11, 1971

PVA gum, two phosphor bands	sheets	0.30	–
PVAD gum, two phosphor bands	sheets	0.30	0.30

■ 10p orange, February 25, 1976

PVAD gum, two phosphor bands (base of value above edge of bust)	sheets, booklets	0.30	0.20
PVAD gum, two phosphor bands (base of value at edge of bust)	booklets	0.30	0.25
PVAD gum, two phosphor bands (value narrower)	prestige booklets	8.00	8.00
PVAD gum, all–over phosphor	sheets, booklets	0.30	0.30
PVAD gum, PCPI	sheets	0.30	0.30
PVAD gum, ACP	sheets	0.30	0.25
PVAD gum, one phosphor band (centre)	sheets, booklets, prestige booklets	0.30	0.30
PVAD gum, one phosphor band (left)	booklets, prestige booklets	0.30	0.30
PVAD gum, one phosphor band (right)	booklets	0.75	0.75
PVAD gum, two phosphor bands, PCPI	sheets	0.50	–
PVAD gum, two phosphor bands, PCPI (gutter pair)	sheets	1.25	–

PVAD gum, two phosphor bands, FCP	sheets	0.45	0.35
PVAD gum, two phosphor bands, FCP (gutter pair)	sheets	1.00	1.50
PVAD gum, one phosphor band (centre), PCPI	sheets	0.70	–

■ 10¹/₂p yellow, February 25, 1976

PVAD gum, two phosphor bands	sheets	0.30	0.30

■ 10¹/₂p blue, April 26, 1978

PVAD gum, two phosphor bands	sheets	0.35	0.40

■ 11p orange–pink, February 25, 1976

PVAD gum, two phosphor bands	sheets	0.30	0.30
PVAD gum, PCPI	sheets	0.50	0.50

■ 11¹/₂p sepia, August 15, 1979

PVAD gum, PCP1	sheets	0.30	0.30

■ 11¹/₂p mushroom, January 14, 1981

PVAD gum, one phosphor band (centre)	sheets, coils, booklets	0.30	0.20
PVAD gum, one phosphor band (left)	booklets	0.40	0.40
PVAD gum, one phosphor band (right)	booklets	0.40	0.40

■ 12p yellow–green, January 30, 1980

PVAD gum, PCPI	sheets, coils, booklets	0.30	0.30
PVAD gum, PCPII	sheets	0.80	0.50
PVAD gum, two phosphor bands	booklets, prestige booklets	0.35	0.35

■ 12p emerald–green, October 29, 1985

PVAD gum, one phosphor band (centre)	sheets, booklets, prestige booklets	0.35	0.35
PVAD gum, one phosphor band (centre) (star on gummed side)	sheets	0.40	0.40
PVAD gum, one phosphor band (centre), ACP	sheets	0.40	0.40
PVAD gum, one phosphor band (left)	booklets, prestige booklets	0.40	0.40
PVAD gum, one phosphor band (right)	booklets, prestige booklets	0.40	0.40

■ 12¹/₂p light green, January 27, 1982

PVAD gum, one phosphor band (centre)	sheets, coils, booklets, prestige booklets	0.35	0.35
PVAD gum, one phosphor band (centre), PCPI	sheets	5.00	–
PVAD gum, one phosphor band (left)	booklets, prestige booklets	0.35	0.35
PVAD gum, one phosphor band (right)	booklets, prestige booklets	0.35	0.35
PVAD gum, one phosphor band (centre) (star on gummed side)	booklets	0.55	0.50
PVAD gum, one phosphor band (centre) (simple star on gummed side)	booklets	0.50	0.40

■ 13p olive, August 15, 1979

PVAD gum, PCPI	sheets	0.40	0.40

■ 13p light brown, August 28, 1984

PVAD gum, one phosphor band (centre)	sheets, booklets, prestige booklets	0.30	0.35
PVAD gum, one phosphor band (centre) (star on gummed side)	booklets	0.70	–
PVAD gum, one phosphor band (centre), ACP	sheets	0.30	0.30
PVAD gum, one phosphor band (left)	booklets, prestige booklets	0.30	0.30
PVAD gum, one phosphor band (right)	booklets, prestige booklets	0.30	0.30
PVAD gum, one phosphor band (centre) (litho by Questa)	booklets	0.35	0.35
PVAD gum, one phosphor band (left) (litho by Questa)	booklets	0.35	0.35
PVAD gum, one phosphor band (right) (litho by Questa)	booklets	0.35	0.35

■ 13¹/₂p red–brown, January 30, 1980

PVAD gum, PCPI	sheets	0.50	0.50

■ 14p grey–blue, January 14, 1981

PVAD gum, PCPI	sheets, coils, booklets	0.40	0.30

PVAD gum, PCPII	sheets, coils, booklets	0.50	0.50
PVAD gum, PCP, fluorescent brightener omitted	booklets	2.00	–
PVAD gum, two phosphor bands	booklets	0.40	0.40

■ 14p deep blue, August 23, 1988

PVAD gum, one phosphor band (centre)	sheets, booklets	0.35	0.35
PVAD gum, one phosphor band (right)	booklets	3.00	3.00
PVAD gum, one phosphor band (centre) (litho by Questa)	booklets	1.50	1.50
PVAD gum, one phosphor band (right) (litho by Walsall)	booklets	3.00	3.00

■ 15p blue, August 15, 1979

PVAD gum, PCPI	sheets	0.40	0.45
PVAD gum, PCPII	sheets	0.50	0.55
PVAD gum, one phosphor band (left)	booklets	2.00	2.00
PVAD gum, one phosphor band (centre)	sheets, coils	0.40	0.30
PVAD gum, one phosphor band (right)	booklets	3.00	3.00

■ 15p bright blue, September 26, 1989

PVAD gum, one phosphor band (centre)	sheets, coils	0.45	0.50
PVAD gum, one phosphor band (left)	booklets	1.80	1.50
PVAD gum, one phosphor band (right)	prestige booklets	1.50	1.50

■ 15¹/₂p pale purple, January 14, 1981

PVAD gum, PCPI	sheets, coils, booklets	0.40	0.45
PVAD gum, PCPI	sheets	0.40	0.45
PVAD gum, PCP, fluorescent brightener omitted	sheets	15.00	–
PVAD gum, ACP	sheets, booklets	3.00	2.50
PVAD gum, two phosphor bands	booklets, prestige booklets	0.40	0.45
PVAD gum, two phosphor bands (star on gummed side)	booklets	0.50	0.45

■ 16p light mushroom, March 30, 1983

PVAD gum, PCPI	sheets, booklets, prestige booklets	0.40	0.45
PVAD gum, PCPI ('D' on gummed side)	booklets	0.50	0.45
PVAD gum, ACP	sheets	0.60	0.45
PVAD gum, two phosphor bands	booklets	0.70	0.70

■ 16¹/₂p light brown, January 27 1982

PVAD gum, PCPI	sheets	0.50	0.65
PVAD gum, PCPII	sheets	3.00	2.50

■ 17p sage green, January 30, 1980

PVAD gum, PCPI	sheets	0.50	0.45
PVAD gum, PCPII	sheets	3.00	2.50
PVAD gum, PCP, fluorescent brightener omitted	sheets	1.50	–

■ 17p steel blue, March 30, 1983

PVAD gum, PCPI	sheets, booklets, prestige booklets	0.50	0.45
PVAD gum, PCPI ('D' on gummed side)	booklets	0.50	–
PVAD gum, ACP	sheets, booklets, prestige booklets	0.50	0.45
PVAD gum, two phosphor bands	booklets, prestige booklets	0.45	0.45
PVAD gum, two phosphor bands (stars on gummed side)	booklets	0.50	0.45

■ 17p deep blue, September 4, 1990

PVAD gum, one phosphor band (centre)	sheets	0.50	0.60
PVAD gum, one phosphor band (left)	booklets	1.00	1.00
PVAD gum, one phosphor band (right)	booklets	10.00	10.00
PVAD gum, one phosphor band (centre) (litho by Questa)	booklets	0.40	0.40

■ 17¹/₂p light brown, January 30, 1979

PVAD gum, PCPI	sheets	0.50	0.50
PVAD gum, PCPII	sheets	2.00	1.75

■ **18p violet, January 14, 1981**

PVAD gum, PCPI	sheets	0.50	0.50
PVAD gum, PCPII	sheets	0.70	0.60

■ **18p grey–green, August 28, 1984**

PVAD gum, ACP	sheets	0.40	0.40
PVAD gum, two phosphor bands	booklets	0.50	0.50
PVAD gum, PCP	booklets	0.50	0.50
PVAD gum, PCP (litho by Questa)	booklets	0.50	0.50
PVAD gum, two phosphor bands (litho by Questa)	booklets	5.50	5.50

■ **18p bright green, September 10, 1991**

PVAD gum, one phosphor band (centre)	sheets	0.40	0.45
PVAD gum, one phosphor band (centre) (gravure by Enschedé)	sheets	0.40	0.45
PVAD gum, one phosphor band (centre) (litho by Questa)	booklets	0.50	0.50
PVAD gum, one phosphor band (left) (litho by Questa)	booklets	1.00	1.00
PVAD gum, one phosphor band (right) (litho by Questa)	booklets	0.80	0.90

■ **19p orange–red, August 23, 1988**

PVAD gum, PCP	sheets, booklets	0.50	0.50
PVAD gum, PCP (litho by Questa)	booklets	1.00	1.00
PVAD gum, two phosphor bands (litho by Walsall)	booklets	0.70	0.70

■ **19¹/₂p olive grey, January 27, 1982**

PVAD gum, PCPI	sheets	1.50	1.50

■ **20p dull purple, February 25, 1976**

PVA gum, two phosphor bands (litho by Waddington)	sheets	0.80	0.90
PVAD gum, PCP (litho by Waddington)	sheets	1.00	1.00
PVAD gum, PCP (litho by Waddington) (dull purple and sepia)	sheets	1.00	1.00
PVAD gum, PCP (litho by Questa, perf 15x14)	sheets	0.80	0.50
PVAD gum, two phosphor bands	sheets	0.50	0.50
PVAD gum, PCPI	sheets	0.80	0.80
PVAD gum, PCPII	sheets	0.80	0.80

■ **20p turquoise, August 23, 1988**

PVAD gum, PCP	sheets	0.55	0.50

■ **20p brownish–black, September 26, 1989**

PVAD gum, PCP	sheets, booklets	0.50	0.50
PVAD gum, two phosphor bands	sheets	1.50	1.50

■ **20¹/₂p bright blue, March 30, 1983**

PVAD gum, PCPI	sheets	0.75	0.50

■ **22p deep blue, October 22, 1980**

PVAD gum, PCPI	sheets	0.55	0.50
PVAD gum, PCPII	sheets	0.55	0.50
PVAD gum, experimental coated paper	sheets	2.50	2.00

■ **22p yellow–green, August 28, 1984**

PVAD gum, ACP	sheets	0.55	0.50
PVAD gum, two phosphor bands (litho by Questa)	booklets	5.50	5.50

■ **22p orange–red, September 4, 1990**

PVAD gum, FCP	sheets	0.80	0.70
PVAD gum, PCP	sheets	0.55	0.55
PVAD gum, PCP (litho by Questa)	booklets	0.60	0.50

■ **23p rose, March 30, 1983**

PVAD gum, PCPI	sheets	1.00	1.00

■ 23p bright green, August 23, 1988

PVAD gum, PCP	sheets	0.80	0.80

■ 24p light purple, August 28, 1984

PVAD gum, ACP	sheets	1.00	1.00

■ 24p red, September 26, 1989

PVAD gum, ACP	sheets	1.50	1.50

■ 24p chestnut, September 10, 1991

PVAD gum, ACP	sheets	0.40	0.40
PVAD gum, ACP (litho by Questa)	booklets	0.40	0.40
PVAD gum, two phosphor bands (litho by Questa)	booklets	1.25	1.25
PVAD gum, ACP (litho by Walsall)	booklets	0.75	0.70

■ 25p purple, January 14, 1981

PVAD gum, PCPI	sheets	1.25	0.70
PVAD gum, PCPII	sheets	0.65	0.60

■ 25p rose red, February 6, 1996

PVAD gum, two phosphor bands	coils	7.00	7.00

■ 26p red, January 27, 1982

PVAD gum, PCPI	sheets	0.65	0.60
PVAD gum, ACP	sheets	0.65	0.50
PVAD gum, two phosphor bands	prestige booklets	5.00	5.00
PVAD gum, ACP, narrow value	booklets	5.50	5.50

■ 26p drab, September 4, 1990

PVAD gum, ACP	sheets	1.00	1.00

■ 27p chestnut, August 23, 1988

PVAD gum, ACP	sheets, booklets	0.70	0.70

■ 27p mauve, September 4, 1990

PVAD gum, ACP	sheets	0.70	0.70

■ 28p violet, March 30, 1983

PVAD gum, PCPI	sheets	0.80	0.90
PVAD gum, ACP	sheets	0.80	0.90

■ 28p ochre, August 23, 1988

PVAD gum, ACP	sheets	0.75	0.75

■ 28p blue–grey, September 10, 1991

PVAD gum , ACP	sheets	0.80	0.80

■ 29p sepia, January 27, 1982

PVAD gum, PCPI	sheets	0.80	0.80
PVAD gum, PCPII	sheets	4.00	4.00

■ 29p mauve, September 26, 1989

PVAD gum, ACP	sheets	1.50	1.50
PVAD gum, two phosphor bands (litho by Walsall)	booklets	3.00	3.00
PVAD gum, ACP (litho by Walsall)	booklets	3.00	3.00

■ 30p olive, September 26, 1989

PVAD gum, ACP	sheets	0.80	0.80

■ 31p purple, March 30, 1983

PVAD gum, PCPI	sheets	0.70	0.70

PVAD gum, ACP	sheets	1.00	1.00
PVAD gum, two phosphor bands	prestige booklets	6.00	6.00

■ **31p ultramarine, September 4, 1990**

PVAD gum, ACP	sheets	1.00	0.90
PVA gum, ACP (litho by Walsall)	booklets	1.00	1.00

■ **32p green–blue, August 23, 1988**

PVAD gum, ACP	sheets	1.10	1.10

■ **33p emerald, September 4, 1990**

PVAD gum, ACP	sheets	0.90	0.30
PVA gum, ACP (litho by Questa)	booklets	1.50	1.50
PVAD gum, two phosphor bands (litho by Questa)	booklets	1.00	1.00
PVA gum, ACP (litho by Walsall)	booklets	1.00	1.00

■ **34p sepia, August 28, 1984**

PVAD gum, PCP	sheets	0.90	0.90
PVAD gum, two phosphor bands	prestige booklets	3.75	4.00
PVAD gum, ACP	sheets	1.40	1.25
PVAD gum, two phosphor bands (litho by Questa)	booklets	2.40	2.40

■ **34p blue–grey, September 26, 1989**

PVAD gum, ACP	sheets	1.10	1.10

■ **34p mauve, September 10, 1991**

PVAD gum, ACP	sheets	1.25	1.25

■ **35p sepia, August 23, 1988**

PVAD gum, ACP	sheets	1.00	1.00

■ **35p yellow, September 10, 1991**

PVAD gum, ACP	sheets	1.00	1.00

■ **37p rosine, September 26, 1989**

PVAD gum, ACP	sheets	1.25	1.25

■ **39p mauve, September 10, 1991**

PVAD gum, ACP	sheets	1.10	0.50
PVAD gum, two phosphor bands (litho by Questa)	booklets	1.00	1.00
PVA gum, phosphor paper (litho by Walsall)	booklets	1.10	1.00

■ **50p dull brown, February 2, 1977**

PVAD gum, two phosphor bands	sheets	1.30	0.50
PVAD gum, no phosphor	sheets	2.25	1.50

■ **50p ochre, March 13, 1990**

PVAD gum, ACP	sheets	7.75	7.00
PVAD gum, two phosphor bands	sheets	2.00	2.00

■ **75p deep grey, January 30, 1980**

PVAD gum, no phosphor (litho by Questa, perf 13½x14)	sheets	2.00	2.00
PVA gum, no phosphor (litho by Questa, perf 15x14)	sheets	3.00	1.50
PVAD gum, no phosphor (litho by Questa, perf 15x14)	sheets	3.00	2.00
PVA gum, no phosphor (litho by Questa, perf 15x14, Coated Paper)	sheets	3.75	–

■ **75p grey and black, February 23, 1988**

PVA gum (litho by Questa)	sheets	3.00	3.00

■ **75p grey and black, July 26, 1988**

PVAD gum, no phosphor	sheets	3.00	3.00

FIRST DAY COVERS

First day cover (February 15, 1971)	
½p, 1p, 1½p, 2p, 2½p, 3p, 3½p, 4p, 5p, 6p, 7½p, 9p	2.50
First day cover (August 11, 1971)	
10p	1.00
First day cover (October 24, 1973)	
4½p, 5½p, 8p	1.25
First day cover (September 4, 1974)	
6½p	1.00
First day cover (January 15, 1975)	
7p	1.00
First day cover (September 24, 1975)	
8½p	1.00
First day cover (February 25, 1976)	
9p, 9½p, 10p, 10½p, 11p, 20p	2.25
First day cover (February 2, 1977)	
50p	1.50
First day cover (April 26, 1978)	
10½p	1.00
First day cover (August 15, 1979)	
11½p, 13p, 15p	1.00
First day cover (January 30, 1980)	
4p, 12p, 13½p, 17p, 17½p, 75p	1.50
First day cover (October 22, 1980)	
3p, 22p	1.00
First day cover (January 14, 1981)	
2½p, 11½p, 14p, 15½p, 18p, 25p	1.50
First day cover (January 27, 1982)	
5p, 12½p, 16½p, 19½p, 26p, 29p	1.75
First day cover (March 30, 1983)	
3½p, 16p, 17p, 20½p, 23p, 28p, 31p	2.00
First day cover (August 28, 1984)	
13p, 18p, 22p, 24p, 34p	2.00
First day cover (October 29, 1985)	
7p, 12p	1.00
First day cover (August 23, 1988)	
14p, 19p, 20p, 23p, 27p, 28p, 32p, 35p	2.50
First day cover (September 26, 1989)	
15p, 20p, 24p, 29p, 30p, 34p, 37p	3.00
First day cover (September 4, 1990)	
10p, 17p, 22p, 26p, 27p, 31p, 33p	3.00
First day cover (September 10, 1991)	
6p, 18p 24p, 28p, 34p, 35p, 39p	3.00
First day cover (February 6, 1996)	
25p	10.00

BOOKLET PANES WITHOUT ELLIPTICAL PERFORATIONS, 1971–93

■ **Panes of four with PVA gum**

Two **2p** with two ½p	
vertically se-tenant	3.00
horizontally se-tenant, OCP	3.00
horizontally se-tenant, FCP	0.75
Two **1p** with two 1½p	
vertically se-tenant	3.00
horizontally se-tenant, OCP	3.00
horizontally se-tenant, FCP	1.25

■ **Panes of six with PVA gum**

Five ½p with label 'B ALAN LTD for GB STAMPS'	
perforated label	2.50
imperforate label	4.00
Five ½p with label 'LICK battery failure'	
perforated label	2.50
imperforate label	4.00
Five ½p with label 'MAKE YOUR LUCKY FIND PAY'	
imperforate label only	2.00
Four 2½p (one centre band) with labels	
'UNIFLO STAMPS' and 'STICK FIRMLY'	
perforated labels	3.50
imperforate labels	6.00
Five 2½p (one centre band) with label 'STICK FIRMLY'	
perforated label	2.50
imperforate label	6.00
Five 2½p (one centre band) with label 'TEAR OFF to ESSO'	
perforated label	2.50
imperforate label	8.00
Five 2½p (one centre band) with label 'STAMP COLLECTIONS'	
imperforate label only	2.75
Four 2½p (one centre band) with labels 'DO YOU	
COLLECT GB STAMPS' and 'BUYING OR SELLING'	
imperforate label only	2.75
Five 2½p (one centre band) with label 'B ALAN'	
imperforate label only	2.50
Five 3p (two bands) with label '£4,315 FOR YOU'	
perforated label	2.00
imperforate label, OCP	2.50
imperforate label, FCP	2.00
Four 3p (two bands) with two 2½p (one band at left)	
OCP	9.50
FCP	3.00
Six 3p (two bands)	
OCP	4.00
FCP	2.00
Five 3p (one centre band) with blank label	
imperforate label only	3.00
Five 3½p (two bands) with blank label	
imperforate label only	3.00

■ **Panes of four with PVAD gum**

Two **2p** horizontally se-tenant with two ½p	1.25
Two **1p** horizontally se-tenant with two 1½p	1.50

■ **Panes of six with PVAD gum**

Five **3p** (one centre band) with blank imperforate label	2.00
Five **3½p** (two bands) with blank imperforate label	2.00
Five **3½p** (one centre band) with blank imperforate label	2.00
Five **4½p** (two bands) with blank imperforate label	2.00

SE-TENANT COIL STRIPS WITHOUT ELLIPTICAL PERFORATIONS, 1971–95

■ **Strips with gum Arabic**
One **2p**, two **½p**, two **1p**

OCP		1.50
OCP with silicone		£200
FCP with silicone		3.50

■ **Strips with PVA gum**

One **6p**, one **2p**, one **1p**, two **½p** (two bands), OCP		2.50

■ **Strips with PVAD gum**

One **2p**, two **½p**, two **1p** (two bands), FCP		0.80
One **6p**, one **2p**, one **1p**, two **½p** (two bands), FCP		0.80
Two **½p**, one **7p**, two **1p** (one centre band), FCP		0.50
One **8p**, two **1p**, two labels (one centre band), FCP		0.50
One **2½p** rose, three **3p** pink, PCP		0.60
fluorescent brightener omitted		40.00
One **½p**, three **4p** blue, PCP		0.80
fluorescent brightener omitted		£150
perfect gum		£1,500
One **1p** and three **4p** blue, PCP		0.80
One **2p**, three **4p**, PCP		1.20
Three **4p**, one **3p**, PCP		1.25
Three **4p**, one **5p**, PCP		1.00
Two **5p**, two **4p**, PCP		0.80
Three **5p**, one **4p**, PCP		1.20

NON–VALUE INDICATORS WITHOUT ELLIPTICAL PERFORATIONS, 1989–93

From retail stamp books (at least one edge may be imperforate) or prestige stamp books (marked *).

■ **2nd bright blue (August 22, 1989)**
Printed in gravure by Harrison

with one centre phosphor band	1.00	1.50
with one phosphor band at right*	1.50	1.50

Printed in litho by Walsall

with one centre phosphor band	1.00	1.00

Printed in litho by Questa

with one centre phosphor band	1.00	1.00
with one phosphor band at left*	1.00	1.00
with one phosphor band at right*	1.50	1.50

■ **2nd deep blue (August 7, 1990)**
Printed in gravure by Harrison

with one centre phosphor band	1.00	0.50

Printed in litho by Walsall

with one centre phosphor band	1.00	1.00

Printed in litho by Questa

with one centre phosphor band	1.25	0.90
with one phosphor band at left*	1.25	1.30

■ **1st brownish black (August 22, 1989)**
Printed in gravure by Harrison

on phosphor paper	1.50	1.50
with two phosphor bands*	2.00	2.00

Printed in litho by Walsall

with two phosphor bands	3.00	3.00

Printed in litho by Questa

on phosphor paper	2.10	1.10

■ **1st orange red (August 7, 1990)**
Printed in gravure by Harrison

on phosphor paper	1.10	0.65

Printed in litho by Walsall

on phosphor paper. Perf: 14	1.50	0.65
on phosphor paper. Perf: 13	1.50	1.00

Printed in litho by Questa

on phosphor paper	1.20	0.85
with two phosphor bands*	1.20	1.00

First day cover (August 22, 1989)		
2nd bright blue, 1st brownish black	–	1.50
First day cover (August 7, 1990)		
2nd deep blue, 1st orange red	–	1.50

HIGH VALUES WITHOUT ELLIPTICAL PERFORATIONS, 1970–77

■ **1970, June 17. Large format**
Des: Arnold Machin. Printed in recess by Bradbury, Wilkinson.
No wmk. Perf: 12.

10p cerise, phosphor paper	0.40	0.35
20p olive–green	0.40	0.35
50p ultramarine	1.00	0.40
phosphor paper (Feb 1, 1973)	2.00	0.45
£1 black (Dec 6, 1972)	2.00	0.45
First day cover (10p, 20p, 50p)	–	2.50
First day cover (£1)	–	3.25

(*The £1 differs from the 1969 issue only in that the denomination is in a different typeface.)

1977, February 2. Large format
Des: Arnold Machin. Printed in photogravure by Harrison. Perf: 14x15.

£1 olive, deep green	2.00	0.30
£1.30 steel blue, buff (Aug 3, 1983)	3.00	2.50
£1.33 lilac, deep blue (Aug 28, 1984)	3.50	3.00
£1.41 deep blue, pale blue, green (Sep 17, 1985)	4.00	3.50
£1.50 rose-lilac, blue-black (Sep 2, 1986)	3.25	2.50
£1.60 buff, blue-green (Sep 15, 1987)	3.25	2.75
£2 emerald, deep purple	3.00	0.50
£5 pink, blue	7.50	2.50
Set	24.00	24.00
Gutter pairs	£100	–
Traffic light gutter pairs	£110	–
First day cover (£1, £2, £5)	–	5.00
First day cover (£1.30)	–	3.00
First day cover (£1.33)	–	3.00
First day cover (£1.41)	–	3.00
First day cover (£1.50)	–	3.00
First day cover (£1.60)	–	3.00

SPECIAL ISSUES WITHOUT ELLIPTICAL PERFORATIONS, 1990–2017

1990, January 10. 150th Anniversary of the Penny Black
Des: Jeffery Matthews. Issued in sheets and booklets; the stamps from booklets can have one or more edges imperforate.

Printed in photogravure by Harrison. Issued in sheets, booklets and, where marked *, in the London Life prestige stamp book

15p bright blue (one centre phosphor band)	0.50	0.75
(one phosphor band at left)*	1.75	1.75
(one phosphor band at right)*	1.75	1.75
20p brownish-black and cream (PCP)	0.50	0.50
(two phosphor bands)*	1.00	1.00
29p mauve (PCP)	0.75	0.75
(two phosphor bands)*	4.00	4.00

34p blue-grey	1.00	1.00
37p rosine	1.00	1.00
First day cover	–	3.00

Printed in litho by Walsall. Issued in booklets

15p bright blue (one centre phosphor band)	0.90	0.90
20p brownish-black and cream (PCP)	0.90	0.90

Printed in litho by Questa. Issued in booklets

15p bright blue (one centre phosphor band)	1.50	1.30
20p brownish-black and cream (PCP)	1.50	1.50

Printed in gravure by Walsall. Issued in the 2000 Special by Design prestige stamp book

1st brownish black and cream	1.75	1.75

(*The 1st class and 20p also appear in the 2009 Treasures of the Archive prestige stamp book, printed in litho by Cartor. The 20p also appears in the 2017 Machin Definitive Golden Anniversary miniature sheet, printed in gravure by ISP.)

1999, February 6. Large format
Issued only in the Profile On Print prestige stamp book. Recess stamp engraved by C. Slania.

Printed in litho and embossed by Walsall. Self-adhesive

1st pale grey	1.50	1.50

Printed in recess by Enschedé. Two phosphor bands

1st grey-black	1.50	1.50

Printed in typography by Harrison. Two phosphor bands

1st black	1.50	1.50

2017, June 5. Large format
Issued only in the Machin Definitive Golden Anniversary miniature sheet and the Machin Definitive 50th Anniversary prestige stamp book. Printed in gravure and embossed by International Security Printers.

£1 gold	4.00	4.00

LOW VALUES WITH ELLIPTICAL PERFORATIONS, 1993–2010

With an elliptical perforation towards the lower end of each vertical side.

■ 1993–2005. Printed in gravure by Enschedé

Issued in sheets except where stated. Two phosphor bands, except where stated.

1p crimson (June 8, 1993)	0.30	0.30
2p deep green (April 11, 1995)	0.20	0.20
4p new blue (December 14, 1993)	0.35	0.35
5p claret (June 8, 1993)	0.35	0.35
6p lime green (April 27, 1993)	0.35	0.35
10p orange (June 8, 1993)	0.40	0.40
20p sea green (December 14, 1993)	0.80	0.80
25p salmon pink (October 10, 1995)	0.65	0.70
29p light grey (October 26, 1993)	0.75	0.70
30p grey–green (July 27, 1993)	0.75	0.70
31p deep purple (June 25, 1996)	1.00	0.70
35p deep yellow (August 17, 1993)	0.85	0.70
35p lime–green (April 5, 2005) (one band)	1.00	1.00
35p lime–green (February 23, 2006)		
from Brunel prestige stamp book	1.00	1.00
36p ultramarine (October 26, 1993)	1.65	1.65
37p amethyst (June 25, 1996)	1.00	1.00
38p rosine (October 26, 1993)	1.00	0.80
39p magenta (June 25, 1996)	1.10	1.10
40p turquoise (February 23, 2006)		
from Brunel prestige stamp book	1.80	1.80
41p stone (October 26, 1993)	1.20	1.20
42p olive–grey (May 25, 2004)		
from Glory of the Garden prestige book	1.80	1.80
43p chocolate–brown (June 25, 1996)	1.15	1.10
47p turquoise green (May 25, 2004)		
from Glory of the Garden prestige book	2.25	2.25
50p ochre (December 14, 1993)	1.15	1.20
50p ochre (September 21, 2006)		

from Victoria Cross prestige stamp book	1.15	1.20
63p emerald (June 25, 1996)	1.40	1.30
£1 bluish–violet (August 22, 1995)	2.00	2.00
Stamp card (£1 stamp)	7.50	15.00

■ 1994–1996. Printed in litho by Questa

Issued in booklets and prestige stamp books. Two phosphor bands, except where stated.

1p crimson (July 8, 1995)		
from £1 booklets	0.75	0.55
6p lime–green (July 26, 1994)		
from Northern Ireland prestige stamp book	6.50	5.00
10p deep orange (April 25, 1995)		
from National Trust prestige stamp book	2.30	2.30
19p olive green (July 26, 1994) (one band at left)		
from Northern Ireland prestige stamp book		
and National Trust prestige stamp book	1.00	0.80
(April 25, 1995) (one band at right)		
from National Trust prestige stamp book	1.20	0.80
20p bright green (July 8, 1996) (one centre band)		
from £1 and £2 booklets	1.50	1.30
25p salmon–pink (July 26, 1994)		
from £1 and £2 booklets, and Northern Ireland		
and National Trust prestige stamp books	0.70	0.60
26p red–brown (July 8, 1996)		
from £1 and £2 booklets	0.90	0.80
30p grey–green (April 25, 1995)		
from National Trust prestige stamp book	2.00	2.00
35p deep yellow (April 25, 1995)		
from National Trust prestige stamp book	1.20	1.20
41p drab (April 25, 1995)		
from National Trust prestige stamp book	1.15	1.50

■ 1998–1999. Printed in gravure by Questa

Issued in booklets and prestige stamp books. Two phosphor bands, except where stated.

1p crimson (December 1, 1998)		
from £1 booklets and World Changers		
prestige stamp book	0.75	1.00
2p myrtle–green (April 26, 1999)		
from £1 booklets	0.75	0.75
19p olive green (Apr 26, 1999) (centre phosphor band)		
from £1 and £2 booklets		
and World Changers PSB	0.80	0.80
20p bright green (Dec 1, 1998) (one centre band)		
from £1 and £2 stamp booklets	15.00	15.00
26p red–brown (December 1, 1998)		
from £1 and £2 booklets and		
World Changers prestige stamp book	0.80	0.80

■ 1993–1996. Printed in litho by Walsall

Issued in booklets. Two phosphor bands.

25p salmon–pink (November 1, 1993)		
from £1 booklets	0.80	0.80
35p deep yellow (November 1, 1993)		
from £1.40 booklets	0.90	0.90
37p amethyst (July 8, 1996)		
from £1.48 booklets	2.50	1.50
41p stone (November 1, 1993)		
from £1.64 booklets	1.50	1.50

60p slate–blue (March 19, 1996)
from £2.40 booklets — 1.25 / 1.25
63p emerald (July 8, 1996)
from £2.52 booklets — 1.25 / 1.25

■ 1997–2005. Printed in gravure by Walsall

Issued in booklets and prestige stamp books. Two phosphor bands, except where stated.

10p deep orange (October 13, 1998)
from Breaking Barriers prestige stamp book — 1.00 / 1.00
19p olive–green (Feb 15, 2000) (one band at right)
from Special By Design prestige stamp book — 0.75 / 0.75
30p grey–green (May 5, 1998)
from £1.20 booklet — 0.75 / 0.75
37p amethyst (August 26, 1997)
from £1.48 booklets — 1.00 / 1.00
38p ultramarine (April 26, 1999)
from £1.52 booklet — 1.25 / 1.25
38p ultramarine (February 15, 2000) (perf: 14)
from Special By Design prestige stamp book — 2.00 / 2.00
39p grey (February 24, 2005)
from Bronte prestige stamp book — 5.00 / 5.00
40p grey–blue (April 27, 2000)
from £1.60 booklets — 1.00 / 1.00
42p olive grey (February 24, 2005)
from Bronte prestige stamp book — 5.00 / 5.00
43p chocolate brown (October 13, 1998)
from Breaking Barriers prestige stamp book — 1.50 / 1.50
50p ochre (October 18, 2005)
from Battle of Trafalgar prestige stamp book — 5.00 / 5.00
63p emerald (August 26, 1997)
from £2.52 booklets — 1.50 / 1.50
64p sea–green (April 26, 1999)
from £2.56 booklets — 1.50 / 1.50
65p greenish blue (April 27, 2000)
from £2.60 booklets — 1.50 / 1.50
68p grey–brown (October 18, 2005)
from Battle of Trafalgar prestige stamp book — 5.00 / 5.00

■ 1993–2010. Printed in gravure by Harrisons and later by De La Rue

Issued in sheets. Two phosphor bands, except where stated.

1p crimson (April 1, 1997)	0.30	0.10
2p deep green (May 27, 1997)	0.30	0.10
4p new blue (May 27, 1997)	0.40	0.10
5p claret (May 27, 1997)	0.40	0.20
6p lime green (April 1, 1997)	0.30	0.10
7p light grey (April 20, 1999)	2.25	0.90
7p bright magenta (April 1, 2004)	0.30	0.30
8p deep yellow (April 25, 2000)	0.35	0.30
9p deep orange (April 5, 2005)	0.35	0.25
10p orange (May 8, 1997)	0.40	0.35
12p turquoise (August 1, 2006)	0.40	0.30
14p salmon pink (August 1, 2006)	0.45	0.45
15p shocking pink (April 1, 2008)	0.40	0.40
16p bright pink (March 27, 2007)	0.40	0.40
17p olive green (March 31, 2009)	0.50	0.30
19p olive (Oct 26, 1993) (one band)	0.45	0.40
20p bright green (June 25, 1996) (one centre band)	0.45	0.35

(September 23, 1997) (one band at right)	1.00	1.10
(April 20, 1999) (two bands)	0.45	0.50
22p stone (March 31, 2009)	0.65	0.35
25p salmon–pink		
(October 26, 1993) (PCP)	0.60	0.60
(December 20, 1994)	0.60	0.60
26p reddish brown (June 25, 1996)	0.60	0.60
26p gold (April 29, 1997)	0.60	0.55
30p grey–green (May 12, 1997)	0.75	0.75
31p deep mauve (August 26, 1997)	0.80	0.80
33p slate–blue (April 25, 2000)	0.65	0.65
34p lime green (May 6, 2003)	4.00	4.00
35p yellow (Nov 1, 1993) (PCP)	5.00	5.00
35p sepia (April 1, 2004)	1.00	0.75
35p lime–green (April 26, 2005)	1.00	1.00
37p amethyst (July 8, 1996)	1.15	1.15
37p bright mauve (August 7, 1997)	1.15	1.15
37p deep grey (July 4, 2002)	1.25	1.25
37p olive green (March 28, 2006)	0.85	0.45
38p ultramarine (April 20, 1999)	1.50	0.70
39p magenta (May 12, 1997)	1.10	1.10
39p grey (April 1, 2004)	1.20	1.20
40p greyish blue (April 20, 1999)	1.20	1.20
40p turquoise (April 1, 2004)	1.20	1.20
41p drab (Nov 1, 1993) (PCP)	5.50	4.50
41p rosine (April 20, 1999)	1.00	1.00
42p olive–grey (July 4, 2002)	1.30	1.30
43p chocolate–brown (July 8, 1996)	2.95	2.95
43p brown (March 21, 1997)	4.00	3.50
43p emerald (April 1, 2004)	1.20	0.95
44p stone (April 20, 1999)	3.00	3.00
44p ultramarine (March 28, 2006)	1.00	1.00
45p mauve (April 20, 1999)	1.00	0.85
46p light brown (April 5, 2005)	1.95	0.80
47p turquoise green (July 4, 2002)	1.25	1.25
48p purple (March 27, 2007)	1.00	1.00
49p rust (March 28, 2006)	1.50	1.50
50p ochre (April 1, 1997)	1.50	1.50
50p grey (March 27, 2007)	1.00	0.95
54p rust (March 27, 2007)	1.30	1.30
56p lime green (April 1, 2008)	1.20	1.20
60p emerald green (March 30, 2010)	1.15	1.15
62p red (March 31, 2009)	1.20	1.20
63p emerald (December 12, 1996)	1.35	1.35
64p sea green (April 20, 1999)	2.35	2.35
65p greenish blue (April 25, 2000)	1.85	1.85
67p rhododendron (March 30, 2010)	1.25	1.25
68p grey–brown (July 4, 2002)	2.00	2.00
72p red (March 28, 2004)	1.75	1.75
78p emerald green (March 27, 2007)	1.50	1.50
81p sea green (April 1, 2008)	1.50	1.50
88p shocking pink (March 30, 2010)	1.60	1.60
90p ultramarine (March 31, 2009)	1.75	1.75
97p mauve (March 30, 2010)	2.00	1.60
£1 bluish–violet (April 1, 1997)	2.40	2.40
£1 ruby (June 5, 2007)	2.00	2.00
£1.48 dark turquoise (March 30, 2010)	2.50	2.50
Stamp cards (24 values current in September 2008, including non–value–indicators)	30.00	50.00

(*The 2p, 5p, 37p deep grey, 46p, 48p and £1 ruby also appear in prestige stamp books, and the £1 ruby and £1 bluish-violet in the 40th Anniversary of the Machin miniature sheet of 2007.)

■ 2009. Printed in litho by De La Rue
Issued in prestige stamp books.

5p deep claret (February 12, 2009)		
from Darwin prestige stamp book	1.00	1.00
10p orange (February 12, 2009)		
from Darwin prestige stamp book	1.50	1.50
48p purple (February 12, 2009)		
from Darwin prestige stamp book	1.80	1.80

■ 2009–2010. Printed in litho by Cartor
Issued in prestige stamp books.

1p crimson (September 17, 2009)		
from Royal Navy Uniforms prestige book	1.50	1.50
5p deep claret (February 25, 2010) with wrong font		
from Classic Album Covers prestige book	2.50	2.00
5p deep claret (May 13, 2010)		
from Britain Alone prestige book	1.75	1.75
10p orange-brown (February 25, 2010)		
from Classic Album Covers		
and Britain Alone prestige books	2.00	2.00
16p bright pink (January 13, 2009)		
from Design Classics prestige book	2.00	2.00
17p olive green (August 18, 2009)		
from Treasures of the Archive and		
Royal Navy Uniforms prestige books	1.25	1.25
20p bright green (February 25, 2010)		
from Classic Album Covers prestige book	2.00	2.00
22p stone (August 18, 2009)		
from Treasures of the Archive, Classic Album		
Covers and Royal Society prestige books	2.95	2.95
50p grey (January 13, 2009)		
from Design Classics prestige book	3.00	2.00
54p rust (February 25, 2010) with wrong font		
from Classic Album Covers and		
Royal Society prestige books	2.50	2.50
60p emerald-green (May 13, 2010)		
from Britain Alone prestige book	5.00	5.00
62p red (August 18, 2009)		
from Treasures of the Archive and		
Classic Album Covers prestige books	1.95	2.25
90p ultramarine (September 17, 2009)		
from Royal Navy Uniforms prestige book	3.50	3.50

(*Two prestige stamp books issued in 2010 included definitives using the wrong font for the '5' of 5p and '54' of 54p.)

First day cover (October 26, 1993)		
19p, 25p, 29p, 36p, 38p, 41p	–	4.00
First day cover (August 9, 1994)		
60p	–	1.50
First day cover (August 22, 1995)		
£1	–	1.75
First day cover (June 25, 1996)		
20p, 26p, 31p, 37p, 39p, 43p, 63p	–	4.25
First day cover (April 21, 1997)		
26p, together with 1st gold	–	2.00
First day cover (April 20, 1999)		
7p, 38p, 44p, 64p	–	3.50

First day cover (April 25, 2000)		
8p, 33p, 40p, 41p, 45p, 65p	–	4.00
First day cover (July 4, 2002)		
37p, 42p, 47p, 68p	–	4.00
First day cover (May 6, 2003)		
34p	–	2.00
First day cover (April 1, 2004)		
7p, 35p, 39p, 40p, 43p	–	7.00
First day cover (April 5, 2005)		
9p, 35p, 46p	–	3.50
First day cover (March 28, 2006)		
37p, 44p, 49p, 72p	–	6.00
First day cover (August 1, 2006)		
12p, 14p, with Pricing in Proportion stamps	–	4.50
First day cover (March 27, 2007)		
16p, 48p, 50p, 54p, 78p	–	5.50
First day cover (June 5, 2007)		
£1	–	4.00
First day cover (April 1, 2008)		
15p, 56p, 81p	–	3.50
First day cover (March 31, 2009)		
17p, 22p, 62p, 90p	–	4.00
First day cover (March 30, 2010)		
60p, 67p, 88p, 97p, £1.46, with Europe, Worldwide NVIs		6.00

NON-VALUE INDICATORS WITH ELLIPTICAL PERFORATIONS, 1993–2000

Issued in sheets, booklets or coils. 2nd class stamps have one centre phosphor band; the others have two phosphor bands, except where stated.

■ 1993–1999. Printed in gravure by Harrison or (from 1999) De La Rue

2nd bright blue (September 7, 1993)	1.25	1.20
1st orange-red		
(April 6, 1993) (PCP)	1.20	1.00
(April 4, 1995) (two phosphor bands)	1.20	1.00
1st gold (April 21, 1997)	1.30	1.00
E deep blue (October 5, 1999)	2.00	2.00
Stamp card (1st gold)	2.50	7.00

1993. Printed in litho by Walsall

2nd bright blue (April 6, 1993)	1.00	0.80
1st orange–red (April 6, 1993)	1.20	1.00

1997–1999. Printed in gravure by Walsall

2nd bright blue (April 29, 1997)	1.00	0.80
1st gold (April 21, 1997)	1.20	1.20
1st orange–red (August 26, 1997)	1.20	1.20
E deep blue (January 19, 1999)	2.00	2.00

1993. Printed in litho by Questa

2nd bright blue (April 6, 1993)	1.00	0.80
1st orange–red (April 6, 1993)	1.20	1.20

1998–2000. Printed in gravure by Questa

2nd bright blue (Dec 1, 1998) (perf: 14)	1.20	1.20
2nd bright blue (Apr 27, 2000) (perf: 15x14)	1.00	0.90
1st orange–red (Dec 1, 1998) (perf: 14)	1.20	1.20
1st orange–red (Apr 27, 2000) (perf: 15x14)	1.20	1.20

First day cover (April 6, 1993)		
2nd bright blue, 1st orange–red	–	6.00
First day cover (April 21, 1997)		
1st gold, together with 26p	–	2.00
First day cover (January 19, 1999)		
E deep blue	–	2.00

(*The 2nd class bright blue printed in gravure by Enschedé and Walsall, the 1st class orange–red printed in gravure by Questa, the 1st class gold printed in gravure by De La Rue, Enschedé, Questa and Walsall, and the E deep blue printed in gravure by Enschedé and Questa also appear in prestige stamp books.)

NON–VALUE INDICATORS WITH ELLIPTICAL PERFORATIONS IN GREETINGS CARD SHEETLETS, 1994–97

Small sheets including one 1st class orange–red stamp sold in conjunction with greetings cards, through Boots and other retail outlets.

1994–1995. Printed in litho by Questa

1st sheetlet with Boots logo (Aug 17, 1994)	1.50	2.00
1st sheetlet with no logo (Sep 11, 1995)	1.50	1.20

1997. Printed in litho by Enschedé

1st sheetlet with no logo (Apr 29, 1997)	1.50	1.15

PRICING IN PROPORTION ISSUES WITH ELLIPTICAL PERFORATIONS, 2006–07

2006–07. Printed in gravure by De La Rue or Enschedé

Issued in sheets, business sheets and coils.

2nd blue (August 1, 2006)	1.00	1.00
2nd Large blue (August 1, 2006)	1.30	1.20
1st gold (August 1, 2006)	1.20	1.10
1st Large gold (August 1, 2006)	1.60	1.60
First day cover (together with 12p, 14p)		5.00

(*All four values printed in gravure by De La Rue, and the 1st class printed in gravure by Enschedé, also appear in prestige stamp books.)

HIGH VALUES WITH ELLIPTICAL PERFORATIONS, 1999–2003

1999. Printed in intaglio by Enschedé

£1.50 red (March 9, 1999)	2.75	2.00
£2 blue (March 9, 1999)	3.50	2.00
£3 violet (March 9, 1999)	5.00	4.00
£5 brown (March 9, 1999)	8.00	6.00
First day cover	–	12.50

2000. Printed in intaglio by De La Rue

£1.50 red (April 11, 2000)	2.75	2.00
£2 blue (April 11, 2000)	3.50	3.00
£3 violet (April 11, 2000)	5.00	4.00
£5 brown (April 11, 2000)	8.00	7.00
First day cover	–	30.00

2003. Printed in gravure by De La Rue

£1.50 brown–red (July 1, 2003)	2.75	2.75
£2 blue–green (July 1, 2003)	3.50	3.00
£3 mauve (July 1, 2003)	5.50	3.00
£5 grey–blue (July 1, 2003)	8.50	5.00
First day cover	–	15.00

SPECIAL ISSUES, 2000–17

2000, January 6. Millennium definitive

Des: R. Scholey.
Printed in gravure by De La Rue. Perf: 15x14. Issued in sheets

1st olive–brown	1.20	1.00

Printed in gravure by Walsall. Perf: 15x14. Issued in booklets

1st olive–brown	1.20	1.00

Printed in gravure by Walsall. Perf: 14. Issued in the Special By Design and Treasury Of Trees prestige stamp books

1st olive–brown	1.10	1.00

Printed in gravure by Questa. Perf: 14. Issued in booklets

1st olive–brown	1.10	1.00

Printed in gravure by Questa. Perf: 15x14. Issued in the Queen Elizabeth The Queen Mother prestige stamp book

1st olive–brown	1.30	1.20
First day cover	–	2.00
Stamp card	9.00	30.00

(*This design also appears in the 2017 Machin Definitive Golden Anniversary miniature sheet and the 2017 Machin Definitive 50th Anniversary prestige stamp book, printed in gravure by ISP.)

2000, May 22. Stamp Show 2000 Exhibition Souvenir

Des: Jeffery Matthews. Printed by De La Rue. Phosphor paper. Miniature sheet comprising 4p blue, 5p claret, 6p lime green, 10p orange, 31p purple, 39p magenta, 64p sea–green, £1 bluish violet, plus labels featuring the Royal Mail crest and the Jeffery Matthews colour palette.

Miniature sheet	15.00	15.00
First day cover	–	10.00

2010, May 8. London 2010 Festival of Stamps Exhibition Souvenir

Printed by De La Rue. Two phosphor bands. Miniature sheet comprising 1p, 2p, 5p, 9p, 10p, 20p, 60p, 67p, 88p, 97p, £1.46, plus a label featuring the London 2010: Festival of Stamps logo.

Miniature sheet	5.00	5.00
First day cover	–	9.00

2011, September 14. Centenary of the Birth of Arnold Machin

Printed by Cartor. Miniature sheet comprising ten 1st class gold, with security overlay.

Miniature sheet	12.00	12.00
First day cover	–	12.00

2017, June 5. The Machin Definitive Golden Anniversary Celebration

Des: Atelier Works. Printed in gravure by ISP. Miniature sheet comprising 5p violet (1971), 20p brownish–black and cream Penny Black Anniversary (1990), 1st orange–red (1993), 1st olive–brown (2000), 1st gold Pricing in Proportion (2006), 1st red (2013; source code MMIL, date code 17), £1 gold (2017).

Miniature sheet	8.00	12.00
First day cover	–	12.00
Press sheet	50.00	

SELF–ADHESIVES, 1993–2010

All with elliptical perforations except where otherwise stated.

■ 1993, October 19
Des: Jeffery Matthews. Printed in litho by Walsall. Horizontal format. Issued only in booklets of 20.

1st orange–red	1.10	1.10
Stamp card	6.00	7.00
First day cover	–	1.50

(*This design also appears, with standard gum, in the 2017 Machin Definitive Golden Anniversary miniature sheet, printed in gravure.)

■ 1997, March 18
Des: Jeffery Matthews. Printed in gravure by Enschedé. Horizontal format with 'st' or 'nd' in large size. Issued only in rolls of 100.

2nd bright blue	1.35	1.20
1st orange–red	1.35	1.20
First day cover	–	3.00

■ 1998, April 6
Printed in gravure by Walsall in booklets and business sheets of 100, by Questa in business sheets of 100 (1st class only) and by Enschedé in rolls of 200 and business sheets of 100. Die–cut perf: 15x14 except where stated.

2nd bright blue	1.00	1.00
2nd bright blue (Perf: 14½x14)	£175	£175

1st orange–red	1.10	1.10
1st orange–red (Perf: 14½x14)	£135	£155

(*Perf: 14½x14 stamps were printed only by Walsall, and sold only individually through Royal Mail's philatelic service.)

■ 2002, June 5
Printed in gravure by De La Rue, Questa and Walsall in retail booklets, and by Enschedé and Walsall in business sheets of 100.

1st gold	1.20	1.00

■ 2002, July 4. Overseas rates
Printed in gravure by Walsall. Issued only in retail booklets.

E deep blue	2.25	1.60
42p olive–grey	4.50	2.50
68p grey–brown	5.00	2.60

■ 2003–2010. Overseas rates with airmail chevrons
Des: Sedley Place. Printed in gravure by Walsall. Issued only in booklets, although individual stamps were sold through Royal Mail's philatelic service.

Europe up to 40g (March 27, 2003)	1.95	1.95
Europe up to 20g (March 30, 2010)	1.95	1.95
Worldwide up to 40g (March 27, 2003)	2.20	2.20
Worldwide up to 20g (March 30, 2010)	2.95	2.95
Worldwide Postcard (April 1, 2004)	2.95	2.95
First day cover (March 27, 2003)	–	3.00
First day cover (April 1, 2004)	–	3.25
First day cover (March 30 2010, with other values)	–	7.00
Stamp cards (E40g, W40g)	2.50	10.00

■ 2006. Pricing in Proportion
Des: Jeffery Matthews. Printed in gravure by Walsall and Enschedé. Issued in booklets, coils and business sheets.

2nd blue (September 12, 2006)	1.00	1.00
2nd Large blue (August 15, 2006)	1.50	1.50
1st gold (September 12, 2006)	1.10	1.10
1st Large gold (August 15, 2006)	1.85	1.85
First day cover (2nd Large, 1st Large)	–	3.00
First day cover (2nd, 1st)	–	3.00

DEFINITIVES WITH ADDITIONAL SECURITY FEATURES, 2009 to date

Stamps feature U–shaped security slits, and/or an iridescent wavy–line overlay text inscribed 'Royal Mail', with variant letters which indicate the source of the stamp (if not from counter sheets), and the year of production (from 2010).

Source codes are 'FOYAL' or 'MF1L' (booklets of four), 'MSIL' (booklets of six), 'MTIL' (booklets of 12), 'MCIL' (booklets which include special issues), 'ROYBL' or 'MBIL' (business sheets), 'MRIL' (rolls), 'MPIL' (prestige stamp books) and 'MMIL' (miniature sheets).

Year codes are 'MA10' (2010), 'MA11' or 'M11L' (2011), 'MA12' or 'M12L' (2012), 'MA13' or 'M13L' (2013), 'MA14' or 'M14L' (2014), 'M15L' (2015), 'M16L' (2016), 'M17L' (2017) and 'M18L' (2018).

From 2016, mint stamps also feature security backing paper (SBP) with underlay text. This text can be found all upright, or upright and inverted in alternating double lines.

■ 2009 to date. Non–value indicators

Printed in gravure by De La Rue (sheets up to 2017) or Walsall (sheets from 2018, booklets and business sheets), or litho by Cartor (prestige stamp books). Self–adhesive, with slits and overlay text, except where stated.

2nd blue (February 17, 2009)

no source code, no date code	2.00	2.00
no source code, date code 10	2.75	2.75
no source code, date code 11	3.95	3.95
no source code, date code 12	1.50	1.50
no source code, date code 13	1.50	1.50
no source code, date code 14	1.50	1.30
no source code, date code 15	1.50	1.30
no source code, date code 16	1.50	1.50
no source code, date code 17	1.75	1.75
no source code, date code 17, SBP	1.50	1.50
no source code, date code 18, SBP	1.50	1.50
no source code, date code 19, SBP	1.50	1.50
source code MTIL, no date code	1.75	1.75
source code MTIL, date code 10	4.75	4.75
source code MTIL, date code 11	2.00	2.00
source code MTIL, date code 12	2.00	2.00
source code MTIL, date code 13	1.75	1.75
source code MTIL, date code 14	1.50	1.50
source code MTIL, date code 15	1.50	1.50
source code MTIL, date code 16	1.75	1.75
source code MTIL, date code 16, SBP	3.00	3.00
source code MTIL, date code 17, SBP	1.75	1.75
source code MTIL, date code 18, SBP	1.75	1.75

source code MBIL, no date code	2.50	2.50
source code MBIL, date code 10	4.50	4.50
source code MBIL, date code 11	3.00	2.50
source code MBIL, date code 12	1.75	1.75
source code MBIL, date code 13	1.75	1.75
source code MBIL, date code 14	1.75	1.75
source code MBIL, date code 15	1.75	1.75
source code MBIL, date code 16	1.75	1.75
source code MBIL, date code 16, SBP	2.00	2.00
source code MBIL, date code 17, SBP	1.80	1.80
source code MBIL, date code 18, SBP	1.80	1.80
source code MBIL, date code 19, SBP	1.50	1.50
source code MRIL, no date code	3.00	3.00
source code MRIL, date code 10	–	30.00
source code MRIL, date code 10, gum, no slits	2.50	2.00
source code MRIL, date code MA12	3.00	3.00
source code MRIL, date code M12L	3.00	3.00
source code MRIL, date code 15	3.00	3.00
source code MPIL, date code 10	5.00	5.00
source code MPIL, date code 15, gum, no slits	1.50	1.50
source code MPIL, date code 17, gum, no slits	1.50	1.50

2nd Large blue (February 17, 2009)

no source code, no date code	3.75	3.75
no source code, date code 10	7.95	7.95
no source code, date code 11	2.00	2.00
no source code, date code 12	2.00	2.00
no source code, date code 13	1.75	1.75
no source code, date code 14	1.75	1.75
no source code, date code 15	1.75	1.75
no source code, date code 16	1.75	1.75
no source code, date code 17, SBP	1.75	1.75
no source code, date code 18, SBP	1.75	1.75
no source code, date code 19, SBP	1.75	1.75
source code FOYAL, no date code	2.50	2.50
source code MFIL, date code 10	16.00	16.00
source code MFIL, date code 11	2.00	2.00
source code MFIL, date code 12	2.75	2.75
source code MFIL, date code 13	3.00	3.00
source code MFIL, date code 14	2.00	2.00
source code MFIL, date code 15	4.50	4.50
source code MFIL, date code 16	5.00	5.00
source code MFIL, date code 16, SBP	2.25	2.25
source code MFIL, date code 17, SBP	2.25	2.25
source code MFIL, date code 18, SBP	2.25	2.25
source code MFIL, date code 19 SBP	2.25	2.25
source code ROYBL, no date code	2.50	2.50
source code MBIL, date code 10	16.00	16.00

source code MBIL, date code 11	2.25	2.25
source code MBIL, date code 12	2.25	2.25
source code MBIL, date code 13	2.00	2.00
source code MBIL, date code 14	1.95	1.95
source code MBIL, date code 15	2.50	2.50
source code MBIL, date code 16	2.00	2.00
source code MBIL, date code 16, SBP	2.00	2.00
source code MBIL, date code 17, SBP	2.25	2.25
source code MBIL, date code 19, SBP	2.25	2.25

1st gold (February 17, 2009)

no source code, no date code	2.50	2.50
no source code, date code 10	2.50	2.50
no source code, date code 11	2.00	2.00
no source code, date code 12	1.50	1.50
source code MSIL, no date code	3.25	3.25
source code MSIL, date code 10	2.50	2.50
source code MSIL, date code 11	2.50	2.50
source code MTIL, no date code	1.75	1.75
source code MTIL, date code 10	3.00	3.00
source code MTIL, date code 11	2.00	2.00
source code MTIL, date code 12	5.00	5.00
source code MCIL, no date code	1.50	1.50
source code MCIL, date code 10	2.00	2.00
source code MCIL, date code 11	2.00	2.00
source code MPIL, date code 10	1.95	1.95
source code MPIL, date code 11, gum, no slits	5.00	5.00
source code MBIL, no date code	2.50	2.50
source code MBIL, date code 10	5.00	5.00
source code MBIL, date code 11	3.00	3.00
source code MRIL, no date code	3.00	3.00
source code MRIL, date code 10	4.50	4.50
source code MRIL, date code 10, gum, no slits	2.50	3.00
source code MRIL, date code 12	3.00	3.00

(*The 1st gold also exists with slits but no overlay text, from rolls.)

1st Large gold (February 17, 2009)

no source code, no date code	2.50	2.50
no source code, date code 10	5.00	5.00
no source code, date code 11	4.00	4.00
source code FOYAL, no date code	3.00	3.00
source code MFIL, date code 10	5.00	5.00
source code MFIL, date code 11	2.50	2.50
source code ROYBL, no date code	2.50	2.50
source code MBIL, date code 10	5.75	5.75
source code MBIL, date code 11	3.50	3.50

1st red (January 3, 2013)

no source code, date code 12	1.40	1.40
no source code, date code 13	1.50	1.50
no source code, date code 14	1.50	1.50
no source code, date code 15	3.00	3.00
no source code, date code 16	1.50	1.50
source code MBIL, date code 12	1.50	1.50
source code MBIL, date code 13	1.50	1.50
source code MBIL, date code 14	1.50	1.50
source code MBIL, date code 15	3.25	3.25
source code MBIL, date code 16	1.60	1.60
source code MSIL, date code 12	1.75	1.75
source code MSIL, date code 13	2.20	2.20
source code MSIL, date code 14	1.60	1.60
source code MSIL, date code 15	2.75	2.75
source code MTIL, date code 12	1.75	1.75
source code MTIL, date code 13	1.75	1.75
source code MTIL, date code 14	1.50	1.50
source code MTIL, date code 15	2.50	2.50
source code MTIL, date code 16	1.60	1.60
source code MCIL, date code 12	1.60	1.60
source code MCIL, date code 13	1.50	1.50
source code MCIL, date code 14	1.25	1.25
source code MCIL, date code 15	1.50	1.50
source code MRIL, date code 12	2.00	2.00
source code MRIL, date code 13	2.00	2.00
source code MPIL, date code 13, gum, no slits	1.75	1.00
source code MPIL, date code 15, gum, no slits	2.35	2.35
source code MPIL, date code 16, gum, no slits	2.50	2.50
source code MPIL, date code 17, gum, no slits	2.25	2.25
source code MMIL, date code 17, gum, no slits	2.25	2.25

1st Large red (January 3, 2013)
no source code, date code 12	2.25	2.25
no source code, date code 13	3.50	3.50
no source code, date code 14	2.25	2.25
no source code, date code 15	2.00	2.00
no source code, date code 16	2.00	2.00
source code MBIL, date code 12	2.25	2.25
source code MBIL, date code 13	2.25	2.25
source code MBIL, date code 14	2.25	2.25
source code MBIL, date code 15	3.25	3.25
source code MBIL, date code 16	2.25	2.25
source code MFIL, date code 12	2.00	2.00
source code MFIL, date code 13	2.50	2.50
source code MFIL, date code 14	2.00	2.00
source code MFIL, date code 15	2.50	2.50
source code MFIL, date code 16	2.60	2.60

1st deep red (October 20, 2016)
no source code, date code 17, SBP	1.50	1.50
no source code, date code 18, SBP	1.90	1.90
no source code, date code 19, SBP	2.50	2.50
source code MBIL, date code 16	2.50	2.50
source code MBIL, date code 16, SBP	2.50	2.50
source code MBIL, date code 17, SBP	2.50	2.50
source code MBIL, date code 18, SBP	2.50	2.50
source code MBIL, date code 19, SBP	2.50	2.50
source code MCIL, date code 16	1.50	1.50
source code MCIL, date code 17, SBP	1.50	1.50
source code MCIL, date code 18, SBP	1.50	1.50
source code MCIL, date code 19, SBP	1.50	1.50
source code MSIL, date code 16	1.50	1.50
source code MSIL, date code 16, SBP	1.70	1.70
source code MSIL, date code 17, SBP	1.70	1.70
source code MSIL, date code 18, SBP	1.70	1.70
source code MPIL, date code 16, gum, no slits	2.25	2.25
source code MPIL, date code 18, gum, no slits	1.75	1.75
source code MTIL, date code 16	1.65	1.65
source code MTIL, date code 16, SBP	1.95	1.95
source code MTIL, date code 17, SBP	1.95	1.95
source code MTIL, date code 18, SBP	1.80	1.80

1st Large deep red (October 20, 2016)
no source code, date code 17, SBP	2.50	2.50
no source code, date code 18, SBP	2.75	2.75
no source code, date code 19, SBP	2.75	2.75
source code MBIL, date code 16	2.40	2.40
source code MBIL, date code 17, SBP	2.40	2.40
source code MBIL, date code 18, SBP	2.40	2.40
source code MFIL, date code 16	2.60	2.60
source code MFIL, date code 17, SBP	2.60	2.60
source code MFIL, date code 18, SBP	2.60	2.60

■ **2009 to date. Denominated definitives**
Printed in gravure by De La Rue or Walsall (sheets), or litho by Cartor (prestige stamp books). Self–adhesive, with security slits and iridescent overlay text, except where stated.
1p dark maroon (March 8, 2011)
no overlay text	0.20	0.20
no source code, date code 12	0.25	0.25

no source code, date code 15	0.25	0.25
no source code, date code 16	0.25	0.25
no source code, date code 17	0.25	0.25
no source code, date code 17, SBP	0.25	0.25
no source code, date code 18, SBP	0.25	0.25
no source code, date code 19, SBP	0.25	0.25
source code MPIL, date code 13, gum, no slits	1.50	1.50
source code MPIL, date code 14, gum, no slits	1.00	1.00
source code MPIL, date code 18, gum, no slits	1.00	1.00
source code M IL, date code 18, gum, no slits	1.00	1.00

2p dark green (March 8, 2011)

no overlay text	0.30	0.30
no source code, date code 12	0.30	0.30
no source code, date code 14	0.30	0.30
no source code, date code 15	0.30	0.30
no source code, date code 16	0.30	0.30
no source code, date code 17	0.45	0.45
no source code, date code 17, SBP	0.45	0.45
no source code, date code 18, SBP	0.45	0.45
source code MPIL, date code 13, gum, no slits	1.25	1.25
source code MPIL, date code 14, gum, no slits	1.00	1.00
source code MPIL, date code 16, gum, no slits	1.00	1.00
source code MPIL, date code 18, gum, no slits	0.20	0.20
source code MPIL, date code 19, gum, no slits	0.20	0.20

5p ash pink (March 8, 2011)

no overlay text	0.35	0.35
no source code, date code 12	0.40	0.40
no source code, date code 14	1.95	2.00
no source code, date code 15	0.40	0.40
no source code, date code 16	0.40	0.40
no source code, date code 17, SBP	0.40	0.40
no source code, date code 18, SBP	0.40	0.40
source code MPIL, date code 12, gum, no slits	1.50	1.50
source code MPIL, date code 13, gum, no slits	1.50	1.50
source code MPIL, date code 15, gum, no slits	0.40	0.40
source code MPIL, date code 16, gum, no slits	0.40	0.40
source code MPIL, date code 17, gum, no slits	0.40	0.40
source code M IL, date code 18, gum, no slits	0.40	0.40

10p light tan (March 8, 2011)

no overlay text	0.30	0.30
no source code, date code 12	0.40	0.40
no source code, date code 13	0.40	0.40
no source code, date code 14	0.40	0.40
no source code, date code 15	0.40	0.40
no source code, date code 16	0.40	0.40
no source code, date code 17	0.50	0.50
no source code, date code 17, SBP	0.50	0.50
no source code, date code 18, SBP	0.50	0.50
no source code, date code 19, SBP	0.50	0.50
source code MPIL, date code 12, gum, no slits	1.50	1.50
source code MPIL, date code 13, gum, no slits	1.50	1.50
source code MPIL, date code 14, gum, no slits	1.00	1.00
source code MPIL, date code 15, gum, no slits	0.35	0.35
source code MPIL, date code 16, gum, no slits	0.35	0.35
source code MPIL, date code 18, gum, no slits	0.35	0.35

20p light green (March 8, 2011)

no overlay text	0.65	0.65
no source code, date code 12	0.75	0.75
no source code, date code 13	1.15	1.15
no source code, date code 14	0.60	0.40

no source code, date code 15	0.60	0.60
no source code, date code 16	0.65	0.65
no source code, date code 17, SBP	0.65	0.65
no source code, date code 18, SBP	0.65	0.65
no source code, date code 19, SBP	0.65	0.65
source code MPIL, date code 12, gum, no slits	0.50	0.50
source code MPIL, date code 14, gum, no slits	1.00	1.00
source code MPIL, date code 17, gum, no slits	0.60	0.60
source code MPIL, date code 18, gum, no slits	0.75	0.75
source code M IL, date code 18, gum, no slits	0.75	0.75

50p grey (February 17, 2009)

no source code, no date code	1.25	1.25
source code MPIL, date code 10	7.00	7.00
source code MPIL, date code 11	3.00	3.00

50p slate–grey (January 3, 2013)

no source code, date code 12	1.35	1.35
no source code, date code 17, SBP	1.45	1.45
source code MPIL, date code 13, gum, no slits	2.00	2.00
source code MPIL, date code 15, gum, no slits	1.75	1.75
source code MPIL, date code 18, gum, no slits	1.75	1.75
source code MPIL, date code 19, gum, no slits	1.75	1.75

68p sea green (March 29, 2011)

no source code, date code 11	1.50	1.50
no source code, date code 12	6.25	6.25
source code MPIL, date code 11, gum, no slits	3.25	3.25

76p bright pink (March 29, 2011)

no source code, date code 11	1.50	1.50
no source code, date code 12	1.75	1.75
source code MPIL, date code 11, gum, no slits	5.00	5.00

78p orchard mauve (March 27, 2013)

no source code, date code 13 (Walsall)	1.75	1.75
no source code, date code 13 (De La Rue)	3.00	3.00

81p holly green (March 26, 2014)

no source code, date code 14	1.70	1.70

81p sea green (February 19, 2015)

source code MPIL, date code 14, gum, no slits	1.70	1.70

87p orange (April 25, 2012)

no source code, date code 12	3.00	3.00
source code MPIL, date code 12, gum, no slits	4.00	4.00

88p amber yellow (March 27, 2013)

no source code, date code 13 (Walsall)	1.95	1.95
no source code, date code 13 (De La Rue)	2.50	2.50

97p purple (March 26, 2014)

no source code, date code 14	1.90	1.90
source code MPIL, date code 14, gum, no slits	2.50	2.50

£1 ruby (February 17, 2009)

no source code, no date code	2.00	2.00
no source code, date code 11	5.00	5.00
no source code, date code 12	4.00	4.00
source code MPIL, date code 17, gum, no slits	2.00	2.00

£1 wood brown (January 3, 2013)

no source code, date code 12	3.50	3.50
no source code, date code 14	2.50	2.50
no source code, date code 15	2.50	2.50
no source code, date code 16	3.00	3.00
no source code, date code 18, SBP	2.50	2.50
no source code, date code 19, SBP	2.50	2.50
source code MPIL, date code 14, gum, no slits	2.50	2.50
source code MPIL, date code 15, gum, no slits	2.50	2.50

£1.05 gooseberry green (March 22, 2016)

no source code, date code 16	2.25	2.25
source code MPIL, date code 16, gum, no slits	2.50	2.50
£1.10 lime green (March 29, 2011)		
no source code, date code 11	2.50	2.50
no source code, date code 12	£400	–
£1.17 sunrise red (March 21, 2017)		
no source code, date code 17	2.25	2.25
no source code, date code 17, SBP	2.50	2.50
source code MPIL, date code 17, gum, no slits	2.25	2.25
source code M IL, date code 18, gum, no slits	2.25	2.25
£1.25 holly green (March 20, 2018)		
no source code, date code 18, SBP	2.50	2.50
source code MPIL, date code 18, gum, no slits	2.25	2.25
source code M IL, date code 18, gum, no slits	2.25	2.25
£1.28 emerald green (April 25, 2012)		
no source code, date code 12	3.75	3.75
no source code, date code 13	3.75	3.75
no source code, date code 14	2.75	2.75
£1.33 amber yellow (March 24, 2015)		
no source code, date code 15	2.35	2.35
no source code, date code 16	2.75	2.75
£1.35 orchid mauve (March 19, 2019)		
no source code, date code 19, SBP	2.50	2.50
£1.40 dark pine green (March 21, 2017)		
no source code, date code 17	2.50	2.50
no source code, date code 17, SBP	2.50	2.50
source code MPIL, date code 17, gum, no slits	2.50	2.50
£1.45 dove grey (March 20, 2018)		
no source code, date code 18, SBP	2.75	2.75
source code M IL, date code 18, gum, no slits	2.75	2.75
£1.47 dove grey (March 26, 2014)		
no source code, date code 14	2.75	2.75
£1.50 brown–red (February 17, 2009)		
no source code, no date code	2.75	2.75
£1.52 orchid mauve (March 24, 2015)		
no source code, date code 15	2.25	2.25
£1.55 marine turquoise (March 20, 2018)		
no source code, date code 18, SBP	3.00	3.00
no source code, date code 19, SBP	3.00	3.00
source code MPIL, date code 18, gum, no slits	3.00	3.00
£1.57 tarragon green (March 21, 2017)		
no source code, date code 17	2.50	2.50
no source code, date code 17, SBP	2.50	2.50
£1.60 amber yellow (March 19, 2019)		
no source code, date code 19, SBP	2.75	2.75
£1.65 sage green (March 29, 2011)		
no source code, date code 11	3.50	3.50
no source code, date code 12	£400	–
£1.88 orchard mauve (March 27, 2013)		
no source code, date code 13 (Walsall)	3.25	3.25
no source code, date code 13 (De La Rue)	3.25	3.25
£1.90 rhododendron (April 25, 2012)		
no source code, date code 12	3.50	3.50
£2 blue–green (February 17, 2009)		
no source code, no date code	3.40	3.40
no source code, date code 13	5.50	5.50
£2.15 turquoise (March 26, 2014)		
no source code, date code 14	3.50	3.50
£2.25 plum purple (March 24, 2015)		
no source code, date code 15	3.25	3.25

no source code, date code 16	7.00	7.00
no source code, date code 18, SBP	4.00	4.00
£2.27 harvest gold (March 21, 2017)		
no source code, date code 17	3.50	3.50
no source code, date code 17, SBP	3.50	3.50
£2.30 gooseberry green (March 19, 2019)		
no source code, date code 19, SBP	4.00	4.00
£2.45 spruce green (March 24, 2015)		
no source code, date code 15	3.50	3.50
£2.55 garnet red (March 21, 2017)		
no source code, date code 17	4.00	4.00
no source code, date code 17, SBP	4.00	4.00
£2.65 purple heather (March 20, 2018)		
no source code, date code 18, SBP	4.00	4.00
£2.80 spruce green (March 19, 2019)		
no source code, date code 19, SBP	4.00	4.00
£3 mauve (February 17, 2009)		
no source code, no date code	4.75	4.75
£3.15 aqua green (March 24, 2015)		
no source code, date code 15	4.25	4.25
£3.30 rose pink (March 24, 2015)		
no source code, date code 15	4.25	4.25
£3.45 dark pine green (March 19, 2019)		
no source code, date code 19, SBP	5.00	5.00
£3.60 bright orange (March 19, 2019)		
no source code, date code 19, SBP	6.00	6.00
£5 azure (February 17, 2009)		
no source code, no date code	7.50	7.50

(*The 5p and 50p with source code MPIL and date code 13 exist in gummed form with the elliptical perforation towards the top, from the Merchant Navy prestige stamp book. The 2p, 5p and 10p also exist in gummed form, without overlay text, from prestige stamp books.)

First day cover (February 17, 2009)		
2nd, 2nd Large, 1st, 1st Large, 50p, £1	–	6.50
First day cover (February 17, 2009)		
£1.50, £2, £3, £5	–	20.00
First day cover (March 29, 2011)		
1p, 2p, 5p, 10p, 20p	–	2.00
First day cover (March 29, 2011)		
68p, 76p, £1.10, £1.65	–	6.00
First day cover (April 25, 2012)		
87p, £1.28, £1.90, with 1st Large Diamond Jubilee	–	8.00
First day cover (January 3, 2013)		
1p, 2p, 5p, 10p, 20p, 50p, £1, 1st red, 1st Large red	–	6.00
First day cover (March 27, 2013)		
78p, 88p, £1.88, with 1st Signed For, 1st Large Signed For	7.00
First day cover (March 26, 2014)		
81p, 97p, £1.47, £2.15	–	9.00
First day cover (March 24, 2015)		
£1.33, £1.52, £2.25, £2.45, £3.15, £3.30	–	24.00
First day cover (March 22, 2016)		
£1.05	–	2.50
First day cover (March 21, 2017)		
£1.17, £1.40, £1.57, £2.27, £2.55	–	15.00
First day cover (March 20, 2018)		
£1.25, £1.45, £1.55, £2.65	–	16.00
First day cover (March 19, 2019)		
£1.35, £1.60, £2.30, £2.80, £3.45, £3.60	–	20.00

SPECIFIC SERVICE ISSUES WITH ADDITIONAL SECURITY FEATURES

■ **2009, November 7. Recorded/Signed For**
Printed in gravure by De La Rue. Self-adhesive, with slits and iridescent overlay text.

1st orange–red and yellow

no source code, no date code	3.50	3.50
no source code, date code 10	9.00	9.00

1st Large orange–red and yellow

no source code, no date code	4.00	4.00
no source code, date code 10	9.00	9.00
First day cover	–	5.00

■ **2010, October 26. Special Delivery**
Printed in gravure by De La Rue (up to 2017) or ISP (from 2018). Self-adhesive, with slits and iridescent overlay text.

1st up to 100g silver and blue

no source code, date code 10	9.00	9.00
no source code, date code 14	12.50	12.50
no source code, date code 15	11.50	11.50
no source code, date code 16	10.50	10.50
no source code, date code 17	10.50	10.50
no source code, date code 18, SBP	11.00	11.00
no source code, date code 19, SBP	11.00	11.00

1st up to 500g blue and silver

no source code, date code 10	10.00	10.00
no source code, date code 14	12.50	12.50
no source code, date code 16	11.50	11.50
no source code, date code 18, SBP	11.50	11.50
First day cover	–	15.00

■ **2013, March 27. Royal Mail/Signed For**
Printed in gravure by De La Rue (up to 2017) or ISP (from 2018). Self-adhesive, with slits and iridescent overlay text.

1st orange–red and yellow

no source code, date code 13	4.00	4.00
no source code, date code 15	4.00	4.00
no source code, date code 16	4.00	4.00
no source code, date code 17, SBP	4.00	4.00

1st Large orange–red and yellow

no source code, date code 13	4.00	4.00
no source code, date code 15	4.50	4.50
no source code, date code 16	4.50	4.50
no source code, date code 17	4.50	4.50
no source code, date code 18, SBP	5.00	5.00
First day cover (with 78p, 88p, £1.88)	–	7.00

SPECIAL ISSUES WITH ADDITIONAL SECURITY FEATURES

■ **2012, February 6. Diamond Jubilee**
Printed in gravure by De La Rue (counter sheets, business sheets) or Walsall (booklets, business sheets). Self-adhesive, with slits and overlay text reading 'DIAMOND JUBILEE'.

1st diamond blue

no source code (counter sheets)	1.50	1.50
source code MSND (booklets of 6)	1.50	1.50
source code MTND (booklets of 12)	1.50	1.50
source code MCND (special issue booklets)	1.75	1.75
source code MBND (business sheets)	2.20	2.20

source code MPND (PSBs), gum, no slits	1.25	1.25
source code MMND (mini sheet), gum, no slits	–	2.25

1st Large diamond blue (April 25, 2012)

no source code (counter sheets)	2.50	2.50
source code JUBILFE (booklets of 4)	2.50	2.50
source code JUBILBE (business sheets)	2.50	2.50
First day cover (1st)	–	2.00
First day cover (1st Large, with 87p, £1.28, £1.90)	–	11.00

(*The 1st Large was released early by a number of post offices.)

■ **2015, September 9. Long To Reign Over Us**
Printed in gravure by De La Rue (counter sheets) or ISP (booklets). Self-adhesive, with slits and overlay text reading 'LONG TO REIGN OVER US'.
1st amethyst purple

no source code, date code 15	1.60	1.60
no source code, date code 16	1.60	1.60
source code REIGS, date code 15	1.60	1.60
source code REIGS, date code 16	1.60	1.60
source code REIGC, date code 15	1.60	1.60
source code REIGC, date code 16	1.60	1.60
source code REIGP, date code 16, gum. no slits	1.60	1.60
First day cover	–	2.00

■ **2017, February 6. 65th Anniversary of the Accession**
Printed in gravure by ISP. Gummed, with overlay text reading '65TH ANNIVERSARY OF ACCESSION'.

£5 sapphire blue	10.00	10.00
First day cover	–	10.00

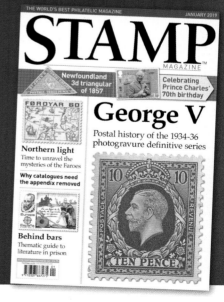

P14 PASSCHENDAELE Historic World War One commemorative cover for the 100th Anniv. of the Battle of Passchendaele. Limited issue of only 60 covers. Bears Royal Mail WWI commem. with Illustrated Passchendaele postmark.....Price £9.25

NE58 GREAT BRITAIN SPECIALISED 1971 POSTAL STRIKE COLLECTION Dating back to the short period in British Postal History when the Post Office granted licenses to private delivery companies to deliver mail in the U.K. This important GB postal history collection comprising of postal strike stamps in singles & blocks also has scarcer multiples and "Tete-beche" stamps. Used and unused with many unmounted mint (FOC noted). ....Price £14

NK39 NORTH KOREA An unusual collection of D.P.R. (North) Korean stamps including controversial and highly political propaganda communist stamps depicting its Kim-Jong-Il, father of the current leader Kim-Jong-un. Includes scarcer blocks, se-tenant and single stamps. Over 100 stamps.........Price £10.75

HUTT4 HUTT RIVER PROVINCE A lovely collection of unmounted mint stamps from the Hutt River Province. This collection includes complete mint sets including se-tenant pairs. Local issues from this Western Australian territory which claims to be an independent sovereign state, rarely offered for sale... ....Price £16

CS473 CEYLON A fabulous collection of hundreds of different Ceylon and Sri Lanka stamps. Definitive and commemorative stamps dating back to Queen Victoria with King Edward VII, King George V, a superb group of King George VI engraved stamps, following through to Queen Elizabeth II and later independent Sri Lankan stamps. A perfect collection to build upon. ....Price £18.50

WD399 WALT DISNEY A fantastic collection of only unmounted mint stamps covering the Walt Disney theme mostly British Commonwealth countries noted including Lesotho, St. Vincent, Grenada, Sierra Leone, Antigua, Turks & Caicos Islands, Anguilla, Maldives & Barbuda. Other countries noted include Bhutan, Gambia, and stamps of the Union Island. All the favourite Disney characters are included, namely Mickey & Minnie Mouse, Donald Duck, Goofy. Famous Disney films includes 101 Dalmatians, the Lion King, Hunchback of Notre-Dame and Pocahontas. Several complete sets in miniature sheetlets format plus a mass of other mini Disney stamps. Hundreds of stamps, plus special mini sheetlets ....Price £23

KE8 KING EDWARD VII SCARCE ABDICATION COVER This valuable cover commemorates the abdication of K.E.VII illustrated with an iconic portrait of the King, the cover bears the complete British issue of the K.E.VIII stamps tied to the cover with purple cachet inscribed "G.P.O. Postage Stamp Issue September 1936" in combination with Royal Mail House of Windsor Royal badge stamps postmarked with official Windsor Castle abdication postmark. Only 80 of this scarce cover are known to exist ....Price £26

MA30 GREAT BRITAIN RARE IMPERFORATE MACHIN STAMPS 1p black. This highly collectable specialist Machin item is a special printing by Harrison and Sons. With Post Office official approval of the 1p Machin definitive stamp printed in black on thin card. Unusual printer's item, rarely seen. ....Price £11.50

MZ112 MOZAMBIQUE COMPANY An impressive old collection of the stamps of the Mozambique Company dating back to the 1930s and earlier. With mint and used stamps in singles and blocks including postage dues and early air mail issues. The stamps are classically engraved and superbly printed approx. 80 stamps...Price £9.75

UK84 GREAT BRITAIN Royal Mail Elusive Mount Pleasant Sorting Office Cover. Issued to commemorate the 125th Anniversary of the GPO Mount Pleasant Office, officially opened on 30/8/1889, on the site of Coldbath Prison. Once acknowledged as the largest post sorting office in the world, it continues to handle millions of postal items daily. Only 100 of this important cover were ever produced. Bearing the iconic Machin stamp postmark. Dated 30/8/14. Offered in superb condition. ....Price £7.50

MS561 GB MINI SHEETS A specialised collection of Great Britain Stamp Exhibition Miniature Sheets. Comprising of over a dozen mint miniature sheets issued for British Stamp Exhibitions. Includes Stampex and International Exhibitions with Royal Mail postally valid sheets and scarcer sheets with post office approval; which were not available generally from the Royal Mail. The whole collection..............Price £9.75

BR.COL.388 KING GEORGE VI British & Colonial collection mainly King George VI but includes earlier K.G.V stamps mostly used but mint noted. Good range of countries.................................Price £13.75

LU328A LUNDY ISLAND A superb collection of unmounted mint British local stamps of Lundy Island in blocks, large multiples and singles + miniature sheets. Starts off Puffin stamps overprinted with 1950s & 1960s stamps on to more recent. With lots of "Puffin" stamps, definitives, commemoratives & Air Mail stamps. Hundreds of unmounted mint Lundy stamps.. Price..Price £27.25

GB85 - GREAT BRITAIN An important error on the 1966 Battle of Hastings 6d. value. The wrong colour gold leaf was used in error on the Queens Head. Error – yellow gold instead of normal bronze gold. We can offer the unmounted mint error plus normal stamp for comparison .... Price £7.50

E32 GREAT BRITAIN XMAS ERROR Spectacular error on 1966 XMAS 3d value (SG713) shift of gold colour, causing Queens Head Shift Error, superb unmounted mint together with normal stamp for comparison. ....Price £4.25

SJ53a BARDSEY ISLAND (Welsh Local Issue) A superb specialised group of Unmounted Mint (complete sets). Stamps from this small Welsh Island rarely get offered for sale ....Price £7

CH28 GREAT BRITAIN The GB Churchill Commemorative 4d White Brown and Black with startling broken white line error. The white line dividing Churchill from the Queens head on the stamp is broken; causing Churchill's shoulder to be dislocated. We offer the unmounted mint error stamp plus normal stamp for comparison ....Price £7.75

BE822 THE BEATLES A fantastic collection of Beatles stamps. "The Fab Four" John Lennon, Paul McCartney, George Harrison, and Ringo Star. Contains various Beatles stamps including mint and used and miniature sheets with catalogued and scarcer uncatalogued issues. Scarce Beatles FDCs included, with Royal Mail Beatles official postmarks. The important collection of Beatles stamps FDCs and miniature sheets from different countries including GB Royal Mail issue......... ....Price £16

J.208 JERSEY NAZI OCCUPATION World War II occupation stamps ½d green and 1d red. SG 1c & 2c in unmounted mint imperforate pairs. Catalogue value is over £500. However, we are not certain if these are genuine or faux, so they are being sold "as is" without guarantee. The stamps form part of a collection of mint Jersey stamps. If genuine the catalogue value, would be in excess of £570.00.. Price £22

E2R.GP1 GREAT BRITAIN Rare Machin gutter pair cover. One of the most sought after Machin definitive covers. The Royal Mail illustrated cover bears the scarce blue 2nd class definitive Machin gutter pair with gold coronation anniv. Royal Mail crown design in Gutter Pair. The cover is postmarked with the official London E2R Coronation Anniv. postmark dated 1/1/13. This is of postal history importance as the Machin Coronation Gutter Pair is scarce as mint and rare used on cover. .... Price £27

SCI.8H ALBERT EINSTEIN A special cover commemorating the 100th Anniversary of Einstein's theory of relativity. The illustrated cover depicts Einstein and bears a Royal Mail commemorative officially postmarked by the Royal Mail with Mount Pleasant 11/05/16 postmark. In combination with Jersey Einstein commemorative issue tied to the cover with large circular red Theory of Relativity cachet dated 11/05/16. The cover came from a severely restricted issue of only 60 covers. Price £18

CL5 CLEMENT ATTLEE A scarce political cover commemorating the 70th anniversary of Clement Attlee becoming Prime Minister. Attlee won a landslide election victory in 1945 bringing the Labour party into power. The scarce cover depicts Clement Attlee in his World War I army uniform. The cover bears the official Royal Mail Attlee commemorative stamp issue with London 26/7/15 postmark. Only 50 of this scarce political cover are known to exist. ....Price £19

M27A CORONATION STREET A specialised and most unusual thematic collection of Coronation Street stamps with complete unm. mint sets. From various British Local Islands, including scarcer High Values and several £1.00 values. Personalities depicted on stamps include: Jack & Annie Walker, Stan & Hilda Ogden, Ken & Irma Barlow, Jack & Vera Duckworth, Martha Longhurst, Ena Sharples, Mike & Alma Baldwin, Kevin Webster, Raquel Wolstenholme, Ray Langton, Liz McDonald, Alf Roberts, Bet Gilroy, Curly Watts, Emily Bishop, Martin Platt, Leonard Swindly, Elsie Tanner, Reg Holdsworth + others ....Price £12

DJ98 DJIBOUTI A small but specialised collection of Djibouti stamps, mostly used but mint noted. Contains many better catalogued, high denomination stamps..Price £13

MAL62 Malaya A substantial collection of Malaya, Malaysia with Singapore. Contains several hundred unmounted mint and fine used stamps in blocks and singles. Noted: Perak, Selangor, Kedah, Sabah, Perlis, Trengganu, Palau Pinang, Negri Sembilan, Kelantan, Sarawak, Melaka, Johor, Parhang; with strength in Singapore. Several hundred stamps ....Price £17

ALB. 7 ALBANIA A lovely collection of Albanian stamps, including scarcer older stamps issued for King Zog, unmounted mint. Unusual items noted include 1952 stamps issued by the Albanian Govt. in exile. Also better overprinted stamps. Containing over 100 stamps with blocks and singles mint and used... ....Price £15

GUSTAMPS

Established 1971

12 Prince Albert Street, Brighton, Sussex, BN1 1HE
Tel: 01273 326994
Telephone orders accepted.
Payment by mastercard or Visa credit cards
We have no e-mail address, please contact us by telephone
Dealing in stamps for over 40 years

GB11. WINSTON CHURCHILL A superb cover commemorating the 75th Anniversary of Sir Winston Churchill becoming Prime Minister. The cover depicts the great man and his quote "All my past life has been but a preparation for this hour and this trial." The cover bears the Winston Churchill Royal Mail commemorative stamp issue and illustrated Royal Mail Churchill postmark (from a limited issue of only 100 covers)..Price £27

GB.8 KEIR HARDIE Scarce political cover for the Centenary of the death of Keir Hardie. This must be one of the scarcest political covers, due to the fact that only 50 covers were produced; issued to commemorate the centenary of the death of Keir Hardie, the founder of the British Labour Party. The cover depicts the famous man with Royal Mail stamp tied to the cover by official Royal Mail Edinburgh Postmark dated 26/09/15, one hundred years to the day of Keir Hardie's death.........................Price £11

RSA14 SOUTH AFRICA A large and valuable collection of South African stamps containing only unmounted mint stamps in superb condition; includes singles, blocks, plate blocks, complete sets and miniature sheets. Hundreds of stamps plus miniature sheets all unmounted mint..........Price £27

GBX5 GREAT BRITAIN PRESENTATION PACKS A valuable and highly collectable collection of elusive Royal Mail Presentation packs. Some earlier pre-decimal GPO packs noted, but mainly modern Royal Mail recent issues. High face values with catalogue value of over £200. ....Price £58.50

GB482 GREAT BRITAIN Impressive collection of over 500 British stamps dating back to K.G.V. including Wilding, Machins and commemoratives. Includes mint but mainly used stamps also contains miniature sheets & F.D.C's. With decimal & pre-decimal G.P.O. & Royal Mail issues.............Price £23

GBX13 GREAT BRITAIN Royal Mail presentation packs and illustrated First Day covers. Also unmounted mint commemoratives, definitives and miniature sheets. Not counting mint stamps, the presentation packs and First Day covers have a combined catalogue value of over £160. ....
....Price £41.25

MA92 GREAT BRITAIN RARE IMPERFORATE MACHIN STAMPS ½p imperforate pair printed on thin paper, these were printed octagonal by special authority of the Post Office at Somerset House. Sought after and missing from most Machin stamp collections ....Price £28

HRH72 KING EDWARD VIII Great Britain K.E.VIII special commemorative cover. The scarce cover commemorated the 120th Anniv. of the birth of K.E. VIII, quoting the famous abdication speech. "I found it impossible to carry the heavy burden of responsibility and to discharge my duty as King, as I would wish, without the help and support of the woman I love." From a severely restricted world-wide issue of only 60 covers. The cover bears the K.E.VIII Royal Mail commemorative with first day of issue Royal Family Tree Postmark dated 2/2/12. Unusually the cover was re-posted on 23/6/14 and cancelled with the official Royal House of Windsor Arms pmk. The cover also bears the complete British original K.E.VIII set of 1936 definitive stamps, tied to the cover with boxed purple cache, inscribed "King Edward III GPO postage stamp Issue September 1936". We offer this important and valuable cover for sale. ...Price £24.50

HK145 HONG KONG A fine collection of used stamps of Hong Kong. Almost all the stamps pre date the handover to China. Including $ values and popular Chinese New Year Commemoratives. Totally unchecked for catalogue value, over 100 old Hong Kong stamps..Price £11

VR7 GREAT BRITAIN POSTAL HISTORY 1d BLACK VALUABLE COVER Issued to commemorate the first known use of the 1d Black. This scarce cover is illustrated with the Mulready design and bears an imperforate 1d Black stamp (four margins). Issued by the Royal Mail ex-special exhibition sheet tied to the cover with superb red Maltese Cross postmark. In addition, the cover bears duel Royal Mail official postmarks both "Bath" one dated 2/5/15 exactly 175 years to the day of the first 1d Black ever postmarked. A second official Royal Mail postmark in Red inscribed "Bath" 2/5/1840 ties Royal Mail 1d Black and 2d Blue commem. stamps to the cover on first official day of issue 6/5/15. The cover's restricted issue of only 75 must surely make this highly desirable cover one of the rarest of all Royal Mail 1d Black commemorative covers. ....
....Price £38

R88A NAZI GERMANY Occupation of World War II various Croatia Bohemia and Moravia. Occupation of Poland General government (Theresienstsdt and Lodz Ghetto these may not be genuine) plus various other Germany war period Hitler issues. Mainly genuine unmounted mint/used. ....Price £10

NJB.30 JAMES BOND A fantastic collection of James Bond stamps including sets, miniature sheets and singles with several scarcer unlisted. James Bond stamp sets ....Price £19.25

EUR 33 EUROPA - A specialised European thematic Collection of Europa stamps, spanning from the 1950's to more modern stamps. Includes Italy, France, Germany, Iceland, Belgium, Luxembourg ......Price £15

E2R.GP1 GREAT BRITAIN Rare Machin gutter pair cover. One of the most sought after Machin definitive covers. The Royal Mail illustrated cover bears the scarce blue 2nd class definitive Machin gutter pair with gold coronation Anniv. Royal Mail crown design in Gutter Pair. The cover is postmarked with the official London E2R Coronation Anniv. postmark dated 1/1/13. This is of postal history importance as the Machin Coronation Gutter Pair is scarce as mint and rare used on cover ....Price £27

NE832 BRITISH LOCALS A phenomenal and valuable collection of British Local Island's stamps. Only unmounted mint, including Lundy Island, Davaar Island, Cain Iar, Isle of Easdale, Bemara Island, Staffa, Stroma, Isle of Pabay, Bardsey, Herm, Calf of Man, Hildasay – Shetland Islands, Jethou, Alderney, St Kilda, St Marys, Calvey Island, Gugh, St. Martins. With blocks, multiples, singles and miniature sheets. This important and valuable collection with only unmounted mint stamps and many high £ values. The normal face value is well over £150.....Price £33

ALF.3 Great Britain Postal History Cover Special cover for the 10th anniversary of the A.L.F. (Automatic Letter Facing Machine), 1961-1971. Bears Machin issue tied to the cover with pictorial "A.L.F" postmark 31/7/1971, Southampton.............
....Price £5

F.95 Marine Life A spectacular specialised of fish and sea life. Includes just about every type of fish imaginable plus seals, dolphins, shells. A "virtual aquarium" of over 500 fish stamps mint and used ....
....Price £39.50

GB 32EP GREAT BRITAIN ACID RAIN ERROR STAMP A super GB stamp error has recently come to light. The error a "must" for any complete GB collection shows a "full stop" at the base of the 24p denomination. As it is a constant error only one stamp appears in each sheet of 100 stamps. So, it is 99 times scarcer than the normal stamp (SG 1629) Many serious GB stamps collectors are now realising that their collections are incomplete without this important value denomination variety. We offer the Acid Rain error stamp denomination variety, togther with a normal stamp for comparison...................................Price £8.75

LOT K3 GREAT BRITAIN, COMMEMS & DEFINS. UNSORTED ACCUMULATION With stamps in blocks, multiples and singles. Items noted include Traffic Light Gutter Pairs and miniature sheets. Well over 500 stamps, only unmounted mint. ....Price £18

FEM2 GREAT BRITAIN UNIVERSAL SUFFRAGE An important GB cover for the Centenary of the release of all Suffragettes from prison on 10/8/1914. The British Government after negotiations with Emmeline Pankhurst announced it was releasing all suffragettes from prison. In return the Women's Social and Political Union agreed to end all militant activity and assist in the war effort. The cover with iconic suffragette votes for women illustration bears a British definitive stamp with official Royal Mail Victorian style duplex Berkhamsted 66 pmk. On the anniversary dated 10/8/14. The cover also bears the votes for women commemorative stamp issue tied with red cachet inscribed "Universal Suffrage – Votes for Women". Severely restricted and limited issue of 100 covers (few available)....................Price £12.75

MC334 MUSIC An awesome & valuable collection of music stamps begins with an orchestra of musical instrument stamps. The specialist classical section includes: Mozart, Beethoven, Bach, Tchaikovsky, Verdi, Bartok. Also jazz and pop music stamps, with Louis Armstrong, Frank Sinatra, Oasis, Marlene Dietrich. With G.B. Royal Mail stamps of Freddy Mercury, The Beatles and Pink Floyd. A multiple of other issues for Rolling Stones, Jimi Hendrix, Michael Hendrix, Michael Jackson, Kylie Minogue, Elvis Presley and many more. Hundreds of stamps – mint and used with several miniature sheets. The best music collection we have ever seen.......Price £29.25

SP45 Sports A superb collection of sports stamps from many countries which includes miniature sheets and sport related covers including scarcer signed covers. Hundreds of sports stamps plus covers and miniature sheets ....Price £16

CD389 Cats & Dogs A fantastic collection of cats & dogs on stamps. A vast variety of different breeds of these popular pets. Hundreds of different cats & dogs stamps..Price £17

SJ92 Great Britain 1961 Post Office Savings Bank Error on SG624. (3d value). A most impressive and amusing error due to a shift of the Orange colour, the owl in the top right-hand corner of the stamp has turned and is looking sideways. Unusual to find such an impressive error turn up over 44 years after it was issued. We can offer the shifty-eye owl error, (together with normal stamp for comparison)...Price £8

EXP 14 THE BRITISH ICELANDIC EXPEDITION A scarce expedition cover for the British-Icelandic expedition of 1981. This is the official illustrated cover flown from the UK to KEFLAVIC (Iceland)and bears the P.O. expedition postmark. The cover has been additionally signed by Mike Todd,(Chairman of the B.S.A.C.)An important postal history cover for sale...Price £12

QUEEN ELIZABETH II
DECIMAL SPECIAL ISSUES

In this section, prices are quoted in two columns: unmounted mint (left) and fine used (right). Most issues, as well as gutter pairs and stamp cards, are priced for complete sets only except where stated.

Except where otherwise stated, all stamps were printed in photogravure by Harrison. Gutter pairs and traffic–light gutter pairs appear from November 1972, blue–tinted polyvinyl alcohol dextrin (PVAD) gum from November 1973 and phosphor–coated paper from September 1979.

'A Mountain Road' by T. P. Flanagan (3p)
'Deer's Meadow' by Tom Carr (7½p)
'Slieve na Brock' by Colin Middleton (9p)

■ **1971, June 16. Ulster Paintings**
Des: S. Rose.

Set	0.50	0.60
First day cover	–	1.00

John Keats (3p)
Thomas Gray (5p)
Sir Walter Scott (7½p)

■ **1971, July 28. Literary Anniversaries**
Des: Rosalind Dease.

Set	0.50	0.60
First day cover	–	1.00

British Legion: servicemen and nurse (3p)
City of York: Roman centurion (7½p)
Rugby Football Union: rugby players (9p)

■ **1971, August 25. Anniversaries**
Des: F. Wegner.

Set	0.55	0.65
First day cover	–	1.75

University College, Aberystwyth (3p)
University of Southampton (5p)
University of Leicester (7½p)
University of Essex (9p)

■ **1971, September 22. Modern University Buildings**
Des: N. Jenkins.

Set	0.85	1.00
First day cover	–	1.00

'Dream of the Wise Men' (2½p)
'Adoration of the Magi' (3p)
'Ride of the Magi' (7½p)

■ **1971, October 13. Christmas**
Des: Clarke, Clement and Hughes, based on stained glass windows at Canterbury Cathedral.

Set	0.40	0.60
First day cover	–	1.00

Sir James Clarke Ross (3p)
Sir Martin Frobisher (5p)
Sir Henry Hudson (7½p)
Robert Scott (9p)

■ **1972, February 16. Polar Explorers**
Des: Marjorie Seynor.

Set	0.60	1.00
First day cover	–	1.00

Tutankhamun discovery: statuette (3p)
H.M. Coastguard: 19th–century coastguard (7½p)
Ralph Vaughan Williams: portrait and score (9p)

■ **1972, April 26. Anniversaries**
Des: Rosalind Dease (3p), F. Wegner (7½p), C. Abbott (9p)

Set	0.50	0.60
First day cover	–	1.00

St. Andrew's, Greensted–juxta–Ongar, Essex (3p)
All Saints, Earls Barton, Northamptonshire (4p)
St. Andrew's, Lethringsett, Norfolk (5p)
St. Andrew's, Helpringham, Lincolnshire (7½p)
St. Mary the Virgin, Huish Episcopi, Somerset (9p)

■ **1972, June 21. Village Churches**
Des: R. Maddox.

Set	1.00	1.40
First day cover	–	1.50

BBC: microphones (3p)
BBC: horn loudspeaker (5p)
BBC: colour television (7½p)
Marconi: oscillator and spark transmitter (9p)

■ **1972, September 13. Broadcasting Anniversaries**
Des: D. Gentleman.

Set	0.75	0.95
First day cover	–	1.25

Angel with trumpet (2½p)
Angel with lute (3p)
Angel with harp (7½p)

■ **1972, October 18. Christmas**
Des: Sally Stiff.

Set	0.50	0.40
First day cover	–	1.00

Queen Elizabeth II and Prince Phillip (3p, 20p)

■ **1972, November 20. Royal Silver Wedding**
Des: J. Matthews from photograph by Norman Parkinson.
All–over phosphor (3p), no phosphor (20p).
Printed on a Rembrandt machine

Set	0.90	0.80
First day cover	–	1.00

Printed on a Jumelle machine

3p	0.50	0.50
Gutter pair	1.00	–
Traffic light gutter pair	20.00	–

(*The portraits tend to be lighter on the Jumelle printing.)

Jigsaw pieces representing Europe (3p, 5p, 5p)

■ **1973, January 3. Britain's Entry into European Communities**
Des: P. Murdoch.

Set	0.60	0.75
First day cover	–	1.00

Oak tree (9p)

■ **1973, February 28. British Trees, 1st issue**
Des: D. Gentleman.

9p	0.20	0.25
First day cover	–	0.50

Self-portrait by Joshua Reynolds (3p)
Self-portrait by Henry Raeburn (5p)
'Nelly O'Brien' by Reynolds (7½p)
'The Skating Minister' by Raeburn (9p)

■ **1973, July 4. British Painters**
Des: S. Rose.

Set	0.70	0.70
First day cover	–	1.00

David Livingstone (3p)
Henry Stanley (3p)
Sir Francis Drake (5p)
Sir Walter Raleigh (7½p)
Charles Sturt (9p)

Court masque costumes (3p)
St Paul's Church, Covent Garden (3p)
Prince's Lodging, Newmarket (5p)
Court masque stage scene (5p)

■ **1973, April 18. British Explorers**
Des: Marjorie Seynor. All-over phosphor.

Set	0.90	1.00
First day cover	–	1.25

■ **1973, August 15. 400th Anniversary of Birth of Inigo Jones**
Des: Rosalind Dease. Printed in litho and typo by Bradbury, Wilkinson.

Set	0.65	0.75
First day cover	–	1.00
Stamp card (of 3p St Paul's)	£100	£300

W. G. Grace batting (3p)
W. G. Grace watching the ball (7½p)
W. G. Grace leaving the wicket (9p)

Palace of Westminster from Whitehall (8p)
Palace of Westminster from Millbank (10p)

■ **1973, May 16. Centenary of County Cricket**
Des: E Ripley, based on drawings by Harry Furniss.

Set	1.00	1.00
First day cover	–	1.50
Stamp card (of 3p design)	40.00	–

■ **1973, September 12. Commonwealth Parliamentary Conference**
Des: R. Downer. Printed in recess and litho by Bradbury, Wilkinson.

Set	0.40	0.50
First day cover	–	0.75
Stamp card (of 8p design)	20.00	£175

Princess Anne and Captain Mark Phillips (3½p), (20p)

■ 1973, November 14. Royal Wedding
Des: C. Clements and E. Hughes, based on photograph by Lord Lichfield.

Set	0.50	0.55
Gutter pair	1.75	–
Traffic light gutter pair	70.00	–
First day cover	–	0.75
Stamp card (of 3½p design)	5.00	25.00

(*The 3½p exists from sheets guillotined in the wrong place, giving incorrect inscriptions within the gutter; price £30.)

Good King Wenceslas, the carol story (3p, 3p, 3p, 3p, 3p)
Good King Wenceslas, the page and the peasant (3½p)

■ 1973, November 28. Christmas
Des: D. Gentleman. 3p values have one phosphor band. These stamps exist with either gum Arabic (3p), PVA gum (3½p) or dextrin gum (both values); prices are the same.

Set	1.25	1.25
First day cover	–	1.25

Horse chestnut (10p)

■ 1974, February 27. British Trees, 2nd issue
Des: D. Gentleman.

10p	0.25	0.25
Gutter pair	1.00	–
Traffic light gutter pair	50.00	–
First day cover	–	0.75
Stamp card	80.00	75.00

First motor fire engine, 1904 (3½p)
Prizewinning fire engine, 1863 (5½p)
First steam fire engine, 1830 (8p)
Fire engine, 1766 (10p)

■ 1974, April 24. Bicentenary of the Fire Prevention Act
Des: D. Gentleman. Dextrin gum except where stated.

Set	0.75	0.80
3½p with PVA gum	0.90	–
Gutter pairs	2.75	–
Traffic light gutter pairs	37.00	–
First day cover	–	1.50
Stamp card (of 3½p design)	67.00	70.00

P&O Packet Steamer 'Peninsular', 1888 (3½p)
First official airmail, 1911 (5½p)
Airmail van and postbox, 1930 (8p)
Imperial Airways flying boat, 1937 (10p)

■ 1974, June 12. Centenary of the UPU
Des: Rosalind Dease.

Set	0.55	0.75
Gutter pairs	1.75	–
Traffic light gutter pairs	40.00	–
First day cover	–	1.00

Robert the Bruce (4½p)
Owain Glyndwr (5½p)
King Henry V (8p)
The Black Prince (10p)

■ 1974, July 10. Medieval Warriors
Des: F. Wegner.

Set	0.70	0.70
Gutter pairs	3.00	–
Traffic light gutter pairs	42.00	–
First day cover	–	1.50
Stamp cards	14.00	40.00

Lord Warden of the Cinque Ports (4½p)
Prime Minister (5½p)
Secretary for War and Air (8p)
War correspondent in South Africa (10p)

■ 1974, October 9. Birth Centenary of Sir Winston Churchill
Des: C. Clements and E. Hughes.

Set	1.00	0.85
8p with PVA gum	0.50	–
Gutter pairs	1.75	–
Traffic light gutter pairs	24.00	–
First day cover	–	1.00
Stamp card (of 5½p design)	3.00	20.00

'Adoration of the Magi', York Minster (3½p)
'The Nativity', St. Helen's Church, Norwich (4½p)
'Virgin and Child', Ottery St. Mary Church (8p)
'Virgin and Child', Worcester Cathedral (10p)

■ 1974, November 27. Christmas
Des: Peter Hatch Partnership, based on church roof bosses.

3½p with phos band to right	0.20	0.25
Set	0.50	0.60
Gutter pairs	2.25	–
Traffic light gutter pairs	27.00	–
First day cover	–	1.00

Disabled person in wheelchair (4½p + 1½p)

■ 1975, January 22. Health and Handicap Charities
Des: P. Sharland. Surcharge donated to charity.

4½p + 1½p	0.15	0.15
Gutter pair	0.30	–
Traffic light gutter pair	2.50	–
First day cover	–	0.50

'Peace: Burial at Sea' (4½p)
'Snowstorm' (5½p)
'The Arsenal, Venice' (8p)
'St. Laurent' (10p)

■ 1975, February 19. Bicentenary of the Birth of J. M. W. Turner
Des: S. Rose.

Set	0.50	0.60
Gutter pairs	1.25	–
Traffic light gutter pairs	6.00	–
First day cover	–	0.75
Stamp card (of 5½p design)	20.00	12.00

Charlotte Square, Edinburgh (7p)
The Rows, Chester (7p)
Royal Observatory, Greenwich (8p)
St. George's Chapel, Windsor (10p)
National Theatre, London (12p)

■ 1975, April 23. European Architectural Heritage Year
Des: P. Gauld.

Set	0.80	1.00
Gutter pairs	3.50	–
Traffic light gutter pairs	15.00	–
First day cover	–	1.00
Stamp cards (of 7p and 8p designs)	6.00	25.00

Sailing dinghies (7p)
Racing keel boats (8p)
Cruising yachts (10p)
Multihulls (12p)

■ 1975, June 11. Sailing
Des: A. Restall. Printed in photogravure and recess by Harrison.

Set	0.60	0.75
Gutter pairs	1.50	–
Traffic light gutter pairs	18.00	–
First day cover	–	1.00
Stamp card (of 8p design)	3.50	15.00

(*The 7p exists from sheets guillotined in the wrong place, giving gutter pairs with the wrong inscriptions, priced at £45.)

Stephenson's Locomotion, 1825 (7p)
Waverley class, 1876 (8p)
Caerphilly Castle, 1923 (10p)
Inter–City High Speed Train, 1975 (12p)

■ 1975, August 13. 150th Anniversary of Public Railways
Des: B. Cracker.

Set	0.80	0.80
Gutter Pairs	2.25	–
Traffic light gutter pairs	8.00	–
First day cover	–	1.00
Stamp cards (set)	32.00	35.00

Palace of Westminster (12p)

■ 1975, September 3. Inter–Parliamentary Union Conference
Des: R. Downer

12p	0.25	0.25
Gutter pair	0.60	–
Traffic light gutter pair	2.50	–
First day cover	–	0.50

Emma and Mr. Woodhouse, from Emma (8½p)
Catherine Morland, from Northanger Abbey (10p)
Mr. Darcy, from Pride and Prejudice (11p)
Mary and Henry Crawford, from Mansfield Park (13p)

■ 1975, October 22. Birth Bicentenary of Jane Austen
Des: Barbara Brown.

Set	0.80	0.70
Gutter pairs	1.40	–
Traffic light gutter pairs	7.50	–
First day cover	–	1.00
Stamp cards (set)	10.00	30.00

Angel with harp and lute (6½p)
Angel with mandolin (8½p)
Angel with horn (11p)
Angel with trumpet (13p)

■ 1975, November 25. Christmas
Des: R. Downer. Dextrin gum except where stated. The 8½p has the phosphor in the green printing ink

6½p with PVA gum	0.50	–
Set	0.75	0.75
Gutter pairs	1.40	–
Traffic light gutter pairs	5.50	–
First day cover	–	1.00

Housewife with telephone (8½p)
Policeman with telephone (10p)
District nurse with telephone (11p)
Industrialist with telephone (13p)

■ 1976, March 10. Centenary of First Telephone Call by Alexander Graham Bell
Des: P. Sharland.

Set	0.75	0.80
Gutter pairs	1.50	–
Traffic light gutter pairs	12.00	–
First day cover	–	0.75

Mining coal: Thomas Hepburn (8½p)
Machinery: Robert Owen (10p)
Sweeping a chimney: Lord Shaftesbury (11p)
Prison bars: Elizabeth Fry (13p)

■ 1976, April 28. Social Reformers
Des: D. Gentleman.

Set	0.70	0.80
Gutter pairs	1.50	–
Traffic light gutter pairs	5.50	–
First day cover	–	0.75
Stamp card (of 8½p design)	3.00	7.50

Benjamin Franklin (11p)

■ 1976, June 2. Bicentennial of American Independence
Des: P. Sharland.

11p	0.25	0.25
Gutter pair	0.50	–
Traffic light gutter pair	2.50	–
First day cover	–	0.75
Stamp card	2.50	10.00

Elizabeth of Glamis (8½p)
Grandpa Dickson (10p)
Rosa mundi (11p)
Sweet briar (13p)

■ 1976, June 30. Centenary of the Royal National Rose Society
Des: Kristin Rosenberg.

Set	0.70	0.80
Gutter pairs	1.50	–
Traffic light gutter pairs	6.50	–
First day cover	–	1.00
Stamp cards	15.00	25.00

Royal National Eisteddfod of Wales: archdruid (8½p)
Morris dancing (10p)
Highland Gathering: piper (11p)
Royal National Eisteddfod of Wales: harpist (13p)

■ 1976, August 4. British Cultural Traditions
Des: Marjorie Seynor.

Set	0.80	0.80
Gutter pairs	1.50	–
Traffic light gutter pairs	6.50	–
First day cover	–	0.75
Stamp cards	8.00	15.00

Woodcut from 'The Canterbury Tales' (8½p)
Extract from 'The Tretyse of Love' (10p)
Woodcut from 'The Game and Playe of Chesse' (11p)
Early printing press (13p)

■ 1976, September 29. 500th Anniversary of British Printing
Des: R. Gay.

Set	0.80	0.75
Gutter pairs	1.50	–
Traffic light gutter pairs	5.50	–
First day cover	–	1.00
Stamp cards	6.00	15.00

Virgin and child, embroidery c.1272 (6½p)
Angel with crown, embroidery c.1340 (8½p)
Angel appearing to shepherds, embroidery c.1320 (11p)
The three kings, embroidery c.1330 (13p)

■ 1976, November 24. Christmas.
Des: Enid Marx, based on medieval English embroideries.

Set	0.80	0.70
6½p with one phos band	0.15	0.10
Gutter pairs	1.50	–
Traffic light gutter pairs	5.00	–
First day cover	–	0.75
Stamp cards	2.00	17.00

Lawn tennis (8½p)
Table tennis (10p)
Squash (11p)
Badminton (13p)

■ 1977, January 12. Racket Sports
Des: A. Restall.

Set	0.75	0.80
Gutter pairs	1.75	–
Traffic light gutter pairs	6.00	–
First day cover	–	1.00
Stamp cards	4.00	12.00

Steroids: conformational analysis (8½p)
Vitamin C: synthesis (10p)
Starch: chromatography (11p)
Salt: crystallography (13p)

■ 1977, March 2. Centenary of the Royal Institute of Chemistry
Des: J. Karo.

Set	0.75	0.75
Gutter pairs	1.75	–
Traffic light gutter pairs	6.00	–
First day cover	–	0.75
Stamp cards	4.00	10.00

'ER' and Queen Elizabeth II (8½p, 9p, 10p, 11p, 13p)

■ 1977, May 11. Silver Jubilee
Des: Professor R. Guyatt. 9p issued on June 15.

Set	1.00	1.00
Gutter pairs	2.50	–
Traffic light gutter pairs	8.00	–
First day cover (8½p, 10p, 11p, 13p)	–	1.00
First day cover (9p)	–	0.50
Stamp cards	6.00	11.00

Symbol of meeting (13p)

■ 1977, June 8. Commonwealth Heads of Government Meeting, London
Des: P. Murdoch. Printed in photogravure and recess by Harrison.

13p	0.25	0.25
Gutter pair	0.50	–
Traffic light gutter pair	2.00	–
First day cover	–	0.75
Stamp card	1.50	2.50

Hedgehog *Erinaceus europaeus*

OIL

Hedgehog (9p)
Hare (9p)
Red squirrel (9p)
Otter (9p)
Badger (9p)

North Sea oil (9p)
Coal pithead (10½p)
Natural gas flame (11p)
Electricity (13p)

■ 1977, October 5. British Wildlife
Des: P Oxenham.

Set (se–tenant strip of five)	0.90	1.20
Gutter strip	1.25	–
Traffic light gutter strip	5.50	–
First day cover	–	1.25
Stamp cards	2.00	5.50

(*Gutter strips normally comprise a horozontal strip of four designs separated from the fifth design by a gutter.)

■ 1978, January 25. Energy Resources
Des: P. Murdoch.

Set	0.65	0.75
Gutter pairs	1.50	–
Traffic light gutter pairs	5.00	–
First day cover	–	0.75
Stamp cards	1.50	3.50

THE TWELVE DAYS OF CHRISTMAS

Tower of London·The White Tower

Three hens, two turtle doves, a partridge in a pear tree (7p)
Six geese, five gold rings, four colly birds (7p)
Eight maids, seven swans (7p)
Ten pipers, nine drummers (7p)
Twelve lords, eleven ladies (7p)
Partridge in a pear tree (9p)

Tower of London (9p)
Palace of Holyroodhouse (10½p)
Caernarvon Castle (11p)
Hampton Court Palace (13p)

■ 1977, November 23. Christmas
Des: D. Gentleman, based on the song 'The Twelve Days of Christmas'. The 7p values, issued se–tenant, have one phosphor band.

Set	0.75	0.85
Gutter strip	1.50	–
Traffic light gutter strip	4.00	–
First day cover	–	1.00
Stamp cards	2.00	5.00

(*Gutter strips of the 7p values comprise two horizontal se–tenant strips of five separated by a gutter.)

■ 1978, March 1. Historic Buildings
Des: R. Maddox; miniature sheet by J. Matthews.

Set	0.75	0.80
Gutter pairs	1.60	–
Traffic light gutter pairs	4.50	–
First day cover	–	0.75
Stamp cards	1.50	3.50
Miniature sheet (one of each value)	1.025	1.50
Miniature sheet first day cover	–	1.25

(*The miniature sheet was sold at 53½p, the extra 10p being donated towards the cost of staging the International Stamp Exhibition. London 1980, which the sheet itself publicised.)

State Coach (9p)
St. Edward's Crown (10½p)
Sovereign's Orb (11p)
Imperial State Crown (13p)

■ **1978, May 31. 25th Anniversary of the Coronation**
Des: J. Matthews.

Set	0.75	0.90
Gutter pairs	1.50	–
Traffic light gutter pairs	4.50	–
First day cover	–	1.00
Stamp cards	1.50	3.50

Shire horse (9p)
Shetland pony (10½p)
Welsh pony (11p)
Thoroughbred (13p)

■ **1978, July 5. Horses**
Des: P. Oxenham.

Set	0.70	0.75
Gutter pairs	1.50	–
Traffic light gutter pairs	4.75	–
First day cover	–	0.75
Stamp cards	1.50	3.50

Penny Farthing and Safety Bicycle, 1884 (9p)
Touring bicycles, 1920 (10½p)
Modern small–wheel bicycles (11p)
Road racers, 1978 (13p)

■ **1978, August 2. Cycling**
Des: F. Wegner.

Set	0.70	0.75
Gutter pairs	1.50	–
Traffic light gutter pairs	4.50	–
First day cover	–	0.75
Stamp cards	1.50	3.50

Singing carols around a Christmas tree (7p)
The waits (9p)
18th–century carol singers (11p)
The boar's head carol (13p)

■ **1978, November 22. Christmas**
Des: Faith Jaques. 7p has one phosphor band.

Set	0.70	0.70
Gutter pairs	1.25	–
Traffic light gutter pairs	4.75	–
First day cover	–	0.75
Stamp cards	1.50	3.00

Old English sheepdog (9p)
Welsh springer spaniel (10½p)
West Highland terrier (11p)
Irish setter (13p)

■ **1979, February 7. British Dogs**
Des: P. Barrett.

Set	0.70	0.75
Gutter pairs	1.25	–
Traffic light gutter pairs	4.00	–
First day cover	–	0.75
Stamp cards	1.50	3.50

Primrose (9p)
Daffodil (10½p)
Bluebell (11p)
Snowdrop (13p)

■ 1979, March 21. Spring Wild Flowers

Des: P. Newcombe.

Set	0.70	0.75
Gutter pairs	1.50	–
Traffic light gutter pairs	4.25	–
First day cover	–	0.75
Stamp cards	1.50	3.50

Hands placing flags into ballot boxes (9p, 10½p, 11p, 13p)

■ 1979, May 9. First Direct Elections to the European Assembly

Des: S. Cliff.

Set	0.70	0.75
Gutter pairs	1.50	–
Traffic light gutter pairs	4.25	–
First day cover	–	0.75
Stamp cards	1.50	3.00

Saddling Mahmoud for the Derby, 1936 (9p)
Liverpool Great National Steeplechase, 1839 (10½p)
First Spring Meeting at Newmarket, 1793 (11p)
Racing at Dorsett Ferry, Windsor, 1684 (13p)

■ 1979, June 6. 200th Anniversary of the Derby. Horse Racing Paintings

Des: S. Rose.

Set	0.70	0.75
Gutter pairs	1.50	–
Traffic light gutter pairs	4.25	–
First day cover	–	0.75
Stamp cards	1.50	3.00

'The Tale of Peter Rabbit' by Beatrix Potter (9p)
'The Wind in the Willows' by Kenneth Grahame (10½p)
'Winnie the Pooh' by A. A. Milne (11p)
'Alice's Adventures in Wonderland' by Lewis Carroll (13p)

■ 1979, July 11. International Year of the Child

Des: E. Hughes.

Set	0.85	0.85
Gutter pairs	1.75	–
Traffic light gutter pairs	4.00	–
First day cover	–	0.75
Stamp cards	1.50	4.00

Sir Rowland Hill (10p)
General Post, 1839 (11½p)
London Post, 1839 (13p)
Uniform Penny Post, 1840 (15p)

■ **1979, August 22. Centenary of the Death of Sir Rowland Hill**
Des: E. Stemp (set) and J. Matthews (miniature sheet).

Set	0.75	0.75
Gutter pairs	1.60	–
Traffic light gutter pairs	4.00	–
First day cover	–	0.75
Stamp cards	1.50	3.50
Miniature sheet (one of each value)	1.00	1.25
Miniature sheet first day cover	–	1.00

(*The miniature sheet, issued on October 24, 1979, was sold at 59½p, the extra 10p being donated towards the cost of staging the International Stamp Exhibition, London 1980, which the sheet itself publicised.)

Policeman talking to two children (10p)
Street patrol (11½p)
Policewoman on horseback (13p)
River police (15p)

■ **1979, September 26. 150th Anniversary of the Metropolitan Police**
Des: B. Sanders.

Set	0.80	0.85
Gutter pairs	1.60	–
Traffic light gutter pairs	4.25	–
First day cover	–	0.75
Stamp cards	1.50	3.00

Three kings following the star (8p)
Angel appearing to shepherds (10p)
Nativity (11½p)
Joseph and Mary travelling to Bethlehem (13p)
Annunciation (15p)

■ **1979, November 21. Christmas**
Des: F. Wegner. 8p has one phosphor band.

Set	0.90	0.90
Gutter pairs	1.80	–
Traffic light gutter pairs	4.25	–
First day cover	–	0.75
Stamp cards	150	3.00

Kingfisher (10p)
Dipper (11½p)
Moorhen (13p)
Yellow wagtail (15p)

■ **1980, January 16. Water Birds**
Des: Michael Warren.

Set	0.80	0.80
Gutter pairs	2.00	–
First day cover	–	1.00
Stamp cards	1.50	3.50

George Stephenson's Rocket (12p)
First and second class carriages (12p)
Third class carriage and cattle truck (12p)
Open coach on truck and horsebox (12p)
Goods wagon and mail coach (12p)

■ **1980, March 12. 150th Anniversary of the Liverpool & Manchester Railway**
Des: D. Gentleman.

Se–tenant strip of five	1.00	1.00
Gutter strip	2.25	–
First day cover	–	1.00
Stamp cards	3.00	3.50

(*Gutter strips comprise two horizontal se–tenant strips separated by a gutter.)

Montage of London buildings and monuments (50p)

■ 1980, April 9. London 1980 International Stamp Exhibition
Des: J. Matthews. Printed in recess by Harrisons. No phosphor.

50p	0.80	0.75
Gutter pair	2.00	–
First day cover	–	0.75
Stamp card	0.75	1.75
Miniature sheet	1.00	1.25
Miniature sheet first day cover	–	1.25

(*The miniature sheet, issued on May 7, 1980, was sold at 75p, the extra 25p being donated towards the cost of staging the International Stamp Exhibition, London 1980. The stamp is known to exist in shades of green, caused by the speed of the ink–drying operation, and fakes of these shades exist.)

Buckingham Palace (10½p)
Albert Memorial (12p)
Royal Opera House (13½p)
Hampton Court (15p)
Kensington Palace (17½p)

■ 1980, May 7. London Landmarks
Des: Sir Hugh Casson.

Set	1.00	1.00
Gutter pairs	2.50	–
First day cover	–	1.25
Stamp cards	1.50	3.00

Charlotte Brontë: Jane Eyre

Charlotte Brontë and 'Jane Eyre' (12p)
George Eliot and 'The Mill on the Floss' (13½p)
Emily Brontë and 'Wuthering Heights' (15p)
Elizabeth Gaskell and 'North and South' (17½p)

■ 1980, July 9. Famous Authoresses (Europa)
Des: Barbara Brown.

Set	0.90	0.90
Gutter pairs	2.50	–
First day cover	–	1.00
Stamp cards	1.75	3.00

Queen Elizabeth, the Queen Mother (12p)

■ 1980, August 4. Queen Mother's 80th Birthday
Des: Jeffery Matthews.

12p	0.40	0.30
Gutter pair	1.00	–
First day cover	–	0.75
Stamp card	0.75	1.75

Sir Henry Wood (12p)
Sir Thomas Beecham (13½p)
Sir Malcolm Sargent (15p)
Sir John Barbirolli (17½p)

■ 1980, September 10. British Conductors
Des: Peter Gauld.

Set	0.90	0.90
Gutter pairs	2.25	–
First day cover	–	1.25
Stamp cards	1.50	2.75

(*These stamps exist on paper with differences in the degree of 'shine' on the surface.)

Athletics (12p)
Rugby (13½p)
Boxing (15p)
Cricket (17½p)

■ 1980, October 10. Sport Centenaries
Des: Robert Goldsmith. Printed in litho by Questa.

Set	0.90	1.00
Gutter pairs	2.25	–
First day cover	–	1.25
Stamp cards	1.50	2.75

Christmas tree (10p)
Candles, ivy and ribbon (12p)
Mistletoe and apples (13½p)
Paper chains with crown and bell (15p)
Holly wreath and ornaments (17½p)

■ 1980, November 10. Christmas
Des: Jeffery Matthews. 10p has one phosphor band.

Set	1.00	1.00
Gutter pairs	2.50	–
First day cover	–	1.25
Stamp cards	1.50	3.00

(*These stamps exist on paper with differences in the degree of 'shine' on the surface.)

St. Valentine's Day (14p)
Morris dancers (18p)
Lammastide (22p)
Medieval mummers (25p)

■ 1981, February 6. Folklore (Europa)
Des: Fritz Wegner.

Set	1.25	1.25
Gutter pairs	3.00	–
First day cover	–	1.25
Stamp cards	1.50	2.75

Blind man walking with guide dog (14p)
'Deaf' spelt in sign language (18p)
Man in wheelchair (22p)
Disabled artist foot painting (25p)

■ 1981, March 25. International Year of Disabled People
Des: John Gibbs.

Set	1.20	1.20
Gutter pairs	3.00	–
First day cover	–	1.00
Stamp cards	1.50	2.75

Small Tortoiseshell

Small tortoiseshell (14p)
Large blue (18p)
Peacock (22p)
Chequered skipper (25p)

■ 1981, May 13. British Butterflies
Des: Gordon Beningfield.

Set	1.25	1.25
Gutter pairs	3.50	–
First day cover	–	1.25
Stamp cards	1.50	2.75

Glenfinnan, Scotland (14p)
Derwentwater, England (18p)
Stackpole Head, Wales (20p)
Giant's Causeway, Northern Ireland (22p)
St. Kilda, Scotland (25p)

■ 1981, June 24. British Landscapes
Des: Michael Fairclough.

Set	1.45	1.60
Gutter pairs	3.50	–
First day cover	–	1.50
Stamp cards	1.50	2.75

Prince Charles and Lady Diana Spencer (14p, 25p)

■ 1981, July 22. Wedding of Prince Charles and Lady Diana Spencer
Des: Jeffery Matthews, from a portrait by Lord Snowdon.

Set	0.80	0.75
Gutter pair	2.00	–
First day cover	–	2.00
Stamp cards	1.50	2.75

Expeditions (14p)
Skills (18p)
Service (22p)
Recreation (25p)

■ 1981, August 12. 25th Anniversary of the Duke of Edinburgh's Award Scheme
Des: Philip Sharland. Printed in litho by Waddingtons.

Set	1.25	1.25
Gutter pairs	3.50	–
First day cover	–	1.25
Stamp cards	1.50	2.75

Cockle dredging (14p)
Hauling side trawl net (18p)
Lobster potting (22p)
Hauling Seine net (25p)

■ 1981, September 23. Fishing Industry
Des: Brian Sanders.

Set	1.25	1.25
Gutter pairs	3.50	–
First day cover	–	1.00
Stamp cards	1.50	2.75

Father Christmas with sacks of toys (11½p)
Jesus Christ (14p)
Angel in flight (18p)
Joseph and Mary with donkey (22p)
Three wise men on camels following the star (25p)

■ 1981, November 18. Christmas

Des: Samantha Brown (11½p), Tracy Jenkins (14p), Lucinda Blackmore (18p), Stephen Moore (22p), Sophie Sharp (25p). The 11½p has one phosphor band.

Set	1.40	1.35
Gutter pairs	3.00	–
First day cover	–	1.00
Stamp cards	1.50	3.00

Darwin and giant tortoises (15½p)
Darwin and marine iguanas (19½p)
Darwin and finches (26p)
Darwin and prehistoric skulls (29p)

■ 1982, February 10. Centenary of the Death of Charles Darwin.

Des: David Gentleman.

Set	1.40	1.30
Gutter pairs	3.50	–
First day cover	–	1.00
Stamp cards	1.50	3.50

Boys' Brigade (15½p)
Girls' Brigade (19½p)
Boy Scouts (26p)
Girl Guides and Brownies (29p)

■ 1982, March 24. Youth Organisations

Des: Brian Sanders.

Set	1.40	1.40
Gutter pairs	3.50	–
First day cover	–	1.25
Stamp cards	1.50	3.50

Ballet (15½p)
Pantomime (19½p)
Shakespearean drama (26p)
Opera (29p)

■ 1982, April 28. British Theatre (Europa)

Des: Adrian George.

Set	1.35	1.35
Gutter pairs	3.50	–
First day cover	–	1.25
Stamp cards	2.50	3.50

King Henry VIII and Mary Rose (15½p)
Admiral Blake and Triumph (19½p)
Lord Nelson and H.M.S. Victory (24p)
Lord Fisher and H.M.S. Dreadnought (26p)
Viscount Cunningham and H.M.S. Warspite (29p)

■ 1982, June 16. Maritime Heritage

Des: Marjorie Seynor. Printed in recess and photogravure by Harrison.

Set	1.60	2.00
Gutter pairs	4.00	–
First day cover	–	1.25
Stamp cards	1.50	3.50

'Strawberry Thief', 1883, by William Morris (15½p)
Untitled work 1906, by F. Steiner and Co (19½p)
'Cherry Orchard', 1930, by Paul Nash (26p)
'Chevrons', 1973, by Andrew Foster (29p)

■ 1982, July 23. British Textiles
Des: Peter Hatch Partnership.

Set	1.40	1.60
Gutter pairs	3.00	–
First day cover	–	1.25
Stamp cards	3.25	3.50

History of communications (15½p)
Modern technology (26p)

■ 1982, September 8. Information Technology Year
Des: Brian Delaney and Darrell Ireland.

Set	0.75	0.90
Gutter pair	2.00	–
First day cover	–	1.00
Stamp cards	1.00	3.50

Austin Seven and Metro (15½p)
Ford Model T and Escort (19½p)
Jaguar SS1 and XJ6 (26p)
Rolls Royce Silver Ghost and Silver Spirit (29p)

■ 1982, October 13. British Motor Cars
Des: Stanley Paine. Printed in litho by Questa.

Set	1.50	1.50
Gutter pairs	3.50	–
First day cover	–	1.25
Stamp cards	1.50	3.50

'While Shepherds Watched' (12½p)
'The Holly and the Ivy' (15½p)
'I Saw Three Ships' (19½p)
'We Three Kings' (26p)
'Good King Wenceslas' (29p)

■ 1982, November 17. Christmas
Des: Barbara Brown. 12½p has one phosphor band.

Set	1.50	1.50
Gutter pairs	3.50	–
First day cover	–	1.25
Stamp cards	1.50	3.50

Salmon (15½p)
Pike (19½p)
Trout (26p)
Perch (29p)

■ 1983, January 26. British River Fish
Des: Alex Jardine.

Set	1.50	1.50
Gutter pairs	3.50	–
First day cover	–	1.25
Stamp cards	2.50	3.50

Tropical island (15½p)
Arid desert (19½p)
Lush arable land (26p)
Cold mountainous region (29p)

■ 1983, March 9. Commonwealth Day
Des: Donald Hamilton Fraser.

Set	1.50	1.50
Gutter pairs	3.50	–
First day cover	–	1.25
Stamp cards	1.50	3.50

Humber Bridge (16p)
Thames Flood Barrier (20½p)
Iolair oilfield emergency support vessel (28p)

■ 1983, May 25. Engineering Achievements (Europa)
Des: Michael Taylor.

Set	1.25	1.25
Gutter pairs	4.00	–
First day cover	–	1.25
Stamp cards	1.50	3.50

Musketeer and pikeman, Royal Scots, 1633 (16p)
Fusilier and ensign, Royal Welch Fusiliers, 18th century (20½p)
Riflemen, 95th Rifles (Royal Green Jackets), 1805 (26p)
Sergeant and guardsman, Irish Guards, 1900 (28p)
Paratroopers, Parachute Regiment, 1983 (31p)

■ 1983, July 6. British Army Uniforms
Des: Eric Stemp.

Set	1.75	1.75
Gutter pairs	4.50	–
First day cover	–	1.75
Stamp cards	1.50	3.50

Sissinghurst, 20th century (16p)
Biddulph Grange, 19th century (20½p)
Blenheim Palace, 18th century (28p)
Pitmedden, 17th century (31p)

■ 1983, August 24. British Gardens
Des: Liz Butler. Printed in litho by Waddingtons.

Set	1.50	1.50
Gutter pairs	4.00	–
First day cover	–	1.25
Stamp cards	1.50	3.50

Merry-go-round (16p)
Menagerie and fairground rides (20½p)
Side shows (28p)
Produce fair (31p)

■ 1983, October 5. British Fairs
Des: Andrew Restall.

Set	1.40	1.50
Gutter pairs	3.25	–
First day cover	–	1.25
Stamp cards	1.50	3.50

Birds posting Christmas cards (12½p)
Chimney pots with a dove and cat (16p)
Dove and blackbird under an umbrella (20½p)
Dove and blackbird under a street lamp (28p)
Hedge sculpture of dove (31p)

■ 1983, November 16. Christmas
Des: Tony Meeuwissen. 12½p has one phosphor band.

Set	1.50	1.60
Gutter pairs	3.50	–
First day cover	–	1.25
Stamp cards	1.50	3.50

Arms of The College of Arms (16p)
Arms of King Richard III (20½p)
Arms of the Earl Marshal of England (28p)
Arms of the City of London (31p)

■ 1984, January 17. Quincentenary of the College of Arms
Des: Jeffery Matthews.

Set	1.50	1.60
Gutter pairs	3.50	–
First day cover	–	1.50
Stamp cards	1.50	3.50

Highland cow (16p)
Chillingham wild bull (20½p)
Hereford bull (26p)
Welsh black bull (28p)
Irish moiled cow (31p)

■ 1984, March 6. British Cattle
Des: Barry Driscoll.

Set	1.75	1.80
Gutter pairs	4.00	–
First day cover	–	1.50
Stamp cards	2.50	3.50

Liverpool: International Garden Festival (16p)
Durham: Milburngate Shopping Centre (20½p)
Bristol: Bush House, City Docks (28p)
Perth: Commercial Street Housing Scheme (31p)

■ 1984, April 19. Urban Renewal
Des: Trickett and Webb, and Ronald Maddox.

Set	1.60	1.60
Gutter pairs	3.50	–
First day cover	–	1.50
Stamp cards	1.50	3.50

Europa 'bridge' and CEPT emblem (16p, 20½p)
Abduction of Europa and European Parliament emblem (16p, 20½p)

■ 1984, May 15. 25th Anniversary of CEPT and Second Elections to the European Parliament (Europa)
Des: J. Larriviere (16p), Fritz Wegner (20½p). The two designs of each value were printed in se–tenant pairs.

Set	1.40	1.60
Gutter pairs	3.25	–
First day cover	–	1.50
Stamp cards	1.50	3.50

Lancaster House with flags of participating nations (31p)

■ 1984, June 5. London Economic Summit
Des: Paul Hogarth.

31p	0.70	0.70
Gutter pair	1.75	–
First day cover	–	1.00
Stamp card	0.75	3.50

Earth from space (16p)
Navigational chart of the English Channel (20½p)
Aerial photograph of the Greenwich Observatory (28p)
Sir George Airy's transit circle telescope (31p)

■ 1984, June 21. Centenary of the Greenwich Meridian
Des: J. Barney and H. Waller. Printed in litho by Questa.

Set	1.60	1.60
Gutter pairs	4.00	–
First day cover	–	1.25
Stamp cards	1.50	3.50

Bath mail coach, 1784 (16p)
Attack on the Exeter mail, 1816 (16p)
Norwich mail coach in a thunderstorm, 1827 (16p)
Holyhead and Liverpool mails leaving London, 1828 (16p)
Edinburgh mail coach snowbound, 1831 (16p)

■ 1984, July 31. 200th Anniversary of the First Mail Coach Run from Bristol and Bath to London
Des: Keith Bassford and Stanley Paine. Printed in recess and photogravure by Harrison.

Set	1.50	1.50
Gutter strip	3.50	–
First day cover	–	1.50
Stamp cards	1.75	3.50

(*Gutter strips comprise two horizontal se-tenant strips of five separated by a gutter.)

Education for development, Nigeria (17p)
Promoting the arts, Greece (22p)
Technical training, Sri Lanka (31p)
Language and libraries, Middle East (34p)

■ 1984, September 25. 50th Anniversary of the British Council
Des: Francis Newell, John Sorrell and Brian Sanders.

Set	1.50	1.50
Gutter pairs	3.75	–
First day cover	–	1.50
Stamp cards	2.00	3.50

(*Sheets of these stamps sold at the international stamp exhibition held in Melbourne, Australia, had the gutter margins overprinted with the exhibition logo.)

Holy family (13p)
Arrival in Bethlehem (17p)
Shepherd and lamb (22p)
Virgin and Child (31p)
Offering of frankincense (34p)

■ 1984, November 20. Christmas
Des: Yvonne Gilbert. 13p has one centre phosphor band.

Set	1.75	1.60
13p (stars printed on gummed side)	0.60	–
Gutter pairs	4.00	–
First day cover	–	1.50
Stamp cards	1.75	3.50

(*The 13p exists with a five-pointed-star pattern printed on the gummed side, from a booklet sold at a discount.)

Flying Scotsman, c.1947 (17p)
Golden Arrow, c.1960 (22p)
Cheltenham Flyer, c.1938 (29p)
Royal Scot, c.1959 (31p)
Cornish Riviera, c.1935 (34p)

■ 1985, January 22. Famous Trains
Des: Terence Cuneo.

Set	2.50	2.50
Gutter pairs	6.50	–
First day cover	–	1.50
Stamp cards	4.00	6.00

Buff-tailed bumble bee (17p)
Seven-spotted ladybird (22p)
Wart-biter bush-cricket (29p)
Stag beetle (31p)
Emperor butterfly (34p)

■ 1985, March 12. Insects
Des: Gordon Beningfield.

Set	2.00	2.00
Gutter pairs	5.00	–
First day cover	–	1.50
Stamp cards	2.00	3.00

'Water Music' by George Handel (17p)
'The Planets Suite' by Gustav Holst (22p)
'The First Cuckoo' by Frederick Delius (31p)
'Sea Pictures' by Edward Elgar (34p)

■ 1985, May 14. European Music Year. British Composers (Europa)
Des: Wilson McLean.

Set	2.25	2.00
Gutter pairs	6.00	–
First day cover	–	1.50
Stamp cards	3.50	3.00

RNLI lifeboat and signal flags (17p)
Beachy Head Lighthouse and chart (22p)
MARECS A communications satellite and aerials (31p)
Trinity House buoyage (34p)

■ 1985, June 18. Safety at Sea
Des: Newell and Sorell. Printed in litho by Waddingtons.

Set	1.60	1.60
Gutter pairs	4.00	–
First day cover	–	1.50
Stamp cards	1.50	3.00

Datapost motorcyclist and plane in London (17p)
Postbus in countryside (22p)
Parcel delivery by van in winter (31p)
Postman delivering letters on foot (34p)

■ 1985, July 30. 350th Anniversary of Royal Mail Service to the Public
Des: Paul Hogarth.

Set	1.75	1.75
17p ('D' pattern on gummed side)	0.60	–
Gutter pairs	4.25	–
First day cover	–	1.50
Stamp cards	1.50	3.00

(*The 17p exists with a 'D' pattern printed on the gummed side, from a booklet sold at a discount.)

King Arthur and Merlin (17p)
The Lady of the Lake (22p)
Queen Guinevere and Sir Lancelot (31p)
Sir Galahad (34p)

■ **1985, September 3. Arthurian Legend**
Des: Yvonne Gilbert.

Set	1.75	1.85
Gutter pairs	4.50	–
First day cover	–	1.50
Stamp cards	2.50	3.00

Peter Sellers, photographed by Bill Brandt (17p)
David Niven, photographed by Cornel Lucas (22p)
Charles Chaplin, photographed by Lord Snowdon (29p)
Vivien Leigh, photographed by Angus McBean (31p)
Alfred Hitchcock, photographed by Howard Coster (34p)

■ **1985, October 8. British Film Year**
Des: Keith Bassford.

Set	2.25	2.25
Gutter pairs	6.00	–
First day cover	–	2.25
Stamp cards	2.00	3.00

Principal boy (12p)
Genie (17p)
Pantomime dame (22p)
Good fairy (31p)
Pantomime cat (34p)

■ **1985, November 19. Christmas. Pantomime Characters**
Des: Adrian George. 12p has one phosphor band.

Set	1.75	1.75
12p (stars on gummed side)	0.55	–
Gutter pairs	5.00	–
First day cover	–	1.50
Stamp cards	1.50	3.00

(*The 12p exists with a star pattern printed on the gummed side, from a booklet sold at a discount.)

Energy: light bulb and North Sea oil rig (17p)
Health: thermometer and laboratory (22p)
Manufacture: garden hoe and steelworks (31p)
Agriculture: loaf of bread and cornfield (34p)

■ **1986, January 14. Industry Year**
Des: Keith Bassford. Printed in litho by Questa.

Set	1.75	1.75
Gutter pairs	5.00	–
First day cover	–	1.50
Stamp cards	1.50	3.00

Sir Edmond Halley as the comet (17p)
Giotto space probe approaching the comet (22p)
'Maybe twice in a lifetime' (31p)
The comet's orbit (34p)

■ **1986, February 18. Halley's Comet**
Des: Ralph Steadman.

Set	1.75	1.75
Gutter pairs	4.75	–
First day cover	–	1.50
Stamp cards	1.50	3.00

The Queen at the age of 2, 16 and 26 (17p, 34p)
The Queen at the age of 32, 47 and 56 (17p, 34p)

■ 1986, April 21. The Queen's 60th Birthday
Des: Jeffery Matthews.

Set	2.25	2.50
Gutter pairs	5.00	–
First day cover	–	2.25
Stamp cards	1.50	3.00

Barn owl (17p)
Pine marten (22p)
Wild cat (31p)
Natterjack toad (34p)

■ 1986, May 20. Nature Conservation (Europa)
Des: Ken Lilly.

Set	1.75	1.75
Gutter pairs	4.00	–
First day cover	–	1.75
Stamp cards	1.50	3.00

Peasants working the land (17p)
Freemen and their crafts (22p)
A knight and his retinue (31p)
A lord at a banquet (34p)

■ 1986, June 17. 900th Anniversary of the Domesday Book
Des: Tayburn.

Set	1.75	1.75
Gutter pairs	5.00	–
First day cover	–	1.75
Stamp cards	1.50	3.00

Athletics (17p)
Rowing (22p)
Weightlifting (29p)
Shooting (31p)
Hockey (34p)

■ 1986, July 15. Commonwealth Games, Edinburgh, and World Hockey Cup, London
Des: Nick Cudworth.

Set	2.00	2.00
Gutter pairs	5.00	–
First day cover	–	2.00
Stamp cards	1.75	3.00

Prince Andrew and Sarah Ferguson (12p, 17p)

■ 1986, July 22. Royal Wedding
Des: Jeffery Matthews.

Set	0.85	0.75
Gutter pairs	2.00	–
First day cover	–	1.00
Stamp cards	1.00	2.00

Cross on ballot paper (34p)

1986, August 19. Commonwealth Parliamentary Association Conference
Des: John Gibbs. Printed in litho by Questa.

34p	0.75	0.80
Gutter pairs	2.00	–
First day cover	–	1.00
Stamp card	0.75	2.00

Lord Dowding and Hawker Hurricane (17p)
Lord Tedder and Hawker Typhoon (22p)
Lord Trenchard and De Havilland DH9A (29p)
Sir Arthur Harris and Avro Lancaster (31p)
Lord Portal and De Havilland Mosquito (34p)

1986, September 16. Royal Air Force
Des: Brian Sanders.

Set	3.25	2.50
Gutter pairs	5.00	–
First day cover	–	2.25
Stamp cards	1.75	3.00

The Glastonbury Thorn (12p, 13p)
The Tanad Valley Plygain (18p)
The Hebrides Tribute (22p)
The Dewsbury Church Knell (31p)
The Hereford Boy Bishop (34p)

1986, November 18. Christmas. Folk Customs
Des: Lynda Gray. 12p has one phosphor band and was issued on December 2, 1986; 13p has one phosphor band

Set	2.00	2.00
13p (stars on gummed side)	0.60	–
Gutter Pairs	4.50	–
First day covers	–	1.75
Stamp cards	1.75	3.00

(*The 13p exists with a star pattern printed on the gummed side, from a booklet and a pack sold at a discount.)

Gaillardia (18p)
Echinops (22p)
Echeveria (31p)
Colchicum (34p)

1987, January 6. Flowers
Des: Jeffery Matthews from photographs by Alfred Lammer.

Set	1.75	1.75
Gutter pairs	4.50	–
First day cover	–	1.75
Stamp cards	1.50	3.00

'Principia Mathematica': apple (18p)
Motion of bodies in ellipses: planets orbiting around sun (22p)
'Optick Treatise': flask of water refracting light (31p)
'The System of the World': Earth and artificial satellite (34p)

1987, March 24. Sir Isaac Newton
Des: Sarah Goodwin.

Set	1.75	1.75
Gutter pairs	4.50	–
First day cover	–	1.75
Stamp cards	1.75	3.00

Willis Faber Dumas Building, Ipswich (18p)
Pompidou Centre, Paris (22p)
Staatgalerie, Stuttgart (31p)
European Investment Bank, Luxembourg (34p)

■ **1987, May 12. British Architects in Europe (Europa)**
Des: Minale Tattersfield Studio.

Set	1.75	1.75
Gutter pairs	4.50	–
First day cover	–	1.75
Stamp cards	1.50	3.00

Arms of the Lord Lyon, King of Arms (18p)
Arms of the Duke of Rothesay (22p)
Arms of the Royal Scottish Academy of Painting,
Sculpture and Architecture (31p)
Arms of the Royal Society of Edinburgh (34p)

■ **1987, July 21. 300th Anniversary of the Revival of the Order of the Thistle**
Des: Jeffery Matthews.

Set	1.75	1.75
Gutter pairs	4.50	–
First day cover	–	1.75
Stamp cards	1.50	3.00

First aid duties, 1887 (18p)
First aid in wartime, 1940 (22p)
First aid at events, 1965 (31p)
Transporting transplant organs by air, 1987 (34p)

■ **1987, June 16. St John Ambulance Centenary**
Des: Debbie Cook. Printed in litho by Questa.

Set	1.75	1.75
Gutter pairs	4.50	–
First day cover	–	1.75
Stamp cards	1.50	3.00

Landseer's painting 'Monarch of the Glen', the Great Exhibition,
Grace Darling (18p)
Brunel's S.S. Great Eastern, Mrs Beeton's 'Book of Household
Management', Prince Albert (22p)
Albert Memorial, Benjamin Disraeli, the first ballot box (31p)
Marconi's broadcast to Paris, the Diamond Jubilee, the Relief of
Mafeking (34p)

■ **1987, September 8. 150th Anniversary of the Accession of Queen Victoria**
Des: Carroll and Dempsey Studio. Printed in recess and
photogravure by Harrison.

Set	1.75	1.75
Gutter pairs	4.50	–
First day cover	–	1.75
Stamp cards	1.75	3.00

Pot by Bernard Leach (18p)
Pot by Elizabeth Fritsch (26p)
Pot by Lucie Rie (31p)
Pot by Hans Coper (34p)

■ **1987, October 13. Studio Pottery**
Des: Tony Evans.

Set	1.75	1.75
Gutter pairs	4.50	–
First day cover	–	1.75
Stamp cards	3.50	3.00

Child decorating a Christmas tree (13p)
Child looking out of a window (18p)
Child sleeping, and Father Christmas in his sleigh (26p)
Child reading a book surrounded by toys (31p)
Child playing a recorder, watched by snowman (34p)

■ **1987, November 17. Christmas**
Des: M. Foreman. 13p has one phosphor band.

Set	1.75	1.75
13p (stars on gummed side)	0.70	–
Gutter pairs	4.50	–
First day cover	–	1.75
Stamp cards	1.75	3.00

(*The 13p exists with a star pattern printed on the gummed side, from a pack sold at a discount.)

Short–spined sea scorpion (18p)
Yellow waterlily (26p)
Bewick's swan (31p)
Morel mushroom (34p)

■ **1988, January 19. Bicentenary of the Linnean Society**
Des: E. Hughes.

Set	1.75	1.75
Gutter pairs	4.50	–
First day cover	–	1.75
Stamp cards	1.50	3.00

Reverend William Morgan, Bible translator 1588 (18p)
William Salesbury, New Testament translator 1567 (26p)
Bishop Richard Davies, New Testament translator 1567 (31p)
Bishop Richard Parry, Welsh Bible editor 1620 (34p)

■ **1988, March 1. 400th Anniversary of the Welsh Bible**
Des: K. Bowen.

Set	1.75	1.75
Gutter pairs	4.50	–
First day cover	–	1.75
Stamp cards	1.50	3.00

Gymnastics: British Amateur Gymnastics Association (18p)
Skiing: Ski Club of Great Britain (26p)
Tennis: Lawn Tennis Association (31p)
Football: Football League (34p)

■ **1988, March 22. Sports Organisations**
Des: J. Sutton.

Set	1.75	1.75
Gutter pairs	4.50	–
First day cover	–	1.75
Stamp cards	1.50	3.00

Mallard train and mailbags (18p)
Queen Elizabeth liner and transatlantic mail (26p)
Glasgow tram and pillar box (31p)
Imperial Airways Handley Page HP45 and airmail (34p)

■ 1988, May 10. Transport and Mail Services (Europa)
Des: M. Dempsey.

Set	1.75	1.75
Gutter pairs	4.50	–
First day cover	–	1.75
Stamp cards	1.50	3.00

(*The Handley Page design also exists as an imprinted 33p value on a set of airmail postal cards issued on March 2, 1993; price £5.)

Early settler and sailing clipper (18p)
British and Australian parliaments and Queen Elizabeth II (18p)
W. G. Grace and tennis racquet (34p)
Shakespeare, John Lennon and Sydney Opera House (34p)

■ 1988, June 21. Bicentenary of Australian Settlement
Des: G. Emery. Printed in litho by Questa.

Set (two se-tenant pairs)	1.80	1.80
Gutter pairs	4.00	–
First day cover	–	1.75
Stamp cards	1.50	3.00

Spanish ship off The Lizard (18p)
English fleet leaving Plymouth (18p)
Engagement off the Isle of Wight (18p)
English fire-ships attack off Calais (18p)
Spanish ships in North Sea storm (18p)

■ 1988, July 19. 400th anniversary of the Spanish Armada
Des: G. Evernden.

Set (se-tenant strip of five)	1.50	1.50
Gutter pairs	4.00	–
First day cover	–	1.75
Stamp cards	1.75	3.00

'The owl and the pussy cat went to sea' (19p)
Self-portrait of Edward Lear as a bird (27p)
'Cat' (32p)
'There was a young lady whose bonnet...' (35p)

■ 1988, September 6. Centenary of the Death of Edward Lear
Des: M. Swatridge and S. Dew.

Set	1.75	1.75
Gutter pairs	4.50	–
First day cover	–	1.75
Stamp cards	1.50	3.00
Miniature sheet (one of each value)	3.75	4.00
Miniature sheet first day cover	–	4.00

(*The miniature sheet, issued on September 27, 1988, was sold with a surcharge towards the cost of staging the international stamp exhibition, Stamp World London 90.)

Carrickfergus Castle (£1)
Caernarfon Castle (£1.50)
Edinburgh Castle (£2)
Windsor Castle (£5)

■ 1988, October 18. Castle high value definitives
Engraved by C. Matthews from photographs by Prince Andrew. Recess-printed by Harrison.

Set	16.00	4.50
Gutter pairs	35.00	–
Gutter blocks of four (centre cross)	75.00	–
First day cover	–	20.00

Journeying to Bethlehem (14p)
Shepherds following the star (19p)
Three wise men (27p)
Nativity (32p)
Annunciation (35p)

■ 1988, November 15. Christmas. Christmas Cards
Des: L. Trickett. 14p has one phosphor band.

Set	1.90	1.90
Gutter pairs	4.00	–
First day cover	–	1.75
Stamp cards	1.75	3.00

(*Examples of the 14p are known with the denomination of 13p in error.)

Atlantic puffin (19p)
Avocet (27p)
Oystercatcher (32p)
Northern gannet (35p)

■ 1989, January 17. Centenary of the Royal Society for the Protection of Birds
Des: D. Cordery.

Set	1.75	1.75
Gutter pairs	5.00	–
First day cover	–	1.75
Stamp cards	2.75	3.00

Teddy bear (19p)
Rose (19p)
Cupid (19p)
Yachts (19p)
Fruit (19p)

■ 1989, January 31. Greetings
Des: P. Sutton. Se–tenant strip of five. Issued in booklets in panes of ten containing two of each design.

Set (se–tenant strip of five)	10.00	13.00
Booklet pane (of 10)	23.00	–
Booklet	25.00	–
First day cover	–	9.00
Stamp cards	5.00	10.00

Fruit and vegetables (19p)
Meat products (27p)
Dairy products (32p)
Cereal products (35p)

■ 1989, March 7. Food and Farming Year
Des: Sedley Place.

Set	1.75	1.75
Gutter pairs	4.50	–
First day cover	–	1.75
Stamp cards	1.50	3.00

150th anniversary of public education: mortar board (19p)
Third elections to European Parliament: cross on ballot (19p)
26th Postal, Telegraph and Telephone Congress: posthorn (35p)
Inter–Parliamentary Union Conference: globe (35p)

■ 1989, April 11. Anniversaries and Events
Des: Lewis Moberly. 19p and 35p issued in se–tenant pairs.

Set (two se–tenant pairs)	1.75	1.75
Gutter pairs	4.50	–
First day cover	–	1.75
Stamp cards	1.50	3.00

Toy aeroplane and locomotive (19p)
Building bricks (27p)
Board games and dice (32p)
Toy robot, boat and doll's house (35p)

■ **1989, May 16. Games and Toys (Europa)**
Des: D. Fern.

Set	1.75	1.75
Gutter pairs	4.50	–
First day cover	–	1.75
Stamp cards	1.50	3.00

Snowflake (19p)
Fly (27p)
Blood cells (32p)
Microchip (35p)

■ **1989, September 5. 150th Anniversary of the Royal Microscopical Society**
Des: K. Bassford. Printed in litho by Questa.

Set	1.75	1.75
Gutter pairs	4.50	–
First day cover	–	1.75
Stamp cards	1.50	3.00

Ironbridge, Shropshire (19p)
Tin mine, St Agnes Head, Cornwall (27p)
Cotton Mills, New Lanark, Strathclyde (32p)
Pontcysyllte Aqueduct, Clwyd (35p)

■ **1989, July 4. Industrial Archaeology**
Des: R. Maddox.

Set	1.75	1.75
Gutter pairs	4.50	–
First day cover	–	1.75
Stamp cards	1.50	3.00
Miniature sheet	3.50	3.50
Miniature sheet first day cover	–	3.50

(*The miniature sheet, issued on July 25, 1989, contained one of each value but with the designs in a horizontal format, with a surcharge towards the cost of staging the international stamp exhibition, Stamp World London 90.)

Royal Mail coach (20p)
Escort of the Blues and Royals (20p)
Lord Mayor's coach (20p)
St Paul's Cathedral (20p)
Blues and Royals drum horse (20p)

■ **1989, October 17. Lord Mayor's Show, London**
Des: P. Cox.

Set (se-tenant strip of five)	1.50	1.50
Gutter pairs	4.00	–
First day cover	–	1.70
Stamp cards	1.75	3.00

(*The Royal Mail Coach design also appears in the Treasures of the Archive prestige stamp book issued on August 18, 2009, printed in litho.)

14th century peasants, from stained glass window (15p)
Arches and roundels from West Front (15p+1p)
Octagon Tower (20p+1p)
Arcade from West Transept (34p+1p)
Triple arch from West Front (37p+1p)

■ **1989, November 14. Christmas. 800th Anniversary of Ely Cathedral**
Des: D. Gentleman. 15p and 15p+1p have one phosphor band.

Set	2.25	2.25
Gutter pairs	5.00	–
First day cover	–	1.75
Stamp cards	2.25	3.00

(*Four of these stamps carried a surcharge for charity.)

■ **1990, January 10. 150th Anniversary of the Penny Black**
See under Decimal Machin definitives.

Kitten (20p)
Rabbit (29p)
Duckling (34p)
Puppy (37p)

■ **1990, January 23. 150th Anniversary of the Royal Society for the Prevention of Cruelty to Animals**
Des: T. Evans. Printed in litho by Questa.

Set	2.00	2.00
Gutter pairs	5.00	–
First day cover	–	1.75
Stamp cards	1.75	3.00

Teddy Bear (20p)
Dennis the Menace (20p)
Punch (20p)
Cheshire Cat (20p)
The Man in the Moon (20p)
The Laughing Policeman (20p)
Clown (20p)
Mona Lisa (20p)
Queen of Hearts (20p)
Stan Laurel (20p)

■ **1990, February 6. Greetings: Smiles**
Des: Michael Peters and Partners. Issued se–tenant in booklet panes of ten comprising one of each design.

Booklet pane (of 10)	11.00	12.00
Booklet	14.00	–
First day cover	–	11.00

Alexandra Palace, London (20p)
School of Art, Glasgow (20p)
British Philatelic Bureau, Edinburgh (29p)
Templeton Carpet Factory, Glasgow (37p)

■ **1990, March 6. Glasgow 1990 European City of Culture and Stamp World Exhibition (Europa)**
Des: P. Hogarth.

Set	1.75	1.75
Gutter pairs	4.25	–
First day cover	–	1.75
Stamp cards	1.50	3.00

(*The 20p Alexandra Palace design also appears in the £5 London Life prestige stamp book issued on March 20, 1990.)

Export Achievement Award (20p and 37p)
Technological Achievement Award (20p and 37p)

■ 1990, April 10. 25th Anniversary of The Queen's Awards for Export and Technology
Des: S. Broom. Printed in litho by Questa.

Set (two se–tenant pairs)	1.75	1.75
Gutter pairs	4.00	–
First day cover	–	1.80
Stamp cards	1.50	3.00

Portraits of Queen Victoria and Queen Elizabeth II (20p)

■ 1990, May 3. Stamp World London 90 International Exhibition
Des: Sedley Place Design; engraved by C. Matthews. Printed in recess and photogravure by Harrison.

Miniature sheet	2.50	2.50
First day cover	–	2.75

(*The border illustrates the 1840 Penny Black but this was not valid for postage. The sheets were sold at £1 each, the surcharge going towards the cost of staging the exhibition.)

Cycad and Sir Joseph Banks Building (20p)
Stone pine and Princess of Wales Conservatory (29p)
Willow tree and Palm House (34p)
Cedar tree and Pagoda (37p)

■ 1990, June 5. 150th Anniversary of Kew Gardens
Des: P. Leith.

Set	1.75	1.75
Gutter pairs	4.00	–
First day cover	–	1.75
Stamp cards	1.50	3.00

Thomas Hardy and Clyffe Clump, Dorset (20p)

■ 1990, July 10. 150th Anniversary of the Birth of Thomas Hardy
Des: J. Gibbs.

20p	0.40	0.40
Gutter pair	1.00	–
First day cover	–	1.00
Stamp card	1.00	1.50

Queen Elizabeth as The Queen Mother (20p)
Queen Elizabeth as Queen (29p)
Queen Elizabeth as Duchess of York (34p)
Queen Elizabeth as Lady Elizabeth Bowes–Lyon (37p)

■ **1990, August 2. 90th Birthday of Queen Elizabeth, The Queen Mother**
Des: J. Gorham from photographs by Norman Parkinson, Dorothy Wilding, B. Park and Rita Martin.

Set	2.75	2.75
Gutter pairs	7.00	–
First day cover	–	2.50
Stamp cards	1.50	3.00

(*The same designs were used in the Queen Mother Memorial issue of April 2002, but with the borders changed to black.)

Victoria Cross (20p)
George Cross (20p)
Distinguished Service Cross, Distinguished Service Medal (20p)
Military Cross and Military Medal (20p)
Distinguished Flying Cross, Distinguished Flying Medal (20p)

■ **1990, September 11. Gallantry Awards**
Des: J. Gibbs and J. Harwood.

Set	1.75	1.75
Gutter pairs	4.50	–
First day cover	–	2.00
Stamp cards	2.25	3.00

(*The 20p also appears in the miniature sheet and the prestige stamp book with the Victoria Cross issue on September 21, 2006.)

Armagh Observatory, Jodrell Bank & La Palma telescopes (22p)
Early telescope and moon and tides diagram by Newton (26p)
Greenwich Old Observatory and astronomical equipment (31p)
Stonehenge, armillary sphere and navigation by the stars (37p)

■ **1990, October 16. Astronomy**
Des: J. Fisher. Printed in litho by Questa.

Set	1.75	1.75
Gutter pairs	4.50	–
First day cover	–	2.00
Stamp cards	1.50	3.00

Building a snowman (17p)
Fetching a Christmas tree (22p)
Carol singers (26p)
Tobogganing (31p)
Ice–skating (37p)

■ **1990, November 13. Christmas**
Des: J. Gorham and A. Davidson. The 17p has one phosphor band.

Set	2.00	2.00
Gutter pairs	5.00	–
First day cover	–	1.75
Stamp cards	1.75	3.00

(*The 17p was also sold in booklets.)

'King Charles Spaniel' (22p)
'A Pointer' (26p)
'Two Hounds in a Landscape' (31p)
'A Rough Dog' (33p)
'Fino and Tiny' (37p)

■ **1991, January 8. Dogs. Paintings by George Stubbs**
Des: Carroll, Dempsey and Thirkell.

Set	2.25	2.25
Gutter pairs	5.50	–
First day cover	–	2.25
Stamp cards	1.75	3.00

Thrush's nest (1st)
Shooting star and rainbow (1st)
Magpies and charm bracelet (1st)
Black cat (1st)
Kingfisher and key (1st)
Mallard and frog (1st)
Four-leaf clover, boot and matchbox (1st)
Pot of gold at the end of the rainbow (1st)
Butterflies (1st)
Wishing well and sixpence (1st)

■ 1991, February 5. Greetings: Good Luck
Des: T. Meeuwissen. Issued se-tenant in booklet panes of 10 containing one of each design.

Booklet pane (of 10)	10.00	10.00
Booklet	10.00	–
First day cover	–	10.00

Michael Faraday, electricity (22p)
Charles Babbage, computer (22p)
Robert Watson Watt, radar (31p)
Frank Whittle, jet engine: Gloster Whittle E28/39 aircraft (37p)

■ 1991, March 5. Scientific Achievements
Des: P. Till (22p, 22p), J. Harwood (31p, 37p).

Set	2.00	2.00
Gutter pairs	5.00	–
First day cover	–	1.75
Stamp cards	1.50	3.00

■ 1991, March 26. Greetings: Smiles
Designs as for the Greetings stamps of February 6, 1990, but with all values changed to 1st class. Issued se-tenant in booklet panes of ten containing one of each design.

Booklet pane (of 10)	9.00	10.00
Booklet	9.00	–
First day cover	–	10.00

(*These designs were also used for Smilers sheets in 2000 and 2001.)

Man looking at space (22p, 22p)
Space looking at man (37p, 37p)

■ 1991, April 23. Europe in Space (Europa)
Des: J-M. Folon.

Set (two se-tenant pairs)	2.25	2.25
Gutter pairs	6.00	–
First day cover	–	2.50
Stamp cards	1.50	3.00

Fencing (22p)
Hurdling (26p)
Diving (31p)
Rugby (37p)

■ 1991, June 11. World Student Games, Sheffield, and Rugby World Cup
Des: Huntley Muir Partners.

Set	2.25	2.25
Gutter pairs	6.00	–
First day cover	–	2.25
Stamp cards	1.50	3.00

Silver Jubilee rose (22p)
Madame Alfred Carrière rose (26p)
Rosa Moyesii rose (31p)
Harvest Fayre rose (33p)
Mutabilis rose (37p)

■ 1991, July 16. World Congress of Roses, Belfast
Des: Yvonne Skargon. Printed in litho by Questa.

Set	2.25	2.25
Gutter pairs	6.00	–
First day cover	–	2.25
Stamp cards	2.00	3.00

Iguanodon (22p)
Stegosaurus (26p)
Tyrannosaurus (31p)
Protoceratops (33p)
Triceratops (37p)

■ 1991, August 20. 150th Anniversary of the Identification of Dinosaurs by Richard Owen
Des: B. Kneale.

Set	2.50	2.50
Gutter pairs	6.00	–
First day cover	–	3.00
Stamp cards	2.00	3.00

Map of Hamstreet, Kent, in 1816 (24p)
Map of Hamstreet, Kent, in 1906 (28p)
Map of Hamstreet, Kent, in 1959 (33p)
Map of Hamstreet, Kent, in 1991 (39p)

■ 1991, September 17. Bicentenary of Ordnance Survey
Des: H. Brown. Printed in recess and litho by Harrison (24p), in litho by Harrison (28p), and in litho by Questa (33p, 39p).

Set	2.25	2.25
Gutter pairs	6.00	–
First day cover	–	2.50
Stamp cards	1.50	3.00

(*Examples of the 28p are known with the denomination of 26p, from supplies printed before an increase in postage rates and issued in error.)

Adoration of the Magi (18p)
Mary with Jesus in stable (24p)
Holy family and angel (28p)
Annunciation (33p)
Flight into Egypt (39p)

■ 1991, November 12. Christmas
Des: D. Driver, from the Acts Of Mary & Jesus illuminated manuscript. The 18p has one phosphor band.

Set	2.25	2.25
Gutter pairs	6.00	–
First day cover	–	2.50
Stamp cards	1.75	3.00

(*The 18p was also sold in booklets.)

Fallow deer in Scottish forest (18p)
Hare on North Yorkshire moors (24p)
Fox in the Fens (28p)
Redwing in the Home Counties (33p)
Welsh mountain sheep in Snowdonia (39p)

■ 1992, January 14. The Four Seasons: Wintertime
Des: J. Gorham and K. Bowen. 18p has one phosphor band.

Set	2.25	2.25
Gutter pairs	5.00	–
First day cover	–	2.25
Stamp cards	1.75	3.75

(*The 39p also appears in the Cymru Wales prestige stamp booklet issued on February 25, 1992.)

Spray of flowers (1st)
Double locket (1st)
Key (1st)
Toy car and cigarette cards (1st)
Compass and map (1st)
Pocket watch (1st)
Penny Red stamp and pen (1st)
Pearl necklace (1st)
Marbles (1st)
Starfish and a bucket and spade (1st)

■ 1992, January 28. Greetings: Memories

Des: Trickett and Webb Ltd. Issued se-tenant in booklet panes of ten, containing one of each design.

Booklet pane (of 10)	10.00	10.00
Booklet	10.00	–
First day cover	–	10.00

Queen Elizabeth II, in Coronation robes (24p)
Queen Elizabeth II, in Garter robes (24p)
Queen Elizabeth II, with Prince Andrew as a baby (24p)
Queen Elizabeth II, at Trooping of the Colour (24p)
Queen Elizabeth II, with emblem of the Commonwealth (24p)

■ 1992, February 6. 40th Anniversary of the Accession

Des: Why Not Associates. Printed in litho by Questa.

Set (se-tenant strip of five)	3.25	3.50
Gutter pairs	7.50	–
First day cover	–	3.50
Stamp cards	1.75	3.75

Tennyson in 1888 and 'The Beguiling of Merlin' by Burne-Jones (24p)
Tennyson in 1856 and 'April Love' by Hughes (28p)
Tennyson in 1864 and 'I Am Sick Of The Shadows' by Waterhouse (33p)
Tennyson as a young man and 'Mariana' by Rossetti (39p)

■ 1992, March 10. Centenary of the Death of Alfred, Lord Tennyson

Des: Irene von Treskow.

Set	2.25	2.25
Gutter pairs	5.00	–
First day cover	–	2.25
Stamp cards	1.50	3.75

Barcelona Olympics: British Olympic Association logo (24p)
Barcelona Paralympics: British Paralympic Association logo (24p)
Discovery of America by Columbus: 'Santa Maria' (24p)
Operation Raleigh Grand Regatta: 'Kaisei' (39p)
Expo '92 in Seville: British Pavilion (39p)

■ 1992, April 7. International Events (Europa)

Des: K. Bassford (Olympics, Paralympics and Expo), K. Bassford and S. Paine (Columbus and Raleigh). Printed in litho by Questa (Olympics, Paralympics and Expo) or in recess and litho by Harrison (Columbus and Raleigh). The Olympics and Paralympics designs were issued as a se-tenant pair.

Set	2.50	2.60
Gutter pairs	6.00	–
First day cover	–	2.50
Stamp cards	1.75	3.75

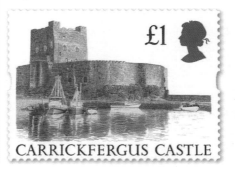

Carrickfergus Castle (£1)
Caernarfon Castle (£1.50)
Edinburgh Castle (£2)
Windsor Castle (£5)

■ 1992, March 24. Castle high value definitives

As issue of October 18, 1988, but with the Queen's head in silhouette, printed in optically variable ink which changes colour from gold to green depending on the angle at which it is viewed, and with an elliptical perforation along each side.

Set	23.00	6.00
Gutter pairs	70.00	–
Gutter blocks of four (centre cross)	£140	–
First day cover	–	15.00
Stamp cards	8.00	55.00

(*The £1.50, £2 and £5 exist with either blue-tinted PVAD gum or white PVA gum.)

Pikeman (24p)
Drummer (28p)
Musketeer (33p)
Standard bearer (39p)

■ 1992, June 16. 350th Anniversary of the Civil War

Des: J. Sancha.

Set	2.25	2.25
Gutter pairs	6.00	–
First day cover	–	2.25
Stamp cards	2.50	3.75

'The Yeoman of the Guard' (18p)
'The Gondoliers' (24p)
'The Mikado' (28p)
'The Pirates of Penzance' (33p)
'Iolanthe' (39p)

■ 1992, July 21. Gilbert and Sullivan Operas

Des: Lynda Gray. 18p has one phosphor band.

Set	2.50	2.50
Gutter pairs	6.00	–
First day cover	–	2.50
Stamp cards	1.75	3.75

Acid rain kills (24p)
Ozone layer (28p)
Greenhouse effect (33p)
Bird of hope (39p)

■ 1992, September 15. Protection of the Environment

Des: C. Hall (24p), L. Fowler (28p), S. Warren (33p) and A. Newton–Mold (39p). All paintings by children, in conjunction with the BBC Television programme 'Blue Peter'.

Set	2.25	2.25
Gutter pairs	5.50	–
First day cover	–	2.25
Stamp cards	1.50	3.75

European star (24p)

■ 1992, October 13. Single European Market

Des: D. Hockney.

24p	0.50	0.45
Gutter pair	1.50	–
First day cover	–	1.00
Stamp card	1.00	2.50

Angel Gabriel, from St. James's, Pangbourne (18p)
Madonna and Child, from St. Mary's, Bilbury (24p)
King with gold, from Our Lady and St. Peter, Leatherhead (28p)
Shepherds, from All Saints, Porthcawl (33p)
Kings with gifts, from Our Lady and St. Peter, Leatherhead (39p)

■ 1992, November 10. Christmas. Stained–Glass Windows
Des: Carroll, Dempsey and Thirkell. The 18p has one phosphor band.

Set	2.25	2.25
Gutter pairs	5.00	–
First day cover	–	2.50
Stamp cards	1.75	3.75

(*The 18p was also sold in booklets.)

Mute swan cob and St. Catherine's Chapel (18p)
Cygnet and decoy (24p)
Swans and cygnet (28p)
Eggs in nest and Tithe Barn (33p)
Young swan (39p)

■ 1993, January 19. 600th Anniversary of Abbotsbury Swannery
Des: David Gentleman. The 18p has one phosphor band.

Set	4.00	4.00
Gutter pairs	10.00	–
First day cover	–	4.00
Stamp cards	1.75	5.00

William (1st)
Long John Silver (1st)
Tweedledum and Tweedledee (1st)
Mole and Toad (1st)
Teacher and Wilfred (1st)
Peter Rabbit and Mrs Rabbit (1st)
Snowman and Father Christmas (1st)
The Big Friendly Giant and Sophie (1st)
Bill Badger and Rupert Bear (1st)
Aladdin and the Genie (1st)

■ 1993, February 2. Greetings: Gift Giving
Des: Newell and Sorrell. Issued se–tenant in booklet panes of ten containing one of each design.

Booklet pane (of 10)	10.00	10.00
Booklet	10.00	–
First day cover	–	10.00
Stamp cards	8.00	15.50

(*The Peter Rabbit and Mrs Rabbit design also appears in the Story of Beatrix Potter prestige stamp book issued on August 10, 1993.)

H4 chronometer: decorated enamel dial (24p)
H4 chronometer: escapement, remontoire and fusée (28p)
H4 chronometer: balance and spring (33p)
H4 chronometer: movement seen from back (39p)

■ 1993, February 16. 300th Anniversary of the Birth of John Harrison
Des: H. Brown and D. Penny. Printed in litho by Questa.

Set	2.25	2.25
Gutter pairs	5.50	–
First day cover	–	2.25
Stamp cards	1.75	5.00

Britannia (£10)

■ **1993, March 2. £10 definitive**
Des: M. Denney and B. Craddock. Printed in litho by Questa, with die-stamping and braille embossing.

£10	20.00	8.50
First day cover	–	15.00
Stamp card	4.50	50.00

Dendrobium hellwigianum (18p)
Paphiopedilum Maudiae 'Magnificum' (24p)
Cymbidium lowianum (28p)
Vanda Rothschildiana (33p)
Dendrobium vexillarius var. albiviride (39p)

■ **1993, March 16. World Orchid Conference, Glasgow**
Des: Pandora Sellars. The 18p has one phosphor band.

Set	2.25	2.25
Gutter pairs	5.50	–
First day cover	–	2.25
Stamp cards	1.75	5.00

'Family Group' by Henry Moore (24p)
'Kew Gardens' by Edward Bawden (28p)
'St Francis and the Birds' by Stanley Spencer (33p)
'Still Life: Odyssey 1' by Ben Nicholson (39p)

■ **1993, May 11. Contemporary Art (Europa)**
Des: A. Dastor.

Set	2.25	2.25
Gutter pairs	6.00	–
First day cover	–	2.25
Stamp cards	1.50	5.00

Emperor Claudius, from gold coin (24p)
Emperor Hadrian, from bronze head (28p)
Goddess Roma, from gemstone (33p)
Christ, from mosaic at Hinton St. Mary (39p)

■ **1993, June 15. Roman Britain**
Des: J. Gibbs.

Set	2.25	2.25
Gutter pairs	6.00	–
First day cover	–	2.25
Stamp cards	1.50	5.00

Narrowboats on Grand Junction Canal (24p)
Humber keels on Stainforth and Keadby Canal (28p)
Horse-drawn barges on Brecknock and Abergavenny Canal (33p)
Steam barges and fishing boats on Crinan Canal (39p)

■ **1993, July 20. Inland Waterways**
Des: T. Lewery. Printed in litho by Questa.

Set	2.25	2.25
Gutter pairs	6.00	–
First day cover	–	2.25
Stamp cards	2.00	5.00

Horse chestnut (18p)
Blackberry (24p)
Hazel (28p)
Rowan (33p)
Pear (39p)

■ **1993, September 14. The Four Seasons: Autumn**
Des: Charlotte Knox. The 18p has one phosphor band.

Set	2.25	2.25
Gutter pairs	6.00	–
First day cover	–	2.25
Stamp cards	2.00	5.00

'The Reigate Squire' (24p)
'The Hound of the Baskervilles' (24p)
'The Six Napoleons' (24p)
'The Greek Interpreter' (24p)
'The Final Problem' (24p)

■ 1993, October 12. Sherlock Holmes
Des: A. Davidson. Printed in litho by Questa.

Set (se–tenant strip of five)	2.25	2.50
Gutter pairs	6.00	–
First day cover	–	2.50
Stamp cards	5.00	4.50

Bob Cratchit and Tiny Tim (19p)
Mr. and Mrs. Fezziwig (25p)
Mr. Scrooge (30p)
The prize turkey (35p)
Mr. Scrooge's nephew (41p)

■ 1993, November 9. Christmas. 150th Anniversary of 'A Christmas Carol' by Charles Dickens
Des: Q. Blake. The 19p has one phosphor band.

Set	2.40	2.50
Gutter pairs	6.00	–
First day cover	–	2.75
Stamp cards	2.50	5.00

(*The 19p and 25p were also sold in booklets.)

Class 5 and Class B1 on the West Highland Line (19p)
Class A1 at Kings Cross (25p)
Class 4 at Blyth North (30p)
Class 4 near Wigan Central (35p)
Castle class crossing Worcester & Birmingham Canal (41p)

■ 1994, January 18. The Age of Steam
Des: B. Delaney, from photographs by Colin Gifford. The 19p has one phosphor band.

Set	2.40	3.00
Gutter pairs	6.00	–
First day cover	–	2.50
Stamp cards	3.00	5.50

Dan Dare (1st)
The Three Bears (1st)
Rupert Bear (1st)
Alice in Wonderland (1st)
Noggin and the Ice Dragon (1st)
Peter Rabbit (1st)
Little Red Riding Hood (1st)
Orlando the Marmalade Cat (1st)
Biggles (1st)
Paddington Bear (1st)

■ 1994, February 1. Greetings: Messages
Des: Newell and Sorrell. Issued se–tenant in booklet panes of ten containing one of each design.

Booklet pane (of 10)	10.00	10.00
Booklet	10.00	–
First day cover	–	10.00
Stamp cards	8.00	15.50

Chirk Castle, Clwyd, Wales (19p)
Ben Arkle, Sutherland, Scotland (25p)
Mourne Mountains, County Down, Northern Ireland (30p)
Dersingham, Norfolk, England (35p)
Dolwyddelan, Gwynedd, Wales (41p)

■ 1994, March 1. 25th Anniversary of the Investiture of The Prince of Wales

Des: paintings by the Prince of Wales. The 19p has one phosphor band.

Set	2.40	2.50
Gutter pairs	6.00	–
First day cover	–	2.75
Stamp cards	2.50	5.50

(*The 30p also appears in the Northern Ireland prestige stamp book issued on July 26, 1994.)

Bathing at Blackpool (19p)
'Where's my little lad?' (25p)
'Wish you were here' (30p)
Punch and Judy show (35p)
Tower Crane machine (41p)

■ 1994, April 12. Centenary of Picture Postcards

Des: M. Dempsey and B. Dare. Printed in litho by Questa. The 19p has one phosphor band, and the other values have two.

Set	2.40	2.50
Gutter pairs	6.50	–
First day cover	–	2.75
Stamp cards	2.00	5.50

British lion and French cockerel (25p, 41p)
Hands over a train (25p, 41p)

■ 1994, May 3. Opening of the Channel Tunnel

Des: G. Hardie (lion and cockerel), J.–P. Cousin (hands and train).

Set (two se–tenant pairs)	2.50	2.50
Gutter pairs	6.50	–
First day cover	–	2.75
Stamp cards	2.00	5.50

Ground crew servicing Douglas Boston aircraft (25p)
HMS Warspite (25p)
Commandos on Gold Beach (25p)
Infantry on Sword Beach (25p)
Tank and infantry at Ouistreham (25p)

■ 1994, June 6. 50th Anniversary of D–Day

Des: K. Bassford. Printed in litho by Questa.

Set (se–tenant strip of five)	2.50	2.75
Gutter pairs	6.00	–
First day cover	–	2.75
Stamp cards	2.50	5.50

St. Andrew's, old course (19p)
Muirfield, 18th hole (25p)
Carnoustie, 15th hole (30p)
Royal Troon, 8th hole (35p)
Turnberry, 9th hole (41p)

■ 1994, July 5. Scottish Golf Courses

Des: P. Hogarth. The 19p has one phosphor band.

Set	2.50	2.50
Gutter pairs	6.50	–
First day cover	–	2.50
Stamp cards	2.50	5.50

Royal Welsh Show, Llanelwedd (19p)
All England Tennis Championships, Wimbledon (25p)
Cowes Week (30p)
Test Match, Lord's (35p)
Braemar Gathering (41p)

■ 1994, August 2. The Four Seasons: Summertime

Des: M. Cook. The 19p has one phosphor band.

Set	2.50	2.50
Gutter pairs	6.00	–
First day cover	–	2.50
Stamp cards	3.25	5.50

Ultrasonic imaging (25p)
Scanning electron microscopy (30p)
Magnetic resonance imaging (35p)
Computed tomography (41p)

■ 1994, September 27. Medical Discoveries (Europa)
Des: P. Vermier and J.–P. Tibbles. Printed in photogravure by Enschedé.

Set	2.25	2.25
Gutter pairs	6.00	–
First day cover	–	2.50
Stamp cards	2.00	5.50

Mary and Joseph (19p)
Three wise men (25p)
Mary with doll (30p)
Shepherds (35p)
Angels (41p)

■ 1994, November 1. Christmas. Children's Nativity Plays
Des: Yvonne Gilbert. The 19p has one phosphor band.

Set	2.40	2.50
Gutter pairs	6.00	–
First day cover	–	2.50
Stamp cards	2.50	5.50

(*The 19p and 25p were also sold in booklets.)

Black cat (19p)
Siamese and tabby cat (25p)
Ginger cat (30p)
Tortoiseshell and Abyssinian cat (35p)
Black and white cat (41p)

■ 1995, January 17. Cats
Des: Elizabeth Blackadder. Printed in litho by Questa. The 19p has one phosphor band, other values two phosphor bands.

Set	2.50	2.50
Gutter pairs	6.00	–
First day cover	–	2.50
Stamp cards	3.00	6.50

Dandelions (19p)
Chestnut leaves (25p)
Garlic leaves (30p)
Hazel leaves (35p)
Spring grass (41p)

■ 1995, March 14. The Four Seasons: Springtime
Des: plant sculptures by Andy Goldsworthy. The 19p has one phosphor band, other values two phosphor bands.

Set	2.25	2.40
Gutter pairs	6.00	–
First day cover	–	2.50
Stamp cards	2.50	6.50

'La Danse à la Campagne' by Pierre–Auguste Renoir (1st)
'Troilus and Criseyde' by Peter Brookes (1st)
'The Kiss' by Auguste Rodin (1st)
'Girls on the Town' by Beryl Cook (1st)
'Jazz' by Andrew Mockett (1st)
'Girls Performing a Kathak Dance' (1st)
'Alice Keppel With Her Daughter' by Alice Hughes (1st)
'Children Playing' by L. S. Lowry (1st)
'Circus Clowns' by Emily Firmin and Justin Mitchell (1st)
'All the Love Poems of Shakespeare' by Eric Gill (1st)

■ **1995, March 21. Greetings: Art**
Des: Newell and Sorrell. Printed in litho by Walsall. Issued
se–tenant in booklet panes of ten containing one of each design.

Booklet pane (of 10)	10.00	10.00
Booklet	10.00	–
First day cover	–	10.00
Stamp cards	9.00	15.50

Fireplace decoration (19p)
Oak seedling (25p)
Carved table leg (30p)
St David's Head, Dyfed, Wales (35p)
Elizabethan window (41p)

■ **1995, April 11. Centenary of The National Trust**
Des: T. Evans. The 19p has one phosphor band, the 25p and 35p
two phosphor bands, the 30p and 41p phosphor paper.

Set	2.25	2.25
Gutter pairs	6.00	–
First day cover	–	2.50
Stamp cards	2.50	6.50

(*The 25p also appears in the National Trust prestige stamp
book issued on April 25, 1995.)

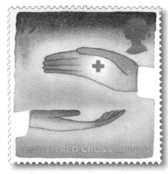

End of World War II: British troops and French civilians (19p)
British Red Cross: symbolic hands and Red Cross emblem (19p)
Victory: searchlights in a 'V' over St. Paul's Cathedral (25p)
United Nations: hand releasing dove of peace (25p)
United Nations: symbolic hands uplifted (30p)

■ **1995, May 2. Peace & Freedom (Europa)**
Des: J–M. Folon (Red Cross 19p, Dove 25p, 30p), J. Gorham
(Troops 19p, Searchlights 25p). The 19p has one phosphor band,
other values two phosphor bands.

Set	2.25	2.25
Gutter pairs	6.00	–
First day cover	–	2.50
Stamp cards	3.00	6.50

(*The St Paul's Cathedral design was also used as a 1st class
stamp in the End of the War miniature sheet in 2005.)

'The Time Machine' (25p)
'The First Men in the Moon' (30p)
'The War of the Worlds' (35p)
'The Shape of Things to Come' (41p)

■ **1995, June 6. Novels of H. G. Wells**
Des: Siobhan Keaney. Printed in litho by Questa.

Set	2.25	2.25
Gutter pairs	5.00	–
First day cover	–	2.50
Stamp cards	3.00	6.50

The Swan Theatre, 1595 (25p)
The Rose Theatre, 1592 (25p)
The Globe Theatre, 1599 (25p)
The Hope Theatre, 1613 (25p)
The Globe Theatre, 1614 (25p)

■ **1995, August 8. Reconstruction of Shakespeare's Globe
Theatre**
Des: C. Hodges. Printed in litho by Walsall.

Set (se–tenant strip of five)	2.25	2.50
Gutter pairs	5.00	–
First day cover	–	2.50
Stamp cards	3.00	6.50

■ 1995, August 22. Castle high–value definitive

Des: as issue of March 24, 1992, but new value, replacing the £1.

£3	8.50	1.75
Gutter pair	20.00	–
Gutter block of four (centre cross)	40.00	–
First day cover	–	5.00
Stamp card	8.00	21.00

(*This stamp exists with either blue tinted PVAD gum or white PVA gum.)

Sir Rowland Hill and Uniform Penny Postage petition (19p)
Sir Rowland Hill and Penny Black (25p)
Guglielmo Marconi and early wireless (41p)
Guglielmo Marconi and the sinking of the 'Titanic' (60p)

■ 1995, September 5. Pioneers of Communications

Des: The Four Hundred; engraved by C. Slania. Printed in recess and litho by Harrison. The 19p has one phosphor band.

Set	2.50	2.50
Gutter pairs	6.00	–
First day cover	–	2.50
Stamp cards	2.50	6.50

Harold Wagstaff (19p)
Gus Risman (25p)
Jim Sullivan (30p)
Billy Batten (35p)
Brian Bevan (41p)

■ 1995, October 3. Centenary of Rugby League

Des: C. Birmingham. The 19p has one phosphor band, other values two phosphor bands.

Set	2.50	2.60
Gutter pairs	6.00	–
First day cover	–	2.50
Stamp cards	2.50	6.50

Robin in letter box (19p)
Robin on railings (25p)
Robin on milk bottles (30p)
Robin on road sign (41p)
Robin on door handle (60p)

■ 1995, October 30. Christmas. Robins

Des: K. Lilly. The 19p has one phosphor band, other values two phosphor bands.

Set	2.50	2.80
Gutter pairs	6.00	–
First day cover	–	2.80
Stamp cards	3.25	6.50

(*The 19p, 25p and 60p were also sold in booklets, and the 19p was used in Smilers sheets in 2000 and 2001.)

'Wee, fleeket, cowran, tim'rous beastie' (19p)
'O, my love's like a red, red rose' (25p)
'Scots, wha hae wi Wallace bled' (41p)
'Should auld acquaintance be forgot' (60p)

■ 1996, January 25. Bicentenary of the Death of Robert Burns

Des: Tayburn Consultancy. Printed in litho by Questa. The 19p has one phosphor band, other values two phosphor bands.

Set	2.25	2.25
Gutter pairs	5.50	–
First day cover	–	2.50
Stamp cards	2.50	6.50

'I'm writing to you because you don't listen to a word I say' (1st)
'More! Love' (1st)
'Sincerely' (1st)
'Do you have something for the human condition?' (1st)
'Mental floss' (1st)
'4:55pm. Don't ring' (1st)
'Dear lottery prize winner' (1st)
'Fetch this, fetch that. Let the cat do it' (1st)
'My day starts before I'm ready for it' (1st)
'The cheque in the post' (1st)

■ 1996, February 26. Greetings: Cartoons
Des: M. Wolff. Printed in litho by Walsall. All-over phosphor.
Issued se-tenant in booklet panes of ten containing one of each design.

Booklet pane (of 10)	9.00	9.00
Booklet	9.00	–
First day cover	–	9.00
Stamp cards	9.00	16.00

Muscovy duck (19p)
Lapwing (25p)
White-front goose (30p)
Bittern (35p)
Whooper swan (41p)

■ 1996, March 12. 50th Anniversary of the Wildfowl and Wetlands Trust
Des: Moseley Webb, from paintings by C. F. Tunnicliffe. The 19p has one phosphor band.

Set	2.25	2.25
Gutter pairs	6.00	–
First day cover	–	2.75
Stamp cards	3.00	6.50

Odeon, Harrogate (19p)
Laurence Olivier and Vivien Leigh in 'Lady Hamilton' (25p)
Cinema ticket (30p)
Pathé News (35p)
Cinema sign, Odeon, Manchester (41p)

■ 1996, April 16. Centenary of Cinema
Des: The Chase. The 19p has one phosphor band, other values two phosphor bands.

Set	2.50	2.50
Gutter pairs	6.00	–
First day cover	–	2.75
Stamp cards	4.00	6.50

Dixie Dean (19p)
Bobby Moore (25p)
Duncan Edwards (30p)
Billy Wright (35p)
Danny Blanchflower (41p)

■ 1996, May 14. European Football Championship
Des: H. Brown. Printed in litho by Questa. The 19p has one phosphor band, other values two phosphor bands.

Set	2.75	3.00
Gutter pairs	6.50	–
First day cover	–	3.00
Stamp cards	4.00	6.50

(*All five values also appear in the European Football Championship prestige stamp book issued on May 14, 1996.)

Athlete on starting blocks (26p)
Throwing the javelin (26p)
Basketball (26p)
Swimming (26p)
Athlete and Olympic rings (26p)

■ **1996, July 9. Olympic and Paralympic Games, Atlanta, USA**
Des: N. Knight. Printed in litho by Questa.

Set (se-tenant strip of five)	2.40	2.60
Gutter pairs	6.00	–
First day cover	–	2.75
Stamp cards	3.00	6.50

Dorothy Hodgkin (20p)
Margot Fonteyn (26p)
Elizabeth Frink (31p)
Daphne du Maurier (37p)
Marea Hartman (43p)

■ **1996, August 6. Famous Women (Europa)**
Des: Stephanie Nash. The 20p has one phosphor band, other values two phosphor bands.

Set	2.50	2.60
Gutter pairs	6.50	–
First day cover	–	3.00
Stamp cards	2.50	6.50

Muffin the Mule (20p)
Sooty (26p)
Stingray (31p)
The Clangers (37p)
Dangermouse (43p)

■ **1996, September 3. 50th Anniversary of Children's Television**
Des: Tutssels. Printed in photogravure by Enschedé. The 20p has one phosphor band, other values two phosphor bands.

Set	2.50	2.50
Gutter pairs	6.50	–
First day cover	–	3.00
Stamp cards	3.00	6.50

(*The 20p also appears in the 75th Anniversary of the BBC prestige stamp booklet issued on September 23, 1997, printed in photogravure by Harrison; price £1.00 mint or used.)

Triumph TR3 (20p)
MG TD (26p)
Austin Healey 100 (37p)
Jaguar XK120 (43p)
Morgan Plus 4 (63p)

■ **1996, October 1. Classic Sports Cars**
Des: S. Clay. The 20p has one phosphor band, other values two phosphor bands.

Set	3.00	3.00
Gutter pairs	8.50	–
First day cover	–	3.50
Stamp cards	5.00	6.50

Three kings (2nd)
Annunciation (1st)
Journey to Bethlehem (31p)
Nativity (43p)
Shepherds (63p)

■ 1996, October 28. Christmas

Des: Laura Stoddart. The 2nd class has one phosphor band, other values two phosphor bands.

Set	3.00	3.25
Gutter pairs	8.50	–
First day cover	–	3.50
Stamp cards	3.50	6.50

(*The 2nd class and 1st class were also sold in booklets.)

■ 1996, November 11. Greetings: Cartoons

As issue of February 26, but with two phosphor bands. Issued se-tenant in booklet panes of ten containing one of each design.

Booklet pane (of 10)	25.00	27.00
Booklet	25.00	–

(*These designs were also used for Smilers sheets in 2001 and 2002.)

Iris latifolia (1st)
Gentiana acaulis (1st)
Magnolia grandiflora (1st)
Camellia japonica (1st)
Tulipa (1st)
Fuchsia 'Princess of Wales' (1st)
Tulipa gesneriana (1st)
Gazania splendens (1st)
Hippeastrum rutilum (1st)
Passiflora coerulea (1st)

■ 1997, January 6. Greetings: 19th-Century Flower Paintings

Des: Tutssels. Printed in litho by Walsall. Two phosphor bands. Issued se-tenant in booklet panes of ten containing one of each design.

Booklet pane (of 10)	10.00	10.00
Booklet	10.00	–
First day cover	–	11.00
Stamp cards	12.00	20.00

(*The *Gentiana acaulis*, *Tulipa* and *Iris latifolia* designs also appear in the Glory of the Garden prestige stamp book of 2004, and the *Tulipa* and *Iris latifolia* designs in the 50th Anniversary of NAFAS booklet of May 21, 2009, in self adhesive form. All the designs were also used in a Smilers sheet issued in 2003.)

King Henry VIII (26p)
Catherine of Aragon (26p)
Anne Boleyn (26p)
Jane Seymour (26p)
Anne of Cleves (26p)
Catherine Howard (26p)
Catherine Parr (26p)

■ 1997, February 21. 450th Anniversary of the Death of King Henry VIII

Des: Kate Stephens. Two phosphor bands. The wives designs were issued in a se-tenant strip of six.

Set	3.50	4.00
Gutter pairs	9.00	–
First day cover	–	4.00
Stamp cards	7.50	6.50

St Columba in boat (26p)
St Columba on Iona (37p)
St Augustine with King Ethelbert (43p)
St Augustine with a model of cathedral (63p)

■ 1997, March 11. Religious Anniversaries

Des: Claire Melinsky. Printed in photogravure by Enschedé. Two phosphor bands.

Set	2.75	2.75
Gutter pairs	7.00	–
First day cover	–	3.50
Stamp cards	2.50	6.50

Dracula (26p)
Frankenstein (31p)
Dr Jekyll and Mr Hyde (37p)
The Hound of the Baskervilles (43p)

■ 1997, May 13. Horror Stories (Europa)

Des: J. Pollock. Printed in photogravure by Walsall. Two phosphor bands and features printed in fluorescent ink which are visible only under ultra–violet light.

Set	2.50	2.75
Gutter pairs	6.50	–
First day cover	–	3.00
Stamp cards	2.50	6.50

Supermarine Spitfire MkIIA and Reginald Mitchell (20p)
Avro Lancaster MkI and Roy Chadwick (26p)
De Havilland Mosquito B MkXVI and Ronald Bishop (37p)
Gloster Meteor T Mk7 and George Carter (43p)
Hawker Hunter FGA Mk9 and Sir Sydney Camm (63p)

■ 1997, June 10. British Aircraft Designers

Des: Turner Duckworth. The 20p has one phosphor band, other values two phosphor bands.

Set	3.25	3.25
Gutter pairs	8.00	–
First day cover	–	3.25
Stamp cards	3.00	6.50

(*The 20p value also appears in the Pilot To Plane: RAF Uniforms prestige stamp book issued on September 18, 2008.)

Carriage horse (20p)
Lifeguards horse (26p)
Blues and Royals drum horse (43p)
Duke of Edinburgh's horse (63p)

■ 1997, July 8. All The Queen's Horses. 50th Anniversary of the British Horse Society

Des: J.–L. Benard. Printed in litho by Walsall. The 20p has one phosphor band, other values two phosphor bands.

Set	2.50	2.75
Gutter pairs	7.00	–
First day cover	–	3.00
Stamp cards	2.50	6.50

Caernarfon Castle (£1.50)
Edinburgh Castle (£2)
Carrickfergus Castle (£3)
Windsor Castle (£5)

■ 1997, July 29. Castle high–value definitives

Des: as the issues of March 24, 1992, and August 22, 1995, but re-engraved by Inge Madlé. Printed in recess and silk screen (for Queen's portrait) by Enschedé.

Set	45.00	13.00
Gutter pairs	£125	–
Gutter blocks of four (centre cross)	£275	–
First day cover	–	25.00

Haroldswick, Shetland (20p)
Painswick, Gloucestershire (26p)
Beddgelert, Gwynedd (43p)
Ballyroney, County Down (63p)

■ **1997, August 12. Sub Post Offices**
Des: T. Millington. Printed in photogravure by Enschedé. The 20p has one phosphor band, other values two phosphor bands.

Set	2.50	2.75
Gutter pairs	7.00	–
First day cover	–	3.00
Stamp cards	2.00	6.50

Enid Blyton's *Malory Towers*

'Noddy' (20p)
'Famous Five' (26p)
'Secret Seven' (37p)
'Faraway Tree' (43p)
'Malory Towers' (63p)

■ **1997, September 9. Centenary of the Birth of Enid Blyton**
Des: C. Birmingham. Printed in photogravure by Enschedé. The 20p has one phosphor band, other values two phosphor bands.

Set	2.75	3.00
Gutter pairs	7.00	–
First day cover	–	3.00
Stamp cards	3.00	6.50

Father Christmas and children pulling a cracker (2nd)
Father Christmas holding a cracker (1st)
Father Christmas riding on a cracker (31p)
Father Christmas riding on a snowball (43p)
Father Christmas on a chimney (63p)

■ **1997, October 27. Christmas. 150th Anniversary of the Christmas Cracker**
Des: M. Thomas (1st) and J. Gorham (others). The 2nd class has one phosphor band, other values two phosphor bands.

Set	3.25	3.25
Gutter pairs	8.00	–
First day cover	–	3.50
Stamp cards	3.25	6.50

(*The 2nd class and 1st class also appear in booklets, and the 1st class was used in Smilers sheets in 2000 and 2001.)

Queen Elizabeth II and Prince Philip, wedding photograph of 1947 (20p, 43p)
Queen Elizabeth II and Prince Philip, photographed in 1997 (26p, 63p)

■ **1997, November 13. Royal Golden Wedding**
Des: D. Driver (20p, 43p), Lord Snowdon (26p, 63p). The 20p has one phosphor band, other values two phosphor bands.

Set	3.75	3.75
Gutter pairs	9.00	–
First day cover	–	3.50
Stamp cards	2.50	6.50

Common dormouse (20p)
Lady's slipper orchid (26p)
Song thrush (31p)
Shining ram's-horn snail (37p)
Mole cricket (43p)
Devil's bolette (63p)

■ **1998, January 20. Endangered Species**
Des: R. Maude. Printed in litho by Questa. The 20p has one phosphor band, other values two phosphor bands.

Set	4.00	4.00
Gutter pairs	10.00	–
First day cover	–	3.75
Stamp cards	3.50	6.50

Princess Diana wearing necklace, 1997 (26p)
Princess Diana dressed in blue, 1997 (26p)
Princess Diana wearing tiara, 1991 (26p)
Princess Diana dressed in black and white checks, 1995 (26p)
Princess Diana wearing black evening dress, 1987 (26p)

■ 1998, February 3. Diana, Princess of Wales Memorial
Des: B. Robinson. Two phosphor bands.

Set (se-tenant strip of five)	2.40	2.25
Gutter pairs	6.00	–
First day cover	–	3.50

Lion of England and Griffin of Edward III (26p)
Falcon of Plantagenet and Bull of Clarence (26p)
Lion of Mortimer and Yale of Beaufort (26p)
Greyhound of Richmond and Dragon of Wales (26p)
Unicorn of Scotland and Horse of Hanover (26p)

■ 1998, February 24. The Queen's Beasts. 650th Anniversary of the Order of the Garter
Des: Jeffery Matthews. Printed in recess and litho by Harrison. Two phosphor bands.

Set (se-tenant strip of five)	2.50	2.60
Gutter pairs	6.00	–
First day cover	–	3.00
Stamp cards	3.00	6.50

Wilding design of 1952–67 (20p, 26p, 37p)

■ 1998, March 10. Wilding definitives
Des: Dew Gibbons Design Group, from original design by G. Knipe. Printed in gravure by Walsall. Issued only in the Wilding Definitives prestige stamp book.

20p light green (phos band at left)	0.70	0.75
20p light green (phos band at right)	0.70	0.75
26p red-brown	0.75	0.80
37p light purple	1.75	1.85

St John's Point lighthouse (20p)
Smalls lighthouse (26p)
Needles Rock lighthouse (37p)
Bell Rock lighthouse (43p)
Eddystone lighthouse (63p)

■ 1998, March 24. Lighthouses
Des: D. Davis and J. Boon. Printed in litho by Questa. The 20p has one phosphor band, other values two phosphor bands.

Set	3.25	3.25
Gutter pairs	8.50	–
First day cover	–	3.50
Stamp cards	2.50	6.50

Tommy Cooper (20p)
Eric Morecambe (26p)
Joyce Grenfell (37p)
Les Dawson (43p)
Peter Cook (63p)

■ 1998, April 23. Comedians
Des: Gerald Scarfe. Printed in litho by Questa. The 20p has one phosphor band, other values two phosphor bands.

Set	3.25	3.25
Gutter pairs	8.00	–
First day cover	–	3.50
Stamp cards	3.00	6.50

Hands forming the shape of a heart (20p)
Adult holding the hand of a child (26p)
Hands forming a cradle (43p)
Hand taking a pulse (63p)

■ 1998, June 23. 50th Anniversary of the National Health Service

Des: V. Frost, using photographs by A. Wilson. Printed in litho by Questa. The 20p has one phosphor band, other values two phosphor bands.

Set	2.60	2.60
Gutter pairs	7.00	–
First day cover	–	3.25
Stamp cards	3.50	6.50

'The Hobbit' by J. R. R. Tolkien (20p)
'The Lion, The Witch and The Wardrobe' by C. S. Lewis (26p)
'The Phoenix and the Carpet' by E. Nesbit (37p)
'The Borrowers' by Mary Norton (43p)
'Through The Looking Glass' by Lewis Carroll (63p)

■ 1998, July 21. Children's Fantasy Novels

Des: P. Malone. Printed in photogravure by De La Rue. The 20p has one phosphor band, other values two phosphor bands.

Set	3.25	3.25
Gutter pairs	7.50	–
First day cover	–	3.50
Stamp cards	5.00	6.50

Woman in costume of yellow feathers (20p)
Woman in blue costume (26p)
Children in white and gold robes (43p)
Child dressed as a tree (63p)

■ 1998, August 25. Notting Hill Carnival (Europa)

Des: T. Hazael. Printed in photogravure by Walsall. The 20p has one phosphor band, other values two phosphor bands.

Set	2.75	2.75
Gutter pairs	7.00	–
First day cover	–	3.25
Stamp cards	2.00	6.50

Bluebird of Sir Malcolm Campbell, 1925 (20p)
Sunbeam of Sir Henry Segrave, 1926 (26p)
Babs of John Parry Thomas, 1926 (30p)
Railton Mobil Special of John Cobb, 1947 (43p)
Bluebird CN7 of Donald Campbell, 1964 (63p)

■ 1998, September 29. British Land Speed Records

Des: Roundel Design Group. Printed in photogravure by De La Rue. The 20p has one phosphor band, other values two phosphor bands.

Set	3.00	3.25
Gutter pairs	7.50	–
First day cover	–	3.25
Stamp cards	2.50	6.50

(*The 20p also appears in the Breaking Barriers prestige stamp book issued on October 13, 1988, but printed in photogravure by Walsall, and with one phosphor band printed on the left or right of the stamp; price £1.00 each mint or used)

Angel with hands in blessing (20p)
Angel praying (26p)
Angel playing lute (30p)
Angel playing flute (43p)
Angel praying (63p)

■ **1998, November 2. Christmas. Angels**
Des: Irene von Treskow. Printed in photogravure by De La Rue.
The 20p has one phosphor band, other values two phosphor
bands.

Set	3.25	3.25
Gutter pairs	9.00	–
First day cover	–	3.25
Stamp cards	2.50	6.50

(*The 20p and 26p values were also sold in booklets.)

During 1999 and 2000 Royal Mail produced a series of special
stamp issues to mark the new millennium. Each design includes
the inscription 'Millennium', the year of issue and a serial
number. The designs for 1999 looked back over the previous
millennium under 12 different themes. The designs for 2000
highlighted projects undertaken to celebrate the millennium.

Timekeeping: Greenwich Meridian and clock face (20p)
Steam Power: worker and blast furnace (26p)
Photography: photograph of leaves (43p)
Computers: computer inside head (63p)

■ **1999, January 12. The Inventors' Tale**
Des: David Gentleman (20p), P. Howson (26p), Z. and B. Baran
(43p), E. Paolozzi (63p). Printed in photogravure by Enschedé
(26p), or De La Rue (20p, 43p, 63p). The 20p has one phosphor
band, other values two phosphor bands.

Set	3.00	4.25
Gutter pairs	7.50	–
First day cover	–	4.50
Stamp cards	2.00	6.50

(*The 63p value also appears in the World Changers prestige
stamp book issued on September 21, 1999, but printed in
photogravure by Questa; price £2.25 mint or used.)

Jet Travel: globe surrounded by aircraft (20p)
Liberation By Bike: woman on bicycle (26p)
Linking The Nation: railway station (43p)
Cook's Endeavour: Captain Cook and Maori (63p)

■ **1999, February 2. The Travellers' Tale**
Des: G. Hardie (20p), S. Fanelli (26p), J. Lawrence (43p), A.
Klimowski (63p). Printed in photogravure by Enschedé (20p, 63p)
or De La Rue (26p), or litho by Enschedé (43p). The 20p has one
phosphor band, other values two phosphor bands.

Set	3.00	4.25
Gutter pairs	7.50	–
First day cover	–	3.75
Stamp cards	2.00	6.50

Jenner's Vaccination: cow with markings of vaccinated child (20p)
Nursing Care: patient on trolley (26p)
Fleming's Penicillin: penicillin mould (43p)
Test Tube Baby: sculpture of baby (63p)

■ 1999, March 2. The Patients' Tale
Des: P. Brookes (20p), S. Macfarlane (26p), M. Dempsey (43p), A. Gormley (63p. Printed in photogravure by Questa. The 20p has one phosphor band, other values two phosphor bands.

Set	3.00	4.25
Gutter pairs	7.50	–
First day cover	–	3.75
Stamp cards	3.00	6.50

(*The 20p also appears in the World Changers prestige stamp book issued on September 21, 1999.)

Migration To Scotland: Norman settler and dove (20p)
Pilgrim Fathers: settlers and Red Indian (26p)
Destination Australia: sailing ship and aspects of settlement (43p)
Migration To UK: face superimposed on hummingbird (63p)

■ 1999, April 6. The Settlers' Tale
Des: J. Byrne (20p), W. McLean (26p), J. Fisher (43p), G. Powell (63p). Printed in litho (20p) or photogravure (26p, 43p, 63p) by Walsall. The 20p has one phosphor band, other values two phosphor bands.

Set	3.00	4.25
Gutter pairs	7.50	–
First day cover	–	3.75
Stamp cards	2.00	6.50

(*The 26p also appears in a booklet issued on May 12, 1999.)

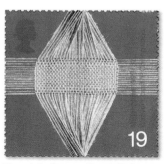

Weaver's Craft: woven threads (19p)
Mill Towns: Salts Mill, Saltaire (26p)
Shipbuilding: hull on slipway (44p)
City Finance: Lloyd's Building, London (64p)

■ 1999, May 4. The Workers' Tale
Des: P. Collingwood (19p), D. Hockney (26p), R. Sanderson (44p), B. Neiland (64p). Printed in litho (19p) or photogravure (26p, 44p, 64p) by De La Rue. The 19p has one phosphor band, other values two phosphor bands.

Set	3.00	4.25
Gutter pairs	7.50	–
First day cover	–	3.75
Stamp cards	3.00	6.50

(*The 26p also appears in a booklet issued on May 12, 1999, printed in photogravure by Walsall; price £1.75 mint or used.)

Mercury's Magic: Freddie Mercury of Queen on stage (19p)
World Cup: Bobby Moore holding the trophy (26p)
Doctor Who: dalek (44p)
Chaplin's Genius: Charlie Chaplin (64p)

■ 1999, June 1. The Entertainers' Tale
Des: P. Blake (19p), M. White (26p), Lord Snowdon (44p), R. Steadman (64p). Printed in photogravure by Enschedé. The 19p has one phosphor band, other values two phosphor bands.

Set	3.00	4.25
Gutter pairs	7.50	–
First day cover	–	3.75
Stamp cards	4.50	6.50

Prince Edward and Miss Sophie Rhys–Jones facing front (26p)
Prince Edward and Miss Sophie Rhys–Jones facing sideways (64p)

■ 1999, June 15. Royal Wedding
Des: J. Gibbs, from photographs by John Swannell. Printed in photogravure by De La Rue.

Set	1.50	2.75
Gutter pairs	4.00	–
First day cover	–	2.50
Stamp cards	2.50	3.50

Equal Rights: suffragette behind bars (19p)
Right To Health: tap (26p)
Right To Learn: children at school (44p)
First Rights: Magna Carta (64p)

■ 1999, July 6. The Citizens' Tale
Des: N. Kerr (19p), M. Craig–Martin (26p), A. Drummond (44p),
A. Kitching (64p). Printed in photogravure by De La Rue. The 19p
has one phosphor band, other values two phosphor bands.

Set	3.00	4.25
Gutter pairs	7.50	–
First day cover	–	3.75
Stamp cards	2.00	6.50

Decoding DNA: molecular structures (19p)
Darwin's Theory: Galapagos finch and skeleton (26p)
Faraday's Electricity: light polarised by magnetism (44p)
Newton: Saturn, from Hubble Space Telescope (64p)

■ 1999, August 3. The Scientists' Tale
Des: M. Curtis (19p), R. Harris Ching (26p), C. Gray (44p),
photograph (64p). Printed in photogravure (19p, 64p) or litho
(26p, 44p) by Questa. The 19p has one phosphor band, other
values two phosphor bands.

Set	3.00	4.25
Gutter pairs	7.50	–
First day cover	–	3.75
Stamp cards	2.00	6.50

(*The 26p and 44p also appear in the World Changers prestige
stamp book of September 21, 1999; price £3.50 for the pair. The
64p also appears in the miniature sheet of August 11, 1999.)

Saturn, from Hubble Space Telescope (64p)

■ 1999, August 11. Solar Eclipse
Des: four 64p values from the issue of August 3. Printed in
photogravure by De La Rue.

Miniature sheet	12.00	18.00
First day cover	–	12.50

Strip Farming: upland landscape (19p)
Mechanical Farming: horse–drawn seed drill (26p)
Food From Afar: peeling potato (44p)
Satellite Agriculture: combine harvester in field (64p)

■ 1999, September 7. The Farmers' Tale
Des: D. Tress (19p), C. Wormell (26p), T. Traeger (44p), R. Cooke
(64p). Printed in photogravure by De La Rue. The 19p has one
phosphor band, other values two phosphor bands.

Set	3.00	4.25
Gutter pairs	6.50	–
First day cover	–	3.75
Stamp cards	2.00	6.50

(*The 26p also appears in a booklet issued on September 21, 1999,
printed in gravure by Walsall; price £2.00 mint or used.)

Bannockburn: Robert the Bruce (19p)
Civil War: cavalier and horse (26p)
World Wars: war graves (44p)
Peace–Keeping: soldiers with boy (64p)

■ 1999, October 5. The Soldiers' Tale
Des: A. Davidson (19p), R. Kelly (26p), D. McCullin (44p), C. Corr
(64p). Printed in litho (19p) or photogravure (26p, 44p, 64p)
by Walsall. The 19p has one phosphor band, other values two
phosphor bands.

Set	3.00	4.25
Gutter pairs	6.50	–
First day cover	–	3.75
Stamp cards	2.00	6.50

Wesley: 'Hark the Herald Angels Sing' (19p)
King James Bible: King James I and Authorised Version (26p)
St. Andrews Pilgrimage: St. Andrews Cathedral, Fife (44p)
First Christmas: nativity (64p)

■ 1999, November 2. The Christians' Tale
Des: B. Neuenschwander (19p), C. Melinsky (26p), C. Yass (44p),
C. Aitchison (64p). Printed in photogravure by De La Rue. The 19p
has one phosphor band, other values two phosphor bands.

Set	3.00	4.25
Gutter pairs	6.50	–
First day cover	–	3.75
Stamp cards	2.00	6.50

(*The 19p and 26p were also sold in booklets.)

World Of The Stage: dancers behind curtain (19p)
World Of Music: coloured stripes (26p)
World Of Literature: untitled book (44p)
New Worlds: rainbow abstract (64p) ·

■ 1999, December 7. The Artists' Tale
Des: A. Jones (19p), B. Riley (26p), L. Milroy (44p), Sir H. Hodgkin
(64p). Printed in photogravure by Walsall. The 19p has one
phosphor band, other values two phosphor bands.

Set	3.00	4.25
Gutter pairs	7.00	–
First day cover	–	3.75
Stamp cards	2.00	6.50

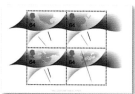

Clock face and globe showing North America (64p)
Clock face and globe showing Asia (64p)
Clock face and globe showing Middle East (64p)
Clock face and globe showing Europe (64p)

■ 1999, December 14. Millennium Timekeeper
Des: David Gentleman. Printed in gravure by De La Rue.

Miniature sheet	12.00	18.00
First day cover	–	11.00
Stamp cards	11.00	19.00

(*The miniature sheet also exists with the margin overprinted
'Earls Court, London 22–28 May 2000 The Stamp Show 2000',
sold at £10 with tickets to the exhibition from March 1, 2000;
price £18.00 mint.)

Third Millennium, Muncaster: barn owl (19p)
National Space Centre, Leicester: night sky (26p)
Torrs Walkway, New Mills: River Goyt and textile mills (44p)
Seabird Centre, North Berwick: cape gannets (64p)

■ 2000, January 18. Above and Beyond
Printed in litho (44p) and gravure (19p, 26p, 64p) by Questa. The
19p has one phosphor band, other values two phosphor bands.

Set	3.50	3.50
Gutter pairs	8.50	–
First day cover	–	4.50
Stamp cards	2.00	6.50

(*The 26p design also appears, as a 1st class value, in a booklet
issued on May 26, 2000, printed in gravure by Walsall; price
£3.00 mint.)

Beacons Across The Land: millennium beacon (19p)
Rheilffordd Eryri, Snowdonia: Garratt locomotive and train (26p)
Dynamic Earth Centre, Edinburgh: lightning (44p)
Lighting Croydon's Skyline: floodlighting (64p)

■ 2000, February 1. Fire and Light
Printed in gravure by De La Rue. The 19p has one phosphor band,
other values two phosphor bands.

Set	3.50	3.50
Gutter pairs	8.50	–
First day cover	–	4.50
Stamp cards	2.50	6.50

Turning The Tide, Durham: beach pebbles (19p)
National Pondlife Centre, Merseyside: frog's legs and lilies (26p)
Parc Arfordirol, Llanelli: cliff boardwalk (44p)
Portsmouth Harbour: reflections in water (64p)

■ 2000, March 7. Water and Coast
Printed in litho (44p) or gravure (19p, 26p, 64p) by Walsall. The
19p has one phosphor band, other values two phosphor bands.

Set	3.50	3.50
Gutter pairs	8.50	–
First day cover	–	4.50
Stamp cards	2.50	6.50

ECOS, Ballymena: River Braid reed beds (2nd)
Web Of Life, London Zoo: leaf–cutter ants (1st)
Earth Centre, Doncaster: solar sensors (44p)
Project Suzy, Teesside: hydroponic leaves (64p)

■ 2000, April 4. Life and Earth
Printed in gravure by De La Rue. The 2nd class has one phosphor
band, other values two phosphor bands.

Set	3.50	3.50
Gutter pairs	9.50	–
First day cover	–	4.50
Stamp cards	2.50	6.50

(*The 1st class also appears in a booklet issued on May 26, 2000.)

Ceramica Museum, Stoke–on–Trent: pottery glaze (2nd)
Tate Modern, London: bankside galleries (1st)
Cycle Network: road markings for bicycles (45p)
Lowry Centre, Salford: people in Salford (65p)

■ 2000, May 2. Art and Craft
Printed in gravure by Enschedé. The 2nd class has one phosphor
band, other values two phosphor bands.

Set	3.50	3.50
Gutter pairs	9.50	–
First day cover	–	4.50
Stamp cards	2.50	6.50

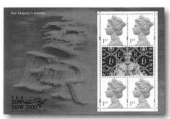

Coronation design of 1953 (£1)
Definitives (1st, 1st. 1st, 1st)

■ 2000, May 23. Her Majesty's Stamps. Stamp Show 2000
Des: Delaney Design Consultants, the £1 based on the 1953
Coronation 1/3 design by Edmund Dulac. Printed in gravure by
De La Rue.

Miniature sheet	10.00	10.00
First day cover	–	10.00
Stamp cards	11.00	35.00

Millennium Greens Project: children playing (2nd)
Millennium Bridge, Gateshead: bridge (1st)
Mile End Park, London: daisies (45p)
On The Meridian Line: African hut and thatched cottage (65p)

■ 2000, June 6. People and Places
Printed in gravure (2nd, 45p) or litho (1st, 65p) by Walsall. The
2nd class has one phosphor band, other values two bands.

Set	3.50	3.50
Gutter pairs	9.50	–
First day cover	–	4.50
Stamp cards	2.50	6.50

Strangford Stone, Killyleagh: raising the stone (2nd)
Trans–Pennine Trail, Derbyshire: horse's hooves (1st)
Kingdom Of Fife Cycle Ways: cyclist and reflection (45p)
Groundwork's Changing Places: bluebell wood (65p)

2000, July 4. Stone and Soil
Printed in gravure in Enschedé. The 2nd class has one phosphor
band, other values two phosphor bands.

Set	3.50	3.50
Gutter pairs	9.50	–
First day cover	–	4.50
Stamp cards	2.50	6.50

(*The 1st class also appears in a booklet issued on September
5, 2000, printed in gravure by Walsall; price 75p mint. The 65p
design also appears in the Treasury of Trees prestige stamp book
issued on September 18, 2000, printed in gravure by Walsall;
price £1.50 mint.)

Yews For The Millennium: tree roots (2nd)
Eden Project, St. Austell: sunflower (1st)
Millennium Seed Bank, Ardingly: sycamore seeds (45p)
Forest For Scotland: highland forest (65p)

2000, August 1. Tree and Leaf
Printed in gravure in De La Rue. The 2nd class has one phosphor
band, other values two phosphor bands.

Set	3.50	3.50
Gutter pairs	9.50	–
First day cover	–	4.50
Stamp cards	2.50	6.50

(*The 1st class also appears in a booklet issued on September
5, 2000, printed in gravure by Walsall; price 75p mint. The 2nd,
45p and 65p also appear in the Treasury of Trees prestige stamp
book issued on September 18, 2000, printed in gravure by
Walsall; price £3 each mint.)

Queen Elizabeth II (27p)
Prince William (27p)
The Queen Mother (27p)
Prince Charles (27p)

2000, August 4. 100th Birthday of The Queen Mother
Des: J. Gibbs. Photograph by J. Swannell. Printed in gravure by
De La Rue.

Miniature sheet	6.00	6.00
First day cover	–	6.00
Stamp cards	10.00	11.50

(*The Queen Mother design, and the entire miniature sheet but
in a slightly larger size, appear in the Life Of The Century
prestige stamp book issued on August 4, 2000, printed in
gravure; price £1.50 mint or used.)

Wildscreen At Bristol: head of ant (2nd)
Norfolk & Norwich Project: gathering water lilies on Broads (1st)
Millennium Point, Birmingham: X–ray of hand on mouse (45p)
Scottish Cultural Resources Network: tartan wool holder (65p)

2000, September 5. Mind and Matter
Printed in litho by Walsall. The 2nd class has one phosphor
band, other values two phosphor bands.

Set	3.50	3.50
Gutter pairs	9.50	–
First day cover	–	4.50
Stamp cards	2.50	6.50

Body Zone, Millennium Dome: acrobats (2nd)
Hampden Park, Glasgow: footballers (1st)
Bath Spa Project: bather (45p)
Centre For Life, Newcastle: hen's egg under magnification (65p)

2000, October 3. Body and Bone
Printed in litho (2nd) or gravure (1st, 45p, 65p) by Questa. The
2nd class has one phosphor band, other values two phosphor
bands.

Set	3.50	3.50
Gutter pairs	9.50	–
First day cover	–	4.50
Stamp cards	2.50	6.50

St. Edmundsbury Cathedral, Suffolk: stained glass window (2nd)
Church Floodlighting: St. Peter and St. Paul, Overstowey (1st)
St. Patrick Centre, Downpatrick: Latin gradual (45p)
Mystery Plays, York Minster: Chapter House ceiling (65p)

■ 2000, November 7. Spirit and Faith
Printed in gravure by De La Rue. The 2nd class has one phosphor band, other values two phosphor bands.

Set	3.50	3.50
Gutter pairs	9.50	–
First day cover	–	4.50
Stamp cards	2.50	6.50

(*The 2nd class and 1st class also appear in booklets.)

Ringing In The Millennium: church bells (2nd)
Year Of The Artist: eye (1st)
Canolfan Mileniwm, Cardiff: top of a harp (45p)
Talent & Skills 2000: figure in latticework (65p)

■ 2000, December 5. Sound and Vision
Printed in gravure by De La Rue. The 2nd class has one phosphor band, other values two phosphor bands.

Set	3.50	3.50
Gutter pairs	9.00	–
First day cover	–	4.50
Stamp cards	2.50	6.50

Children's face painting: flower (2nd)
Children's face painting: tiger (1st)
Children's face painting: owl (45p)
Children's face painting: butterfly (65p)

■ 2001, January 16. Rights of the Child
Des: Why Not Associates. Printed in gravure by De La Rue. The 2nd class has one phosphor band, other values two phosphor bands.

Set	3.50	3.50
Gutter pairs	8.50	–
First day cover	–	3.75
Stamp cards	3.25	6.50

Hallmark: 'Love' (1st)
Hallmark: 'Thanks' (1st)
Hallmark: 'ABC' (1st)
Hallmark: 'Welcome' (1st)
Hallmark: 'Cheers' (1st)

■ 2001, February 6. Occasions (issue 1)
Des: Springpoint Design. Printed in gravure by Enschedé.

Set	4.50	4.50
Gutter pairs	11.00	–
First day cover	–	5.00
Stamp cards	4.50	7.50

(*These designs were also used for Smilers sheets in 2001.)

Dog in bath (1st)
Dog and man on a bench (1st)
Dog at dog show (1st)
Cat in handbag (1st)
Cat on gate (1st)
Dog in car (1st)
Cat at window (1st)
Dog looking over fence (1st)
Cat watching bird (1st)
Cat in wash basin (1st)

■ 2001, February 13. Cats and Dogs
Des: Johnson Banks. Printed in gravure by Walsall. Self-adhesive. Issued as a sheetlet which could be folded to form a booklet, containing one of each of the ten designs.

Sheetlet	10.00	10.00
First day cover	–	8.00
Stamp cards	5.00	16.00

(*All these designs, along with two 1st class definitives, also appear in a booklet issued on February 13, 2001.)

Quadrant of a barometer: rain (19p)
Quadrant of a barometer: fair (27p)
Quadrant of a barometer: stormy (45p)
Quadrant of a barometer: very dry (65p)

2001, March 13. The Weather

Des: H. Brown and T. Meeuwissen. Printed in gravure by De La Rue. The 19p has one phosphor band, other values two phosphor bands.

Set	3.50	3.50
Gutter pairs	8.50	–
First day cover	–	3.50
Miniature sheet (one of each value)	11.00	11.00
Miniature sheet first day cover	–	11.00
Stamp cards	4.00	9.00

Vanguard class submarine (2nd)
Swiftsure class submarine (1st)
Unity class submarine (45p)
Holland class submarine (65p)

2001, April 10. Centenary of Royal Navy Submarine Service

Des: D. Davis. Printed in gravure by Questa. Perf: 15x14. PVA gum. The 2nd class has one phosphor band, other values two phosphor bands.

Set	3.25	3.25
Gutter pairs	7.50	–
First day cover	–	3.50
Stamp cards	4.00	6.50

(*All four stamps also appear in the Unseen And Unheard prestige stamp book issued on October 22, 2001, perf: 15x15; price £10.00 mint or used. The 1st class also appears in self–adhesive form in a booklet issued on April 17, 2001; price £35 mint or used. See also the issue of October 22, 2001.)

Leyland X2, B Type, Leyland Titan TD1, AEC Regent I (1st)
AEC Regent I, Daimler COG5, Guy Arab II, AEC Regent III (1st)
AEC Regent III, Bristol K, AEC Routemaster, Bristol Lodekka FSF (1st)
Bristol Lodekka FSF, Leyland PD3, Leyland Atlantean, Daimler Fleetline (1st)
Daimler Fleetline, MCW Metrobus, Leyland Olympian, Dennis Trident (1st)

2001, May 15. 150th Anniversary of the Double–Decker Bus

Des: M. English. Printed in gravure by Questa. The illustrations extend into the sheet margins, and across the sheet, so that some of the illustrations span two stamps.

Set (se–tenant strip of five)	4.75	4.75
Gutter pairs	11.50	–
First day cover	–	5.00
Miniature sheet (one of each value)	7.00	7.00
Miniature sheet first day cover	–	8.00
Stamp cards	6.50	16.00

Toque hat by Pip Hackett(1st)
Butterfly hat by Dai Rees (E)
Top hat by Stephen Jones (45p)
Spiral hat by Philip Treacy (65p)

2001, June 19. Fashion Hats

Des: Rose Design, from photographs by N. Knight. Printed in litho by Enschedé.

Set	3.50	3.50
Gutter pairs	9.00	–
First day cover	–	3.50
Stamp cards	3.00	6.50

Common frog (1st)
Great diving beetle (E)
Three-spined stickleback (45p)
Southern hawker dragonfly (65p)

■ 2001, July 10. Pond Life (Europa)
Des: J. Gibbs. Printed in gravure by De La Rue.

Set	3.75	3.75
Gutter pairs	9.00	–
First day cover	–	5.25
Stamp cards	3.00	6.50

Policeman (1st)
Mr Punch (1st)
Clown (1st)
Judy (1st)
Beadle (1st)
Crocodile (1st)

■ 2001, September 4. Punch and Judy Puppets
Des: K. Bernstein, from puppets made by Bryan Clarkez. Printed in gravure by Walsall. PVA gum. Perf: 14x15.

Set (se-tenant strip of six)	6.00	6.00
Gutter pairs	15.00	–
First day cover	–	7.00
Stamp cards	4.75	8.50

(*The Mr Punch and Judy designs also appear in self-adhesive form in a booklet issued on September 4, 2001, printed in gravure by Questa, perf: 14x15½; price £15 mint per pair.)

Carbon molecule, printed in litho and silk screen (2nd)
Globe, printed in litho and recess (1st)
Dove, printed in litho and embossing (E)
Crosses, printed in litho (40p)
'The Addressing of Cats' by T. S. Eliot, printed in litho (45p)
Boron molecule, printed in litho with hologram (65p)

■ 2001, October 2. Centenary of Nobel Prizes
Des: P. Vermier, with engraving by Inge Madle (1st). Printed by Enschedé. The 2nd class has one phosphor band, other values a phosphor frame around the design.

Set	8.50	8.50
Gutter pairs	22.00	–
First day cover	–	6.50
Stamp cards	10.00	8.50

White Ensign (1st)
Union Flag (1st)
Jolly Roger (1st)
Flag of Chief of Defence Staff (1st)

■ 2001, October 22. Centenary of Royal Navy Submarine Service. Flags and Ensigns
Des: D. Davis. Printed in gravure by Questa. PVA gum.

Miniature sheet	6.00	6.00
First day cover	–	5.50
Stamp cards	7.00	14.00

(*The White Ensign and Jolly Roger designs also appear in self-adhesive form in a booklet issued on October 22, 2001; price £16 mint or used per pair. The Union Jack and White Ensign designs were used in Smilers sheets from 2005, and also appear in the Ian Fleming's James Bond prestige stamp book issued on January 8, 2008. See also the issue of April 10, 2001.)

Robins with snowman (2nd)
Robins on bird table (1st)
Robins skating on bird bath (E)
Robins with Christmas pudding hanging from tree (45p)
Robins in nest made of paper chains (65p)

■ 2001, November 6. Christmas. Robins

Des: A. Robins and H. Brown. Printed in gravure by De La Rue. Self-adhesive.

Set	4.50	4.50
First day cover	–	4.50
Stamp cards	3.50	7.50

(*The 2nd class and 1st class values also appear in booklets, and were used for Smilers sheets in 2003 and 2005.)

'The Elephant's Child' (1st)
'How the Whale got his Throat' (1st)
'How the Camel got his Hump' (1st)
'How the Rhinoceros got his Skin' (1st)
'How the Leopard got his Spots' (1st)
'The Sing Song of Old Man Kangaroo' (1st)
'The Beginning of the Armadillos' (1st)
'The Crab that Played with the Sea' (1st)
'The Cat that Walked by Himself' (1st)
'The Butterfly that Stamped' (1st)

■ 2002, January 15. Centenary of the Just So Stories by Rudyard Kipling

Des: I. Cohen. Printed in gravure by Walsall. Self-adhesive. Issued as a sheetlet which could be folded to form a booklet, containing one of each of the ten designs.

Sheetlet	10.00	10.00
First day cover	–	10.00
Stamp cards	5.00	20.00

Queen Elizabeth II in 1952, by Dorothy Wilding (2nd)
Queen Elizabeth II in 1968, by Cecil Beaton (1st)
Queen Elizabeth II in 1978, by Lord Snowdon (E)
Queen Elizabeth II in 1984, by Yousef Karsh (45p)
Queen Elizabeth II in 1996, by Tim Graham (65p)

■ 2002, February 6. Golden Jubilee

Des: Kate Stephens. Printed in gravure by De La Rue. Wmk: 50 (sideways). The 2nd class has one phosphor band, other values two phosphor bands.

Set	4.50	4.50
Gutter pairs	12.00	–
First day cover	–	4.50
Stamp cards	2.50	7.00

(*All the stamps also appear in the Gracious Accession prestige book, but with the Wmk upright; price £13 mint, £13 used.)

Wilding design of 1952–67 (2nd)
Wilding design of 1952–67 (1st)

■ 2002, February 6. Wilding definitives

Des: M. Farrar–Bell (2nd), Enid Marx (1st). Printed in gravure by Enschedé. Wmk: 50. The 2nd class has one phosphor band, the 1st class two phosphor bands. Issued only in the £7.29 Gracious Accession prestige stamp book. One pane had a tilted stamp, resulting in a diagonal watermark.

2nd carmine–red	1.50	1.50
2nd carmine–red (Wmk diagonal)	2.50	2.50
1st green	1.25	1.25

Love (1st)
Rabbits, inscribed 'a new baby' (1st)
'Hello' written in sky (1st)
Bear pulling topiary tree in shape of house (1st)
Flowers inscribed 'best wishes' (1st)

■ 2002, March 5. Occasions (issue 2)

Des: I. Bilbey (Rabbits and Flowers), A. Kitching (Love), Hoop Associates (Hello), G. Percy (Bear). Printed in litho by Questa.

Set	5.50	5.50
Gutter pairs	12.00	–
First day cover	–	5.75
Stamp cards	3.25	7.00

(*The Hello design also appears, in self-adhesive form, in a booklet issued on March 4, 2003; price £3.50 mint or used. All designs were also used in Smilers sheets.)

Studland Bay, Dorset (27p)
Luskentyre, South Harris (27p)
Cliffs of Dover, Kent (27p)
Padstow Harbour, Cornwall (27p)
Broadstairs, Kent (27p)
St Abb's Head, Berwickshire (27p)
Dunster Beach, Somerset (27p)
Newquay Beach, Cornwall (27p)
Portrush, County Antrim (27p)
Sand spit, Conwy, (27p)

■ 2002, March 19. British Coastlines
Des: R. Cooke. Printed in litho by Walsall.

Set (se-tenant block of ten)	4.50	4.50
Gutter pairs	13.00	–
First day cover	–	5.00
Stamp cards	4.50	13.50

Slack wire act (2nd)
Lion tamer (1st)
Trick tricyclists (E)
Krazy kar (45p)
Equestrienne (65p)

■ 2002, April 10. Circus (Europa)
Des: R. Fuller. Printed in gravure by Questa. The 2nd class has one phosphor band, other values two phosphor bands.

Set	4.50	4.50
Gutter pairs	11.00	–
First day cover	–	4.75
Stamp cards	3.25	7.50

Queen Mother: 20p design from the 1990 issue (1st)
Queen Mother: 29p design from the 1990 issue (E)
Queen Mother: 34p design from the 1990 issue (45p)
Queen Mother: 37p design from the 1990 issue (65p)

■ 2002, April 25. Queen Mother Memorial
Des: J. Gorham, as the issue of August 2, 1990, but with frames and Queen's head in black. Printed in gravure by De La Rue.

Set	4.25	4.25
Gutter pairs	10.00	–
First day cover	–	4.25

Airbus A340–600, 2002 (2nd)
Concorde, 1976 (1st)
Trident, 1964 (E)
VC10, 1964 (45p)
Comet, 1952 (65p)

■ 2002, May 2. Airliners
Des: Roundel. Printed in gravure by De La Rue. The 2nd class has one phosphor band, other values two phosphor bands.

Set	6.00	6.00
Gutter pairs	15.00	–
First day cover	–	4.25
Miniature sheet (one of each value)	8.00	8.50
Miniature sheet first day cover	–	8.00
Stamp cards	3.50	14.00

(*The 1st class design also appears in self-adhesive form in a booklet issued on May 2, 2002, printed in gravure; price £3.50 mint or used. It also appears in the British Design Classics prestige stamp book issued on January 13, 2009.)

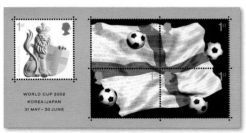

Lion with shield of St. George (1st)
Top left quarter of English flag with football (1st)
Top right quarter of English flag with football (1st)
Bottom left quarter of English flag with football (1st)
Bottom right quarter of English flag with football (1st)

■ 2002, May 21. Football World Cup, Japan and Korea

Des: Sedley Place (lion), H. Brown (flag). Printed in gravure by Walsall. The St. George design was issued in counter sheets, and all five designs in a miniature sheet.

1st (St. George design)	1.50	1.50
Gutter pair (St. George design)	4.00	–
First day cover	–	2.75
Miniature sheet	5.50	5.50
Miniature sheet first day cover	–	6.00
Stamp cards (set of six)	3.50	11.00

(*The 1st class designs showing the top left and top right of the flag also appear in self-adhesive form in a booklet issued on May 21, 2002; price £5.50 per pair. The 1st class design showing the bottom right of the flag was used in Smilers sheets.)

Swimming (2nd)
Running (1st)
Cycling (E)
Long jump (47p)
Wheelchair racing (68p)

■ 2002, July 16. 17th Commonwealth Games, Manchester

Des: Madeleine Bennett. Printed in gravure by Enschedé. The 2nd class has one phosphor band, other values two phosphor bands.

Set	5.00	5.00
Gutter pairs	12.50	–
First day cover	–	4.50
Stamp cards	3.00	10.00

Tinkerbell (2nd)
Wendy, John and Michael Darling flying past Big Ben (1st)
Crocodile and the alarm clock (E)
Captain Hook (47p)
Peter Pan (68p)

■ 2002, August 20. Peter Pan

Des: Tutsells. Printed in gravure by De La Rue. The 2nd class has one phosphor band, other values two phosphor bands.

Set	5.00	5.00
Gutter pairs	12.00	–
First day cover	–	6.00
Stamp cards	4.00	8.00

Millennium Bridge, 2001 (2nd)
Tower Bridge, 1894 (1st)
Westminster Bridge, 1864 (E)
Blackfriars Bridge, 1800 (47p)
London Bridge, 1670 (68p)

■ 2002, September 10. Bridges of London

Des: Sarah Davies and Robert Maude. Printed in litho by Questa. The 2nd class has one phosphor band, other values two phosphor bands.

Set	6.50	6.50
Gutter pairs	15.00	–
First day cover	–	5.50
Stamp cards	3.50	10.00

(*The 1st class design also appears in self-adhesive form in a booklet issued on September 10, 2002, printed in gravure by Questa; price £3.50 mint or £3 used.)

Planetary nebula in Aquila (1st)
Seyfert 2 galaxy in Pegasus (1st)
Planetary nebula in Norma (1st)
Seyfert 2 galaxy in Circinus (1st)

■ 2002, September 24. Astronomy

Des: Rose. Printed in gravure by Questa.

Miniature sheet	4.50	4.50
First day cover	–	5.50
Stamp cards	3.50	10.00

(*The miniature sheet also appears, in a larger format, in the Across The Universe prestige stamp book issued on September 21, 2002.)

Green pillar box, 1857 (2nd)
Horizontal–aperture pillar box, 1874 (1st)
Blue air mail box, 1934 (E)
Double–aperture pillar box, 1939 (47p)
Modern pillar box, 1980 (68p)

■ 2002, October 8. 150th Anniversary of the First Pillar Box

Des: Silk Pearce; engraved by C. Slania. Printed in recess and litho by Enschedé. The 2nd class has one phosphor band, other values two phosphor bands.

Set	4.50	4.50
Gutter pairs	12.00	–
First day cover	–	5.50
Stamp cards	3.50	7.50

Blue spruce (2nd)
Holly (1st)
Ivy (E)
Mistletoe (47p)
Pine cone (68p)

■ 2002, November 5. Christmas

Des: Rose. Printed in gravure by De La Rue. Self–adhesive. The 2nd class has one phosphor band, other values two phosphor bands.

Set	5.50	5.50
First day cover	–	5.00
Stamp cards	3.50	7.50

(*The 2nd class and 1st class stamps also appear in booklets.)

The Wilding definitives collection I ~ 1952 - 1953

Wilding designs of 1952–67 (1p, 2p, 5p, 2nd, 1st, 33p, 37p, 47p, 50p)

■ 2002, December 5. 50th Anniversary of the Wilding Definitives (1st issue)

Des: Rose (based on the original designs of 1952). Printed in gravure by De La Rue. Wmk: 50. The 2nd class has one phosphor band, other values two phosphor bands.

Miniature sheet	5.50	5.50
First day cover	–	5.00
Stamp cards	5.00	15.50

(*The 47p value also appears in the Perfect Coronation prestige stamp book issued on June 2, 2003.)

Barn owl in flight, five different views (1st, 1st, 1st, 1st, 1st)
Kestrel in flight, five different views (1st, 1st, 1st, 1st, 1st)

■ 2003, January 14. Birds of Prey

Des: J. Gibbs, from photographs by S. Dalton. Printed in litho by Walsall.

Set (se–tenant block of ten)	9.50	9.50
Gutter pairs	24.00	–
First day cover	–	9.50
Stamp cards	5.50	15.00

Gold star, See me, Playtime (1st)
I 'love' U, XXXX, S.W.A.L.K. (1st)
Angel, Poppet, Little terror (1st)
Yes, No, Maybe (1st)
Oops! Sorry, Will try harder (1st)
I did it! You did it! We did it! (1st)

■ 2003, February 4. Occasions (issue 3)

Des: UNA, S. Wiegand and M. Exon. Printed in litho by Questa.

Set (se–tenant block of six)	5.50	5.50
Gutter pairs	21.00	–
First day cover	–	6.00
Stamp cards	3.50	9.00

(*All these designs were used in Smilers sheets.)

Genome **The End of the Beginning**

The genetic jigsaw (2nd)
Ape looking at scientist behind bars (1st)
DNA snakes and ladders (E)
Animals dressed as scientists (47p)
Looking into a DNA crystal ball (68p)

■ 2003, February 25. 50th Anniversary of the Discovery of DNA

Des: William Murray Hamm and P. Brookes. Printed in litho by Enschedé. The 2nd class has one phosphor band, other values two phosphor bands.

Set	5.25	5.25
Gutter pairs	14.00	–
First day cover	–	5.00
Stamp cards	3.00	8.50

(*The 2nd class and E designs also appear in the Microcosmos prestige stamp book issued on February 25, 2003.)

Red pepper (1st)
Strawberry (1st)
Potato (1st)
Apple (1st)
Pear (1st)
Orange (1st)
Tomato (1st)
Lemon (1st)
Brussels sprout (1st)
Aubergine (1st)

■ 2003, March 25. Fun Fruit and Veg

Des: Johnson Banks. Printed in gravure by Walsall. Issued as a self-adhesive sheetlet containing one each of the ten designs.

Sheetlet	10.00	10.00
First day cover	–	9.50
Stamp cards	7.50	22.00

(*This sheetlet came with a pane of self-adhesive stickers, such as of eyes, ears and mouths, so that the fruit and vegetables could be customised to resemble faces. These designs were also used in Smilers sheets.)

Amy Johnson with biplane (2nd)
The 1953 Everest team in the Himalayas (1st)
Freya Stark in the Arabian desert (E)
Ernest Shackleton in the Antarctic (42p)
Francis Chichester with 'Gipsy Moth IV' (47p)
Robert Falcon Scott at the South Pole (68p)

■ 2003, April 29. Extreme Endeavours

Des: H. Brown. Printed in gravure by Questa. The 2nd class has one phosphor band, other values two phosphor bands. Perf: 15x14½.

Set	6.00	6.00
Gutter pairs	15.00	–
First day cover	–	6.00
Stamp cards	3.00	10.00

(*The 1st class design also appears, in self adhesive form, in a booklet issued on April 29, 2003, printed in gravure by De La Rue, Perf: 14½; price £3.50 mint, £3.50 used.)

The Wilding definitives collection II ~ 1953 - 1959

Wilding designs of 1952–67 (4p, 8p, 10p, 20p, 28p, 34p, E, 42p, 68p)

■ 2003, May 20. 50th Anniversary of the Wilding Definitives (2nd issue)

Des: Rose (based on the original designs of 1952). Printed in gravure by De La Rue. Wmk: 50. The 20p has one phosphor band, other values two phosphor bands.

Miniature sheet	5.00	5.50
First day cover	–	6.50

(*The 68p value also appears in the Perfect Coronation prestige stamp book issued on June 2, 2003.)

Coronation procession (1st)
Children reading poster (1st)
Queen seated in the Coronation Chair (1st)
Children producing royal montage (1st)
Queen in Coronation robes, by Cecil Beaton (1st)
Children racing during street party (1st)
Coronation Coach passing through Admiralty Arch (1st)
Children in fancy dress (1st)
Coronation Coach outside Buckingham Palace (1st)
Children at street party (1st)

■ 2003, June 2. 50th Anniversary of the Coronation
Des: Kate Stephens. Printed in gravure by De La Rue.

Set (se–tenant block of ten)	9.00	9.00
Gutter pairs	23.00	
First day cover	–	8.50
Stamp cards	6.00	19.00

(*Eight of these designs also appear in the Perfect Coronation prestige stamp book issued on June 2, 2003.)

Photograph of Prince William by Brendan Beirne (28p)
Photograph of Prince William by Tim Graham (E)
Photograph of Prince William by Camera Press (47p)
Photograph of Prince William by Tim Graham (68p)

■ 2003, June 17. 21st Birthday of Prince William
Des: Madeleine Bennett. Printed in gravure by Walsall.

Set	6.50	6.50
Gutter pairs	15.00	–
First day cover	–	5.00
Stamp cards	4.00	19.00

Loch Assynt, Sutherland (2nd)
Ben More, Isle of Mull (1st)
Rothiemurchus, Cairngorms (E)
Dalveen Pass, Lowther Hills (42p)
Glenfinnan Viaduct, Lochaber (47p)
Papa Little, Shetland Islands (68p)

■ 2003, July 15. A British Journey: Scotland
Des: Phelan Barker. Printed in gravure by De La Rue. The 2nd class has one phosphor band, other values two phosphor bands.

Set	5.50	5.50
Gutter pairs	14.00	–
First day cover	–	6.00
Stamp cards	3.00	9.50

(*The 1st class design also appears, in self adhesive form, in a booklet issued on July 15, 2003; price £3.50 mint or used.)

The Station (1st)
Black Swan (E)
The Cross Keys (42p)
The Mayflower (47p)
The Barley Sheaf (68p)

■ 2003, August 12. Pub Signs (Europa)
Des: Elmwood. Printed in gravure by De La Rue.

Set	5.25	5.25
Gutter pairs	12.50	–
First day cover	–	5.25
Stamp cards	3.00	7.50

(*The 1st class design also appears in the Letters By Night prestige stamp book issued on March 16, 2004.)

MECCANO
Constructor Biplane c 1931

Meccano constructor biplane, 1931 (1st)
Wells–Brimtoy clockwork double–decker bus, 1938 (E)
Hornby M1 clockwork locomotive, 1948 (42p)
Dinky Toys Ford Zephyr, 1956 (47p)
Mettoy friction–drive Eagle space ship, 1960 (68p)

■ 2003, September 18. Classic Transport Toys
Des: Trickett and Webb. Printed in gravure by Enschedé.

Set	5.25	5.25
Gutter pairs	12.00	–
First day cover	–	5.25
Miniature sheet (one of each value)	4.50	4.50
Miniature sheet first day cover	–	7.50
Stamp cards	3.50	13.50

(*The 1st class design also appears, in self–adhesive form, in a booklet issued on September 18, 2003, printed in gravure by De La Rue; price £3.25 mint or used.)

Coffin of Denytenamun, Egypt, c.900 BC (2nd)
Sculpture of Alexander the Great, Greece, c.200 BC (1st)
Anglo–Saxon helmet, Sutton Hoo, c.600 AD (E)
Sculpture of Parvati, India, c.1550 AD (42p)
Aztec mask of Xiuhtecuhtli, Mexico, c.1500 AD (47p)
Statue of Hoa Hakananai'a, Easter Island, c.1000 AD (68p)

■ 2003, October 7. 250th Anniversary of the British Museum
Des: Rose. Printed in gravure by Walsall. The 2nd class has one centre phosphor band, the 42p and 68p one phosphor band at right, other values two phosphor bands.

Set	5.50	5.50
Gutter pairs	14.00	–
First day cover	–	5.75
Stamp cards	3.25	9.50

Ice spiral (2nd)
Icicle star (1st)
Wall of ice blocks (E)
Ice ball (53p)
Ice hole (68p)
Snow pyramids (£1.12)

■ 2003, November 4. Christmas. Ice Sculptures
Des: D. Davis, from ice sculptures by Andy Goldsworthy. Printed in gravure by De La Rue. Self–adhesive. The 2nd class has one phosphor band, other values two phosphor bands.

Set	6.50	6.50
First day cover	–	8.00
Stamp cards	8.00	12.00

(*The 1st class and 2nd class designs also appear in booklets, and were used in Smilers sheets.)

England fans and England flag (1st)
England team huddled in a circle before the final (1st)
Rugby World Cup held aloft (68p)
England team members from the back after the final (68p)

■ 2003, December 19. England's Victory in the Rugby World Cup
Des: Why Not Associates. Printed in litho by Walsall.

Miniature sheet	10.00	10.00
First day cover	–	10.00

'Dolgoch' on the Talyllyn Railway (20p)
CR 439 on the Bo'ness and Kinneil Railway (28p)
GCR 8K on the Great Central Railway (E)
GWR Manor on the Severn Valley Railway (42p)
SR West Country on the Bluebell Railway (47p)
BR Standard on the Keighley and Worth Valley Railway (68p)

■ 2004, January 13. Classic Locomotives

Des: Roundel. Printed in litho by De La Rue. The 2nd class has one phosphor band, other values two phosphor bands.

Set	5.50	5.50
Gutter pairs	14.00	–
First day cover	–	6.00
Miniature sheet (one of each value)	15.00	15.00
Miniature sheet first day cover	–	15.00
Stamp cards	6.50	25.00

(*The 28p, E and 42p designs also appear in the Letters by Night prestige stamp book issued on March 16, 2004.)

Postman (1st)
Face (1st)
Duck (1st)
Baby (1st)
Aircraft (1st)

■ 2004, February 3. Occasions (issue 4)

Des: S. Kambayashi. Printed in litho by De La Rue.

Set (se-tenant strip of five)	5.50	5.50
Gutter pairs	14.00	–
First day cover	–	7.00
Stamp cards	3.00	7.50

(*These designs were used in Smilers sheets.)

Middle Earth (1st)
Forest of Lothlórien (1st)
The Fellowship of the Ring (1st)
Rivendell (1st)
The Hall at Bag End (1st)
Orthanc (1st)
Doors of Durin (1st)
Barad–dûr (1st)
Minas Tirith (1st)
Fangorn Forest (1st)

■ 2004, February 26. The Lord of The Rings by J. R. R. Tolkien

Des: HGV Design. Printed in litho by Walsall.

Set (se-tenant block of ten)	10.00	10.00
Gutter pairs	24.00	–
First day cover	–	10.00
Stamp cards	6.50	15.00

Ely Island, Lower Lough Erne (2nd)
Giant's Causeway, Antrim (1st)
Slemish, Antrim (E)
Banns Road, Mourne Mountains (42p)
Glenelly Valley, Sperrins (47p)
Islandmore, Strangford Lough (68p)

■ 2004, March 16. A British Journey: Northern Ireland

Des: Phelan Barker. Printed in gravure by Enschedé. The 2nd class has one phosphor band, other values two phosphor bands.

Set	4.50	4.50
Gutter pairs	12.00	–
First day cover	–	5.00
Stamp cards	3.50	9.50

(*The 28p design also appears, in self–adhesive form, in a booklet issued on March 16, 2004; price £3.50 mint or used.)

'Lace 1 (trial proof) 1968' by Sir Terry Frost (28p)
'Coccinelle' by Sonia Delaunay (57p)

■ 2004, April 6. Centenary of the Entente Cordiale

Des: Rose. Printed in gravure by Walsall.

Set	2.00	2.00
Gutter pairs	4.50	–
Traffic light gutter pairs	11.00	–
First day cover	–	2.50
Stamp cards	6.00	10.00

(*This was a joint issue with La Poste of France.)

RMS 'Queen Mary 2', 2004 (1st)
SS 'Canberra', 1961 (E)
RMS 'Queen Mary', 1936 (42p)
RMS 'Mauretania', 1907 (47p)
SS 'City of New York', 1888 (57p)
PS 'Great Western', 1838 (68p)

■ 2004, April 13. Ocean Liners

Des: J. Gibbs. Printed in gravure by De La Rue.

Set	5.00	5.00
Gutter pairs	12.50	–
First day cover	–	6.00
Miniature sheet (one of each value)	8.00	8.50
Miniature sheet first day cover	–	7.50
Stamp cards	4.00	16.50

(*The 1st class also appears, in self-adhesive form, in a booklet issued on April 13, 2004; price £3.50 mint or used.)

Dianthus Allwoodii group (2nd)
Dahlia 'Garden Princess' (1st)
Clematis 'Arabella' (E)
Miltonia 'French Lake' (42p)
Lilium 'Lemon Pride' (47p)
Delphinium 'Clifford Sky' (68p)

■ 2004, May 25. Bicentenary of the Royal Horticultural Society

Des: Rose. Printed in gravure by Enschedé. The 2nd class has one phosphor band, other values two phosphor bands.

Set	5.50	5.50
Gutter pairs	14.00	–
First day cover	–	6.00
Miniature sheet (one of each value)	7.00	7.00
Miniature sheet first day cover	–	7.50
Stamp cards	4.00	16.50

(*All values also appear in the Glory of the Garden prestige book issued on May 25, 2004, and the 1st class in Smilers sheets.)

Barmouth Bridge (2nd)
Hyddgen, Plynlimon (1st)
Brecon Beacons (40p)
Pen–pych, Rhondda Valley (43p)
Rhewl, Dee Valley (47p)
Marloes Sands, Pembrokeshire (68p)

■ 2004, June 15. A British Journey: Wales (Europa)

Des: Phelan Barker. Printed in gravure by De La Rue. The 2nd class has one phosphor band, other values two phosphor bands.

Set	4.50	4.50
Gutter pairs	12.00	–
First day cover	–	5.00
Stamp cards	3.50	9.50

(*The 1st class design also appears, in self–adhesive form, in a booklet of June 15, 2004; price £4.50 mint or used.)

Penny Black and citation to Sir Rowland Hill (1st)
William Shipley, founder of the RSA (40p)
R, S and A as typewriter keys and shorthand notation (43p)
George Smart's brush for sweeping chimneys (47p)
Eric Gill's typeface (57p)
'Zero Waste' manifesto (68p)

■ 2004, August 10. 250th Anniversary of the Royal Society of Arts

Des: D. Birdsall. Printed in litho by Walsall.

Set	6.25	6.25
Gutter pairs	15.00	–
First day cover	–	6.50
Stamp cards	3.00	9.50

Pine marten (1st)
Roe deer (1st)
Badger (1st)
Yellow–necked mouse (1st)
Wild cat (1st)
Red squirrel (1st)
Stoat (1st)
Natterer's bat (1st)
Mole (1st)
Fox (1st)

2004, September 16. Woodland Animals
Des: Kate Stephens. Printed in gravure by Enschedé.

Set (se–tenant block of ten)	10.00	10.00
Gutter pairs	25.00	–
Traffic light gutter blocks	45.00	–
First day cover	–	9.00
Stamp cards	5.50	15.00

Scotland definitives (40p, 1st, 2nd, 1st, 40p)

2004, October 5. Opening of the Scottish Parliament Building, Edinburgh
Des: H. Brown. Printed in gravure by De La Rue.

Miniature sheet	4.50	4.50
First day cover	–	5.00

Private McNamara, 5th Dragoon Guards (2nd)
Piper Muir, 42nd Regiment of Foot (1st)
Sergeant Major Edwards, Scots Fusilier Guards (40p)
Sergeant Powell, 1st Regiment of Foot Guards (57p)
Sergeant Major Poole, Royal Sappers and Miners (68p)
Sergeant Glasgow, Royal Artillery (£1.12)

2004, October 12. The Crimean War
Des: Atelier Works, from period photographs. Printed in litho by Walsall. The 2nd class has one phosphor band, other values two phosphor bands.

Set	6.50	6.50
Gutter pairs	16.00	–
Traffic light gutter pairs	40.00	–
First day cover	–	5.50
Stamp cards	3.50	9.50

Father Christmas on roof (2nd)
Father Christmas welcoming the sunrise (1st)
Father Christmas battling against the wind (40p)
Father Christmas holding an umbrella (57p)
Father Christmas holding a torch (68p)
Father Christmas sheltering behind a chimney (£1.12)

2004, November 2. Christmas
Des: R. Briggs. Printed in gravure by De La Rue. Counter stamps self-adhesive, miniature sheet gummed. The 2nd class has one phosphor band, other values two phosphor bands.

Set	5.50	5.50
First day cover	–	6.00
Miniature sheet (one of each value)	7.00	7.00
Miniature sheet first day cover	–	7.00
Stamp cards	5.50	15.00

(*The 1st class and 2nd class designs also appear in booklets, and were used in Smilers sheets.)

Emden geese (1st)
British saddleback pigs (1st)
Khaki Campbell ducks (1st)
Clydeside mare and foal (1st)
Dairy shorthorn cattle (1st)
Border collie dog (1st)
Light Sussex chickens (1st)
Suffolk sheep (1st)
Bagot goat (1st)
Norfolk black turkeys (1st)

■ 2005, January 11. Farm Animals

Des: Rose, from illustrations by C. Wormell. Printed in gravure by Enschedé.

Set (se–tenant block of ten)	9.00	9.00
Gutter pairs	23.00	–
Traffic light gutter blocks	70.00	–
First day cover	–	8.00
Stamp cards	5.00	15.50

Old Harry Rocks, Studland Bay, Dorset (2nd)
Wheal Coates, St Agnes, Cornwall (1st)
Start Point, Start Bay, Devon (40p)
Horton Down, Wiltshire (43p)
Chiselcombe, Exmoor, Devon (57p)
St James's Stone, Lundy Island (68p)

■ 2005, February 8. A British Journey: South–West England

Des: J. Phelan and L. Barker. Printed in gravure by De La Rue. The 2nd class has one phosphor band, other values two phosphor bands.

Set	5.25	5.25
Gutter pairs	12.50	–
First day cover	–	5.50
Stamp cards	3.75	9.50

Scene from 'Jane Eyre': Mr. Rochester (2nd)
Scene from 'Jane Eyre': come to me (1st)
Scene from 'Jane Eyre': in the comfort of her bonnet (40p)
Scene from 'Jane Eyre': La Ligne des Rats (57p)
Scene from 'Jane Eyre': refectory (68p)
Scene from 'Jane Eyre': inspection (£1.12)

■ 2005, February 24. 150th Anniversary of the Death of Charlotte Brontë

Des: P. Willberg, from illustrations by Paula Rego. Printed in litho by Walsall. The 2nd class has one phosphor band, other values two phosphor bands.

Set	6.50	6.50
Gutter pairs	16.00	–
Traffic light gutter blocks	50.00	–
First day cover	–	6.25
Miniature sheet (one of each value)	6.00	6.00
Miniature sheet first day cover	–	6.00
Stamp cards	4.00	15.00

(*All designs also appear in the Brontë Sisters prestige stamp book issued on February 24, 2005.)

Spinning coin trick (1st)
Rabbit and top hat trick (40p)
Knotted scarf trick (47p)
Card trick (68p)
Pyramids under fezzes trick (£1.12)

■ 2005, March 15. Centenary of the Magic Circle

Des: Tathem Design, from illustrations by G. Hardie. Printed in gravure by Walsall. Rubbing the 1st class stamp with a coin reveals either the head or tail of a coin; parts of the 47p and £1.12 designs fade temporarily when exposed to heat.

Set	5.75	5.75
Gutter pairs	15.00	–
First day cover	–	5.50
Stamp cards	3.00	7.50

(*The 1st class design was used in Smilers sheets.)

Carrickfergus Castle (50p)
Caernarvon Castle (£1)
Edinburgh Castle (£1)
Windsor Castle (50p)

■ 2005, March 22. 50th Anniversary of the Castles Definitives

Des: Sedley Place, based on designs of 1955–58 by Lynton Lamb but with new values. Printed by intaglio and litho by Enschedé.

Miniature sheet	4.75	5.00
First day cover	–	6.00
Stamp cards	7.00	15.00

(*The 50p design also appears in the First UK Aerial Post prestige stamp book issued on September 9, 2011.)

The couple at the Mey Highland Games (30p, 30p)
The couple at Birkhall (68p, 68p)

■ 2005, April 8. The Wedding of Prince Charles and Camilla Parker Bowles

Des: Rose, from photographs by Christopher Furlong (30p) and Carolyn Robb (68p). Printed in litho by Enschedé.

Miniature sheet	4.75	4.75
First day cover	–	5.50

(*Whilst the miniature sheet and first day handstamps are dated April 8, the wedding took place on April 9.)

Hadrian's Wall, England (2nd)
Uluru Kata Tjuta National Park, Australia (2nd)
Stonehenge, England (1st)
Wet Tropics of Queensland, Australia (1st)
Blenheim Palace, England (47p)
Greater Blue Mountains, Australia (47p)
Heart of Neolithic Orkney, Scotland (68p)
Pumululu National Park, Australia (68p)

■ 2005, April 21. World Heritage Sites

Des: Jason Godfrey from photographs by Peter Marlow. Litho printed by Enschedé. The 2nd class has one phosphor band, other values two phosphor bands.

Set (four se-tenant pairs)	6.50	6.50
Gutter pairs	16.00	–
Traffic light gutter blocks	35.00	–
First day cover	–	8.00
Stamp cards	4.00	12.50

(*This was a joint issue with Australia Post.)

Ensign of the Scots Guards (2nd)
The Queen taking the salute, 1983 (1st)
Trumpeter of the Household Cavalry (42p)
Welsh Guardsmann (60p)
The Queen on horseback, 1972 (68p)
The Queen and Duke of Edinburgh in carriage, 2004 (£1.12)

■ 2005, June 7. Trooping the Colour

Des: Why Not Associates. Printed in litho by Walsall. The 2nd class has one phosphor band, other values two phosphor bands.

Set	6.00	6.00
Gutter pairs	16.00	–
First day cover	–	6.50
Miniature sheet (one of each value)	6.00	6.00
Miniature sheet first day cover	–	6.00
Stamp cards	3.50	17.50

Searchlights in a 'V' over St. Paul's Cathedral (1st)
Definitives (1st, 1st, 1st, 1st, 1st)

■ **2005, July 5. 60th Anniversary of the End of World War II**
Des: Jeffery Matthews, using the St. Paul's stamp designed by J. Gorham and originally issued on May 2, 1995. Printed in gravure by Enschedé.

Miniature sheet	6.00	6.00
First day cover	–	6.00

1991 **Norton F.1** road version of a race winner

Norton F1, 1991 (1st)
BSA Rocket 3, 1969 (40p)
Vincent Black Shadow, 1949 (42p)
Triumph Speed Twin, 1938 (47p)
Brough Superior, 1930 (60p)
Royal Enfield, 1914 (68p)

■ **2005, July 19. Motorcycles**
Des: Atelier Works, with illustrations by Michael English. Printed in litho by Walsall.

Set	5.00	5.00
Gutter pairs	12.50	–
First day cover	–	6.00
Stamp cards	3.50	9.50

Athletes (1st, 1st, 1st, 1st, 1st, 1st)

■ **2005, August 12. London 2012**
Des: one of each of the five designs issued on July 9, 1996, plus a second of one design, but with Olympic rings omitted and new values. Printed in litho by Walsall.

Miniature sheet	6.00	6.00
First day cover	–	6.00

Woman eating rice (2nd)
Woman drinking tea (1st)
Boy eating sushi (42p)
Woman eating pasta (47p)
Woman eating chips (60p)
Boy eating apple (68p)

■ **2005, August 23. Changing Tastes in Britain (Europa)**
Des: Rose, with illustrations by Catell Ronca. Printed in gravure by Enschedé. The 2nd class has one phosphor band, other values two phosphor bands.

Set	5.00	5.00
Gutter pairs	12.50	–
First day cover	–	5.50
Stamp cards	3.00	9.50

'Inspector Morse' (2nd)
'Emmerdale' (1st)
'Rising Damp' (42p)
'The Avengers' (47p)
'The South Bank Show' (60p)
'Who Wants To Be A Millionaire?' (68p)

■ **2005, September 15. Classic ITV Programmes**
Des: Kate Stephens. Printed in litho by De La Rue. The 2nd class has one phosphor band, other values two phosphor bands.

Set	4.50	4.50
Gutter pairs	11.00	–
First day cover	–	5.50
Stamp cards	3.75	9.00

(*The 1st class design was used in Smilers sheets.)

Gazania splendens (1st)
Hello (1st)
Love (1st)
Union flag (1st)
Teddy bear (1st)
Robin looking through pillar box slit (1st)

■ 2005, October 4. Smilers
Printed by litho by Walsall. Self-adhesive. Issued in booklets containing one of each of the six designs.

Booklet (without PiP information)	10.00	–
Booklet (with PiP information)	9.00	–
First day cover	–	9.50

(*These designs were used in Smilers sheets. For the same designs with elliptical perforations, see the issues of January 16, 2007, and February 28, 2008.)

England team celebrating with Ashes trophy (1st)
Kevin Pietersen, Michael Vaughan and Andrew Flintoff (1st)
Michael Vaughan batting (68p)
Action from Second Test at Edgbaston (68p)

■ 2005, October 6. The Ashes
Des: Why Not Associates. Printed in litho by Cartor.

Miniature sheet	4.50	4.50
First day cover	–	5.50

HMS 'Entreprenante' and HMS 'Belle Isle' (1st)
Nelson wounded on HMS 'Victory' (1st)
HMS 'Entreprenante' and burning French ship 'Achille' (42p)
HMS 'Pickle' and cutter (42p)
British fleet attacking in two columns (68p)
Franco-Spanish fleet putting to sea from Cadiz (68p)

■ 2005, October 18. Bicentenary of the Battle of Trafalgar
Des: Dick Davis from a painting by William Heath. Printed in litho by Walsall. Issued in se-tenant pairs.

Set (three se-tenant pairs)	5.25	5.50
Gutter pairs	14.00	–
First day cover	–	6.00
Stamp cards	3.50	25.00
Miniature sheet (one of each value)	5.00	5.50
Miniature sheet first day cover	–	6.00

(*All values also appear in the Battle of Trafalgar prestige stamp book issued on October 18, 2005.)

Madonna and Child painting, Haitian (2nd)
Madonna and Child painting, European (1st)
Madonna and Child painting, European (42p)
Madonna and Child painting, North American Indian (60p)
Madonna and Child painting, Indian (68p)
Madonna and Child painting, Australian Aboriginal (£1.12)

■ 2005, November 1. Christmas
Des: Irene von Treskow. Printed in gravure by De La Rue. Counter stamps self-adhesive, miniature sheet gummed. The 2nd class has one phosphor band, other values two phosphor bands.

Set	6.00	6.00
First day cover	–	6.50
Miniature sheet (one of each value)	6.00	6.00
Miniature sheet first day cover	–	6.50
Stamp cards	5.00	18.50

(*The 2nd class and 1st class stamps also appear in booklets.)

'The Tale of Mr Jeremy Fisher' by Beatrix Potter (2nd)
'Kipper' by Mick Inkpen (2nd)
'The Enormous Crocodile' by Roald Dahl (1st)
'More About Paddington' by Michael Bond (1st)
'Comic Adventures of Boots' by Satoshi Kitamura (42p)
'Alice's Adventures in Wonderland' by Lewis Carroll (42p)
'The Very Hungry Caterpillar' by Eric Carle (68p)
'Maisy's ABC' by Lucy Cousins (68p)

■ 2006. January 10. Animal Tales
Des: Rose. Printed in litho by De La Rue. Issued in se-tenant pairs.

Set (four se-tenant pairs)	6.50	6.50
Gutter pairs	15.00	–
Traffic light gutter blocks	55.00	–
First day cover	–	7.50
Stamp cards	5.00	12.50

(*This was a joint issue with the United States Postal Service.)

Carding Mill Valley, Shropshire (1st)
Beachy Head, Sussex (1st)
St. Paul's Cathedral, London (1st)
Brancaster, Norfolk (1st)
Derwent Edge, Peak District (1st)
Robin Hood's Bay, Yorkshire (1st)
Buttermere, Lake District (1st)
Chipping Campden, Cotswolds (1st)
St Boniface Down, Isle of Wight (1st)
Chamberlain Square, Birmingham (1st)

■ 2006, February 7. A British Journey: England
Des: Phelan Parker Design Consultants. Printed in gravure by
De La Rue.

Set (se-tenant block of 10)	10.00	10.00
Gutter pairs	25.00	–
First day cover	–	10.00
Stamp cards	5.50	15.00

Royal Albert Bridge (1st)
Box Tunnel (40p)
Paddington Station (42p)
PSS 'Great Britain' (47p)
Clifton Suspension Bridge (60p)
Maidenhead Bridge (68p)

■ 2006, February 23. Bicentenary of the Birth of Isambard Kingdom Brunel
Des: Hat-Trick Design. Printed in litho by Enschedé.

Set	5.00	5.00
Gutter pairs	12.50	–
First day cover	–	6.00
Miniature sheet (one of each value)	5.50	5.50
Miniature sheet first day cover	–	6.00
Stamp cards	5.00	25.00

Wales definitives (68p, 1st, 2nd, 1st, 68p)

■ 2006, March 1. Opening of the Welsh Assembly Building, Cardiff
Des: Silk Pearce. Printed in gravure by De La Rue.

Miniature sheet	5.00	5.00
First day cover	–	5.50

Sabre-tooth cat (1st)
Giant deer (42p)
Woolly rhino (47p)
Woolly mammoth (68p)
Cave bear (£1.12)

■ 2006, March 21. Ice Age Animals
Des: Howard Brown from illustrations by Andrew Davidson.
Printed in litho by Enschedé.

Set	5.25	5.25
Gutter pairs	14.00	–
First day cover	–	6.00
Stamp cards	4.00	8.50

The Queen in 1972 (2nd)
The Queen in 1985 (2nd)
The Queen in 1931 with Duchess of York (1st)
The Queen in 2001 (1st)
The Queen in 1951 (44p)
The Queen in 1960 (44p)
The Queen in 1940 (72p)
The Queen in 1951 with Duke of Edinburgh (72p)

■ 2006, April 18. The Queen's 80th Birthday
Des: Sedley Place. Printed in gravure by Enschedé.

Set	6.50	6.50
Gutter pairs	17.00	–
First day cover	–	6.50
Stamp cards	5.00	16.00

World Cup
Winners

42

England (1st)
Italy (42p)
Argentina (44p)
Germany (50p)
France (64p)
Brazil (72p)

■ **2006, June 6. World Cup Winners**
Des: Getty Images. Printed in litho by Walsall.

Set	5.75	5.75
Gutter pairs	14.00	–
First day cover	–	6.00
Stamp cards	4.00	11.00

30 St Mary Axe, London (1st)
Maggie's Centre, Dundee (42p)
Selfridges, Birmingham (44p)
Downland Gridshell, Chichester (50p)
An Turas, Isle of Tiree (64p)
The Deep, Hull (72p)

■ **2006, June 20. Modern Architecture**
Des: Roundel. Printed in gravure by Walsall.

Set	5.25	5.25
Gutter pairs	13.00	–
First day cover	–	6.25
Stamp cards	3.50	10.00

T. S. Eliot by Patrick Heron (1st)
Sir Winston Churchill by Walter Sickert (1st)
Sir Joshua Reynolds, self-portrait (1st)
Emmeline Pankhurst by Georgina Brackenbury (1st)
Virginia Woolf by George Beresford (1st)
Sir Walter Scott by Sir Francis Chantry (1st)
Mary Seacole by Albert Challen (1st)
William Shakespeare by John Taylor (1st)
Dame Cicely Saunders by Catherine Goodman (1st)
Charles Darwin by John Collier (1st)

■ **2006, July 18. 150th Anniversary of the National Portrait Gallery**
Des: Peter Willberg. Printed in gravure by De La Rue.

Set (se-tenant block of 10)	9.50	9.50
Gutter pairs	24.00	–
Traffic light gutter blocks	42.00	–
First day cover	–	9.50
Stamp cards	8.00	18.00

Definitive (£3)

■ **2006, August 31. The Year of the Three Kings**
Des: Together Design. Printed in gravure by De La Rue.

Miniature sheet	5.75	5.75
First day cover	–	6.00

(*The border illustrates 1d stamps of George V, Edward VIII and George VI, but these are not valid for postage.)

Corporal Agansing Rai (1st)
Boy Seaman First Class Jack Cornwell (1st)
Midshipman Charles Lucas (64p)
Captain Noel Chavasse (64p)
Captain Albert Ball (72p)
Captain Charles Upham (72p)

■ **2006, September 21. Victoria Cross**
Des: Atelier Works. Printed in litho by Enschedé.

Set	6.50	6.50
Gutter pairs	15.00	–
First day cover	–	7.00
Miniature sheet (one of each value, plus the		
Victoria Cross 20p of September 1990)	7.00	7.00
Miniature sheet first day cover	–	7.00
Press sheet	75.00	–
Stamp cards	4.00	20.00

Asian sitar and dancer (1st)
Caribbean base guitar and drum (42p)
Irish fiddle and harp (50p)
Black American saxophone and blues guitar (72p)
Latin American maracas and salsa dancers (£1.19)

■ **2006, October 3. Sounds of Britain (Europa)**
Des: CDT. Printed in litho by Cartor

Set	5.50	5.75
Gutter pairs	14.00	–
Traffic light gutter blocks	30.00	–
First day cover	–	6.50
Stamp cards	4.00	8.00

New baby (1st)
Best wishes (1st)
Thank you (1st)
Balloons (1st)
Firework (1st)
Champagne, flowers and butterflies (1st)

■ **2006, October 17. Smilers**
Des: NB Studio. Printed by litho by Walsall. Self-adhesive. Issued in booklets containing one of each of the six designs.

Booklet	6.50	–
First day cover	–	7.00
Stamp cards	7.00	21.00

(*These designs were used in Smilers sheets. For the same designs with elliptical perforations, see the issue of February 28, 2008.)

Snowman (2nd, 2nd Large)
Father Christmas sitting on chimney (1st, 1st Large)
Reindeer (72p)
Christmas tree (£1.19)

■ **2006, November 7. Christmas**
Des: CDT. Printed in litho by De La Rue. Counter sheets self-adhesive, miniature sheet gummed. The 2nd class has one phosphor band, other values two phosphor bands.

Set	6.50	6.50
Gutter pairs	17.00	–
First day cover	–	7.50
Miniature sheet (one of each value)	7.00	7.00
Miniature sheet first day cover	–	7.50
Stamp cards	6.00	18.00

(*The 2nd class and 1st class designs also appear in booklets.)

Poppies on barbed wire (1st)
Country definitives (72p, 72p, 72p, 72p)

■ **2006, November 9. Lest We Forget (issue 1)**
Des: Hat-Trick Design. Printed in gravure by De La Rue.

Miniature sheet	6.00	6.00
First day cover	–	6.50

(*The 1st class design was used in Smilers sheets.)

Scotland definitive (1st)
Scottish flag (1st)
St Andrew (72p)
Edinburgh Castle (72p)

■ **2006, November 30. Celebrating Scotland**
Des: P. Crowther and C. Melinsky, Silk Pearce. Printed in gravure by De La Rue.

Miniature sheet	4.50	4.50
First day cover	–	5.00
Stamp cards	4.00	15.00

(*The 1st class Scottish Flag design also appears in the Football Heroes prestige stamp book of 2013 and the Classic Locomotives of the UK prestige stamp book of 2014.)

Album cover: 'With The Beatles' (1st)
Album cover: 'Sgt Pepper's Lonely Hearts Club Band' (1st)
Album cover: 'Help!' (64p)
Album cover: 'Abbey Road' (64p)
Album cover: 'Revolver' (72p)
Album cover: 'Let It Be' (72p)

■ 2007, January 9. The Beatles

Des: Johnson Banks, from album sleeve covers. Printed in gravure by Walsall. Self-adhesive, in freeform shape. Available in horizontal pairs.

Set	6.50	6.50
First day cover	–	7.00
Stamp cards (set & miniature sheet)	6.00	22.00

Guitar and badge (1st)
Yellow Submarine lunch box and key rings (1st)
'Love Me Do' vinyl record (1st)
Tea tray and badges (1st)

■ 2007, January 9. The Beatles

Des: Johnson Banks. Printed in litho by Walsall.

Miniature sheet	4.00	4.00
First day cover	–	5.50

■ 2007, January 16. Smilers

Printed in litho by Walsall. Self-adhesive. Design as the 'Love' 1st class stamp of October 4, 2005, but with elliptical perforations along vertical sides. Issued in booklets of six.

Booklet	18.00	–

(*This design also appears in a booklet issued on January 15, 2008, and was used in Smilers sheets.)

Moon jellyfish (1st)
Common starfish (1st)
Beadlet anemone (1st)
Bass (1st)
Thornback ray (1st)
Lesser octopus (1st)
Common mussels (1st)
Grey seal (1st)
Shore crab (1st)
Common sun star (1st)

■ 2007, February 1. Sea Life

Des: A. Ross. Printed in litho by Cartor.

Set (se–tenant block of ten)	10.00	10.00
Gutter pairs	25.00	–
First day cover	–	10.00
Stamp cards	5.00	16.00

Saturn nebula C55 (1st)
Eskimo nebula C39 (1st)
Cat's Eye nebula C6 (50p)
Helix nebula C63 (50p)
Flaming Star nebula C31 (72p)
The Spindle galaxy C53 (72p)

■ 2007, February 13. The Sky at Night

Des: D. Davis. Printed in gravure by Walsall. Self-adhesive. Available in horizontal pairs. Stamps have description of designs on the backing paper.

Set	6.50	6.50
First day cover	–	6.50
Stamp cards	4.50	13.00

Bridge building: iron bridge in Thomas Telford's imagination (1st)
Railways: locomotive billowing track as steam (1st)
Communications: Britain and Australia close on map (64p)
Television: reporter on camera and viewer with screen (64p)
E-mail and internet: world wide web as globe (72p)
Space tourism: couple carrying suitcases on the Moon (72p)

■ 2007, March 1. World of Invention

Des: P. Willberg. Printed in gravure by De La Rue. Counter stamps self-adhesive, with description of designs on the backing paper. Miniature sheet gummed.

Set	6.50	6.50
Gutter pairs	16.00	–
First day cover	–	6.50
Miniature sheet (one of each value)	12.50	12.50
Miniature sheet first day cover	–	6.50
Stamp cards	4.25	22.00

(*All designs also appear, in gummed form, in the World of Invention prestige stamp book issued on March 1, 2007.)

William Wilberforce and abolitionist poster (1st)
Olaudah Equiano and map of slave trade routes (1st)
Granville Sharp and slave ship (50p)
Thomas Clarkson and diagram of slave ship (50p)
Hannah More and title page of 'The Sorrows of Yamba' (72p)
Ignatius Sancho and business card (72p)

■ 2007, March 22. Bicentenary of the Abolition of the Slave Trade

Des: Howard Brown. Printed in litho by Cartor. Issued in se-tenant pairs.

Set	5.50	5.50
Gutter pairs	14.00	–
Traffic light gutter blocks	45.00	–
First day cover	–	6.00
Stamp cards	4.00	13.00

England definitive (1st)
English flag (1st)
St. George (78p)
Houses of Parliament (78p)

■ 2007, April 23. Celebrating England

Des: P. Crowther and C. Melinsky, Silk Pearce. Printed in gravure by De La Rue.

Miniature sheet	5.00	5.00
First day cover	–	5.00
Stamp cards	3.25	14.00

(*The 1st class English Flag design also appears in the Football Heroes prestige stamp book of 2013 and the Classic Locomotives of the UK prestige stamp book of 2014.)

Ice cream cone (1st)
Sand castle (46p)
Merry-go-round (48p)
Beach huts (54p)
Deckchairs (69p)
Donkeys (78p)

■ 2007, May 15. Beside the Seaside

Des: Phelan Barker Design Consultants. Printed in gravure by De La Rue.

Set	6.00	6.00
Gutter pairs	15.00	–
First day cover	–	6.00
Stamp cards	4.00	11.00

(* The 1st class design also appears, in self-adhesive form, in a booklet issued on May 13, 2008: price £2.50 mint.)

Lion with shield of St. George (1st)
England definitives (2nd, 2nd, 78p, 78p)

■ 2007, May 17. Opening of the New Wembley Stadium, London

Des: Roundel. Printed in gravure by De La Rue.

Miniature sheet	5.50	5.50
First day cover	–	5.50

(*The 1st class design was previously issued on May 21, 2002, with an inscription, and was used in Smilers sheets.)

Arnold Machin (1st)
4d Machin olive sepia–brown (1st)
Definitive (£1 bluish–violet)
Definitive (£1 ruby)

■ 2007, June 5. 40th Anniversary of the Machin Definitives

Des: J. Matthews and Together Design. Printed in gravure by De La Rue.

Miniature sheet	5.50	5.50
Press sheet	75.00	–
First day cover	–	5.50
Stamp cards	3.50	16.00

(* The two 1st class designs also appear in The Making of a Masterpiece prestige stamp book. The Arnold Machin design was also used in a generic Smilers sheet.)

Stirling Moss and Vanwall 2.5L, 1957 (1st)
Graham Hill and BRM P57, 1962 (1st)
Jim Clark and Lotus–Climax 25, 1963 (54p)
Jackie Stewart and Tyrrell–Cosworth 006, 1973 (54p)
James Hunt and McLaren–Cosworth M23, 1976 (78p)
Nigel Mansell and Williams–Honda FW11, 1986 (78p)

■ 2007, July 3. Grand Prix

Des: True North, from photographs by James Callaghan. Printed in litho by Cartor.

Set	5.50	5.50
Gutter pairs	15.00	–
First day cover	–	6.50
Stamp cards	4.50	11.00

'Harry Potter and the Philosopher's Stone' (1st)
'Harry Potter and the Chamber of Secrets' (1st)
'Harry Potter and the Prisoner of Azkaban' (1st)
'Harry Potter and the Goblet of Fire' (1st)
'Harry Potter and the Order of the Phoenix' (1st)
'Harry Potter and the Half-Blood Prince' (1st)
'Harry Potter and the Deathly Hallows' (1st)

■ 2007, July 17. Harry Potter

Des: True North, from book covers. Printed in litho by Walsall.

Set	6.75	6.75
Gutter pairs	17.00	–
Traffic light gutter pairs	35.00	–
First day cover	–	6.50
Stamp cards	15.00	42.00

Symbol of Gryffindor house (1st)
Symbol of Hufflepuff house (1st)
Crest of Hogwarts School (1st)
Symbol of Ravenclaw house (1st)
Symbol of Slytherin house (1st)

■ 2007, July 17. Harry Potter

Des: True North. Printed in litho by Walsall.

Miniature sheet	5.00	5.00
First day cover	–	6.00

(*These designs were also used in a generic Smilers sheet.)

Scout looking at the Moon (1st)
Scouts conquering a mountain (46p)
Scout planting a tree (48p)
Scout learning archery (54p)
Scout piloting a glider (69p)
Scouts from many nations (78p)

■ **2007, July 26. Centenary of Scouting (Europa)**
Des: The Workroom. Printed in litho by Enschedé.

Set	5.75	6.00
Gutter pairs	14.00	–
First day cover	–	6.50
Stamp cards	4.00	11.00

White-tailed eagle (1st)
Bearded tit (1st)
Red kite (1st)
Cirl bunting (1st)
Marsh harrier (1st)
Avocet (1st)
Bittern (1st)
Dartford warbler (1st)
Corncrake (1st)
Peregrine (1st)

■ **2007, September 4. Endangered Species. Birds**
Des: Kate Stephens. Printed in litho by De La Rue. Issued in a se-tenant block.

Set (se-tenant block of ten)	9.00	9.00
Gutter pairs	23.00	–
First day cover	–	9.50
Stamp cards	5.00	16.00

NCO, British Military Police, 1999 (1st)
Tank Commander, 5th Royal Tank Regiment, 1944 (1st)
Observer, Royal Field Artillery, 1917 (1st)
Rifleman, 95th Rifles, 1813 (78p)

Grenadier, Royal Regiment of Foot of Ireland, 1704 (78p)
Trooper, Earl of Oxford's Horse, 1661 (78p)

■ **2007, September 20. British Army Uniforms**
Des: Atelier Works, from paintings by Graham Turner. Printed in litho by Enschedé. Issued in se-tenant strips of three.

Set (two se-tenant strips of three)	6.50	6.50
Gutter pairs	14.00	–
Traffic light gutter pairs	32.00	–
First day cover	–	7.50
Stamp cards	3.75	11.00

(*All six stamps also appear in the British Army Uniforms prestige stamp book. The 1st class Observer stamp also appears in the Great War 1915 prestige stamp book issued on May 14, 2015.)

The Queen and Prince Philip, 2006 (1st)
The Queen and Prince Philip, 1997 (1st)
The Queen and Prince Philip, 1980 (54p)
The Queen and Prince Philip, 1969 (54p)
The Queen and Prince Philip, 1961 (78p)
The Queen and Prince Philip, 1947 (78p)

■ **2007, October 16. Royal Diamond Wedding Anniversary**
Des: Pentagram. Printed in gravure by Walsall. Issued in se-tenant pairs.

Set (three se-tenant pairs)	8.00	10.00
Gutter pairs	20.00	–
First day cover	–	8.00
Stamp cards	6.00	28.00

The royal family at Balmoral, 1972 (1st)
Queen Elizabeth and Prince Philip at Buckingham Palace, 2007 (1st)
The royal family at Windsor Castle, 1965 (69p)
The royal family at Clarence House, 1951 (78p)

■ **2007, October 16. Royal Diamond Wedding Anniversary**
Des: Pentagram. Printed in gravure by Walsall. Self-adhesive. The reverse of the sheet shows photographs of the royal couple leading up to their marriage.

Miniature sheet	5.00	5.00
Press sheet	60.00	–
First day cover	–	6.00

Peace: angel playing trumpet (2nd, 2nd Large)
Goodwill: angel playing lute (1st, 1st Large)
Joy: angel playing flute (78p)
Glory: angel playing tambourine (£1.24)

■ 2007, November 6. Christmas. Angels
Des: Rose, with illustrations by Marco Ventura. Printed in gravure by De La Rue. Counter stamps self-adhesive, miniature sheet gummed.

Set	7.50	7.50
Gutter pairs	20.00	
First day cover	–	9.50
Miniature sheet (one of each value)	7.00	7.00
Miniature sheet first day cover	–	7.50
Stamp cards	5.00	17.50

(*The 2nd class and 1st class designs also appear in booklets, and the 2nd, 1st and 78p were used in Smilers sheets.)

'Madonna & Child' by William Dyce (2nd)
'The Madonna of Humility' by Lippo di Dalmasio (1st)

■ 2007, November 6. Christmas. Madonna and Child
Des: Peter Willberg, from paintings. Printed in gravure by De La Rue. Self-adhesive.

Set	2.25	2.25
Gutter pairs	6.00	–
First day cover	–	3.50

(*These stamps were re-issued at Christmas in 2008–2012.)

Soldiers in poppy (1st)
Country definitives (78p, 78p, 78p, 78p)

■ 2007, November 8. Lest We Forget (issue 2)
Des: Hat-Trick Design. Printed in gravure by De La Rue.

Miniature sheet	6.50	6.50
First day cover	–	7.00

(*The 1st class design was also used in a Smilers generic sheet.)

Book covers of 'Casino Royale' (1st)
Book covers of 'Dr No' (1st)
Book covers of 'Goldfinger' (54p)
Book covers of 'Diamonds Are Forever' (54p)
Book covers of 'For Your Eyes Only' (78p)
Book covers of 'From Russia With Love' (78p)

■ 2008, January 8. Centenary of the Birth of Ian Fleming.
James Bond Books
Des: A2. Prined in litho by De La Rue.

Set	6.00	6.00
Gutter pairs	15.00	–
First day cover	–	7.00
Miniature sheet	9.50	9.50
Miniature sheet first day cover	–	8.00
Press sheet	75.00	–
Stamp cards (set and miniature sheet)	6.00	25.00

(*All values also appear in the Ian Fleming's James Bond prestige stamp book, issued on January 8, 2008.)

Assistance dog with letter (1st)
Mountain rescue dog (46p)
Police dog (48p)
Customs dog (54p)
Sheepdog (69p)
Guide dog (78p)

■ 2008, February 5. Working Dogs
Des: Redpath Design. Printed in litho by Cartor.

Set	5.75	5.75
Gutter pairs	14.00	
First day cover	–	6.50
Stamp cards	5.00	14.00

King Henry IV, 1399–1413 (1st)
King Henry V, 1413–22 (1st)
King Henry VI, 1422–61 and 1470–71 (54p)
King Edward IV, 1461–70 and 1471–83 (54p)
King Edward V, 1483 (69p)
King Richard III, 1483–85 (69p)

■ 2008, February 28. Kings and Queens. Houses of Lancaster and York

Des: Ian Chilvers, Atelier Works. Printed in litho by Walsall.

Set	5.25	5.50
Gutter pairs	14.00	–
Traffic light gutter blocks	35.00	–
First day cover	–	7.50
Stamp cards	7.00	26.00

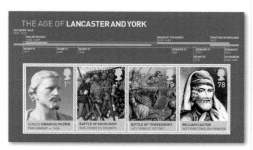

Owain Glyndwr's parliament, 1404 (1st)
Battle of Agincourt, 1415 (1st)
Battle of Tewkesbury, 1471 (78p)
William Caxton, first English printer, 1477 (78p)

■ 2008, February 28. The Age of Lancaster and York

Des: Ian Chilvers. Printed in litho by Walsall.

Miniature sheet	4.25	4.50
First day cover	–	5.25
Press sheet	90.00	–

■ 2008, February 28. Smilers

Printed in litho by Walsall. Self-adhesive. As designs of Hello, Gazania splendens and Union flag 1st class of October 4, 2005, and Champagne, flowers and butterfly, Firework and New baby 1st class of October 17, 2006, but with elliptical perforations on vertical sides. Issued in booklets of six.

Booklet	32.00	32.00
First day cover	–	32.00

(*These designs were used in Smilers sheets.)

Carrickfergus Castle (1st)
Giant's Causeway (1st)
St Patrick (78p)
Queen's Bridge, Belfast (78p)

■ 2008, March 11. Celebrating Northern Ireland

Des: Silk Pearce (sheet) and David Lyons, Clare Melinsky, Tony Pleavin and Ric Ergenbright (stamps). Printed in litho by De La Rue.

Miniature sheet	5.00	5.00
First day cover	–	5.00
Stamp cards	3.25	15.00

Lifeboat at Barra (1st)
Lifeboat and dinghy at Appledore (46p)
Helicopter rescue at Portland (48p)
Lifeboat at St Ives (54p)
Rescue helicopter at Lee-on-Solent (69p)
Lifeboat at Dinbych-y-Pysgod, Tenby (78p)

■ 2008, March 13. Rescue at Sea

Des: Hat Trick Design. Printed in litho by Walsall. 'Dot' and 'dash' shaped perforations at top and bottom.

Set	5.50	6.00
Gutter pairs	14.00	–
First day cover	–	7.00
Stamp cards	4.25	13.00

Field Cricket
Gryllus campestris

Adonis blue butterfly (1st)
Southern damselfly (1st)
Red–barded ant (1st)
Barberry carpet moth (1st)
Stag beetle (1st)
Hazel pot beetle (1st)
Field cricket (1st)
Silver–spotted skipper (1st)
Purbeck mason wasp (1st)
Noble chafer beetle (1st)

■ 2008, April 15. Endangered Species. Insects
Des: Andrew Ross. Printed in litho by De La Rue. Issued in se–tenant blocks of ten.

Set	9.00	9.00
Gutter pairs	21.00	–
First day cover	–	9.00
Stamp cards	7.00	22.00

LICHFIELD CATHEDRAL

Lichfield Cathedral (1st)
Belfast Cathedral (48p)
Gloucester Cathedral (50p)
St. Davids Cathedral (56p)
Westminster Cathedral (72p)
St. Magnus Cathedral, Kirkwall, Orkney (81p)

■ 2008, May 13. Cathedrals
Des: Howard Brown. Printed in litho by Enschedé.

Set	6.50	6.50
Gutter pairs	17.00	–
Traffic light gutter pairs	35.00	–
First day cover	–	7.25
Stamp cards	6.50	27.50

ST PAUL'S CATHEDRAL
BENEATH LIES BURIED THE FOUNDER OF THIS CHURCH AND CITY,
CHRISTOPHER WREN, WHO LIVED MORE THAN 90 YEARS,
NOT FOR HIMSELF BUT FOR THE PUBLIC GOOD.
READER, IF YOU SEEK HIS MONUMENT, LOOK AROUND YOU.

Composite view inside St Paul's Cathedral (1st, 1st, 81p, 81p)

■ 2008, May 13. 300th Anniversary of St. Paul's Cathedral
Des: Howard Brown. Printed in litho by Enschedé.

Miniature sheet	5.00	5.00
First day cover	–	5.50
Press sheet	70.00	–

Poster promoting 'Carry On Sergeant' (1st)
Poster promoting 'Dracula' (48p)
Poster promoting 'Carry on Cleo' (50p)
Poster promoting 'The Curse of Frankenstein' (56p)
Poster promoting 'Carry On Screaming' (72p)
Poster promoting 'The Mummy' (81p)

■ 2008, June 10. Classic Carry On and Hammer Films
Des: Elmwood Design Group, from film posters. Printed in litho by Walsall.

Set	5.75	5.75
Gutter pairs	14.00	–
First day cover	–	6.50
Postcard and stamp set	30.00	–
Stamp cards	4.00	14.00

(*The postcard and stamp set comprised six cards showing the stamp designs against a brick background, together with a folder containing three 1st class and three 56p values.)

Air Displays

Red Arrows aerobatic display, 2006 (1st)
RAF Falcons parachute display, 2006 (48p)
Spectators watching the Red Arrows, 2006 (50p)
Avro Vulcan prototypes and Avro 707S, 1953 (56p)
Parachutist Robert Wyndham and Avro 504, 1933 (72p)
Hendon air race, 1912 (81p)

■ 2008, July 17. Air Displays
Des: Roundel. Printed in litho by Cartor.

Set	6.00	6.00
Gutter pairs	15.00	–
First day cover	–	7.00
Stamp cards	4.00	14.00

(*The 1st class design also appears in the Pilot To Plane: RAF Uniforms prestige stamp book of September 18, 2008, and was used in Smilers sheets.)

National Stadium, Beijing (1st)
London Eye (1st)
Tower of London (1st)
Corner Tower the Forbidden City, Beijing (1st)

■ 2008, August 22. Handover of the Olympic Flag from Beijing to London
Des: Why Not Associates. Printed in litho by Walsall, with the Olympic rings in a silk screen varnish.

Miniature sheet	5.50	5.50
First day cover	–	5.50
Stamp cards	3.00	15.00

Drum Major RAF Central Band 2007

Drum Major, RAF Central Band, 2007 (1st)
Helicopter rescue winchman, 1984 (1st)
Hawker Hunter pilot, 1951 (1st)
Lancaster air gunner, 1944 (81p)
WAAF plotter, 1940 (81p)
Pilot, 1918 (81p)

■ 2008, September 18. RAF Uniforms
Des: Atelier Works, from paintings by Graham Turner. Printed in litho by Walsall. Issued in se-tenant strips of three.

Set	6.50	6.50
Gutter pairs	15.00	–
Traffic light gutter pairs	30.00	–
First day cover	–	7.50
Stamp cards	4.00	14.00

(*All values also appear in the Pilot To Plane: RAF Uniforms prestige stamp book issued on September 18, 2008.)

Northern Ireland 3d design, 1958 (1st)
Northern Ireland 6d design, 1958 (1st)
Northern Ireland 1s 3d design, 1958 (1st)
Scotland 3d design, 1958 (1st)
Scotland 6d design, 1958 (1st)
Scotland 1s 3d design, 1958 (1st)
Wales 3d design, 1958 (1st)
Wales 6d design, 1958 (1st)
Wales 1s 3d design, 1958 (1st)

■ 2008, September 29. 50th Anniversary of the Country Definitives
As the 1958 regional stamps of Northern Ireland, Scotland and Wales, with new values. Printed in gravure by De La Rue.

Miniature sheet	7.50	7.50
Press sheet	80.00	–
First day cover	–	9.50
Stamp cards	11.00	35.00

(*All designs also appear in the Heraldry and Symbol prestige stamp book issued on September 29, 2008.)

Soldier's face in poppy (1st)
Country definitives (81p, 81p, 81p, 81p)

■ 2008, November 6. Lest We Forget (issue 3)
Des: Hat-Trick Design. Printed in litho by De La Rue.

Miniature sheet	6.50	6.50
First day cover	–	7.50

(*The 1st class design was used in a Smilers generic sheet.)

■ 2008, November 6. Lest We Forget
The Poppy designs of November 6, 2006, November 8, 2007, and November 6, 2008, but in se-tenant strips in counter sheets. Printed in litho by De La Rue.

Set (se-tenant strip of three)	3.50	3.50
Gutter pairs	9.00	–
Traffic light gutter pairs	26.00	–
First day cover	–	4.00
Stamp cards (3 stamps, 3 miniature sheets)	10.00	27.00

Millicent Garrett Fawcett: votes for women (1st)
Elizabeth Garrett Anderson: women's health (48p)
Marie Stopes: family planning (50p)
Eleanor Rathbone: family allowance (56p)
Claudia Jones: civil rights (72p)
Barbara Castle: equal pay for women (81p)

■ 2008, October 14. Women of Distinction
Des: Together Design. Printed in gravure by Walsall.

Set	5.75	5.75
Gutter pairs	15.00	–
First day cover	–	7.00
Stamp cards	4.00	14.00

London Underground Map
Designed by Harry Beck

The Ugly Sisters from 'Cinderella' (2nd, 2nd Large)
The Genie from 'Aladdin' (1st, 1st Large)
Captain Hook from 'Peter Pan' (50p)
The Wicked Queen from 'Snow White' (81p)

■ 2008, November 4. Christmas. Pantomime
Des: Steve Haskins, from photographs by Peter Thorpe. Printed in gravure by De La Rue. Counter stamps self-adhesive, miniature sheet gummed.

Set	6.50	6.50
Gutter pairs	16.00	–
First day cover	–	7.00
Miniature sheet (one of each value)	6.00	6.00
Miniature sheet first day cover	–	6.00
Stamp cards	4.25	19.00

(*The 1st class and 2nd class designs also appear in booklets, and the 2nd, 1st and 81p designs were used in Smilers sheets.)

Supermarine Spitfire by R. J. Mitchell (1st)
Mini skirt by Mary Quant (1st)
Mini by Sir Alec Issigonis (1st)
Anglepoise lamp by George Carwardine (1st)
Concorde by BAC and Aerospatiale (1st)
K2 telephone kiosk by Sir Giles Gilbert Scott (1st)
Polypropylene chair by Robin Day (1st)
Penguin book cover by Edward Young (1st)
London Underground map by Harry Beck (1st)
Routemaster bus by A.A.M. Durrant (1st)

■ 2009, January 13. British Design Classics

Des: HGV Design. Printed in litho by Cartor. Issued in se-tenant blocks of 10.

Set	9.00	9.50
Gutter pairs	23.00	–
First day cover	–	10.00
Postcards and stamp set	22.00	–
Stamp cards	5.50	22.00

(*The postcard and stamp set comprises 10 cards reproducing the stamp designs against a Union Flag background, and a set of the stamps. All designs also appear in the British Design Classics prestige stamp book issued on January 13, 2009. The Routemaster, Telephone Kiosk, Mini, Concorde, Spitfire and Mini Skirt designs also appear in self-adhesive form in booklets; price £2.50 each, mint. The Mini and Concorde designs were also used in Smilers generic sheets.)

'A Man's a Man for a' That' (1st)
Portrait of Burns by Alexander Nasmyth (1st)
Scotland definitives (2nd, 1st, 50p, 81p)

■ 2009, January 22. 250th Anniversary of the Birth of Robert Burns

Des: Tayburn. Printed in gravure by Enschedé.

Miniature sheet	5.25	5.50
First day cover	–	6.00
Press sheet	90.00	–
Stamp cards	2.50	12.50

Charles Darwin (1st)
Marine iguana (48p)
Finches (50p)
Atoll (56p)
Bee orchid (72p)
Orang-utan (81p)

■ 2009, February 12. Bicentenary of the Birth of Charles Darwin

Des: Hat-Trick Design. Printed in gravure by De La Rue. Self-adhesive, in freeform shape to resemble jigsaw pieces.

Set	7.50	7.75
Gutter pairs	18.00	–
First day cover	–	8.50
Stamp cards	7.00	28.00

(*All values also appear, in gummed form, in the Charles Darwin prestige stamp book issued on February 12, 2009.)

Flightless cormorant and Galapagos Islands (1st)
Giant tortoise, cactus finch and Galapagos Islands (1st)
Marine iguana and Galapagos Islands (81p)
Floreana mockingbird and Galapagos Islands (81p)

■ 2009, February 12. Bicentenary of the Birth of Charles Darwin. The Galapagos Islands

Des: Howard Brown. Printed in litho by De La Rue.

Miniature sheet	5.00	5.00
First day cover	–	5.50
Press sheet	55.00	–

(*The miniature sheet also appears in the Charles Darwin prestige stamp book issued on February 12, 2009.)

Welsh flag (1st)
Wales definitive (1st)
St. David (81p)
National Assembly for Wales, Cardiff (81p)

■ 2009, February 26. Celebrating Wales

Des: Silk Pearce. Printed in litho by De La Rue.

Miniature sheet	4.50	4.75
First day cover	–	6.00
Stamp cards	3.75	15.00

(*The 1st class Welsh Flag design also appears in the Football Heroes prestige stamp book of 2013 and the Classic Locomotives of the UK prestige stamp book of 2014.)

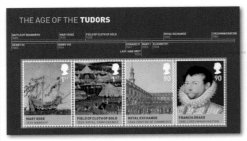

Matthew Boulton, manufacturing (1st)
James Watt, engineering (1st)
Richard Arkwright, textiles (50p)
Josiah Wedgwood, ceramics (50p)
George Stephenson, railways (56p)
Henry Maudslay, machine–making (56p)
James Brindley, canal engineering (72p)
John McAdam, road building (72p)

■ 2009, March 17. Pioneers of the Industrial Revolution

Des: Webb & Webb. Printed in litho by Enschedé. Issued in se-tenant pairs.

Set	7.00	7.00
Gutter pairs	17.00	–
First day cover	–	8.00
Stamp cards	5.00	20.00

King Henry VII, 1485–1509 (1st)
King Henry VIII, 1509–47 (1st)
King Edward VI, 1547–53 (62p)
Lady Jane Grey, 1553 (62p)
Queen Mary 1, 1553–58 (81p)
Queen Elizabeth I, 1558–1603 (81p)

■ 2009, April 21. Kings and Queens. The House of Tudor

Des: Ian Chilvers, Atelier Works. Printed in litho by Walsall.

Set	5.50	5.50
Gutter pairs	15.00	–
Traffic light gutter pairs	32.50	–
First day cover	–	7.00
Stamp cards	6.50	30.00

'Mary Rose' warship, 1510 (1st)
Field of Cloth of Gold conference, 1520 (1st)
Royal Exchange commercial centre, 1565 (90p)
Francis Drake's circumnavigation, 1580 (90p)

■ 2009, April 21. The Age of the Tudors

Des: Ian Chilvers, Atelier Works. Printed in litho by Walsall.

Miniature sheet	4.75	5.00
First day cover	–	6.00
Press sheet	90.00	–

Round–headed leek (1st)
Floating water–plantain (1st)
Lady's slipper orchid (1st)
Dwarf milkwort (1st)
Marsh saxifrage (1st)
Downy woundwort (1st)
Upright spurge (1st)
Plymouth pear (1st)
Sea knotgrass (1st)
Deptford pink (1st)

■ 2009, May 19. Endangered Species: Plants

Des: Studio Dempsey. Printed in litho by Cartor. Issued in se-tenant blocks of ten.

Set	9.00	9.00
Gutter pairs	22.00	–
First day cover	–	11.00
Stamp cards	8.00	35.00

Palm House, Kew Gardens (1st)
Millennium Seed Bank, Wakehurst Place (1st)
Pagoda, Kew Gardens (90p)
Sackler Crossing, Kew Gardens (90p)

■ 2009, May 19. 250th Anniversary of the Royal Botanic Gardens, Kew

Des: Studio Dempsey. Printed in litho by Cartor.

Miniature sheet	4.75	5.00
First day cover	–	6.00
Maximum cards set	12.00	–
Press sheet	70.00	–

(*The maximum cards set comprises four postcards, each with one stamp from the miniature sheet affixed and cancelled on the picture side, sold in a pack with a mint miniature sheet.)

Dragons (1st)
Unicorns (1st)
Giants (62p)
Pixies (62p)
Mermaids (90p)
Fairies (90p)

■ 2009, June 16. Mythical Creatures

Des: Morgan Radcliffe, from illustrations by Dave McKean. Printed in gravure by De La Rue.

Set	6.50	6.50
Gutter pairs	16.00	–
First day cover	–	8.50
Stamp cards	4.00	17.00

George V type B wall box, 1933, at Cookham Rise (1st)
Edward VII Ludlow box, 1901, at Bodiam post office (56p)
Victorian lamp box, 1896, at Hythe (81p)
Elizabeth II type A wall box, 1962, at Slaithwaite sorting office (90p)

■ 2009, August 18. Post Boxes

Des: Elmwood Design Group, from photographs by Peter Marlow. Printed in litho by Cartor.

Miniature sheet	5.00	5.00
First day cover	–	5.50
Press sheet	70.00	–
Stamp cards	3.50	17.00

(*All designs also appear in the Treasures of the Archive prestige stamp book issued on August 18, 2009, and the 1st class design was used in a Smilers generic sheet.)

Firefighting (1st)
Chemical fire (54p)
Emergency rescue (56p)
Flood rescue (62p)
Search and rescue (81p)
Fire safety (90p)

■ 2009, September 1. Fire and Rescue Services

Des: Rose. Printed in gravure by De La Rue.

Set	6.50	6.50
Gutter pairs	16.00	–
First day cover	–	8.00
Stamp cards	3.75	17.00

Flight Deck Officer, 2009 (1st)
Captain, 1941 (1st)
Second Officer WRNS, 1918 (1st)
Able Seaman, 1880 (90p)
Royal Marine, 1805 (90p)
Admiral, 1795 (90p)

■ 2009, September 17. Royal Navy Uniforms

Des: Atelier Works, from paintings by Graham Turner. Printed in litho by Cartor. Issued in se-tenant strips of three.

Set	7.00	7.00
Gutter pairs	17.00	–
Traffic light gutter pairs	32.50	–
First day cover	–	9.00
Stamp cards	3.75	17.00

(*All values also appear in the Royal Navy Uniforms prestige stamp book issued on September 17, 2009.)

Sir Matt Busby 1909–1994
Footballer and football manager

Fred Perry, tennis player (1st)
Henry Purcell, composer (1st)
Sir Matt Busby, football manager (1st)
William Gladstone, statesman (1st)
Mary Wollstonecraft, pioneering feminist (1st)
Sir Arthur Conan Doyle, author (1st)
Donald Campbell, water speed record breaker (1st)
Judy Fryd, founder of Mencap (1st)
Samuel Johnston, lexicographer (1st)
Sir Martin Ryle, radio astronomer (1st)

■ 2009, October 8. Eminent Britons

Des: Together Design. Printed in litho by Cartor. Issued in strips of five se-tenant designs, in two different sheets.

Set	9.50	9.50
Gutter pairs	23.00	–
First day cover	–	10.00
Stamp cards	6.00	26.00

Canoe slalom (1st)
Paralympic archery (1st)
Track athletics (1st)
Aquatics (1st)
Paralympic boccia (1st)
Judo (1st)
Paralympic equestrianism (1st)
Badminton (1st)
Weightlifting (1st)
Basketball (1st)

■ 2009, October 22. London 2012 Olympic and Paralympic Games (issue 1)

Des: John Royle (Canoe), George Hardie (Archery), Nathalie Guinamard (Athletics), Julian Opie (Aquatics), David Doyle (Boccia), Paul Slater (Judo), Andrew Davidson (Equestrian), David Holmes (Badminton), Guy Billout (Weightlifting), Huntley Muir (Basketball), Studio David Hillman (set). Printed in litho by Cartor. Issued in strips of five se-tenant designs in two different sheets.

Set	9.50	9.50
Gutter pairs	23.00	–
First day cover	–	10.00
Postcard and stamp set (Athletics)	9.00	–
Postcard and stamp set (Badminton)	9.00	–
Postcard and stamp set (Equestrian)	9.00	–
Postcard and stamp set (Judo)	9.00	–
Stamp cards	7.00	26.00

(All values also appear in a commemorative sheet. The Judo, Archery, Track Athletics and Basketball designs also appear, in self-adhesive from, in booklets; price £2.00 each, mint.)

Angel by William Morris (2nd, 2nd large)
Madonna & Child by Henry Holiday (1st, 1st Large)
Joseph by Henry Holiday (56p)
Wise Man by Sir Edward Burne-Jones (90p)
Shepherd by Henry Holiday (£1.35)

■ 2009, November 3. Christmas

Des: Andrew Ross, from stained glass windows. Printed in gravure by De La Rue. Counter sheets self-adhesive, miniature sheet gummed.

Set	8.75	8.75
Gutter pairs	22.00	–
First day cover	–	9.50
Miniature sheet (one of each value)	7.50	7.50
Miniature sheet first day cover		8.50
Stamp cards	5.00	27.50

(* The 1st and 2nd class designs also appear in booklets, and the 2nd, 1st, 56p and 90p designs were used in Smilers sheets.)

'The Division Bell' by Pink Floyd, 1994 (1st)
'A Rush of Blood to the Head' by Coldplay, 2002 (1st)
'Parklife' by Blur, 1994 (1st)
'Power, Corruption and Lies' by New Order, 1983 (1st)
'Let It Bleed' by The Rolling Stones, 1969 (1st)
'London Calling' by The Clash, 1979 (1st)
'Tubular Bells' by Mike Oldfield 1973 (1st)
'IV' by Led Zepplin, 1971 (1st)
'Screamadelica' by Primal Scream, 1991 (1st)
'The Rise & Fall of Ziggy Stardust' by David Bowie, 1972 (1st)

■ 2010, January 7. Classic Album Covers

Des: Studio Dempsey. Counter sheets printed in gravure by De La Rue, self-adhesive in freeform shape, in strips of five in two different sheets. Miniature sheet printed in litho by Cartor, gummed.

Set	10.00	10.00
Gutter pairs	25.00	–
First day cover	–	10.00
Miniature sheet (one of each value)	25.00	26.00
Miniature sheet first day cover	–	30.00
Stamp cards	10.00	26.00

(*The stamps also appear in the Classic Album Covers prestige stamp book, litho-printed. A souvenir sheet of 10 of the Division Bell design was issued on March 6, 2010, but was not available from post offices; price £6.50.)

Aircraft (1st)
Sports car (1st)
Wax seal with crown (1st)
Birthday cake with 'Happy birthday' message (1st)
Bird with envelope (Europe up to 20g)
Steam locomotive (1st)
Ocean liner (1st)
Poppies on barbed wire (1st)
Wrapped present (1st)
Aircraft with 'Hello' message (Worldwide up to 20g)

■ 2010, January 26. Stamps for Smilers and Business Customised Sheets

Des: Andrew Davidson (Aircraft, Sports car, Steam locomotive, Ocean liner), Hat-Trick (Seal, Poppies), Annabel Wright (Cake, Present) and Lucy Davey (Europe, Worldwide). Printed in litho by Cartor.

Miniature sheet	10.00	10.00
First day cover	–	9.00
Stamp cards	10.00	35.00

(*These designs were issued primarily for use in Smilers sheets, where they are self-adhesive. The Poppies design was also issued in self-adhesive counter sheets in 2012.)

Rainbows and activities (1st)
Brownies and activities (56p)
Guides and activities (81p)
Senior Section and activities (90p)

■ 2010, February 2. Centenary of Girlguiding

Des: Together Design. Printed in litho by Cartor.

Miniature sheet	5.00	5.00
First day cover	–	6.00
Stamp cards	3.00	22.00

Robert Boyle, chemistry (1st)
Isaac Newton, optics (1st)
Benjamin Franklin, electricity (1st)
Edward Jenner, vaccination (1st)
Charles Babbage, computing (1st)
Alfred Russel Wallace, evolution (1st)
Joseph Lister, antiseptic surgery (1st)
Ernest Rutherford, atomic structure (1st)
Dorothy Hodgkin, crystallography (1st)
Nicholas Shackleton, earth science (1st)

■ **2010, February 25. 350th Anniversary of The Royal Society**
Des: Hat–Trick. Printed in litho by Cartor. Issued in se–tenant blocks of ten.

Set (se–tenant block of 10)	10.00	10.00
Gutter pairs	25.00	–
First day cover	–	11.00
Stamp cards	6.25	25.00

(* All designs also appear in The Royal Society prestige stamp book.)

Pixie, mastiff cross (1st)
Button, cat (1st)
Herbie, mongrel (1st)
Mr Tumnus, cat (1st)
Tafka, border collie (1st)
Boris, bulldog cross (1st)
Casey, lurcher (1st)
Tigger, cat (1st)
Leonard, Jack Russell cross (1st)
Tia, terrier cross (1st)

■ **2010, March 11. 150th Anniversary of Battersea Dogs & Cats Home**
Des: CDT Design Ltd. Printed in litho by Cartor. Issued in se–tenant blocks of ten.

Set (se–tenant block of 10)	10.00	10.00
Gutter pairs	25.00	–
First day cover	–	11.00
Stamp cards	6.25	25.00

King James I of Scotland, 1406–37 (1st)
King James II of Scotland, 1437–60 (1st)
King James III of Scotland, 1460–88 (1st)
King James IV of Scotland, 1488–1513 (62p)
King James V of Scotland, 1513–42 (62p)
Mary Queen of Scots, 1542–67 (81p)
King James VI of Scotland, 1567–1625 (81p)

■ **2010, March 23. Kings and Queens. The House of Stewart**
Des: Atelier Works. Printed in litho by Cartor.

Set	7.50	7.50
Gutter pairs	19.00	–
Traffic light gutter pairs	32.50	–
First day cover	–	8.50
Stamp cards	7.00	35.00

St. Andrews University, 1413 (1st)
College of Surgeons, 1505 (1st)
Court of Session, 1532 (81p)
John Knox and the Reformation, 1559 (81p)

■ **2010, March 23. The Age of the Stewarts**
Des: Atelier Works. Printed in litho by Cartor.

Miniature sheet	5.00	5.00
First day cover	–	5.50
Press sheet	75.00	–

Humpback whale (1st)
Wildcat (1st)
Brown long–eared bat (1st)
Polecat (1st)
Sperm whale (1st)
Water vole (1st)
Greater horseshoe bat (1st)
Otter (1st)
Dormouse (1st)
Hedgehog (1st)

■ **2010, April 13. Endangered Species. Mammals**
Des: Jason Godfrey. Printed in litho by Cartor. Issued in se–tenant blocks of ten.

Set	10.00	10.00
Gutter pairs	25.00	–
First day cover	–	11.00
Stamp cards	6.25	25.00

(* The Otter and Hedgehog designs also appear, in self–adhesive form, in booklets; price £3.50 each mint or used.)

Machin portrait of Queen Elizabeth II and Mackennal portrait of King George V (1st)
Mackennal and Downey portraits of King George V (£1)

■ **2010, May 6. London 2010 Festival of Stamps. Centenary of the Accession of King George V**
Des: Sedley Place. Printed in litho by Cartor. 1st class design printed in sheets; 1st and £1 designs issued in miniature sheets.

1st class	2.00	2.00
Gutter pair (1st class)	5.00	–
First day cover	–	4.00
Miniature sheet	4.00	4.00
Miniature sheet first day cover	–	12.50
Press sheet	45.00	–

(*These stamps also appear in the King George V prestige stamp book. The miniature sheet was issued on May 8, 2010, with an additional overprint in the border reading 'BUSINESS DESIGN

CENTRE, LONDON, 8–15 May 2010'; price £11.00 mint, £13.00 on first day cover. Stamp cards showing the stamps and miniature sheets of this issue were included in the issue of May 8.)

1924 British Empire Exhibition 1d stamp (1st)
1924 British Empire Exhibition 1½d stamp (1st)
1913–34 'Seahorses' £1 definitive (£1)
1913–34 'Seahorses' 10/– definitive (£1)

■ **2010, May 8. London 2010 Festival of Stamps. The King's Stamps**
Des: Sedley Place. Printed in intaglio and litho by Enschedé.

Miniature sheet	5.00	5.50
First day cover	–	12.50
Press sheet	40.00	–
Stamp cards (issues of May 6 and May 8)	5.00	28.00

(*All designs also appear in the King George V prestige stamp book.)

Winston Churchill (1st)
Land girls (1st)
Home Guard (60p)
Evacuees (60p)
Air raid wardens (67p)
Women in factories (67p)
Royal broadcast, 1940 (97p)
Fire service (97p)

■ **2010, May 13. Britain Alone**
Des: Why Not Associates. Printed in litho by Cartor.

Set	8.00	8.00
Gutter pairs	20.00	–
First day cover	–	9.00
Stamp cards	7.50	37.50

(*All values also appear in the Britain Alone prestige stamp book.)

Evacuation of British soldiers from Dunkirk (1st)
Vessels involved in 'Operation Dynamo' (60p)
British soldiers on board a Royal Navy destroyer (88p)
Two boats from the Dunkirk evacuation (97p)

■ 2010, May 13. 70th Anniversary of the Evacuation of Dunkirk
Des: Why Not Associates. Printed in litho by Cartor.

Miniature sheet	5.50	5.50
First day cover	–	6.00

(*All values also appear in the Britain Alone prestige stamp book.)

King James I, 1603–25 (1st)
King Charles I, 1625–49 (1st)
King Charles II, 1660–85 (60p)
King James II, 1685–88 (60p)
King William III, 1689–1702 (67p)
Queen Mary II, 1689–94 (67p)
Queen Anne, 1702–14 (88p)

■ 2010, June 15. Kings and Queens. The House of Stuart
Des: Atelier Works. Printed in litho by Cartor.

Set	6.75	6.75
Gutter pairs	16.00	–
Traffic light gutter pairs	32.50	–
First day cover	–	9.00
Stamp cards	7.00	35.00

William Harvey and discovery of blood circulation, 1628 (1st)
Battle of Naseby, 1645 (60p)
John Milton and 'Paradise Lost', 1667 (88p)
John Vanbrugh and Castle Howard, 1712 (97p)

■ 2010, June 15. The Age of the Stuarts
Des: Atelier Works. Printed in litho by Cartor.

Miniature sheet	5.50	5.50
First day cover	–	5.75
Press sheet	85.00	–

Paralympic rowing (1st)
Shooting (1st)
Modern pentathlon (1st)
Taekwondo (1st)
Cycling (1st)
Paralympic table tennis (1st)
Hockey (1st)
Football (1st)
Paralympic goalball (1st)
Boxing (1st)

■ 2010, July 27. London 2012 Olympic and Paralympic Games (issue 2)
Des: Marian Hill (Rowing), David Hillman (Shooting), Katherine Baxter (Modern pentathlon), James Fryer (Taekwondo), Matthew Dennis (Cycling), Michael Craig-Martin (Table tennis), Darren Hopes (Hockey), Alex Williamson (Football), Tobatron (Goalball), Stephen Ledwidge (Boxing), Studio David Hillman (set). Printed in litho by Cartor. Issued in se-tenant strips of five in two different sheets.

Set	10.00	10.00
Gutter pairs	24.00	–
First day cover	–	10.00
Postcard and stamp set (Boxing)	9.00	–
Postcard and stamp set (Rowing)	9.00	–
Stamp cards	6.00	25.00

(*The Rowing, Table Tennis, Football and Cycling designs also appear, in self-adhesive form, in booklets; price £2.00 each mint or used. All values were used in a commemorative sheet.)

LMS: Coronation Class locomotive (1st)
BR: Class 9F locomotive (1st)
GWR: King Class locomotive (67p)
LNER: Class A1 locomotive (67p)
SR: King Arthur Class locomotive (97p)
LMS: NCC Class WT locomotive (97p)

■ 2010, August 19. Great British Railways
Des: Delaney Design Consultants. Printed in gravure by De La Rue.

Set	6.50	6.50
Gutter pairs	20.00	–
First day cover	–	7.00
Stamp cards	7.50	17.50

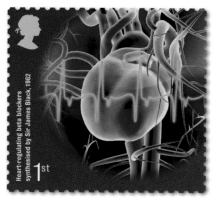

Heart-regulating beta-blockers, 1962 (1st)
Discovery of antibiotic properties of penicillin, 1928 (58p)
Total hip replacement, 1962 (60p)
Artificial lens implant surgery, 1949 (67p)
Proof of malaria transmission by mosquitoes, 1897 (88p)
Computed tomography scanning, 1971 (97p)

■ 2010, September 16. Medical Breakthroughs
Des: Howard Brown. Printed in litho by Cartor.

Set	6.50	6.50
Gutter pairs	20.00	–
First day cover	–	9.00
Stamp cards	4.00	17.50

(*The Beta-Blockers design also appears, in self-adhesive form, in booklets; price £2.00 mint or used.)

Winnie-the-Pooh, Piglet and Christopher Robin (1st)
Winnie-the-Pooh and Piglet (58p)
Winnie-the-Pooh and Rabbit (60p)
Winnie-the-Pooh and Eeyore (67p)
Winnie-the-Pooh and Friends (88p)
Winnie-the-Pooh and Tigger (97p)

■ 2010, October 12. Winnie-the-Pooh (Europa)
Des: Magpie Studio, from the illustrations of E. H. Shepard. Printed in litho by Cartor.

Set	6.50	6.50
Gutter pairs	20.00	–
First day cover	–	9.00
Stamp cards	9.00	36.00

Winnie-the-Pooh and Christopher Robin (1st)
Christopher Robin reads to Winnie-the-Pooh (60p)
Winnie-the-Pooh and Christopher Robin set sail (88p)
Christopher Robin pulls on his wellingtons (97p)

■ 2010, October 12. Winnie-the-Pooh
Des: Magpie Studio, from the illustrations of E. H. Shepard. Printed in litho by Cartor.

Miniature sheet	5.00	5.00
First day cover	–	7.00

Wallace and Gromit singing carols (2nd, 2nd Large)
Gromit posting Christmas cards (1st, 1st Large)
Wallace and Gromit decorating a Christmas tree (60p)
Gromit carrying a Christmas pudding (97p)
Gromit wearing a sweater (£1.46)

■ 2010, November 2. Christmas. Wallace and Gromit

Des: Aardman Animations and Nick Park. Printed in gravure by De La Rue. Counter stamps self–adhesive; miniature sheet gummed.

Set	8.50	8.50
Gutter pairs	22.00	–
First day cover	–	10.00
Miniature sheet (one of each design)	8.50	8.50
Miniature sheet first day cover	–	10.00
Stamp cards	13.00	30.00

(*The 2nd and 1st class designs also appear in booklets. The 2nd, 1st, 60p and 97p designs were used in Smilers sheets.)

'Joe 90' (1st)
'Captain Scarlet' (1st)
'Thunderbirds' (1st)
'Stingray' (97p)
'Fireball XL5' (97p)
'Supercar' (97p)

■ 2011, January 11. FAB. The Genius of Gerry Anderson

Des: GBH. Printed in litho by Cartor. Issued in se–tenant strips for each denomination.

Set (se–tenant strips of three)	7.00	7.00
Gutter pairs	17.00	–
First day cover	–	9.00
Stamp cards	11.00	35.00

(*The Thunderbirds design also appears, in self–adhesive form, in a booklet: price £1.75 mint or used.)

Thunderbird 4 (41p)
Thunderbird 3 (60p)
Thunderbird 2 (88p)
Thunderbird 1 (97p)

■ 2011, January 11. Thunderbirds

Des: GBH. Printed with microlenticular technology by Cartor and Outer Aspect, New Zealand.

Miniature sheet	5.50	6.00
First day cover	–	6.50

BR Dean Goods (1st)
Peckett R2 Thor (60p)
Lancashire and Yorkshire Railway 1093 (88p)
BR WD (97p)

■ 2011, February 1. Classic Locomotives of England

Des: Delaney Design Consultants. Printed in litho by Cartor.

Miniature sheet	5.00	5.00
First day cover	–	6.00
Stamp cards	4.00	22.00

(*The 1st class design also appears, in self–adhesive form, in booklets; price £2 mint.)

'Oliver' (1st)
'Blood Brothers' (1st)
'We Will Rock You' (1st)
'Spamalot' (1st)
'Rocky Horror Show' (97p)
'Me and My Girl' (97p)
'Return to the Forbidden Planet' (97p)
'Billy Elliot' (97p)

■ 2011, February 24. Musicals
Des: Webb and Webb. Printed in litho by Cartor.

Set	8.50	8.50
Gutter pairs	20.00	–
Traffic light gutter pairs	27.50	–
First day cover	–	10.00
Stamp cards	6.00	22.00

Rincewind from Terry Pratchett's Discworld series (1st)
Nanny Ogg from Terry Pratchett's Discworld series (1st)
Dumbledore from J. K. Rowling's Harry Potter series (1st)
Lord Voldemort from J. K. Rowling's Harry Potter series (1st)
Merlin from Arthurian legend (60p)
Morgan Le Fay from Arthurian legend (60p)
Aslan from C. S. Lewis's Narnia series (97p)
White Witch from C. S. Lewis's Narnia series (97p)

■ 2011, March 8. Magical Realms
Des: So Design Consultants. Printed in gravure by De La Rue.
Issued in vertical se-tenant pairs.

Set	7.50	7.50
Gutter pairs	18.00	–
First day cover	–	10.00
Stamp cards	6.00	20.00

African elephant (1st)
Mountain gorilla (1st)
Siberian tiger (1st)
Polar bear (1st)
Amur leopard (1st)
Iberian lynx (1st)
Red panda (1st)
Black rhinoceros (1st)
African wild dog (1st)
Golden lion tamarin (1st)

■ 2011, March 22. 50th Anniversary of WWF
Des: Rose Design Consultants. Printed in litho by Cartor. Issued in se-tenant strips of five, in two different sheets.

Set	9.00	9.00
Gutter pairs	23.00	–
First day cover	–	10.00
Stamp cards	9.00	35.00

(*All designs also appear in the WWF prestige stamp book.)

Spider monkey in Amazon rainforest (1st)
Hyacinth macaw in Amazon rainforest (60p)
Poison dart frog in Amazon rainforest (88p)
Jaguar in Amazon rainforest (97p)

■ 2011, March 22. Amazon Alive (Europa)
Des: Janice Nicholson and Rose Design Consultants. Printed in litho by Cartor.

Miniature sheet	5.00	5.00
First day cover	–	6.00

(*The whole sheet also appears in the WWF prestige stamp book.)

'Hamlet' (1st)
'The Tempest' (66p)
'Henry VI' (68p)
'King Lear' (76p)
'A Midsummer's Night Dream' (£1)
'Romeo and Juliet' (£1.10)

■ 2011, April 12. 50th Anniversary of the Royal Shakespeare Company
Des: Hat-Trick Design. Printed in gravure by Walsall.

Set	7.00	7.00
Gutter pairs	17.00	–
First day cover	–	8.50
Stamp cards	7.50	33.00

Royal Shakespeare Theatre, Stratford–upon–Avon (1st)
Swan Theatre, Stratford–upon–Avon (68p)
The Courtyard Theatre, Stratford–upon–Avon (76p)
The Other Place, Stratford–upon–Avon (£1)

■ 2011, April 12. 50th Anniversary of the Royal Shakespeare Company

Des: Hat-Trick. Printed in litho by Cartor.

Miniature sheet	5.00	5.00
First day cover	–	6.00

Prince William and Catherine Middleton, informal (1st, 1st)
Prince William and Catherine Middleton, formal (£1.10, £1.10)

■ 2011, April 21. Royal Wedding of Prince William and Catherine Middleton

Des: Atelier Works, from portraits by Mario Testino. Printed in gravure by Walsall.

Miniature sheet	6.00	6.00
First day cover	–	7.50

'Cray' by William Morris, 1884 (1st)
'Cherries' by Philip Webb, 1867 (1st)
'Seaweed' by John Henry Dearle, 1901 (76p)
'Peony' by Kate Faulkner, 1877 (76p)
'Acanthus' by William Morris and William de Morgan, 1876 (£1.10)
'The Merchant's Daughter' by Edward Burne–Jones, c1864 (£1.10)

■ 2011, May 5. Morris and Co

Des: Kate Stevens. Printed in litho by Cartor.

Set	7.00	7.00
Gutter pairs	17.00	–
First day cover	–	8.50
Stamp cards	5.00	17.50

(*All values also appear in the Morris & Co prestige stamp book.)

Thomas (1st)
James (66p)
Percy (68p)
Daisy (76p)
Toby (£1)
Gordon (£1.10)

■ 2011, June 14. Thomas the Tank Engine

Des: Elmwood, from television stills. Printed in litho by Cartor.

Set	7.50	7.50
Gutter pairs	18.00	–
First day cover	–	8.50
Stamp cards	7.50	35.00

Thomas racing Bertie the Bus (1st)
James has a crash (68p)
Percy ends up in the sea (76p)
Henry walled up in a tunnel (£1)

■ 2011, June 14. Thomas the Tank Engine

Des: Elmwood, from book illustrations by Reginald Dalby and John Kenney. Printed in litho by Cartor.

Miniature sheet	4.50	5.00
First day cover	–	6.00

(*The 1st class design also appears, in self–adhesive form, in booklets; price £2.50 mint.)

Paralympic sailing (1st)
Field athletics (1st)
Volleyball (1st)
Wheelchair rugby (1st)
Wrestling (1st)
Wheelchair tennis (1st)
Fencing (1st)
Gymnastics (1st)
Triathlon (1st)
Handball (1st)

■ **2011, July 27. London 2012 Olympic and Paralympic Games (issue 3)**
Des: Lara Harwood (Sailing), Anthony Pike (Field), Ben Dalling (Volleyball), Matthew Hollings (Wheelchair rugby), Daniel Stolle (Wrestling), David McConochie (Wheelchair tennis), Lyndon Hayes (Fencing), Kathy Wyatt (Gymnastics), Adam Simpson (Triathlon), David Cutter (Handball), Studio David Hillman (set). Printed in litho by Cartor. Issued in se–tenant strips of five in two different sheets.

Set (se–tenant strips of five)	10.00	10.00
Gutter pairs	25.00	–
First day cover	–	11.00
Postcard and stamp set (Sailing)	9.00	–
Postcard and stamp set (Gymnastics)	9.00	–
Composite sheet (entire series of 30)	36.00	–
Stamp cards	7.00	23.00

(*The composite sheet comprises one of each design in the Olympic and Paralympic Games series. The Wheelchair rugby, Paralympic sailing, Gymnastics and Fencing designs also appear, in self–adhesive form, in booklets; price £2.50 each, mint. All values also appear in a commemorative sheet.)

Sovereign's Sceptre with Cross (1st)
St. Edward's Crown (1st)
Rod and Sceptre with Doves (68p)
Queen Mary's Crown (68p)
The Sovereign's Orb (76p)
Jewelled Sword of Offering (76p)
Imperial State Crown (£1.10)
Coronation Spoon (£1.10)

■ **2011, August 23. The Crown Jewels**
Des: Purpose. Printed in litho by Cartor.

Set	9.00	9.50
Gutter pairs	23.00	–
First day cover	–	11.00
Stamp cards	6.00	25.00

Gustav Hamel receives first mailbag (1st)
Hamel ready to leave Hendon (68p)
Greswell's Blériot at Windsor (£1)
Airmail delivered at Windsor (£1.10)

■ **2011, September 9. Centenary of the First UK Aerial Post**
Des: Robert Maude and Sarah Davies, from photography by Geoff Dann. Printed in litho by Cartor.

Miniature sheet	5.50	6.00
Miniature sheet first day cover	–	6.50
Press sheet	£100	–
Stamp cards	4.75	20.00

(*The £1 and £1.10 designs also appear in the First UK Aerial Post prestige stamp book.)

King George I, 1714–27 (1st)
King George II, 1727–60 (1st)
King George III, 1760–1820 (76p)
King George IV, 1820–30 (76p)
King William IV, 1830–37 (£1.10)
Queen Victoria, 1837–1901 (£1.10)

■ **2011, September 15. Kings and Queens. The House of Hanover**
Des: Ian Chilvers, Atelier Works. Printed in litho by Cartor.

Set	7.00	8.50
Gutter pairs	17.00	–
Traffic light gutter pairs	55.00	–
First day cover	–	9.00
Stamp cards	7.50	35.00

Robert Walpole, first Prime Minister, 1721 (1st)
Ceiling of Kedleston Hall by Robert Adam, 1763 (68p)
Penny Black and Uniform Penny Postage, 1840 (76p)
Queen Victoria's Diamond Jubilee, 1897 (£1)

■ 2011, September 15. The Age of the Hanoverians
Des: Ian Chilvers, Atelier Works. Printed in litho by Cartor.

Miniature sheet	5.00	5.00
First day cover	–	6.00
Press sheet	90.00	–

Angel of the North (1st)
Blackpool Tower (1st)
Carrick-a-Rede (1st)
Downing Street, London (1st)
Edinburgh Castle (1st)
Forth Railway Bridge (1st)
Glastonbury Tor (1st)
Harlech Castle (1st)
Ironbridge (1st)
Jodrell Bank (1st)
Kursaal, Southend (1st)
Lindisfarne Priory (1st)

■ 2011, October 13. UK A–Z (issue 1)
Des: Robert Maude and Sarah Davies. Printed in litho by Cartor.
Issued in se-tenant strips of six in two different sheets.

Set (se-tenant strips of six)	11.00	11.00
Gutter pairs	27.00	–
Traffic light gutter pairs	50.00	–
First day cover	–	1200
Stamp cards	9.00	27.00

The angel visits Joseph, from Matthew 1:21 (2nd, 2nd Large)
Madonna and child, from Matthew 1:23 (1st, 1st Large)
Jesus in the manger, from Luke 2:7 (68p)
The angel visits the shepherds, from Luke 2:10 (£1.10)
The wise men and the star, from Matthew 2:10 (£1.65)

■ 2011, November 8. Christmas. 400th Anniversary of the King James Bible
Des: Peter Malone, The Artworks and Together Design. Printed in gravure by De La Rue. Counter stamps self-adhesive; miniature sheet gummed.

Set	9.00	9.00
First day cover	–	11.00
Miniature sheet (one of each design)	9.00	9.00
Miniature sheet first day cover	–	10.50
Stamp cards	6.25	32.00

(*The 2nd, 1st and 1st class also appear in booklets. The 2nd, 1st, 68p, £1.10 and £1.50 were used in Smilers generic sheets, and the 2nd, 1st, 68p and £1.10 in customised Smilers sheets.)

Olympic Games logo (1st, Worldwide up to 20g)
Paralympic Games logo (1st, Worldwide up to 20g)

■ 2012, January 5. Olympic and Paralympic Games definitives
Des: Studio Dempsey. Printed in gravure by De La Rue. Self-adhesive. The two designs for each value are arranged in a checkerboard fashion in sheets, with the order alternating.

Set	15.00	15.00
Gutter pairs (1st class)	40.00	–
First day cover	–	15.00
Stamp cards	10.00	22.00

(*The 1st class values also appear in booklets, printed by Walsall.)

'Charlie and The Chocolate Factory' (1st)
'Fantastic Mr Fox' (66p)
'James and The Giant Peach' (68p)
'Matilda' (76p)
'The Twits' (£1)
'The Witches' (£1.10)

■ 2012, January 10. Roald Dahl
Des: Magpie Studios. Printed in litho by Cartor.

Set	7.00	7.25
Gutter pairs	17.00	–
Traffic light gutter pairs	32.50	–
First day cover	–	9.50
Stamp cards	8.00	33.00

(*All values also appear in the Roald Dahl prestige stamp book.)

The BFG carrying Sophie (1st)
The BFG and the giants (68p)
Sophie sitting on the Queen's window-sill (76p)
The BFG and Sophie at the writing desk (£1)

■ 2012, January 10. Roald Dahl's The BFG
Des: Magpie Studios. Printed in litho by Cartor.

Miniature sheet	10.00	10.00
Miniature sheet first day cover	–	8.00

(*All values also appear in the Roald Dahl prestige stamp book.)

King Edward VII, 1901–10 (1st)
King George V, 1910–36 (68p)
King Edward VIII, 1936 (76p)
King George VI, 1936–52 (£1)
Queen Elizabeth II, 1952– (£1.10)

■ 2012, February 2. Kings and Queens. The House of Windsor
Des: Ian Chilvers, Atelier Works. Printed in litho by Cartor.

Set	7.00	7.00
Gutter pairs	17.00	–
Traffic light gutter pairs	27.00	–
First day cover	–	7.50
Stamp cards	8.00	32.00

Scott Expedition to the South Pole, 1912 (1st)
Bomb damage in World War I, 1939–45 (68p)
England World Cup winning team, 1966 (76p)
Channel Tunnel opened, 1994 (£1)

■ 2012, February 2. The Age of the Windsors and Saxe–Coburg–Gotha
Des: Ian Chilvers, Atelier Works. Printed in litho by Cartor.

Miniature sheet	5.00	5.00
First day cover	–	6.00
Press sheet	90.00	–

Dorothy Wilding stamp portrait, 1953 (1st)
Robert Austin banknote portrait., 1960 (1st)
Harry Eccleston banknote portrait, 1971 (1st)
Mary Gillick coinage portrait, 1953 (1st)
Arnold Machin coinage portrait, 1968 (1st)
Arnold Machin stamp portrait, 1967 (1st)

■ 2012, February 6. Diamond Jubilee
Printed in gravure by Walsall. The Arnold Machin stamp portrait design has overlay text reading 'Diamond Jubilee' and source code 'MMND'.

Miniature sheet	6.00	6.00
First day cover	–	6.50
Press sheet	60.00	–
Stamp cards	5.00	20.00

(*The Arnold Machin Stamp Portrait design also appears, in self-adhesive form, in counter sheets, business sheets and booklets. The Dorothy Wilding and Arnold Machin Stamp Portrait designs also appear in the Diamond Jubilee prestige stamp book.)

Frederick Delius 1862–1934
Opera, choral and orchestral composer

Coventry Cathedral by Sir Basil Spence (1st)
Frederick Delius, composer (1st)
'Orange Tree' embroidery by Mary 'May' Morris (1st)
Odette Hallowes, wartime secret agent (1st)
Atmospheric steam engine by Thomas Newcomen (1st)
Kathleen Ferrier, opera singer (1st)
Interior of Palace of Westminster by Augustus Pugin (1st)
Montague Rhodes James, author (1st)
Bombe code–breaking machine by Alan Turing (1st)
Joan Mary Fry, social reformer (1st)

■ **2012, February 23. Britons of Distinction**
Des: Purpose. Printed in litho by Cartor. Issued in se–tenant strips of five in two separate sheets.

Set	9.50	9.50
Gutter pairs	23.00	–
First day cover	–	9.50
Stamp cards	8.00	22.00

(*The 1st class Bombe design also appears in the Inventive Britain prestige stamp book of February 19, 2015.)

BR Class D34 locomotive (1st)
BR Class D40 locomotive (68p)
Andrew Barclay No807 locomotive (£1)
BR Class 4P locomotive (£1.10)

■ **2012, March 8. Classic Locomotives of Scotland**
Des: Delaney Design Consultants. Printed in litho by Cartor.

Miniature sheet	5.00	5.50
Miniature sheet first day cover	–	6.50
Stamp cards	4.50	23.00

'The Dandy' and Desperate Dan (1st)
'The Beano' and Dennis the Menace (1st)
'Eagle' and Dan Dare(1st)
'The Topper' and Beryl the Peril (1st)
'Tiger' and Roy of the Rovers (1st)
'Bunty' and The Four Marys (1st)
'Buster' and Buster(1st)
'Valiant' and The Steel Claw (1st)
'Twinkle' and Nurse Nancy (1st)
'2000AD' and Judge Dredd (1st)

■ **2012, March 20. Comics**
Des: The Chase. Printed in litho by Cartor. Issued in se–tenant strips of five in two separate sheets.

Set	9.50	9.50
Gutter pairs	23.00	–
First day cover	–	16.00
Stamp cards	7.00	23.00

Manchester Town Hall

Manchester Town Hall (1st)
Narrow Water Castle (1st)
Old Bailey (1st)
Portmeirion (1st)
Queen's College, Oxford (1st)
Roman Baths (1st)
Stirling Castle (1st)
Tyne Bridge (1st)
Urquhart Castle (1st)
Victoria and Albert Museum (1st)
White Cliffs of Dover (1st)
Station X, Bletchley Park (1st)
York Minster (1st)
ZSL London Zoo (1st)

■ **2012, April 10. UK A–Z (issue 2) (Europa)**
Des: Robert Maude and Sarah Davies. Printed in litho by Cartor. Issued in se–tenant strips of six (M–R and S–X),and in se–tenant pairs (Y–Z), in three different sheets.

Set (se–tenant strips and pairs)	13.00	13.00
Gutter pairs	30.00	–
Traffic light gutter pairs	55.00	–
First day cover	–	16.00
Stamp cards	10.00	37.00
Composite sheet (entire series of 26)	£105	–

(*The 1st class Station X design also appears in the Inventive Britain prestige stamp book of February 19, 2015.)

Ladies' suit by Hardy Amies (1st)
Ladies' outfit by Norman Hartnell (1st)
Men's jacket by Granny Takes A Trip (1st)
Ladies' outfit by Ossie Clark (1st)
Men's suit by Tommy Nutter (1st)
Ladies' outfit by Jean Muir (1st)
Ladies' dress by Zandra Rhodes (1st)
Ladies' dress by Vivienne Westwood (1st)
Men's suit by Paul Smith (1st)
Ladies' dress by Alexander McQueen (1st)

■ **2012, May 15. Great British Fashion**
Des: Johnson Banks. Printed in litho by Cartor. Printed in se-tenant strips of five in two separate sheets.

Set (se-tenant strips of five)	9.50	9.50
Gutter pairs	23.00	–
Traffic light gutter pairs	42.50	–
First day cover	–	12.50
Stamp cards	9.00	24.00

The Queen during her Golden Jubilee, 2002 (1st)
The Queen at the Trooping of the Colour, 1967 (1st)
The Queen inspecting troops of the Royal Welsh, 2007 (77p)
The Queen making her first Christmas TV broadcast, 1957 (77p)
The Queen on a Silver Jubilee Walkabout, 1977 (87p)
The Queen at the Order of the Garter Ceremony, 1997 (87p)
The Queen addressing the United Nations, 1957 (£1.28)
The Queen at the Commonwealth Games, 1982 (£1.28)

■ **2012, May 31. Diamond Jubilee**
Des: Kate Stephens. Printed in litho by Cartor. Issued in se-tenant pairs of each denomination.

Set	11.00	11.00
Gutter pairs	27.00	–

Traffic light gutter pairs	32.00	–
First day cover	–	15.00
Stamp cards	5.00	23.00

(*All values also appear in the Diamond Jubilee prestige stamp book. The Golden Jubilee design also appears, in self-adhesive form, in a booklet; price £2.25 mint or used.)

Mr Bumble from 'Oliver Twist' (2nd)
Mr Pickwick from 'The Pickwick Papers' (1st)
The Marchioness from 'The Old Curiosity Shop' (77p)
Mrs Gamp from 'Martin Chuzzlewit' (87p)
Captain Cuttle from 'Dombey & Son' (£1.28)
Mr Micawber from 'David Copperfield' (£1.90)

■ **2012, June 19. Bicentenary of the Birth of Charles Dickens**
Des: Howard Brown, from illustrations by 'Kyd' (Joseph Clayton Clarke). Printed in litho by Cartor.

Set	9.00	9.00
Gutter pairs	23.00	–
Traffic light gutter pairs	40.00	–
First day cover	–	12.00
Stamp cards	8.00	40.00

Scene from 'Nicholas Nickleby' (1st)
Scene from 'Bleak House' (1st)
Scene from 'Little Dorrit' (1st)
Scene from 'A Tale of Two Cities' (1st)

■ **2012, June 19. Bicentenary of the Birth of Charles Dickens**
Des: Howard Brown, from illustrations by 'Phiz' (Hablot Knight Brown). Printed in litho by Cartor.

Miniature sheet	4.50	4.50
Miniature sheet first day cover	–	5.00

Miniature sheet (1st, 1st, 1st, 1st, 1st, 1st): 29 different sheet designs

■ **2012, July 27–August 12. London 2012 Olympic Games Gold Medal Winners**
Des: True North. Base design printed in litho by Walsall (at Cartor), with photographic image and event-specific inscriptions added in litho by regional printers Acorn Press (Swindon), Allander Print (Edinburgh), Aquatint BSC (London), B&D (Preston), Breckland (Attleborough) and Crescent (Solihull). Self-adhesive miniature sheets comprising six 1st class stamps, issued the day after each gold medal win and initially available from 518 selected post offices.

	Mint	Used	FDC
Miniature sheet Rowing, women's pairs: Heather Stanning, Helen Glover (Aug 2)	7.00	7.00	10.00
Miniature sheet Cycling, men's time trial: Bradley Wiggins (Aug 2)	7.00	7.00	10.00
Miniature sheet Canoeing, men's double slalom: Etienne Stott, Tim Baillie (Aug 3)	7.00	7.00	10.00
Miniature sheet Shooting, men's double trap: Peter Wilson (Aug 3)	7.00	7.00	10.00
Miniature sheet Cycling, men's team sprint: Philip Hindes, Chris Hoy, Jason Kenny (Aug 3)	7.00	7.00	10.00
Miniature sheet Rowing, women's double sculls: Anna Watkins, Katherine Grainger (Aug 4)	7.00	7.00	10.00
Miniature sheet Cycling, men's pursuit: Ed Clancy, Geraint Thomas, Steven Burke, Peter Kennaugh (Aug 4)	7.00	7.00	10.00
Miniature sheet Cycling, women's keirin: Victoria Pendleton (Aug 4)	7.00	7.00	10.00
Miniature sheet Rowing, men's four: Alex Gregory, Tom James, Pete Reed, Andrew Triggs-Hodge (Aug 5)	7.00	7.00	10.00
Miniature sheet Rowing, women's lightweight double sculls: Kat Copeland, Sophie Hosking (Aug 5)	7.00	7.00	10.00
Miniature sheet Cycling, women's team pursuit: Danielle King, Joanna Rowsell, Laura Trott (Aug 5)	7.00	7.00	10.00
Miniature sheet Athletics, women's heptathlon: Jessica Ennis (Aug 5)	7.00	7.00	10.00
Miniature sheet Athletics, men's long jump: Greg Rutherford (Aug 5)	7.00	7.00	10.00
Miniature sheet Athletics, men's 10,000 metres: Mo Farah (Aug 5)	7.00	7.00	10.00
Miniature sheet Sailing, finn class: Ben Ainslie (Aug 6)	7.00	7.00	10.00
Miniature sheet Tennis, men's singles: Andy Murray (Aug 6)	7.00	7.00	10.00
Miniature sheet Equestrian, team show-jumping: Scott Brash, Peter Charles, Ben Maher, Nick Skelton (Aug 7)	7.00	7.00	10.00
Miniature sheet Cycling, men's sprint: Jason Kenny (Aug 7)	7.00	7.00	10.00
Miniature sheet Athletics, men's triathlon: Alistair Brownlee (Aug 8)	7.00	7.00	10.00
Miniature sheet Equestrian, team dressage: Laura Bechtolsheimer, Charlotte Dujardin, Carl Hester (Aug 8)	7.00	7.00	10.00
Miniature sheet Cycling, women's omnium: Laura Trott (Aug 8)	7.00	7.00	10.00
Miniature sheet Cycling, men's keirin: Chris Hoy (Aug 8)	7.00	7.00	10.00
Miniature sheet Equestrian, individual dressage: Charlotte Dujardin (Aug 10)	7.00	7.00	10.00
Miniature sheet Boxing, women's flyweight: Nicola Adams (Aug 10)	7.00	7.00	10.00
Miniature sheet Taekwando, women's under 57kg: Jade Jones (Aug 10)	7.00	7.00	10.00
Miniature sheet Kayaking, men's K1 sprint: Ed McKeever (Aug 12)	7.00	7.00	10.00
Miniature sheet Athletics, men's 5,000 metres: Mo Farah (Aug 12)	7.00	7.00	10.00
Miniature sheet Boxing, men's bantamweight: Luke Campbell (Aug 12)	7.00	7.00	10.00
Miniature sheet Boxing, men's super heavyweight: Anthony Joshua (Aug 13)	7.00	7.00	10.00

Miniature sheet (1st, 1st,): 34 different sheet designs

■ **2012, August 31–September 10. London 2012 Paralympic Games Gold Medal Winners**
Des: True North. Base design printed in litho by Walsall (at Cartor), with photographic image and event-specific inscriptions added in litho by regional printers Acorn Press (Swindon), Allander Print (Edinburgh), Aquatint BSC (London), B&D (Preston), Breckland (Attleborough) and Crescent (Solihull). Self-adhesive miniature sheets comprising two 1st class stamps, issued within four days of each gold medal win and initially available from 518 selected post offices.

	Mint	Used	FDC
Miniature sheet Cycling, women's C5 pursuit: Sarah Storey (Aug 31)	2.75	3.00	4.50
Miniature sheet Swimming, men's S7 100m backstroke: Jonathan Fox (Sep 1)	2.75	3.00	4.50
Miniature sheet Cycling, men's C1 pursuit: Mark Colbourne (Sep 3)	2.75	3.00	4.50
Miniature sheet Athletics, women's T34 100m: Hannah Cockcroft (Sep 3)	2.75	3.00	4.50
Miniature sheet Cycling, men's 1km time trial B: Neil Fachie, Barney Storey (Sep 3)	2.75	3.00	4.50
Miniature sheet Athletics, men's T42 200m: Richard Whitehead (Sep 3)	2.75	3.00	4.50
Miniature sheet Equestrian, individual championship test, grade II: Natasha Baker (Sep 3)	2.75	3.00	4.50
Miniature sheet Cycling, women's 500m time trial C4–5: Sarah Storey (Sep 3)	2.75	3.00	4.50
Miniature sheet Swimming, women's 400m freestyle S6: Ellie Simmonds (Sep 3)	2.75	3.00	4.50
Miniature sheet Rowing, coxed four: Pam Relph, Naomi Riches, David Smith, James Roe, Lily Broecke (Sep 4)	2.75	3.00	4.50
Miniature sheet Athletics, men's F42 discus: Aled Davies (Sep 4)	2.75	3.00	4.50
Miniature sheet Cycling, men's individual sprint B: Anthony Kappes, Craig MacLean (Sep 4)	2.75	3.00	4.50
Miniature sheet Swimming, women's S14 200m freestyle: Jessica-Jane Applegate (Sep 4)	2.75	3.00	4.50
Miniature sheet Equestrian, individual championship test grade Ia: Sophie Christiansen (Sep 4)	2.75	3.00	4.50
Miniature sheet Athletics, men's 5000m T54: David Weir (Sep 4)	2.75	3.00	4.50
Miniature sheet Equestrian, individual freestyle test grade II: Natasha Baker (Sep 4)	2.75	3.00	4.50
Miniature sheet Swimming, women's 200m individual medley SM6: Ellie Simmonds (Sep 4)	2.75	3.00	4.50
Miniature sheet Athletics, men's 100m T53: Mickey Bushell (Sep 5)	2.75	3.00	4.50
Miniature sheet Archery, women's individual compound open: Danielle Brown (Sep 5)	2.75	3.00	4.50
Miniature sheet Swimming, women's 100m backstroke S8: Heather Frederiksen (Sep 5)	2.75	3.00	4.50
Miniature sheet Equestrian, individual freestyle test grade Ia: Sophie Christiansen (Sep 5)	2.75	3.00	4.50
Miniature sheet Athletics, men's T54 1500m: David Weir (Sep 7)	2.75	3.00	4.50
Miniature sheet Cycling, women's time trial C5: Sarah Storey (Sep 7)	2.75	3.00	4.50
Miniature sheet Swimming, men's 200m individual medley SM8: Oliver Hynd (Sep 7)	2.75	3.00	4.50
Miniature sheet Equestrian, team: Sophie Christiansen, Deborah Criddle, Lee Pearson, Sophie Wells (Sep 7)	2.75	3.00	4.50
Miniature sheet Sailing, 2.4mR single-person keelboat: Helena Lucas (Sep 8)	2.75	3.00	4.50
Miniature sheet Cycling, women's C4–5 road race: Sarah Storey (Sep 8)	2.75	3.00	4.50
Miniature sheet Swimming, men's S7 400m freestyle: Josef Craig (Sep 8)	2.75	3.00	4.50
Miniature sheet Athletics, women's T34 200m: Hannah Cockcroft (Sep 8)	2.75	3.00	4.50
Miniature sheet Athletics, men's 800m T54: David Weir (Sep 10)	2.75	3.00	4.50
Miniature sheet Athletics, men's 100m T44: Jonnie Peacock (Sep 10)	2.75	3.00	4.50
Miniature sheet Athletics, women's discus F51/52/53: Josie Pearson (Sep 10)	2.75	3.00	4.50
Miniature sheet Cycling, mixed road race T1–2: David Stone (Sep 10)	2.75	3.00	4.50
Miniature sheet Athletics, men's marathon T54: David Weir (Sep 10)	2.75	3.00	4.50

Fencer and Tower Bridge (1st)
Track athletes and Olympic Stadium (1st)
Diver and Tate Modern (£1.28)
Track cyclist and London Eye (£1.28)

■ **2012, July 27. Welcome to the London 2012 Olympic Games**
Des: Hat–Trick. Printed in litho by Cartor.

Miniature sheet	6.00	6.00
Miniature sheet first day cover	–	11.00
Stamp cards	8.50	25.00

Amputee athlete and Olympic Stadium (1st)
Wheelchair basketball player and Houses of Parliament (1st)
Weightlifter and St. Paul's Cathedral (£1.28)
Cyclist and London Eye (£1.28)

■ **2012, August 29. Welcome to the London 2012 Paralympic Games**
Des: Hat–Trick. Printed in litho by Cartor.

Miniature sheet	6.00	6.00
Miniature sheet first day cover	–	11.00
Stamp cards	8.50	25.00

Paralympic Games: ParalympicsGB team (1st)
Olympic Games: games makers (1st)
Paralympic Games: opening ceremony (£1.28)
Olympic Games: closing ceremony (£1.28)

■ **2012, September 27. Memories of London 2012**
Des: The Chase. Printed in litho by Walsall (at Cartor).

Miniature sheet	10.00	10.00
Miniature sheet first day cover	–	14.00
Stamp cards	12.00	25.00

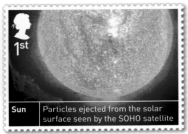

Sun	Particles ejected from the solar surface seen by the SOHO satellite

Sun (1st)
Venus (1st)
Mars (77p)
Lutetia (77p)
Saturn (£1.28)
Titan (£1.28)

■ **2012, October 16. Space Science.**
Des: Osborne Ross Design. Printed in litho by Cartor.

Set	8.00	8.00
Gutter pairs	20.00	–
First day cover	–	11.00
Stamp cards	4.50	25.00

Poppies (1st)

■ **2012, October 23. Lest We Forget**
Des: Hat–Trick Design. Printed in gravure by Walsall. Design as the Poppies 1st class of January 26, 2010, but self–adhesive.

1st	1.75	1.75
Gutter pair	4.50	–

Reindeer (2nd, 2nd Large)
Father Christmas with robin (1st, 1st Large)
Snowman with penguin (87p)
Robin holding star (£1.28)
Christmas tree with cat and mouse (£1.90)

■ 2012, November 6. Christmas

Des: Brian Webb from illustrations by Axel Scheffler. Printed in gravure by De La Rue. Counter sheets self–adhesive; miniature sheet gummed.

Set	10.00	10.50
Gutter pairs	27.00	–
First day cover	–	13.00
Miniature sheet	10.00	10.50
Miniature sheet first day cover	–	13.00
Stamp cards	5.50	35.00

(*The 2nd class and 1st class values also appear in booklets, printed by Walsall. The 2nd class, 1st class, 87p and £1.28 were used in generic and customised Smilers sheets.)

Metropolitan Railway opens, 1863 (2nd)
Tunnelling beneath London, 1898 (2nd)
Commute from the suburbs, 1911 (1st)
Boston Manor station, 1934 (1st)
Classic rolling stock, 1938 (£1.28)
Canary Wharf station, 1999 (£1.28)

■ 2013, January 9. 150th Anniversary of the London Underground

Des: Hat–Trick. Printed in litho by Cartor.

Set	7.50	8.00
Gutter pairs	18.00	–
First day cover	–	10.00
Stamp cards	8.00	45.00

(*The 1st class Boston Manor design also appears, in self–adhesive form, in a booklet; price £2.00, mint or used.)

Posters: Golders Green; To Fresh Air; Summer Sales (1st)
Posters: For The Zoo; Power; The Seen (77p)
Posters: Every 90 Seconds; Thanks; Cut Travelling Time (87p)
Posters: Transport Collection; London Zoo; Tate Gallery (£1.28)

■ 2013, January 9. Art on the London Underground

Des: NB Studios. Printed in litho by Cartor.

Miniature sheet	5.75	6.00
Miniature sheet first day cover	–	7.00

'Pride & Prejudice' (1st)
'Sense & Sensibility' (1st)
'Mansfield Park' (77p)
'Emma' (77p)
'Northanger Abbey' (£1.28)
'Persuasion' (£1.28)

■ 2013, February 21. Jane Austen

Des: Angela Barrett. Printed in litho by Cartor.

Set	8.00	8.50
Gutter pairs	20.00	–
Traffic light gutter pairs	35.00	–
First day cover	–	11.00
Stamp cards	4.50	18.00

The 11th Doctor, played by Matt Smith (1st)
The 10th Doctor, played by David Tennant (1st)
The 9th Doctor, played by Christopher Eccleston (1st)
The 8th Doctor, played by Paul McGann (1st)
The 7th Doctor, played by Sylvester McCoy (1st)
The 6th Doctor, played by Colin Baker (1st)
The 5th Doctor, played by Peter Davison (1st)
The 4th Doctor, played by Tom Baker (1st)
The 3rd Doctor, played by Jon Pertwee (1st)
The 2nd Doctor, played by Patrick Troughton (1st)
The 1st Doctor, played by William Hartnell (1st)

■ 2013, March 26. 50 Years of Doctor Who

Des: GBH. Printed in litho by Cartor. Issued in se–tenant strips of three, four and four in three separate sheets.

Set	10.00	10.00
Gutter pairs	24.00	–
First day covers (set of two)	–	13.00
Stamp cards	20.00	50.00

(*All designs also appear in the 50 Years of Doctor Who prestige stamp book. The Matt Smith and William Hartnell designs also appear, in self–adhesive form, in a booklet; price £6 each, mint or used.)

The Ood (2nd)
Cyberman (2nd)
Weeping Angel (2nd)
Dalek (2nd)
Tardis (1st)

■ 2013, March 26. 50 Years of Doctor Who
Des: GBH. Printed in litho by Cartor. Self-adhesive.

Miniature sheet	9.00	9.00
Miniature sheet first day cover	–	6.00

(*The 1st class design also appears in a booklet and in Smilers sheets. It also appears, in gummed form, in the 50 Years of Doctor Who prestige stamp book; price £2 mint.)

Norman Parkinson (1st)
Vivien Leigh (1st)
Peter Cushing (1st)
David Lloyd George (1st)
Elizabeth David (1st)
John Archer (1st)
Benjamin Britten (1st)
Mary Leakey (1st)
Bill Shankly (1st)
Richard Dimbleby (1st)

■ 2013, April 16. Great Britons
Des: Together Design. Printed in litho by Cartor. Issued in se-tenant strips of five in two separate sheets.

Set (se-tenant strips of five)	9.00	9.00
Gutter pairs	23.00	–
First day cover	–	12.00
Stamp cards	8.00	25.00

Jimmy Greaves (1st)
John Charles (1st)
Gordon Banks (1st)
George Best (1st)
John Barnes (1st)
Kevin Keegan (1st)
Denis Law (1st)
Bobby Moore (1st)
Bryan Robson (1st)
Dave Mackay (1st)
Bobby Charlton (1st)

■ 2013, May 9. Football Heroes
Des: Andrew Kinsman. Printed in litho by Cartor. Issued in se-tenant strips of five and six, in two separate sheets.

Set	10.00	10.00
Gutter pairs	24.00	–
First day cover	–	12.00
Miniature sheet (all 11 designs)	11.00	11.00
Miniature sheet first day cover	–	13.00
Stamp cards	8.50	50.00

(*All designs also appear in the Football Heroes prestige book. The George Best, Bobby Moore, John Charles and Dave Mackay designs also appear, in self-adhesive form, in booklets; price £2.50 each, mint or used.)

Portrait of Queen Elizabeth II by Terence Cuneo, 1953 (2nd)
Portrait of Queen Elizabeth II by Nicola Philipps, 2013 (1st)
Portrait of Queen Elizabeth II by Andrew Festing, 1999 (78p)
Portrait of Queen Elizabeth II by Pietro Annigoni, 1955 (88p)
Portrait of Queen Elizabeth II by Sergei Pavlenko, 2000 (£1.28)
Portrait of Queen Elizabeth II by Richard Stone, 1992 (£1.88)

■ **2013, May 30. 60th Anniversary of the Coronation. Royal Portraits**

Des: Atelier Works. Printed in gravure by Walsall.

Set	9.00	9.00
Gutter pairs	23.00	–
Traffic light gutter pairs	37.50	–
First day cover	–	12.00
Stamp cards	5.00	20.00

UTA W No.103 (1st)
UTA SG3 No.35 (78p)
Peckett No.2 (88p)
CDRJC Class 5 No.4 (£1.28)

■ **2013, June 18. Classic Locomotives of Northern Ireland**

Des: Delaney Design Consultants. Printed in litho by Cartor.

Miniature sheet	6.00	6.00
Miniature sheet first day cover	–	7.50
Stamp cards	4.00	25.00

(*The 1st class design also appears, in self-adhesive form, in a booklet; price £1.50, mint or used.)

Comma (1st)
Orange-tip (1st)
Small copper (1st)
Chalkhill blue (1st)
Swallowtail (1st)
Purple emperor (1st)
Marsh fritillary (1st)
Brimstone (1st)
Red admiral (1st)
Marbled white (1st)

■ **2013, July 11. Butterflies**

Des: Marc & Anna. Printed in litho by Cartor. Issued in se-tenant strips of five in two separate sheets.

Set (in se-tenant strips of 5)	9.00	9.00
Gutter pairs	23.00	–
First day cover	–	12.00
Stamp cards	7.75	25.00

(*The Chalkhill Blue and Comma designs also appear, in self-adhesive form, in a booklet; price £2.50 each, mint or used.)

Andy Murray kissing the championship trophy (1st)
Andy Murray serving (1st)
Andy Murray returning with a backhand (£1.28)
Andy Murray holding the championship trophy (£1.28)

■ **2013. August 8. Andy Murray, Gentlemen's Singles Champion, Wimbledon 2013**

Des: Hat-Trick. Printed in litho by International Security Printers.

Miniature sheet	6.00	6.00
Miniature sheet first day cover	–	7.50

Jaguar E–Type, 1961 (1st)
Rolls–Royce Silver Shadow, 1965 (1st)
Aston Martin DB5, 1963 (1st)
MG MGB, 1962 (£1.28)
Morgan Plus 8, 1968 (£1.28)
Lotus Esprit, 1976 (£1.28)

■ **2013, August 13. British Auto Legends**

Des: Why Not Associates. Printed in litho by Cartor. Issued in se-tenant strips of three in two separate sheets.

Set	9.00	9.00
Gutter pairs	22.00	–
First day cover	–	11.00
Stamp cards	7.50	42.00

Morris Minor van operated by Royal Mail (1st)
Austin FX4 operated as a taxi (1st)
Ford Anglia 105E operated by the police (1st)
Land Rover Defender 110 operated by HM Coastguard (1st)

■ **2013, August 13. British Auto Legends: The Workhorses (Europa)**

Des: Robert Maude and Sarah Davies. Printed in litho by Cartor.

Miniature sheet	4.50	4.50
Miniature sheet first day cover	–	5.00
Press sheet	50.00	–

(*The Morris Minor design also appears, in self-adhesive form, in a booklet printed in gravure by Walsall; price £10 mint or used.)

East Indiaman 'Atlas', 1813 (1st)
Royal Mail ship 'Britannia', 1840 (1st)
Tea clipper 'Cutty Sark', 1870 (1st)
Cargo liner 'Clan Matheson', 1919 (£1.28)
Royal Mail ship 'Queen Elizabeth', 1940 (£1.28)
Bulk carrier 'Lord Hinton', 1986 (£1.28)

Polacanthus (1st)
Ichthyosaurus (1st)
Iguanodon (1st)
Ornithocheirus (1st)
Baryonyx (1st)
Dimorphodon (1st)
Hypsilophodon (1st)
Cetiosaurus (1st)
Megalosaurus (1st)
Plesiosaurus (1st)

■ 2013, September 19. The Merchant Navy
Des: Silk Pearce. Printed in litho by International Security Printers.

Set	9.00	9.00
Gutter pairs	22.00	–
First day cover	–	11.00
Stamp cards	7.50	30.00

(*All designs also appear in the Merchant Navy prestige stamp book, printed by Enschedé. The 1st class Britannia design also appears, in self-adhesive form, in a booklet printed in gravure by Walsall; price £10 mint or used.)

■ 2013, October 10. Dinosaurs
Des: John Sibbick and Why Not Associates. Printed in litho by International Security Printers. Self-adhesive. Issued in strips of five in two separate sheets.

Set	10.00	10.00
Gutter pairs	25.00	–
First day cover	–	12.00
Stamp cards	8.00	25.00

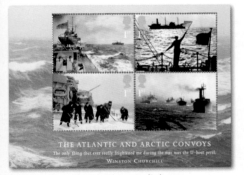

HMS 'Vanoc' escorting Atlantic convoy (1st)
Merchant ship in the Thames Estuary (1st)
Clearing ice on HMS 'King George V' in Arctic waters (1st)
Naval convoy in the North Sea (1st)

■ 2013, September 19. The Merchant Navy: The Atlantic and Arctic Convoys
Des: Silk Pearce. Printed in litho by Enschedé.

Miniature sheet	4.50	4.50
Miniature sheet first day cover	–	5.50

(*All designs also appear in the Merchant Navy prestige stamp book.)

'Virgin and Child with the Young St. John the Baptist', by Antoniazzo Romano (2nd, 2nd Large)
'Madonna and Child', by Francesco Granacci (1st, 1st Large)
'St. Roch Praying to the Virgin for an End to the Plague', by Jacques–Louis David (88p)
'The Virgin of the Lilies', by William–Adolphe Bouguereau (£1.28)
'Theotokos, Mother of God', by Fadi Mikhail (£1.88)

■ 2013, November 5. Christmas. Madonna and Child
Des: Robert Maude and Sarah Davies. Printed in gravure by De La Rue. Counter sheets self-adhesive; miniature sheet gummed.

Set	11.00	11.00
Gutter pairs	27.00	–
First day cover	–	13.00
Miniature sheet	11.00	11.00
Miniature sheet first day cover	–	12.50
Stamp cards	5.50	35.00

(*The 2nd class and 1st class designs also appear in booklets, printed by Walsall. The 2nd, 1st, 88p, £1.28 and £1.88 were used in Smilers sheets. The 2nd and 1st were reissued in 2014 and 2016.)

Three Singing Angels (2nd)
A Jolly Father Christmas (1st)

■ 2013, November 5. Children's Christmas

Des: Rosie Hargreaves, aged 10 (2nd), and Molly Robson, aged 7 (1st). Printed in gravure by International Security Printers. Self-adhesive.

Set	3.50	3.50
First day cover	–	5.50

Andy Pandy (1st)
Ivor the Engine (1st)
Dougal from The Magic Roundabout (1st)
Windy Miller from Camberwick Green (1st)
Mr Benn (1st)
Great Uncle Bulgaria from The Wombles (1st)
Bagpuss (1st)
Paddington Bear (1st)
Postman Pat (1st)
Bob the Builder (1st)
Peppa Pig (1st)
Shaun the Sheep (1st)

■ 2014, January 7. Classic Children's TV

Des: Interabang. Printed in gravure by International Security Printers. Self-adhesive. Issued in strips of six in two separate sheets.

Set	11.00	11.00
Gutter pairs	27.00	–
First day cover	–	14.00
Stamp cards	8.00	30.00

Riding for the Disabled Association (1st)
The King's Troop ceremonial horses (1st)
Dray horses (88p)
Royal Mews carriage horses (88p)
Police horses (£1.28)
Forestry horse (£1.28)

■ 2014, February 4. Working Horses

Des: Michael Denny and Harold Batten. Printed in litho by International Security Printers.

Set	8.50	8.50
Gutter pairs	21.00	–
First day cover	–	11.00
Stamp cards	5.50	18.00

LMS 2F No7720 (1st)
Hunslet No589 'Blanche' (78p)
W&LLR No822 'The Earl' (88p)
BR 5600 No5652 (£1.28)

■ 2014, February 20. Classic Locomotives of Wales

Des: Delaney Design Consultants. Printed in litho by International Security Printers.

Miniature sheet	6.00	6.50
Miniature sheet first day cover	–	7.00
Stamp cards	5.00	25.00

(*All values also appear in the Classic Locomotives of the UK prestige stamp book, printed by Enschedé. The 1st class design also appears, in self-adhesive form, in a booklet, printed in gravure by Walsall; price £2.50 mint or used.)

Dylan Thomas 1914–1953
Bardd ac awdur • Poet and writer

Roy Plomley (1st)
Barbara Ward (1st)
Joe Mercer (1st)
Kenneth More (1st)
Dylan Thomas (1st)
Sir Alec Guinness (1st)
Noorunissa Inayat Khan (1st)
Max Perutz (1st)
Joan Littlewood (1st)
Abram Games (1st)

■ 2014, March 25. Remarkable Lives
Des: Purpose. Printed in litho by International Security Printers.
Issued in se-tenant strips of five.

Set	9.00	9.00
Gutter pairs	23.00	–
First day cover	–	12.00
Stamp cards	8.00	25.00

Buckingham House, c1700 (1st)
Buckingham House, 1714 (1st)
Buckingham House, 1819 (1st)
Buckingham Palace, 1846 (1st)
Buckingham Palace, c1862 (1st)
Buckingham Palace, 2014 (1st)

■ 2014, April 15. Buckingham Palace
Des: Howard Brown. Printed in litho by International Security Printers. Issued in se-tenant strips of three.

Set	6.00	6.00
Gutter pairs	15.00	–
First day cover	–	7.50
Stamp cards	8.50	30.00

(*All designs also appear in the Buckingham Palace prestige stamp book.)

The Throne Room (1st)
The Grand Staircase (1st)
The Blue Drawing Room (1st)
The Green Drawing Room (1st)

■ 2014, April 15. Buckingham Palace
Des: Robert Maude and Sarah Davies. Printed in litho by Enschedé.

Miniature sheet	4.00	4.00
Miniature sheet first day cover	–	5.00

(*All designs also appear in the Buckingham Palace prestige stamp book. The Grand Staircase and Throne Room designs also appear, in self-adhesive form, in a booklet printed in gravure by Walsall; price £2.50 each mint or used.)

'A Matter of Life and Death' (1st)
'Lawrence of Arabia' (1st)
'2001: A Space Odyssey' (1st)
'Chariots of Fire' (£1.28)
'Secrets & Lies' (£1.28)
'Bend It Like Beckham' (£1.28)

■ 2014, May 13. Great British Film
Des: Johnson Banks. Printed in litho by International Security Printers. Issued in se-tenant strips of three.

Set	8.50	9.00
Gutter pairs	22.00	–
First day cover	–	11.00
Stamp cards	8.50	33.00

'Night Mail', 1936 (1st)
'Love on the Wing', 1938 (1st)
'The Colour Box', 1935 (1st)
'Spare Time', 1939 (1st)

■ **2014, May 13. The GPO Film Unit**
Des: Magpie Studio. Printed in litho by Enschedé.

Miniature sheet	5.00	5.00
Miniature sheet first day cover	–	5.50

Herring (1st)
Red gunard (1st)
Dab (1st)
Pouting (1st)
Cornish sardine (1st)
Common skate (1st)
Spiny dogfish (1st)
Wolffish (1st)
Sturgeon (1st)
Conger eel (1st)

■ **2014, June 5. Sustainable Fish**
Des: Kate Stephens. Printed in litho by International Security Printers. Issued in se–tenant strips of five.

Set	9.50	9.50
Gutter pairs	23.00	–
First day cover	–	12.00
Stamp cards	8.00	25.00

(*The Common Skate and Cornish Sardine designs also appear, in self–adhesive form, in a booklet, printed in gravure by Walsall; price £2.50 each mint or used.)

Judo (2nd)
Swimming (1st)
Marathon (97p)
Squash (£1.28)
Netball (£1.47)
Para–sport track cycling (£2.15)

■ **2014, July 17. Commonwealth Games, Glasgow**
Des: Howard Brown and Nanette Hoogslag. Printed in litho by International Security Printers.

Set	10.50	10.50
Gutter pairs	24.00	–
First day cover	–	13.50
Stamp cards	7.00	22.00

(*The Swimming design also appears, in self-adhesive form, in a booklet, printed in gravure by Walsall; price £2.50 mint or used.)

Poppy, by Fiona Strickland (1st)
'For The Fallen', by Laurence Binyon (1st)
Private William Cecil Tickle (1st)
'A Star Shell', by C. R. W. Nevinson (£1.47)
'The Response', by William Goscombe John (£1.47)
Princess Mary's Gift Fund Box (£1.47)

■ **2014, July 28. First World War, 1914**
Des: Hat–Trick. Printed in litho by International Security Printers.

Set	10.00	11.00
Gutter pairs	22.50	–
First day cover	–	12.00
Stamp cards	6.00	20.00

(*All designs also appear in the Great War 1914 prestige stamp book. The 1st class Poppy design also appears, in self–adhesive form, in a booklet issued in 2018.)

Tinside Lido, Plymouth

Harold Wilson

Eastbourne bandstand (1st)
Tinside Lido, Plymouth (1st)
Bangor Pier (97p)
Southwold Lighthouse (97p)
Blackpool Pleasure Beach (£1.28)
Bexhill–on–Sea shelter (£1.28)

■ **2014, September 18. Seaside Architecture (Europa)**
Des: Why Not Associates, after photography by Lee Mawdseley.
Printed in litho by International Security Printers.

Set	9.00	9.00
Gutter pairs	23.00	–
First day cover	–	11.00
Stamp cards	8.50	38.00

Margaret Thatcher (1st)
Harold Wilson (1st)
Clement Attlee (1st)
Winston Churchill (1st)
William Gladstone (1st)
Robert Peel (1st)
Charles Grey (1st)
William Pitt the Younger (1st)

■ **2014, October 14. Prime Ministers**
Des: Together. Printed in litho by International Security Printers.
Issued in se–tenant strips of four.

Set	9.50	10.00
Gutter pairs	23.00	–
First day cover	–	12.50
Stamp cards	6.50	22.00

BRITISH PIERS

Llandudno Pier (1st)
Worthing Pier (1st)
Dunoon Pier (£1.28)
Brighton Pier (£1.28)

■ **2014, September 18. Seaside Architecture. British Piers**
Des: Why Not Associates, after photography by Lee Mawdseley.
Printed in litho by Enschedé.

Miniature sheet	6.50	6.50
Miniature sheet first day cover	–	8.00

Taking home the Christmas tree (2nd, 2nd Large)
Posting cards into a pillar box (1st, 1st Large)
Decorating a snowman (£1.28)
Singing carols (£1.47)
Skating (£2.15)

■ **2014, November 4. Christmas**
Des: True North, after illustrations by Andrew Bannecker. Printed
in gravure by De La Rue. Counter sheets self–adhesive; miniature
sheet gummed.

Set	11.50	11.50
Gutter pairs	28.00	–
First day cover	–	15.00
Miniature sheet	11.50	11.50
Miniature sheet first day cover	–	15.00
Stamp cards	7.00	38.00

(*The 2nd class and 1st class values also appear in booklets,
printed by International Security Printers. The 2nd, 1st, £1.28 and
£1.47 designs were used in Smilers sheets.)

The White Rabbit (2nd)
Down the rabbit hole (2nd)
'Drink Me' (1st)
The White Rabbit's house (1st)
The Cheshire Cat (81p)
A mad tea party (81p)
The Queen of Hearts (£1.28)
The game of croquet (£1.28)
Alice's evidence (£1.47)
A pack of cards (£1.47)

2015, January 6. Alice in Wonderland
Des: Godfrey Design, after illustrations by Grahame Baker–Smith.
Printed in litho by International Security Printers. Issued in vertical
se–tenant pairs.

Set	18.00	21.00
Gutter pairs	45.00	–
First day cover	–	19.00
Stamp cards	7.50	30.00

(*The 1st class designs also appear, in self–adhesive form, in
booklets, printed in gravure by Walsall; price £6 each.)

Well done: '1st' (1st)
Mum: 'Mum Mummy Mother' (1st)
New baby: baby with envelope as nappy (1st)
Wedding: three–tiered cake (1st)
Happy birthday: three smiling candles (1st)
Dad: 'DAD' (1st)
Grandparent: child's hand in adult's hand (1st)
Love: birds in a heart shape (1st)

2015, January 20. Smilers
Des: Webb & Webb (Well Done and DAD), The Chase (Mum), NB
Studio (New Baby, Happy Birthday and Grandparent), Caroline
Gardner (Wedding), Rebecca Sutherland (Love). Printed in litho by
International Security Printers.

Miniature sheet	7.50	7.50
Miniature sheet first day cover	–	10.00
Stamp cards	7.50	30.00

(*All designs also appear, in self–adhesive form, in a booklet.
All values were used in Smilers sheets.)

Colossus (1st)
World Wide Web (1st)
Catseyes (81p)
Fibre optics (81p)
Stainless steel (£1.28)
Carbon fibre (£1.28)
DNA sequencing (£1.47)
i–Limb (£1.47)

2015, February 19. Inventive Britain
Des: GBH. Printed in litho by International Security Printers.
Issued in horizontal se–tenant pairs.

Set	13.50	14.50
Gutter pairs	30.00	–
First day cover	–	17.00
Stamp cards	7.00	26.00

(*All designs also appear in the Inventive Britain prestige stamp
book.)

Tarr Steps, River Barle (1st)
Row Bridge, Mosedale Beck (1st)
Pulteney Bridge, River Avon (1st)
Craigellachie Bridge, River Spey (1st)
Menai Suspension Bridge, Menai Strait (1st)
High Level Bridge, River Tyne (1st)
Royal Border Bridge, River Tweed (1st)
Tees Transporter Bridge, River Tees (1st)
Humber Bridge, River Humber (1st)
Peace Bridge, River Foyle (1st)

2015, March 6. Bridges
Des: GBH. Printed in litho by International Security Printers.
Issued in se–tenant strips of five.

Set	9.50	9.50
Gutter pairs	23.00	–
Traffic light gutter pairs	26.00	–
First day cover	–	12.00
Stamp cards	8.00	25.00

Spike Milligan (1st)
The Two Ronnies (1st)
Billy Connolly (1st)
Morecambe & Wise (1st)
Norman Wisdom (1st)
Lenny Henry (1st)
Peter Cook & Dudley Moore (1st)
Monty Python (1st)
French & Saunders (1st)
Victoria Wood (1st)

■ 2015, April 1. Comedy Greats
Des: The Chase. Printed in litho by International Security Printers.
Issued in se-tenant strips of five.

Set	9.50	9.50
Gutter pairs	23.00	–
First day cover	–	11.50
Stamp cards	7.50	25.00

(*The Norman Wisdom and Morecambe & Wise designs also
appear, in self-adhesive form, in a booklet printed in gravure by
International Security Printers; price £3.00 each, mint or used.)

Penny Black (1st, 1st)
Twopenny Blue (1st, 1st)

■ 2015, May 6. 175th Anniversary of the Penny Black
Printed in litho by International Security Printers.

Miniature sheet	5.00	5.00
Miniature sheet first day cover	–	5.50
Press sheet	55.00	–
Stamp cards	4.00	17.50

(*The Penny Black design also exists, in self-adhesive form, in
a booklet printed in gravure by International Security Printers;
price £5.00 mint or used. Both designs were used in Smilers
sheets, and in the Queen Victoria prestige stamp book of
2019. The miniature sheet also exists with the frame around
the stamps inscribed to note the London 2015 Europhilex
international stamp exhibition, and a serial number, sold only at
the exhibition in a special pack in a limited edition of 7,500.)

Poppy, by Howard Hodgkin (1st)
'All the Hills & Vales Along', by C. H. Sorley (1st)
Rifleman Kulbir Thapa (1st)
'The Kensingtons at Laventie', by Eric Kennington (£1.52)
Cape Helles, Gallipoli, Turkey (£1.52)
London Irish Rifles' football from Loos (£1.52)

■ 2015, May 14. First World War, 1915
Des: Hat-Trick. Printed in litho by International Security Printers.

Set	10.00	10.00
Gutter pairs	23.00	–
First day cover	–	13.00
Stamp cards	6.50	22.00

(*All designs also appear in the Great War 1915 prestige stamp
book.)

Magna Carta, 1215 (1st)
Simon de Montfort's Parliament, 1265 (1st)
Bill of Rights, 1689 (£1.33)
American Bill of Rights, 1791 (£1.33)
Universal Declaration of Human Rights, 1948 (£1.52)
Charter of the Commonwealth, 2013 (£1.52)

■ 2015, June 2. 800th Anniversary of Magna Carta
Des: Howard Brown. Printed in litho by International Security
Printers.

Set	10.50	10.50
Gutter pairs	24.00	–
First day cover	–	13.50
Stamp cards	5.00	21.00

WATERLOO The Scots Greys during the charge of the Union Brigade

The defence of Hougoumont (1st)
The Scots Greys during the charge of the Union Brigade (1st)
The French cavalry's assault on Allied defensive squares (£1.00)
The defence of La Haye Sainte by the King's German Legion (£1.00)
The capture of Plancenoit by the Prussians (£1.52)
The French Imperial Guard's final assault (£1.52)

■ **2015, June 18. 200th Anniversary of the Battle of Waterloo**
Des: Silk Pearce. Printed in litho by International Security Printers.

Set	9.00	9.00
Gutter pairs	22.50	–
First day cover	–	12.50
Stamp cards	10.00	40.00

(*All designs also appear in the Battle of Waterloo prestige stamp book.)

15th Infantry Regiment, IV Corps, Prussian Army (1st)
Light Infantry, King's German Legion, Anglo–Allied Army (1st)
92nd Gordon Highlanders, Anglo–Allied Army (£1.33)
Grenadiers, Imperial Guard, French Army (£1.33)

■ **2015, June 18. 200th Anniversary of the Battle of Waterloo**
Des: Webb and Webb, after illustrations by Chris Collingwood. Printed in litho by International Security Printers.

Miniature sheet	6.00	6.00
Miniature sheet first day cover	–	8.00

(*All designs also appear in the Battle of Waterloo prestige stamp book.)

Pilots scramble to their Hawker Hurricanes (1st)
Supermarine Spitfires on patrol (1st)
Armourer replaces ammunition boxes (1st)
Spotters of the Auxiliary Territorial Service (£1.33)
Operations Room at Bentley Priory (£1.33)
Pilots of 32 Squadron await orders (£1.33)

■ **2015, July 16. 75th Anniversary of the Battle of Britain**
Des: Supple Studio. Printed in litho by International Security Printers.

Miniature sheet	9.00	9.00
Miniature sheet first day cover	–	12.00
Stamp cards	8.00	25.00

(*The 1st class designs also appear in the RAF Centenary prestige stamp book issued on March 20., 2018.)

Bilberry Bumblebee
Bombus monticola

Scabious bee (2nd)
Great yellow bumblebee (1st)
Northern colletes bee (£1.00)
Bilberry bumblebee (£1.33)
Large mason bee (£1.52)
Potter flower bee (£1.28)

■ **2015, August 18. Bees**
Des: Anna Ekelund, after illustrations by Richard Lewington. Printed in litho by International Security Printers.

Set	11.50	12.00
Gutter pairs	25.00	–
First day cover	–	13.50
Stamp cards	7.50	50.00

(*The 1st class design also appears, in self-adhesive form, in booklets; price £2.00, mint or used.)

Waggle dance (1st)
Pollination (1st)
Making honey (£1.33)
Tending young (£1.33)

■ **2015, August 18. The Honeybee**
Des: Interabang, after illustrations by Andy English. Printed in litho by International Security Printers.

Miniature sheet	6.50	6.50
Miniature sheet first day cover	–	7.50

William Wyon's City Medal and Machin portrait (1st)
Wilding portrait and Machin portrait (1st)
Machin definitive, amethyst purple (1st)
Badge of the House of Windsor and Machin portrait (£1.33)
The Queen's personal flag and Machin portrait (£1.33)

■ **2015, September 9. Long To Reign Over Us**
Des: Sedley Place. Printed in intaglio and gravure by International
Security Printers.

Miniature sheet	8.50	8.50
Miniature sheet first day cover	–	11.00
Press sheet	50.00	–
Stamp cards	6.00	30.00

(*The Machin definitive in amethyst purple was also issued in
counter sheets and booklets.)

Tackle (2nd)
Scrum (2nd)
Try (1st)
Conversion (1st)
Pass (£1.00)
Drop goal (£1.00)
Ruck (£1.52)
Line-out (£1.52)

■ **2015, September 18. Rugby World Cup**
Des: Hat-trick; illustrations by Geoff Appleton. Printed in litho by
International Security Printers. Issued in se-tenant pairs.

Set	11.00	11.00
Gutter pairs	28.00	–
First day cover	–	14.00
Stamp cards	6.50	24.00

(*The two 1st class designs also appear, in self-adhesive form, in a
booklet; price £2.00 each, mint or used.)

Darth Vader (1st)
Yoda (1st)
Obi-Wan Kenobi (1st)
Stormtrooper (1st)
Han Solo (1st)
Rey (1st)
Princess Leia (1st)
The Emperor (1st)
Luke Skywalker (1st)
Boba Fett (1st)
Finn (1st)
Kylo Renn (1st)

■ **2015, October 20. Star Wars (issue 1): 'The Force Awakens'**
Des: Interabang, from illustrations by Malcolm Tween. Printed in
litho by International Security Printers. Issued in se-tenant strips
of six in two separate sheets.

Set	11.50	12.00
Gutter pairs	28.00	–
First day cover	–	15.00
Stamp cards	18.00	67.50

(*All designs also appear in the Making of Star Wars prestige
stamp book issued on December 17, 2015. The Han Solo, Yoda,
Darth Vader and Stormtrooper designs were used in Smilers sheets.)

X-Wing T-65 Starfighter (1st)
X-Wing T-70 Starfighter (1st)
Millennium Falcon (1st)
Single-seater TIE Fighter (1st)
Two-seater TIE Fighter (1st)
AT-AT Walker (1st)

■ **2015, October 20. Star Wars: The Vehicles**
Des: GBH. Printed in litho by International Security Printers.
Self-adhesive.

Miniature sheet	6.00	6.00
Miniature sheet first day cover	–	7.50

(*All design also appear in the Making of Star Wars prestige stamp
book issued on December 17, 2015.)

The journey to Bethlehem (2nd, 2nd Large)
The Nativity (1st, 1st Large)
The animals of the Nativity (£1.00)
The Shepherds (£1.33)
The Three Wise Men (£1.52)
The Annunciation (£2.25)

■ 2015, November 3. Christmas
Des: Studio David Hillman, from illustrations by David Holmes.
Printed in gravure by De La Rue. Counter stamps self–adhesive;
miniature sheet gummed.

Set	13.00	13.50
Gutter pairs	32.00	–
First day cover	–	17.50
Miniature sheet	13.00	13.50
Miniature sheet first day cover	–	17.50
Stamp cards	7.50	50.00

(*The 2nd and 1st class designs also appear in booklets, printed by
International Security Printers. The 2nd, 1st, £1.00, £1.33, £1.52 and
£2.25 designs were used in Smilers sheets.)

Entering the Antarctic ice, December 1914 (1st)
'Endurance' frozen in pack ice, January 1915 (1st)
Striving to free 'Endurance', February 1915 (£1.00)
Trapped in a pressure crack, October 1915 (£1.00)
Patience Camp, December 1915, April 1916 (£1.33)
Safe arrival at Elephant Island, April 1916 (£1.33)
Setting out for South Georgia, April 1916 (£1.52)
Rescue of 'Endurance' crew, August 1916 (£1.52)

■ 2016, January 7. Shackleton and the Endurance Expedition
Des: Robert Maude and Sarah Davies. Printed in litho by
International Security Printers. Issued in se–tenant pairs.

Set	13.00	13.50
Gutter pairs	32.00	–
First day cover	–	17.50
Stamp cards	7.50	27.00

Sir Brian Tuke: Master of the Posts in 1516 (1st)
Packet ship: 'Mail Packet off Eastbourne' by Victor Howes (1st)
Penfold pillar box: hexagonal postbox of 1866 (1st)
River post: river postwoman in World War I (£1.52)
Mail coach: London–Glasgow horse–drawn coach (£1.52)
Medway Mail Centre: sorting machines (£1.52)

■ 2016, February 17. Royal Mail 500
Des: Atelier Works. Printed in litho by International Security
Printers.

Set	10.00	10.50
Gutter pairs	24.00	–
Traffic light gutter pairs	22.50	–
First day cover	–	13.00
Stamp cards	9.00	37.00

(*All values also appear in the 500 Years of Royal Mail prestige
stamp book.)

'Quickest Way by Airmail' (1st)
'Address Your Letters Plainly' (1st)
'Pack your Parcels Carefully' (£1.33)
'Stamps in Books Save Time' (£1.33)

■ 2016, February 17. Classic GPO Posters
Des: Purpose. Printed in litho by International Security Printers.

Miniature sheet	9.00	9.00
Miniature sheet first day cover	–	9.00

(*All values also appear in the 500 Years of Royal Mail prestige
stamp book. The miniature sheet also exists with the border
inscribed 'Spring Stampex, 17–20 February 2016', sold only in a
special pack at the exhibition.)

Penny red (1st)

■ 2016, February 18. 175th Anniversary of the Penny Red
Printed in litho by International Security Printers. Self-adhesive. Issued in booklets of six.

1st	2.00	–
First day cover	–	4.00

(*This design also appears, in gummed form, in the 500 Years of Royal Mail prestige stamp book issued on February 24, 2016, and the Queen Victoria prestige stamp book issued on May 24, 2019; price £2. It was also used in Smilers sheets.)

Nicholas Winton (1st)
Sue Ryder (1st)
John Boyd Orr (1st)
Eglantyne Jebb (£1.33)
Joseph Rowntree (£1.33)
Josephine Butler (£1.33)

■ 2016, March 15. British Humanitarians
Des: Hat-Trick Design. Printed in litho by International Security Printers. Issued in se-tenant strips of three.

Set	9.00	9.00
Gutter pairs	22.00	–
First day cover	–	12.00
Stamp cards	5.50	20.00

'To thine own self be true' from Hamlet (1st)
'Cowards die many times...' from Julius Caesar (1st)
'Love is a smoke...' from Romeo and Juliet (1st)
'The fool doth think he is wise...' from As You Like It (1st)
'There was a star danced...' from Much Ado About Nothing (1st)
'But if the while I think on thee...' from Sonnet 30 (1st)
'Love comforteth like sunshine after rain' from Venus and Adonis (1st)
'We are such stuff...' from The Tempest (1st)
'Life's but a walking shadow...' from Macbeth (1st)
'I wasted time...' from Richard II (1st)

■ 2016, April 5. 400th Anniversary of the Death of William Shakespeare
Des: The Chase. Printed in litho by International Security Printers. Issued in se-tenant strips of five in two separate sheets.

Set	17.00	20.00
Gutter pairs	40.00	–
First day cover	–	17.50
Stamp cards	9.00	25.00

Princess Elizabeth II with King George VI, c.1930 (1st)
Queen Elizabeth at the State Opening of Parliament, 2012 (1st)
Queen Elizabeth with Princess Anne and Prince Charles, 1952 (1st)
Queen Elizabeth visiting New Zealand, 1977 (£1.52)
Queen Elizabeth with the Duke of Edinburgh, 1957 (£1.52)
Queen Elizabeth with Nelson Mandela, 1996 (£1.52)

■ 2016, April 21. The Queen's 90th Birthday
Des: Kate Stephens. Printed in litho by International Security Printers. Issued in se-tenant strips of three.

Set	10.00	10.00
Gutter pairs	25.00	–
First day cover	–	13.00
Stamp cards	8.00	45.00

(*All values also appear in the Queen's 90th Birthday prestige stamp book.)

Prince Charles (1st)
Queen Elizabeth II (1st)
Prince George (1st)
Prince William (1st)

■ **2016, April 21. The Queen's 90th Birthday**
Des: photograph by Ranald Mackechnie. Printed in litho by
International Security Printers.

Miniature sheet	4.25	4.50
Miniature sheet first day cover	–	5.00
Press sheet	55.00	–

(*This miniature sheet also appears in the Queen's 90th Birthday
prestige stamp book. All four designs also appear, in self-adhesive
form, in booklets; price £2.50 each, mint or used.)

Woodpecker (1st)
Snake holding a stamp (1st)
Chimpanzee (£1.05)
Bat (£1.05)
Orangutan (£1.33)
Koala with baby (£1.33)

■ **2016, May 17. Animail**
Des: Magpie Studio. Printed in litho by International Security
Printers. Self-adhesive.

Miniature sheet	9.00	9.50
Miniature sheet first day cover	–	12.00
Stamp cards	6.00	37.00

'Battlefield Poppy', by Giles Revell (1st)
'To My Brother', by Vera Brittain (1st)
Munitions worker Lottie Meade (1st)
'Travoys Arriving With wounded', by Stanley Spencer (£1.52)
Thiepval Memorial, Somme, France (£1.52)
Captain A. C. Green's Battle of Jutland commemorative medal (£1.52)

■ **2016, June 21. First World War, 1916**
Des: Hat-Trick. Printed in litho by International Security Printers.

Set	10.00	10.00
Gutter pairs	25.00	–
First day cover	–	13.00
Stamp cards	10.00	37.50

(* All designs also appear in the Great War 1916 prestige stamp
book.)

The Post Office Rifles (1st)
Writing a letter from the Western Front (1st)
Home Depot at Regent's Park, London (£1.33)
Delivering the mail on the Home Front (£1.33)

■ **2016, June 21. The Post Office at War, 1914–1918**
Des: Hat-Trick. Printed in litho by International Security Printers.

Miniature sheet	7.50	10.00
Miniature sheet first day cover	–	8.00

(*All designs also appear in the Great War 1916 prestige stamp book.)

'The Piper at the Gates of Dawn' album cover (1st)
'Atom Heart Mother' album cover (1st)
'The Dark Side of the Moon' album cover (1st)
'Wish You Were Here' album cover (£1.52)
'Animals' album cover (£1.52)
'The Endless River' album cover (£1.52)

■ **2016, July 7. Pink Floyd**
Based on design by Studio Dempsey. Printed in gravure by
International Security Printers. Self-adhesive in free-form shape.

Set	11.00	13.00
Gutter pairs	24.00	–
First day cover	–	13.00
Stamp cards	11.00	50.00

(*The Dark Side of the Moon design also appears in a souvenir
sheet of 10, not available from post offices; price £12.95.)

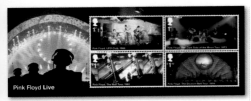

Pink Floyd Live

On stage at the UFO Club, 1966 (1st)
The Dark Side of the Moon tour, 1973 (1st)
The Wall tour, 1981 (£1.52)
The Division Bell tour, 1994 (£1.52)

■ **2016, July 7. Pink Floyd Live**
Printed in litho by International Security Printers.

Miniature sheet	7.00	7.00
Miniature sheet first day cover	–	8.50

Peter Rabbit with his mother (1st)
Peter Rabbit entering Mr. McGregor's garden (1st)
Peter Rabbit feeling sick after eating too much (£1.33)
Peter Rabbit escaping from Mr. McGregor (£1.33)

■ **2016, July 28. The Tale of Peter Rabbit**
Printed in litho by International Security Printers.

Miniature sheet	7.00	7.00
Miniature sheet first day cover	–	8.00

(*All designs also appear in the Beatrix Potter prestige stamp
book.)

'The Tale of Peter Rabbit' (1st)
'The Tale of Mrs Tiggy-Winkle' (1st)
'The Tale of Squirrel Nutkin' (£1.33)
'The Tale of Jemima Puddle-Duck' (£1.33)
'The Tale of Tom Kitten' (£1.52)
'The Tale of Benjamin Bunny' (£1.52)

■ **2016, July 28. 150th Anniversary of the Birth of Beatrix Potter**
Des: Charlie Smith Design. Printed in litho by International
Security Printers. Issued in se-tenant pairs.

Set	11.00	12.00
Gutter pairs	24.00	–
Traffic light gutter pairs	25.00	–
First day cover	–	14.00
Stamp cards	8.50	35.00

(*All designs also appear in the Beatrix Potter prestige stamp
book. The two 1st class designs also appear, in self-adhesive
form, in a booklet printed in gravure; price £2.50 each, mint
or used.)

HIGHCLERE CASTLE | CAPABILITY BROWN

Blenheim Palace (2nd)
Longleat (2nd)
Compton Verney (1st)
Highclere Castle (1st)
Alnwick Castle (£1.05)
Berrington Hall (£1.05)
Stowe (£1.33)
Croome Park (£1.33)

■ **2016, August 16. 300th Anniversary of the Birth of Capability
Brown: Landscape Gardens**
Des: Robert Maude and Sarah Davies. Printed in litho by
International Security Printers. Issued in se-tenant pairs.

Set	11.00	11.00
Gutter pairs	27.00	–
First day cover	–	14.00
Stamp cards	7.00	23.00

(*The two 1st class designs also appear, in self-adhesive form, in a
retail booklet printed in gravure; price £2.00 each, mint or used.)

Sunday, 2nd September 1666. Fire breaks out (1st)
Sunday, 2nd September 1666. Fire spreads rapidly (1st)
Monday, 3rd September 1666. Houses are pulled down (£1.05)
Tuesday, 4th September 1666. Fire reaches St. Paul's (£1.05)
Wednesday, 5th September 1666. Fire dies out (£1.52)
Tuesday, 11th September 1666. Wren develops plans (£1.52)

■ 2016, September 2. 350th Anniversary of the Great Fire of London

Des: The Chase; illustrations by John Higgins. Printed in litho by International Security Printers. Issued in se–tenant pairs.

Set	10.00	10.00
Gutter pairs	25.00	–
First day cover	–	13.00
Stamp cards	6.00	22.00

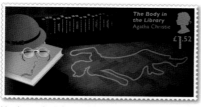

Murder on the Orient Express (1st)
And Then There Were None (1st)
The Mysterious Affair at Styles (£1.33)
The Murder of Roger Ackroyd (£1.33)
The Body in the Library (£1.52)
A Murder is Announced (£1.52)

■ 2016, September 15. Agatha Christie

Des: Studio Sutherland; illustrations by Neil Webb. Printed in litho by International Security Printers. Issued in vertically se–tenant pairs.

Set	11.50	11.50
Gutter pairs	25.00	–
First day cover	–	14.00
Stamp cards	5.50	23.00

Mr. Happy (1st)
Little Miss Naughty (1st)
Mr. Bump (1st)
Little Miss Sunshine (1st)
Mr. Tickle (1st)
Mr. Grumpy (1st)
Little Miss Princess (1st)
Mr. Strong (1st)
Little Miss Christmas (1st)
Mr. Messy (1st)

■ 2016, October 20. Mr. Men and Little Miss

Des: Supple Studio. Printed in litho by International Security Printers. Issued in se–tenant strips of five in two separate sheets.

Set	10.00	11.00
Gutter pairs	23.00	–
First day cover	–	12.50
Stamp cards	8.00	25.00

(*The Mr. Happy and Mr. Tickle designs also appear, in self–adhesive form, in a booklet printed in gravure: price £2.50 each, mint or used. All designs were used, in self–adhesive form, in Smilers sheets.)

Snowman (2nd, 2nd Large)
Robin (1st, 1st Large)
Christmas Tree (£1.05)
Lantern (£1.33)
Stocking full of toys (£1.52)
Christmas pudding (£2.25)

■ 2016, November 8. Christmas

Des: The Chase; paper cuts by Helen Musselwhite, photography by Jonathan Beer. Printed in gravure by De La Rue. Counter stamps self–adhesive; miniature sheet gummed.

Set	13.50	15.00
Gutter pairs	32.00	–
First day cover	–	17.50
Miniature sheet	13.50	14.00
Miniature sheet first day cover	–	17.50
Stamp cards	7.50	52.00

(*The 2nd class and 1st class also appear in booklets, printed by International Security Printers. The 2nd, 1st, £1.05, £1.33, £1.52 and £2.25 designs were used in Smilers sheets.)

Battersea shield, London (1st)
Skara Brae village, Orkney Islands (1st)
Star Carr headdress, Yorkshire (£1.05)
Maiden Castle hill fort, Dorset (£1.05)
Avebury stone circles, Wiltshire (£1.33)
Drumbest horns, County Antrim (£1.33)
Grime's Graves flint mines, Norfolk (£1.52)
Mold cape, Flintshire (£1.52)

■ 2017, January 17. Ancient Britain
Des: True North; illustrations by Rebecca Strickson. Printed in litho by International Security Printers. Issued in se–tenant pairs.

Set	14.50	14.50
Gutter pairs	33.00	
First day cover	–	17.50
Stamp cards	7.25	28.00

The Long Walk (1st)
The Round Tower (1st)
The Norman Gate (1st)
St George's Hall (£1.52)
The Queen's Ballroom (£1.52)
The Waterloo Chamber (£1.52)

■ 2017, February 15. Windsor Castle
Des: Up. Printed in litho by International Security Printers. Issued in se–tenant strips of three.

Set	11.00	11.00
Gutter pairs	24.00	–
First day cover	–	12.00
Stamp cards	8.50	42.00

(*All values also appear in the Windsor Castle prestige stamp book.)

Nave: Sir Reginald Bray roof boss (1st)
Nave: fan–vaulted roof (1st)
Quire: Garter banners (£1.33)
Quire: St George's Cross roof boss (£1.33)

■ 2017, February 15. Windsor Castle: St George's Chapel
Des: Up. Printed in litho by International Security Printers.

Miniature sheet	6.50	7.00
Miniature sheet first day cover	–	8.00
Press sheet	95.00	

(*All designs also appear in the Windsor Castle prestige stamp book. The two 1st class designs also appear, in self-adhesive form, in a booklet printed in gravure: price £2.00 each mint or used. The miniature sheet also exists with the border inscribed 'Spring Stampex 15–18 February 2017', sold only in a special pack at the exhibition.)

'Hunky Dory' album cover (1st)
'Aladdin Sane' album cover (1st)
'Heroes' album cover (1st)
'Let's Dance' album cover (£1.52)
'Earthling' album cover (£1.52)
'Blackstar' album cover (£1.52)

■ 2017, March 14. David Bowie
Studio Dempsey. Printed in gravure by International Security Printers. Self-adhesive.

Set	10.50	11.00
Gutter pairs	24.00	–
First day cover	–	12.00
Stamp cards	11.00	43.00

(*The Aladdin Sane and Heroes designs also appear in a booklet, printed by International Security Printers: price £2.00 each mint or used. All six designs also appear, in gummed form, in four different 'fan sheets' which were sold at a premium and were available only from the philatelic service.)

Ziggy Stardust Tour, 1973 (1st)
Serious Moonlight Tour, 1983 (1st)
Stage Tour, 1978 (£1.52)
A Reality Tour, 2006 (£1.52)

■ **2017, March 14. David Bowie Live**
Printed in litho by International Security Printers.

Miniature sheet	7.00	7.50
Miniature sheet first day cover	–	8.50

Frankel (1st)
Red Rum (1st)
Shergar (£1.17)
Kauto Star (£1.17)
Desert Orchid (£1.40)
Brigadier Gerard (£1.40)
Arkle (£1.57)
Estimate (£1.57)

■ **2017, April 6. Racehorse Legends**
Des: Together Design; illustrations by Mike Heslop. Printed in litho by International Security Printers.

Set	15.00	16.00
Gutter pairs	33.00	–
First day cover	–	17.00
Stamp cards	7.25	29.00

Great Tit (1st)
Wren (1st)
Willow warbler (1st)
Goldcrest (1st)
Skylark (1st)
Blackcap (1st)
Song thrush (1st)
Nightingale (1st)
Cuckoo (1st)
Yellowhammer (1st)

■ **2017, May 4. Songbirds**
Des: Osborne Ross; illustrations by Federico Gemma. Printed in litho by International Security Printers. Issued in se-tenant strips of five in two separate sheets.

Set	11.00	11.00
Gutter pairs	28.00	–
First day cover	–	12.50
Stamp cards	10.00	25.00

Preliminary sketch by Arnold Machin, January 1966 (1st)
Photograph of coin mould, February 1966 (1st)
Essay with coinage head and symbols, April/May 1966 (1st)
Essay with coinage head simplified, October 1966 (1st)
Photograph by John Hedgecoe, August 1966 (1st)
Essay of first plaster cast of the 'Diadem' head, October 1966 (1st)

■ **2017, June 5. The Machin Definitive. 50 Years of a Design Icon**
Des: Atelier Works. Printed in gravure and embossing by International Security Printers.

Miniature sheet	6.50	7.00
Miniature sheet first day cover	–	8.00
Press sheet	50.00	–
Stamp cards	7.50	50.00

(*All designs also appear in the Machin Definitive 50th Anniversary prestige stamp book. The set of stamp cards includes that of the Machin Definitive Golden Anniversary miniature sheet, which is listed in the Machins section of this guide).

Nutley Windmill, East Sussex (1st)
New Abbey Corn Mill, Dumfries and Galloway (1st)
Ballycopeland Windmill, County Down (£1.40)
Cheddleton Flint Mill, Staffordshire (£1.40)
Woodchurch Windmill, Kent (£1.57)
Felin Cochwillan Mill, Gwynedd (£1.57)

■ 2017, June 20. Windmills and Watermills

Des: Atelier Works; photographs by Philip Sayer. Printed in litho by International Security Printers. Issued in vertical se-tenant pairs.

Set	12.00	12.00
Gutter pairs	28.00	–
First day cover	–	14.00
Stamp cards	5.25	23.00

London Aquatics Centre (1st)
Library of Birmingham (1st)
SEC Armadillo, Glasgow (1st)
Scottish Parliament, Edinburgh (1st)
Giant's Causeway Visitor Centre, County Antrim (1st)
National Assembly for Wales, Cardiff (1st)
Eden Project, St Austell, Cornwall (1st)
Everyman Theatre, Liverpool (1st)
Imperial War Museum North, Manchester (1st)
Switch House, Tate Modern, London (1st)

■ 2017, July 13. Landmark Buildings

Des: GBH. Printed in litho by International Security Printers. Issued in se-tenant strips of five.

Set	10.50	11.00
Gutter pairs	24.00	–
First day cover	–	12.00
Stamp cards	10.00	25.00

'Shattered Poppy', by John Ross (1st)
'Dead Man's Dump', by Isaac Rosenberg (1st)
Nurses Elsie Knocker and Mairi Chisholm (1st)
'Dry Docked for Scaling and Painting', by Edward Wadsworth (£1.57)
Tyne Cot Cemetery, Belgium (£1.57)
Private Lemuel Thomas Rees's life-saving Bible (£1.57)

■ 2017, July 31. First World War, 1917

Des: Hat-Trick. Printed in litho by International Security Printers.

Set	11.00	11.00
Gutter pairs	25.00	–
First day cover	–	12.00
Stamp cards	4.50	35.00

(*All designs also appear in the Great War 1917 prestige stamp book.)

Merrythought bear (1st)
Sindy Weekender doll (1st)
Spirograph (1st)
Stickle Bricks (1st)
William Britain Herald Trojan warriors (1st)
Spacehopper (1st)
Fuzzy-Felt farm set (1st)
Meccano ferris wheel (1st)
Action Man Red Devil (1st)
Hornby Dublo TPO mail van (1st)

■ 2017, August 22. Classic Toys

Des: Interabang. Printed in litho by International Security Printers. Issued in se-tenant strips of five.

Set	10.50	11.00
Gutter pairs	24.00	–
First day cover	–	12.00
Stamp cards	10.00	25.00

Adventures From History series (2nd)
Well-Loved Tales series (2nd)
Key Words Reading Scheme series (1st)
Early Tales and Rhymes series (1st)
Hobbies and How It Works series (£1.40)
People At Work series (£1.40)
Nature and Conservation series (£1.57)
Achievements series (£1.57)

■ 2017, September 14. Ladybird Books

Des: True North. Printed in litho by International Security Printers.
Issued in se-tenant pairs.

Set	13.00	13.50
Gutter pairs	32.00	–
First day cover	–	15.00
Stamp cards	7.00	29.00

Maz Kanata (1st)
Chewbacca (1st)
Supreme Leader Snoke (1st)
Porg (1st)
BB–8 (1st)
R2–D2 (1st)
C–3PO (1st)
K–2SO (1st)

■ 2017, October 12. Star Wars (issue 2)

Des: Royal Mail Group Ltd. Printed in litho by International
Security Printers. Issued in se-tenant strips of four.

Set	8.50	9.00
Gutter pairs	20.00	–
First day cover	–	10.00
Stamp cards	9.00	25.00
Composite sheet (entire series of 20)	20.00	25.00

(*The BB–8, R2–D2, Maz Kanata and Chewbacca designs appear, in
self-adhesive form, in booklets, printed in gravure. All the stamps
also appear in the Star Wars: The Making of the Droids, Aliens and
Creatures prestige stamp book issued on December 14, 2017. All
designs were used in Smilers sheets.)

'Virgin and Child', attributed to Gerard David (2nd, 2nd Large)
'Madonna and Child', by William Dyce (1st, 1st Large)
'Virgin Mary with Child', attributed to Quinten Matsijs (£1.17)
'The Small Cowper Madonna', by Raphael (£1.40)
'The Sleep of the Infant Jesus', by Giovanni Battista Salvi (£1.57)
'St Luke Painting the Virgin', by Eduard Jakob von Steinle (£2.27)

■ 2017, November 7. Christmas. Madonna and Child Paintings

Des: Royal Mail Group Ltd, from a concept by Kate Stevens.
Printed in gravure by De La Rue. Counter stamps self-adhesive;
miniature sheet gummed. 2nd, 2nd Large, 1st and 1st Large values
printed in mixed sheets with Children's Competition designs,
resulting in vertical se-tenant pairs.

Set	18.00	18.00
Se-tenant pairs (2nd, 2nd L, 1st, 1st L)	12.00	–
Gutter pairs (£1.17, £1.40, £1.57, £2.27)	25.00	–
First day cover	–	23.00
Miniature sheet	14.00	14.00
Miniature sheet first day cover	–	18.00
Stamp cards	10.00	55.00

(*The 2nd class and 1st class designs also appear in booklets,
printed by International Security Printers. The 2nd, 1st, £1.17, £1.40,
£1.57 and £2.27 designs were used in Smilers sheets. The 2nd and
1st class were reissued on November 1, 2018, printed by ISP.)

Arwen Wilson, age 9

'Snow Family' (2nd, 2nd Large)
'Santa Claus on his Sleigh on a Starry Night' (1st, 1st Large)

■ 2017, November 7. Christmas. Children's Competition

Des: Arwen Wilson, aged 9 (2nd), and Ted Lewis Clark, aged 10
(1st). Printed in gravure by De La Rue. Self-adhesive. Printed
in mixed sheets with Madonna and Child designs, resulting in
vertical se-tenant pairs.

Set	6.00	6.00
Se-tenant pairs	12.00	–
First day cover	–	10.00

(*The 2nd class and 1st class designs also appear in booklets,
printed by International Security Printers, and in Smilers sheets.)

Engagement of Princess Elizabeth and Philip Mountbatten (1st)
Wedding procession (1st)
Princess Elizabeth and Duke of Edinburgh on honeymoon (1st)
Engagement of Princess Elizabeth and Philip Mountbatten (£1.57)
Wedding day (£1.57)
Princess Elizabeth and Duke of Edinburgh on honeymoon (£1.57)

The Iron Throne (1st)
The Night King and white walkers (1st)
Giants (1st)
Direwolves (1st)
Dragons (1st)

■ 2017, November 20. The Royal Wedding: Platinum Anniversary

Design: Mytton Williams. Printed in gravure by International Security Printers.

Miniature sheet	10.50	11.00
Miniature sheet first day cover	–	12.50
Press sheet	£150	–
Stamp cards	6.00	35.00

■ 2018, January 23. Game of Thrones

Des: GBH. Printed in litho by International Security Printers. Self-adhesive.

Miniature sheet	5.50	6.00
Miniature sheet first day cover	–	7.00

(*The Iron Throne design also appears in a booklet. All the designs also appear, in gummed form, in the Game of Thrones prestige stamp book.)

Sansa Stark (1st)
Jon Snow (1st)
Eddard Stark (1st)
Olenna Tyrell (1st)
Tywin Lannister (1st)
Tyrion Lannister (1st)
Cersei Lannister (1st)
Arya Stark (1st)
Jaime Lannister (1st)
Daenerys Targaryen (1st)

Lone suffragette in Whitehall, c.1908 (2nd)
The Great Pilgrimage of Suffragists, 1913 (2nd)
Suffragette leaders at Earl's Court, 1908 (1st)
Women's Freedom League poster parade, c.1907 (1st)
Welsh suffragettes at coronation procession (£1.40)
Mary Leigh and Edith New released from prison, 1908 (£1.40)
Sophia Duleep Singh sells 'The Suffragette', 1913 (£1.57)
Suffragette prisoners' pageant, 1911 (£1.57)

■ 2018, February 15. 100th Anniversary of Votes for Women

Des: Supple Studio. Printed in litho by International Security Printers. Issued in se-tenant pairs.

Set	13.50	14.00
Gutter pairs	30.00	–
First day cover	–	15.00
Stamp cards	6.00	29.00

■ 2018, January 23. Game of Thrones

Des: GBH. Printed in litho by International Security Printers. Issued in se-tenant strips of five.

Set	10.50	11.00
Gutter pairs	23.00	–
First day cover	–	12.00
Stamp cards	11.00	40.00

(*All designs also appear in the Game of Thrones prestige stamp book. All designs were used, in self-adhesive form, in a generic Smilers sheet.)

Lightning F6 (1st)
Hurricane Mk1 (1st)
Vulcan B2 (£1.40)
Typhoon FGR4 (£1.40)
Sopwith Camel F1 (£1.57)
Nimrod MR2 (£1.57)

2018, March 20. Centenary of the Royal Air Force
Des: Royal Mail Group Ltd, from paintings by Michael Turner.
Printed in litho by International Security Printers. Issued in
se-tenant pairs.

Set	11.50	12.00
Gutter pairs	26.00	–
First day cover	–	13.00
Stamp cards	8.00	35.00

(*All the designs also appear in the RAF Centenary prestige stamp
book. The two 1st class designs also appear, in self-adhesive form,
in a booklet.)

'Flypast' formation (1st)
'Swan' formation (1st)
'Synchro' formation (£1.40)
'Python' formation (£1.40)

2018, March 20. Red Arrows
Des: Turner Duckworth. Printed in litho by International Security
Printers.

Miniature sheet	7.00	7.50
Miniature sheet first day cover	–	8.00
Press sheet	75.00	–

(*All the designs also appear in the RAF Centenary prestige stamp
book. The two 1st class designs also appear, in self-adhesive
form, in a booklet.)

Osprey (1st)
Large blue butterfly (1st)
Eurasian beaver (£1.45)
Pool frog (£1.45)
Stinking hawk's-beard (£1.55)
Sand lizard (£1.55)

2018, April 17. Reintroduced Species
Des: Godfrey Design, from illustrations by Tanya Lock. Printed in
litho by International Security Printers. Issued in se-tenant pairs.

Set	11.50	12.00
Gutter pairs	26.00	–
First day cover	–	13.00
Stamp cards	4.50	22.00

Barn owl, adult (1st)
Little owl, adult (1st)
Tawny owl, adult (1st)
Short-eared owl, adult (1st)
Long-eared owl, adult (1st)
Barn owl, juveniles (1st)
Little owl, juveniles (1st)
Tawny owl, juvenile (1st)
Short-eared owl, juvenile (1st)
Long-eared owl, juvenile (1st)

2018, May 11. Owls
Des: Atelier Works. Printed in litho by International Security
Printers. Issued in se-tenant strips of five.

Set	10.50	11.00
Gutter pairs	24.00	–
Traffic light gutter pairs	40.00	–
First day cover	–	12.00
Stamp cards	7.50	25.00

Prince Harry and Meghan Markle, formal portrait (1st, 1st)
Meghan Markle and Prince Harry, informal (£1.55, £1.55)

2018, May 19. Royal Wedding of Prince Henry of Wales and Meghan Markle
Des: The Chase, from photographs by Alexi Lubomirski. Printed in
litho by International Security Printers.

Miniature sheet	7.00	7.50
Miniature sheet first day cover	–	9.00
Press sheet	75.00	–

'Summer Exhibition', by Grayson Perry (1st)
'Queen of the Sky', by Fiona Rae (1st)
'St Kilda: The Great Sea Stacs', by Norman Ackroyd (£1.25)
'Inverleith Allotments and Edinburgh Castle', by Barbara Rae (£1.25)
'Queuing at the RA', by Yinka Shonibare (£1.55)
'Saying Goodbye', by Tracey Emin (£1.55)

■ 2018, June 5. 250th Anniversary of the Royal Academy of Arts
Des: Royal Mail Group Ltd, from artwork by members of the
Royal Academy. Printed in litho by International Security Printers.
Issued in vertical se–tenant pairs.

Set	11.00	12.00
Gutter pairs	29.00	–
First day cover	–	12.50
Stamp cards	4.50	25.00

Sergeant Wilson (2nd)
Private Pike (2nd)
Captain Mainwaring (1st)
Lance Corporal Jones (1st)
Private Walker (£1.45)
Private Frazer (£1.45)
Private Godfrey (£1.55)
Chief Warden Hodges (£1.55)

■ 2018, June 26. 50th Anniversary of Dad's Army
Des: Up. Printed in litho by International Security Printers. Issued
in se–tenant pairs.

Set	13.50	14.00
Gutter pairs	28.00	–
First day cover	–	15.00
Stamp cards	6.00	29.00

(*The two 1st class designs also appear, in self–adhesive form, in a
booklet. All designs were used in a generic Smilers sheet.)

South Front (1st)
West Front (1st)
East Front (1st)
Pond Gardens (£1.55)
Maze (£1.55)
Great Fountain Garden (£1.55)

■ 2018, July 31. Hampton Court Palace
Des: Osborne Ross. Printed in litho by International Security
Printers. Issued in se–tenant strips of three.

Set	10.50	11.00
Gutter pairs	25.00	–
First day cover	–	12.00
Stamp cards	8.00	25.00

Great Hall (1st)
King's Great Bedchamber (1st)
Chapel Royal (£1.45)
King's Staircase (£1.45)

■ 2018, July 31. Hampton Court Palace
Des: Osborne Ross. Printed in litho by International Security
Printers.

Miniature sheet	7.00	7.50
Miniature sheet first day cover	–	9.00
Press sheet	70.00	–

(*The two 1st class designs also appear, in self–adhesive form, in a
booklet.)

Joseph Banks, red passion flower and red-tailed tropicbird (2nd)
The Chief Mourner of Tahiti, palm trees and canoe (2nd)
Captain James Cook and HMB Endeavour (1st)
The transit of Venus, 1769, and sextant (1st)
Scarlet clianthus and Maori chief with facial moko (£1.45)
Sydney Parkinson and blue-black grassquit plant (£1.45)

■ **2018, August 16. Captain Cook and the Endeavour Voyage**
Des: Howard Brown. Printed in litho by International Security
Printers. Issued in se-tenant pairs.

Set	8.00	12.00
Gutter pairs	20.00	–
First day cover	–	11.00
Stamp cards	8.00	25.00

Route of HMB Endeavour to New Zealand and Australia (1st)
Boathouse and canoes on Raiatea, Society Islands (1st)
Maori clifftop fortress in New Zealand (£1.45)
Repairing Endeavour on Australia's Great Barrier Reef (£1.45)

■ **2018, August 16. Captain Cook and the Endeavour Voyage**
Des: Webb & Webb Design. Printed in litho by International
Security Printers.

Miniature sheet	6.50	9.00
Miniature sheet first day cover	–	8.00

'The Dance of Death', 1967, with Laurence Olivier (1st)
'King Lear', 2016, with Glenda Jackson (1st)
'Hamlet', 1975, with Albert Finney (£1.25)
'Hedda Gabler', 1970, with Maggie Smith (£1.25)
'No Man's Land', 1975, with John Gielgud and Ralph Richardson (£1.45)
'Carmen Jones', 1991, with Sharon Benson (£1.45)
'Romeo & Juliet', 1960, with Judi Dench and John Stride (£1.55)
'Henry V', 1955, with Richard Burton (£1.55)

■ **2018, August 30. The Old Vic**
Des: Hat-Trick Design. Printed in litho by International Security
Printers. Issued in se-tenant pairs.

Set	15.00	20.00
Gutter pairs	32.00	–
First day cover	–	19.00
Stamp cards	5.00	30.00

'100 Poppies', by Zafer and Barbara Baran (1st)
'Anthem for Doomed Youth', by Wilfred Owen (1st)
Second Lieutenant Walter Tull (1st)
'We Are Making A New World', by Paul Nash (£1.55)
The Grave of the Unknown Warrior, Westminster Abbey (£1.55)
Lieutenant Francis Hopgood's goggles (£1.55)

■ **2018, September 13. First World War, 1918**
Des: Hat-Trick. Printed in litho by International Security Printers.

Set	10.00	14.00
Gutter pairs	23.00	–
First day cover	–	13.00
Stamp cards	4.50	25.00
Composite sheet (entire series 2014–18)	50.00	

(*All the designs also appear in the Great War 1918 prestige stamp
book. The 100 Poppies 1st class design also appears, in self-
adhesive form, in a booklet.)

Hermione Granger (1st)
Hogwarts Express (1st)
Harry Potter (1st)
Flying Ford Anglia (1st)
Ron Weasley (1st)
Hagrid's motorbike (1st)
Ginny Weasley (1st)
Triwizard Cup (1st)
Neville Longbottom (1st)
Knight bus (1st)

■ 2018, October 16. Harry Potter
Des: True North. Printed in litho by International Security Printers.
Issued in se-tenant strips of five.

Set	10.00	14.00
Gutter pairs	23.00	–
First day cover	–	13.00
Stamp cards	10.00	30.00

(*All designs also appear in the Harry Potter prestige stamp book
issued on December 4, 2018. The Hermione Granger and Harry
Potter designs also appear, in self-adhesive form, in a booklet. All
designs appear in a collector's sheet.)

Pomona Sprout (1st)
Horace Slughorn (1st)
Sybill Trelawney (1st)
Remus Lupin (1st)
Severus Snape (1st)

■ 2018, October 16. Harry Potter
Des: The Chase. Printed in litho by International Security Printers.
Self-adhesive.

Miniature sheet	5.00	7.00
Miniature sheet first day cover	–	7.00
Press sheet	90.00	–

(*All the designs also appear in the Harry Potter prestige stamp
book issued on December 4, 2018.)

King Edward VII wall box (2nd, 2nd Large)
Queen Elizabeth II double-aperture box (1st, 1st Large)
King George VI lamp box (£1.25)
Queen Victoria Penfold box (£1.45)
King Edward VIII pillar box (£1.55)
King George V lamp box (£2.25)

■ 2018, November 1. Christmas: Postboxes
Des: Andrew Davidson. Printed in gravure by International
Security Printers. Counter sheets self-adhesive; miniature sheet
gummed.

Set	14.00	20.00
Gutter pairs (£1.17, £1.40, £1.57, £2.27)	30.00	–
Se-tenant pairs (2018 with 2017 designs)	20.00	–
First day cover	–	18.00
Miniature sheet	14.00	20.00
Miniature sheet first day cover	–	18.00
Stamp cards	7.00	35.00

(* As well as in sheets of 50, the 2nd and 1st designs were
additionally printed as the lower 25 stamps in sheets of 50
with the reissued Madonna & Child 2nd and 1st designs of 2017,
resulting in vertically se-tenant pairs; price £12. The 2nd and 1st
class designs also appear in booklets. All designs were used in a
generic Smilers sheet.)

Prince of Wales in civilian dress (1st)
Prince of Wales and Duchess of Cornwall (1st)
Prince of Wales, Duke of Cambridge and Duke of Sussex (1st)
Prince of Wales, Duke of Cambridge and Duke of Sussex at
Cirencester Park Polo Club (£1.55)
Prince of Wales at the Castle of Mey (£1.55)
Prince of Wales and schoolchildren in Wales (£1.55)

■ 2018, November 14. 70th Birthday of the Prince of Wales
Design: Davies Maude. Printed in gravure by International
Security Printers.

Miniature sheet	10.00	14.00
Miniature sheet first day cover	–	13.00
Press sheet	£125	–
Stamp cards	5.00	25.00

Queen Victoria 1891 £1 green (1st)
King Edward VII 1910 2d Tyrian plum (1st)
King George V 1913 2s 6d brown (1st)
King Edward VIII 1936 1½d red–brown (£1.55)
King George VI 1940 Penny Black Centenary ½d green (£1.55)
Queen Elizabeth II 1953 Coronation 2½d red (£1.55)

■ **2019, January 15. Stamp Classics**
Des: Hat–Trick Design. Printed in litho by International Security
Printers.

Miniature sheet	10.00	14.00
Miniature sheet first day cover	–	13.00
Press sheet	£125	–
Stamp cards	5.00	25.00

(*The miniature sheet exists with the additional text 'Stampex
International 13–16 February 2019' in the border, and a serial
number, sold only at the exhibition in a limited edition of 5,000.)

The skull sectioned (1st)
A sprig of guelder rose (1st)
Studies of cats (1st)
The anatomy of the shoulder and foot (1st)
A star–of–Bethlehem and other plants (1st)
The head of Leda (1st)
The head of a bearded man (1st)
The skeleton (1st)
The head of St Philip (1st)
A woman in a landscape (1st)
A design for an equestrian monument (1st)
The fall of light on a face (1st)

■ **2019, February 13. Leonardo da Vinci**
Des: Kate Stephens, from drawings by Leonardo da Vinci held by
the Royal Collection. Printed in litho by International Security
Printers. Issued in se–tenant strips of six.

Set	12.00	15.00
Gutter pairs	25.00	–
First day cover	–	14.00
Stamp cards	8.00	26.00

(*These stamps also appear in the Leonardo da Vinci prestige
stamp book.)

Spider–Man (1st)
Captain Marvel (1st)
Hulk (1st)
Doctor Strange (1st)
Captain Britain (1st)
Peggy Carter (1st)
Iron Man (1st)
Union Jack (1st)
Black Panther (1st)
Thor (1st)

■ **2019, March 14. Marvel Super Heroes**
Des: Interabang, from illustrations by Alan Davis. Printed in litho
by International Security Printers. Issued in se–tenant strips of
five.

Set	10.00	14.00
Gutter pairs	23.00	–
First day cover	–	13.00
Stamp cards	10.00	35.00

(*The Spider–Man and Hulk designs appear, in self–adhesive
form, in a booklet, printed in gravure. All the stamps also appear
in the Make Mine Marvel prestige stamp book.)

Captain Britain spies a portal opening (£1.45)
Thanos emerges from the portal (1st)
Thor, Doctor Strange and Iron Man deflect a cosmic ray (1st)
Hulk, Spider–Man, Black Panther and Iron Man retaliate (1st)
Captain Britain and the superheroes proclaim their unity (£1.45)

■ **2019, March 14. Marvel Heroes UK**
Des: Interabang, from illustrations by Alan Davis. Printed in litho
by International Security Printers.

Miniature sheet	7.00	9.00
Miniature sheet first day cover	–	8.00
Press sheet	£130	–

(*The miniature sheet also appears in the Make Mine Marvel
prestige stamp book.)

Buzzard
Buteo buteo

White-tailed eagle (1st)
Merlin (1st)
Hobby (1st)
Buzzard (1st)
Golden eagle (1st)
Kestrel (1st)
Goshawk (1st)
Sparrowhawk (1st)
Red kite (1st)
Peregrine falcon (1st)

■ 2019, April 4. Birds of Prey

Des: Royal Mail and GBH, from photography by Tim Flach. Printed in litho by International Security Printers. Issued in se-tenant strips of five.

Set	10.00	14.00
Gutter pairs	23.00	–
First day cover	–	13.00
Stamp cards	7.00	20.00

(*The Buzzard and Hobby designs also appear, in self-adhesive form, in a booklet.)

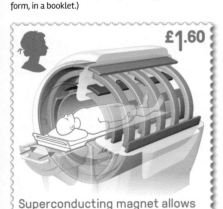

Superconducting magnet allows high-quality imaging in MRI

Raspberry Pi microcomputer (1st)
Falkirk Wheel (1st)
Three-way catalytic converter (£1.55)
Crossrail (£1.55)
Superconducting magnets in MRI scanner (£1.60)
Synthetic bone graft material (£1.60)

■ 2019, May 2. British Engineering

Des: Common Curiosity. Printed in litho by International Security Printers. Issued in se-tenant pairs.

Set	11.00	14.00
Gutter pairs	24.00	–
First day cover	–	13.00
Stamp cards	8.00	25.00

HARRIER JUMP JET
50th ANNIVERSARY

Harrier GR3: short take-off (1st)
Harrier GR3: conventional flight (1st)
Harrier GR3: transition to landing (£1.55)
Harrier GR3: vertical landing (£1.55)

■ 2019, May 2. 50th Anniversary of the Harrier Jump Jet

Des: Turner Duckworth, from photography by Richard Cooke. Printed in litho by International Security Printers.

Miniature sheet	7.00	9.00
Miniature sheet first day cover	–	8.00
Press sheet	90.00	–

1859
Queen Victoria wearing her Robes of State

Queen Victoria portrait by Heinrich Von Angeli, 1890 (1st)
Queen Victoria and Benjamin Disraeli at Osborne House, 1878 (1st)
Queen Victoria on horseback with servant John Brown, 1876 (£1.35)
Queen Victoria wearing her Robes of State, 1859 (£1.35)
Marriage of Queen Victoria and Prince Albert, 1840 (£1.60)
Princess Victoria aged 11, 1830 (£1.60)

■ 2019, May 24. Bicentenary of the Birth of Queen Victoria
Des: Webb & Webb Design. Printed in litho by International Security Printers. Issued in se-tenant pairs.

Set	11.00	14.00
Gutter pairs	24.00	–
First day cover	–	13.00
Stamp cards	8.00	25.00

(*All values also appear in the Victoria: A Long & Glorious Reign prestige stamp book.)

Model Lodge, Kennington (1st)
Balmoral Castle, Scotland (1st)
The New Crystal Palace, Sydenham (£1.55)
Royal Albert Hall, London (£1.55)

■ 2019, May 24. The Legacy of Prince Albert
Des: Common Curiosity. Printed in litho by International Security Printers.

Miniature sheet	7.00	9.00
Miniature sheet first day cover	–	8.00
Press sheet	£100	–

(*All designs also appear in the Victoria: A Long & Glorious Reign prestige stamp book.)

British soldiers are briefed before embarkation (1st)
HMS Warspite shelling in support of beach landings (1st)
Paratroopers synchronising watches (£1.35)
Soldiers wade ashore on Juno (£1.35)
An American light bomber provides air support (£1.60)
British troops take cover as they advance inland (£1.60)

■ 2019, June 6. 75th Anniversary of D-Day
Des: Baxter & Bailey. Printed in litho by International Security Printers. Issued in se-tenant pairs.

Set	11.00	14.00
Gutter pairs	24.00	–
First day cover	–	13.00
Stamp cards	8.00	25.00

Utah (1st)
Omaha (1st)
Gold (1st)
Juno (1st)
Sword (1st)

■ 2019, June 6. 75th Anniversary of D-Day: The Normandy Landings
Des: Baxter & Bailey. Printed in litho by International Security Printers.

Miniature sheet	6.00	8.00
Miniature sheet first day cover	–	7.00

(*The Gold and Sword designs also appear, in self-adhesive form, in a retail stamp book.)

Burning the Clocks, Brighton (2nd)
'Obby 'Oss, Padstow (2nd)
World Gurning Championships, Egremont (1st)
Up Helly Aa, Lerwick (1st)
Cheese Rolling, Cooper's Hill, Brockworth (£1.55)
Halloween, Derry/Londonderry (£1.55)
Horn Dance, Abbots Bromley (£1.60)
Bog Snorkelling, Llanwrtyd Wells (£1.60)

■ 2019, July 9. Curious Customs
Des: NB Studio. from illustrations by Jonny Hannah. Printed in litho by International Security Printers. Issued in se-tenant pairs.

Set	13.00	17.00
Gutter pairs	28.00	–
First day cover	–	16.00
Stamp cards	6.00	20.00

REGIONAL ISSUES

Prices in this section are quoted in two columns: mint (left) and fine used (right).
The definitive issues for Guernsey, the Isle of Man and Jersey pre–date their postal independence in 1969, 1973 and 1969 respectively.

CHANNEL ISLANDS

Gathering seaweed (1d)

Islanders gathering seaweed (2½d)

■ **1948, May 10. Third Anniversary of Liberation**
Des: J.R.R. Stobie (1d), E. Blampied (2½d). Printed in gravure by Harrison. Wmk: Multiple Crowns and GVIR. Perf: 15x14.

Set	0.15	0.20
First day cover	–	17.50

GUERNSEY

2½d

3d, 4d, 5d

■ **1958–1969**
Des: E.A. Piprell. Printed in gravure by Harrison. Perf: 15x14.

Wmk: Multiple St. Edward's Crown. Non phosphor, except where stated

2½d red (June 8, 1964)	0.30	0.35
3d lilac (August 18, 1958)	0.30	0.30
one centre phos band (May 24, 1967)	0.10	0.15
4d ultramarine (February 7, 1966)	0.20	0.25
two phos bands (October 24, 1967)	0.10	0.15
First day cover (2½d)	–	25.00
First day cover (3d)	–	20.00
First day cover (4d)	–	10.00

No watermark. Chalky paper. Two phosphor bands, except where stated

4d ultramarine (April 16, 1968)	0.10	0.15
4d sepia (September 4, 1968)		
one centre phosphor band	0.10	0.15
4d red (February 26, 1969)		
one centre phosphor band	0.10	0.20
5d deep blue (September 4, 1968)	0.10	0.20
First day cover (4d sepia, 5d)	–	2.00
First day cover (4d red)	–	1.50

ISLE OF MAN

2½d

3d, 4d, 5d

■ **1958–1969**
Des: J. Nicholson. Printed in gravure by Harrison. Perf: 15x14.

Wmk: Multiple St. Edward's Crown. Non phosphor, except where stated

2½d carmine-red (June 8, 1964)	0.20	0.35
3d lilac (August 18, 1958)	0.15	0.20
chalky paper (May 17, 1964)	4.50	4.00
one centre phos band (June 27, 1968)	0.10	0.15
4d ultramarine (February 7, 1966)	0.75	0.75
a) two phosphor bands (July 5, 1967)	0.10	0.15
First day cover (2½d)	–	25.00
First day cover (3d)	–	30.00
First day cover (4d)	–	10.00

No watermark. Chalky paper. Two phosphor bands, except where stated

4d ultramarine (June 24, 1968)	0.10	0.15
4d sepia (September 4, 1968)		
one centre phosphor band	0.10	0.15
4d red (February 26, 1969)		
one centre phosphor band	0.20	0.30
5d deep blue (September 4, 1968)	0.20	0.30
First day cover (4d sepia, 5d)	–	2.00
First day cover (4d red)	–	1.50

■ **1971–1973**
Des: J. Matthews. Printed in gravure by Harrison. Perf: 15x14.

2½p magenta (July 7, 1971)	0.15	0.15
3p ultramarine (July 7, 1971)	0.20	0.20
5p violet (July 7, 1971)	0.50	0.50
7½p pale brown (July 7, 1971)	0.60	0.60
First day cover	–	2.50

(*The 2½p and 3p exist on either ordinary coated paper or fluorescent-coated paper.)

JERSEY

2½d

3d, 4d, 5d

■ **1958–1969**
Des: E. Blampied (2½d), W.M. Gardner (others). Printed in gravure by Harrison. Perf: 15x14.

Wmk: Multiple St. Edward's Crown. Non phosphor, except where stated

2½d carmine-red (June 8, 1964)	0.20	0.25
3d lilac (August 18, 1958)	0.25	0.25
one centre phos band (June 9, 1967)	0.10	0.15
4d ultramarine (February 7, 1966)	0.20	0.25
two phos bands (September 5, 1967)	0.10	0.15
First day cover (2½d)	–	25.00
First day cover (3d)	–	20.00
First day cover (4d)	–	10.00

No watermark. Chalky paper, PVA gum. One centre phosphor band (4d), or two phosphor bands (5d).

4d sepia (September 4, 1968)	0.10	0.15
4d red (February 26, 1969)	0.10	0.20
5d deep blue (September 4, 1968)	0.10	0.20
First day cover (4d sepia, 5d)	–	2.00
First day cover (4d red)	–	1.50

NORTHERN IRELAND DEFINITIVES

Prices in this section are quoted in two columns: mint (left) and fine used (right).

PRE–DECIMAL WILDING ISSUES

3d lilac, 4d blue, 5d blue   6d purple, 9d green

1/3 green, 1/6 grey–blue

■ 1958–1969

Des: W. Hollywood (3d, 4d, 5d), L.Philton (6d, 9d), T. Collins (1/3, 1/6). Printed in gravure by Harrisons. Perf 15x14.

Wmk: Multiple St. Edward's Crown. Non-phosphor except where stated

3d lilac (August 18, 1958)	0.15	0.15
3d lilac, one phos band	0.15	0.20
4d blue (February 7, 1966)	0.15	0.15
4d blue, two phos bands	0.15	0.15
6d purple (September 29, 1958)	0.20	0.20
9d green (March 1, 1967). two phos bands	0.35	0.40
1/3 green (September 29, 1958)	0.35	0.40
1/6 grey–blue (March 1, 1967), two phos bands	0.40	0.40
First day cover (3d)	–	25.00
First day cover (6d, 1/3)	–	30.00
First day cover (4d)	–	7.50
First day cover (9d, 1/6)	–	4.00

No wmk. Two phosphor bands and PVA gum except where stated

4d blue, gum Arabic (June 27, 1968)	0.15	0.15
4d sepia (September 4, 1968), one phos band	0.15	0.25
4d red (February 26, 1969)	0.20	0.30

5d blue (September 4, 1968)	0.20	0.20
1/6 grey–blue (May 20, 1969)	1.50	1.40
First day cover (4d sepia, 5d)	–	2.50
First day cover (4d red)	–	1.00

(*The 4d blue also exists with PVA gum, but this was not placed on sale in Northern Ireland; price £8.50 mint.)

DECIMAL MACHIN ISSUES WITHOUT ELLIPTICAL PERFORATIONS

3p blue

Des: J. Matthews. Type I has the symbol close to the top of the design; type II (1983) has the symbol redrawn and edged down.

■ 1971–1980. Printed in gravure by Harrisons

Perf 15x14. Two phosphor bands except where stated.

Original coated paper. PVA gum

2¹/₂p pink (July 7, 1971), one phos band	0.40	0.40
3p blue (July 7, 1971)	0.20	0.20
5p violet (July 7, 1971)	0.50	0.50
7¹/₂p brown (July 7, 1971)	0.90	0.90

Fluorescent coated paper. PVA gum

2¹/₂p pink (June 1973), one phos band	5.25	4.00
3p blue (April 1973)	7.50	7.00
3p blue, one centre band	0.35	0.30

Fluorescent coated paper. PVAD gum

3p blue (January 23, 1974), one phos band	0.10	0.15
3¹/₂p green (January 23, 1974)	0.15	0.20
3¹/₂p green, one centre band	0.15	0.20
4¹/₂p grey–blue (November 6, 1974)	0.15	0.20
5¹/₂p deep violet (January 23, 1974)	0.15	0.25
5¹/₂p deep violet, one centre band	0.15	0.25
6¹/₂p green–blue (January 14, 1976), one band	0.15	0.30
7p red-brown (January 18, 1978), one band	0.15	0.20
8p red (January 23, 1974)	0.20	0.35
8¹/₂p green (January 14, 1976)	0.20	0.35

9p violet–blue (January 18, 1978)	0.20	0.30
10p orange (October 20, 1976)	0.20	0.30
10p orange, one phos band	0.25	0.30
10¹/₂p grey–blue (January 18, 1978)	0.25	0.30
11p red (October 20, 1976)	0.25	0.30

Phosphor coated paper. PVAD gum

12p yellow–green (July 23, 1980)	0.30	0.30
13¹/₂p red–brown (July 23, 1980)	0.35	0.35
15p blue (July 23, 1980)	0.35	0.35

First day cover (2¹/₂p, 3p, 5p, 7¹/₂p)	–	1.70
First day cover (3¹/₂p, 5¹/₂p, 8p)	–	1.40
First day cover (4¹/₂p)	–	1.25
First day cover (6¹/₂p, 8¹/₂p)	–	1.00
First day cover (10p, 11p)	–	1.00
First day cover (7p, 9p, 10¹/₂p)	–	1.00
First day cover (12p, 13¹/₂p, 15p)	–	1.00

■ 1981–1993. Printed in litho by Questa

Perf: 13¹/₂x14. Phosphor coated paper, except 11¹/₂p and 12¹/₂p (left side band). PVA gum (11¹/₂p, 14p, 18p, 22p), PVAD gum (others)

11¹/₂p mushroom (April 8, 1981)	0.45	0.45
12¹/₂p light green (February 24, 1982)	0.35	0.30
14p steel–blue (April 8, 1981)	0.50	0.50
15¹/₂p pale violet (February 24, 1982)	0.60	0.60
16p light mushroom (April 27, 1983)	0.60	0.40
18p mauve (April 8, 1981)	0.50	0.50
19¹/₂p grey–green (February 24, 1982)	1.00	1.00
20¹/₂p bright blue (April 27, 1983)	2.50	2.50
22p deep blue (April 8, 1981)	0.50	0.50
26p red (February 24, 1982), type I	0.60	0.60
28p blue (April 27, 1983), type I	0.65	0.65

Perf: 15x14. One phosphor band (12p, 12¹/₂p, 13p, 14p, 15p), phosphor coated paper (16p, 17p, 18p, 19p, 20p, 22p, 23p, 24p, 31p, 32p, 34p, 37p, 39p), advanced coated paper (22p, 26p, 28p), or as stated. PVAD gum except where stated.

12p emerald green (January 7, 1986)	0.60	0.60
12¹/₂p light green (February 28, 1984)	0.30	0.30
12¹/₂p light green, PVA gum	2.50	–
13p red–brown (October 23, 1984), type I	0.60	0.60
13p deep brown, type II	0.70	0.70
14p deep blue (November 8, 1988)	0.30	0.30
15p bright blue (November 28, 1989)	0.55	0.60
16p light mushroom (February 28, 1984)	4.00	4.00
17p steel blue (October 23, 1984), type I	0.50	0.50
17p steel blue, type I, advanced coated paper	0.50	0.50
17p steel blue, type II, advanced coated paper	£140	£140
18p deep green (January 6, 1987)	0.50	0.50
18p bright green, centre phos band	0.60	0.60
18p bright green, perf 14	5.00	5.00
18p bright green, left phos band	1.20	1.20
19p orange–red (November 8, 1988)	0.40	0.40
20p brownish–black (November 28, 1989)	0.60	0.50
22p yellowish–green (October 23, 1984)	0.60	0.60
22p orange–red (December 4, 1990)	0.50	0.50
23p bright green (November 8, 1988)	0.60	0.60
24p deep red (November 28, 1989)	0.70	0.70
24p chestnut (August 10, 1993), two bands	1.50	1.50

26p red (January 27, 1987), type II	1.40	1.40
26p drab (December 4, 1990), phos paper	0.80	0.80
28p blue (January 27, 1987), type II	0.80	0.80
28p blue–grey (Dec 3, 1991), phos paper	0.80	0.80
31p purple (October 23, 1984), type I	0.90	0.90
31p purple (April 14, 1987), type II	1.50	1.50
32p greenish blue (November 8, 1988)	0.90	0.90
34p bluish grey (November 28, 1989)	0.90	0.90
37p rosine (December 4, 1990)	1.00	1.00
39p mauve (December 3, 1991)	1.00	1.00

(*The 18p with left phosphor band and 24p chestnut with two phosphor bands come from prestige stamp books. The 13p also exists printed on paper supplied by Coated Papers Ltd, with PVA gum, in 1987)

First day cover (11¹/₂p, 14p, 18p, 22p)	–	1.00
First day cover (12¹/₂p, 15¹/₂p, 19¹/₂p, 26p)	–	1.50
First day cover (16p, 20¹/₂p, 28p)	–	1.50
First day cover (13p, 17p, 22p, 31p)	–	1.50
First day cover (12p)	–	1.00
First day cover (18p)	–	1.00
First day cover (14p, 19p, 23p, 32p)	–	2.00
First day cover (15p, 20p, 24p, 34p)	–	2.00
First day cover (17p, 22p, 26p, 37p)	–	2.25
First day cover (18p, 24p, 28p, 39p)	–	2.25

DECIMAL MACHIN ISSUES WITH ELLIPTICAL PERFORATIONS

1st red

■ 1993–1996. Printed in litho by Questa

Perf 15x14. One phosphor band (19p and 20p), or two phosphor bands (others).

19p bistre (December 7, 1993), left band	1.00	1.00
19p bistre, right band	1.35	1.35
20p bright green (July 23, 1996)	1.00	1.40
25p red (December 7, 1993)	0.60	0.60
26p red–brown (July 23, 1996)	0.90	0.90
30p olive–grey (December 7, 1993)	0.90	0.90
37p mauve (July 23, 1996)	1.40	1.40
41p grey–brown (December 7, 1993)	1.00	1.00
63p emerald (July 23, 1996)	2.75	2.50

(* The 19p with phosphor band to right comes from the 1995 National Trust prestige stamp book.)

■ 1997–2000. Printed in gravure by Walsall

Perf 15x14. One phosphor band (19p and 20p), two phosphor bands (others)

19p bistre (June 8, 1999)	2.00	2.00
20p bright green (July 1, 1997)	2.00	2.00
26p chestnut (July 1, 1997)	1.40	1.40
37p mauve (July 1, 1987)	1.50	1.50
38p ultramarine (June 8, 1999)	5.00	5.00
40p azure (April 25, 2000)	3.00	3.00
63p emerald (July 1, 1997)	3.00	3.00
64p turquoise (June 8, 1999)	5.50	5.50
65p greenish blue (April 25, 2000)	3.00	3.00

(*The 20p with right phosphor band, the 26p perf 15x14 and perf 14, and the 37p also exist printed by Harrisons, from prestige stamp books.)

Perf 15x14 except where stated. One phosphor band

1st orange–red (February 15, 2000), perf 14	2.25	2.20
1st orange–red (April 25, 2000)	6.50	6.50

(*The perf 14 stamp was issued only in the Special By Design prestige stamp book.)

First day cover (19p, 25p, 30p, 41p)	–	2.50
First day cover (20p, 26p, 37p, 63p)	–	2.50
First day cover (19p, 38p, 64p)	–	3.00
First day cover (1st, 40p, 65p)	–	3.00

PICTORIAL ISSUES WITHOUT WHITE BORDERS

Basalt columns (2nd)   Patchwork fields (1st)

Linen (E)   Pattern on vase (65p, 68p)

■ 2001–2002

Des: Rodney Miller Associates. Printed in litho by Walsall (2nd, 1st, E, 65p), De La Rue (E, 68p), or Enschedé (2nd, 1st). Perf 15x14. One phosphor band (2nd), two phosphor bands (others).

2nd (March 6, 2001,Walsall)	1.00	1.00
2nd (February 25, 2003, Enschedé)	4.50	4.50
1st (March 6, 2001,Walsall)	1.20	0.90
1st (February 25, 2003, Enschedé)	4.50	4.50
E (March 6, 2001,Walsall)	1.75	1.75
E (October 15, 2002, De La Rue)	2.00	2.00
65p (March 6, 2001)	2.00	2.00
68p (July 4, 2002)	2.00	2.00

(*The 2nd and 1st printed by Enschedé come from the 2003 Microcosmos prestige stamp book.)

First day cover (2nd, 1st, E, 65p)	–	3.00
First day cover (68p)	–	2.00
Stamp cards	8.00	13.00

PICTORIAL ISSUES WITH WHITE BORDERS

Basalt columns (2nd)   Patchwork fields (1st)

Linen (E, 40p, 42p, 44p, 48p, 50p, 56p, 60p, 87p, 88p, 97p, £1.00, £1.05)

Pattern on vase (68p, 72p, 78p, 81p, 90p, 97p, £1.10, £1.28, £1.33)

■ 2003–2016

Des: Rodney Miller Associates. Printed in litho by De La Rue (2nd, 1st, E, 40p, 42p, 44p, 68p, 72p, 78p, 81p), in litho by Walsall (42p), in gravure by De La Rue (2nd, 1st, 48p, 50p, 56p, 60p, 72p, 78p, 81p, 90p, 97p), in litho by Enschedé (1st, in prestige stamp books only) or in litho by Cartor (2nd, 1st, 68p, 87p, 88p, £1.00, £1.05, £1.10, £1.28, £1.33). Perf 15x14. One phosphor band (2nd) or two phosphor bands (others).

2nd (October 14, 2003, De La Rue)	1.00	1.00
2nd (January 3, 2013, Cartor)	1.00	1.00
1st (October 14, 2003, De La Rue)	1.20	1.20
1st (January 3, 2013, Cartor)	1.50	1.50
E (October 14, 2003)	1.70	1.70
40p (May 11, 2004)	1.10	1.10
42p (Walsall, April 5, 2005)	1.70	1.70
42p (De La Rue, July 26, 2005)	2.00	2.00
44p (March 25, 2006)	1.00	1.00
48p (March 27, 2007)	0.80	0.80
50p (April 1, 2008)	1.00	1.00
56p (March 31, 2009)	1.00	1.00
60p (March 30, 2010)	1.20	1.20
68p (October 14, 2003, De La Rue)	2.00	2.00
68p (March 29, 2011, Cartor)	1.30	1.30
72p (March 28, 2006)	2.25	2.25
78p (March 27, 2007)	1.50	1.50
81p (April 1, 2008)	1.75	1.75
87p (April 25, 2012)	2.00	2.00
88p (March 27, 2013)	1.90	1.90
90p (March 31, 2009)	1.70	1.70
97p (March 30, 2010)	2.00	2.00
97p (March 26, 2014)	2.00	2.00
£1.00 (March 24, 2015)	2.00	2.00
£1.05 (March 22, 2016)	2.25	2.25
£1.10 (March 29, 2011)	2.00	2.00
£1.28 (April 25, 2012)	2.20	2.20
£1.33 (March 24, 2015)	2.20	2.20

(*Various values have also appeared in miniature sheets and prestige stamp books. The 1st class also exists, self-adhesive, in Smilers sheets. Although January 3, 2013, was the official date of issue of the 1st class and 2nd class printed by Cartor, both stamps were available earlier from post offices.)

First day cover (2nd, 1st, E, 68p)	–	3.00
First day cover (40p)	–	1.50
First day cover (42p)	–	1.50
First day cover (44p, 72p)	–	2.00
First day cover (48p, 78p)	–	2.50
First day cover (50p, 81p)	–	3.00
First day cover (56p, 90p)	–	3.00
First day cover (60p, 97p)	–	4.00
First day cover (68p, £1.10)	–	4.00
First day cover (87p, £1.28)	–	4.50
First day cover (88p)	–	2.00
First day cover (97p)	–	2.25
First day cover (£1.00, £1.33)	–	4.50
First day cover (£1.05)	–	2.25
Stamp cards	5.00	12.00

Basalt columns (2nd)

Patchwork fields (1st)

Linen
(£1.17, £1.25, £1.35)

Pattern on vase
(£1.40, £1.45, £1.55)

2017 to date
As previous issue but with revised typeface for denomination. Printed in litho by Cartor. Perf 15 x 14. One phosphor band (2nd) or two phosphor bands (others).

2nd (March 20, 2018)	1.75	1.75
1st (March 20, 2018)	1.80	1.80
£1.17 (March 21, 2017)	2.20	2.20
£1.25 (March 20, 2018)	2.40	2.40
£1.35 (March 19, 2019)	2.50	2.50
£1.40 (March 21, 2017)	2.50	2.50
£1.45 (March 20, 2018)	2.75	2.75
£1.55 (March 19, 2019)	2.75	2.75

First day cover (£1.17, £1.40)	–	5.00
First day cover (2nd, 1st, £1.25, £1.45)	–	7.00
First day cover (£1.35, £1.55)	–	5.00

SCOTLAND DEFINITIVES

Prices in this section are quoted in two columns: mint (left) and fine used (right).

PRE-DECIMAL WILDING ISSUES

3d lilac, 4d blue, 5d blue

6d purple, 9d green

1/3 green, 1/6 grey-blue

■ 1958-1970

Des: G. F. Huntly (3d, 4d, 5d), J. B. Fleming (6d, 9d), A. B. Imrie (1/3, 1/6). Printed in gravure by Harrisons. Perf 15x14.

Wmk: Multiple St Edward's Crown. Non-phosphor except where stated

3d lilac (August 18, 1958)	0.15	0.15
3d lilac, two phos bands	8.00	2.00
3d lilac, one left band	0.20	0.35
3d lilac, one right band	0.20	0.35
3d lilac, one centre band	0.20	0.30
4d blue (February 7, 1966)	0.15	0.15
4d blue, two phos bands	0.15	0.15
6d purple (September 29, 1958)	0.15	0.15
6d purple, two phos bands	0.20	0.25
9d green (March 1, 1967), two phos bands	0.35	0.40
1/3 green (September 29, 1958)	0.35	0.25
1/3 green, two phos bands	0.35	0.40
1/6 grey-blue (March 1, 1967), two phos bands	0.40	0.50

First day cover (3d)	–	10.00
First day cover (6d, 1/3)	–	20.00
First day cover (3d, 6d, 1/3 phosphor)	–	£100
First day cover (4d)	–	10.00
First day cover (9d, 1/6)	–	2.75

No watermark. Two phosphor bands except where stated. PVA gum except where stated

3d lilac (May 16, 1968), one band, gum Arabic	0.15	—
3d lilac, one centre band (July 11, 1968)	0.15	0.20
4d blue (November 28, 1967), gum Arabic	0.15	—
4d blue (July 25, 1968)	0.15	0.20
4d sepia (September 4, 1968), one band	0.15	0.20
4d red (February 26, 1969), one band	0.20	0.20
5d blue (September 4, 1968)	0.20	0.25
9d green (September 28, 1970)	3.25	3.25
1/6 grey-blue (December 12, 1968)	1.25	1.00

First day cover (4d sepia, 5d)	–	2.50
First day cover (4d red)	–	1.00

DECIMAL MACHIN ISSUES WITHOUT ELLIPTICAL PERFORATIONS

3½p green

Des: J. Matthews. Type I has the eye on the lion symbol appearing as a circle, while the tongue and claws are thin; type II (1983) has a solid eye and thicker tongue and claws.

■ 1971-1980. Printed in gravure by Harrisons

Perf 15x14. Two phosphor bands except where stated.

Original coated paper. PVA gum

2½p pink (July 7, 1971), one phos band	0.15	0.15
3p blue (July 7, 1971)	0.15	0.15
5p violet (July 7, 1971)	0.50	0.50
7½p brown (July 7, 1971)	0.65	0.65

Fluorescent coated paper. Gum Arabic

2½p pink (Sep 22, 1972), one phos band	0.20	–
3p blue (December 14, 1972)	0.35	–

Fluorescent coated paper. PVA gum

2½p pink (January 1973), one phos band	2.25	2.00
3p blue (January 23, 1974)	11.00	10.50
3p blue, one phos band	0.35	0.30
3½p green (January 23, 1974)	0.20	–
5p violet (January 23, 1974)	22.00	21.50
7½p brown (January 23, 1974)	80.00	70.00

Fluorescent coated paper. PVAD gum

3p blue (November 6, 1974), one phos band	0.10	–
3½p green (November 6, 1974)	0.10	0.10
3½p green, one phos band	0.10	0.10
4½p grey–blue (November 6, 1974)	0.15	0.30
5½p deep violet (January 23, 1974)	0.15	0.25
5½p deep violet, one phos band	0.15	0.30
6½p green–blue (January 14, 1976), one band	0.20	0.30
7p red–brown (January 18, 1974), one band	0.20	0.30
8p red (January 23, 1974)	0.20	0.30
8½p green (January 14, 1976)	0.20	0.30
9p violet–blue (January 18, 1978)	0.20	0.35
10p orange (October 20, 1976)	0.20	0.40
10p orange, one phos band	0.20	0.20
10½p grey–blue (January 18, 1978)	0.30	0.35
11p red (October 20, 1976)	0.30	0.35

Phosphor coated paper. PVAD gum

12p yellow–green (July 23, 1980)	0.35	0.35
13½p red–brown (July 23, 1980)	0.50	0.50
15p blue (July 23, 1980)	0.35	0.35

First day cover (2½p, 3p, 5p, 7½p)	–	1.70
First day cover (3½p, 5½p, 8p)	–	1.40
First day cover (4½p)	–	1.25
First day cover (6½p, 8½p)	–	1.00
First day cover (10p, 11p)	–	1.00
First day cover (7p, 9p, 10½p)	–	1.00
First day cover (12p, 13½p, 15p)	–	1.00

■ 1981–1986. Printed in litho by Waddingtons

Perf 13½x14. Phosphor coated paper, except 11½p, 12p, 12½p, 13p (left side phosphor band), 22p (advanced coated paper). PVAD gum except 11½p, 12½p (PVA).

11½p mushroom (April 8, 1981)	0.40	0.40
12p emerald–green (January7, 1986)	0.80	0.80
12½p light green (February 24, 1982)	0.35	0.35
13p light brown (Oct 23, 1984), type I	0.45	0.45
13p light brown, type II	6.00	6.00
14p grey–blue (April 8, 1981)	0.35	0.35
15½p pale–violet (February 24, 1982)	0.40	0.40
16p light mushroom (April 27, 1983)	0.50	0.50
17p steel blue (October 23, 1984), type I	1.00	1.00
17p steel blue, type II	1.10	1.10
17p steel blue, type II, PVA gum	1.00	1.00
18p violet (April 8, 1981)	0.50	0.50
19½p grey–green (February 24, 1982)	1.00	1.00
20½p bright blue (April 27, 1983)	2.00	2.00
22p deep blue (April 8, 1981)	0.50	0.50
22p yellowish green (Oct 23, 1984), type I	2.00	2.00
22p yellowish green, type II	16.00	16.00
26p red (February 24, 1982), type I	0.60	0.60
28p blue (April 27, 1983), type I	0.60	0.60
31p purple (October 23, 1984), type I	1.10	1.10
31p purple, type II	£135	£100

(*The 16p also exists printed by Harrisons on advanced coated paper in 1983; price £4 mint, £3.75 used.)

First day cover (11½p, 14p, 18p, 22p)	–	1.00
First day cover (12½p, 15½p, 19½p, 26p)	–	1.50
First day cover (16p, 20½p, 28p)	–	1.50

First day cover (13p, 17p, 22p, 31p)	–	1.50
First day cover (12p)	–	1.10

■ 1986–1993. Printed in litho by Questa

Perf 15x14. One centre phosphor band (12p, 13p, 14p, 18p), phosphor coated paper (19p, 20p, 23p, 24p, 26p, 28p, 32p, 34p, 37p, 39p), or as indicated. PVAD gum.

12p emerald–green (April 29, 1986)	1.00	1.00
13p light brown (November 4, 1986)	0.60	0.60
14p deep blue (November 8, 1988)	0.40	0.40
14p deep blue, left band	0.40	0.40
15p bright blue (Nov 28, 1989), left band	0.35	0.35
17p steel blue (April 29, 1986)	0.40	0.40
18p deep green (January 6, 1987)	0.75	0.75
18p bright green (December 3, 1991)	0.75	0.75
18p bright green, perf 14	0.75	0.75
18p bright green, left band	1.20	1.20
19p orange–red (November 8, 1988)	0.50	0.50
19p orange–red, two bands	1.00	1.00
20p brownish–black (November 28, 1989)	0.50	0.50
22p green (Jan 27, 1987), advanced coated paper	0.75	0.80
22p orange–red (Dec 4, 1990), phos paper	0.75	0.75
23p bright green (November 8, 1988)	0.75	0.75
23p bright green, two bands	6.00	6.00
24p deep red (November 28, 1989)	0.45	0.65
24p chestnut (December 3, 1991)	0.70	0.70
24p chestnut, perf 14	5.00	5.00
24p chestnut, two bands	1.20	1.20
26p red (Jan 27, 1987), advanced coated paper	2.00	2.00
26p drab (December 4, 1990)	0.75	0.75
28p blue (Jan 27, 1987), advanced coated paper	0.85	0.85
28p bluish grey (December 3, 1991)	0.80	0.80
28p bluish grey, perf 14	6.00	6.00
31p purple (April 29, 1986)	1.20	1.20
32p greenish blue (November 8, 1988)	0.80	0.80
34p bluish grey (November 28, 1989)	1.00	1.00
37p rosine (December 4, 1990)	1.20	1.20
39p mauve (December 3, 1991)	1.20	1.20
39p mauve, perf 14	10.00	10.00

(*The 19p and 23p with two bands come from the 1989 Scots Connection prestige stamp book. The 13p also exists printed on paper supplied by Coated Papers Ltd, with PVA gum, in 1987)

First day cover (12p, 17p, 31p)	–	10.00
First day cover (13p)	–	9.00
First day cover (18p)	–	1.00
First day cover (22p, 26p, 28p)	–	1.50
First day cover (14p, 19p, 23p, 32p)	–	2.00
First day cover (15p, 20p, 24p, 34p)	–	2.00
First day cover (17p, 22p, 26p, 37p)	–	2.50
First day cover (18p, 24p, 28p, 39p)	–	2.90

DECIMAL MACHIN ISSUES WITH ELLIPTICAL PERFORATIONS

■ 1993–1996. Printed in litho by Questa

Perf 15x14. One phosphor band (19p and 20p), or two phosphor bands (others).

19p bistre (December 7, 1993)	0.60	0.60
19p bistre, one right band	2.00	2.00

20p bright green (July 23, 1996)	0.90	0.90
25p red (December 7, 1993)	0.60	0.60
26p red-brown (July 23, 1996)	1.00	1.00
30p olive-grey (December 7, 1993)	0.90	0.90
37p mauve (July 23, 1996)	1.40	1.40
41p grey-brown (December 7, 1993)	1.00	1.00
63p emerald (July 23, 1996)	3.00	3.00

(* The 19p with phosphor band to right comes from the 1995 National Trust prestige stamp book.)

■ 1997–2000. Printed in gravure by Walsall

Perf 15x14. except where stated. One phosphor band (20p), or two phosphor bands (others).

20p bright green (July 1, 1997)	2.50	2.50
26p chestnut (July 1, 1997)	1.20	1.20
37p mauve (July 1, 1997)	1.30	1.30
63p emerald (July 1, 1997)	3.00	3.00

(*The 20p with right phosphor band, the 26p perf 15x14 and perf 14, and the 37p also exist printed by Harrisons, from prestige stamp books.)

Perf 15x14. One phosphor band

1st orange-red (February 15, 2000)	1.35	1.20

(*This stamp was issued only in the Special By Design prestige stamp book.)

First day cover (19p, 25p, 30p, 41p)	–	3.00
First day cover (20p, 26p, 37p, 63p)	–	3.00

PICTORIAL ISSUES WITHOUT WHITE BORDERS

Scottish flag (2nd)

Scottish lion (1st)

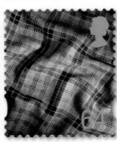

Thistle (E)

Tartan (64p, 65p, 68p)

■ 1999–2002

Des: A. Morris (2nd), F. Pottinger and T. Chalk (1st, E), Tayburn (64p), all adapted by Tayburn. Printed in gravure by Walsall (2nd, 1st, E, 64p, 65p), Questa (2nd, 1st, E, 65p), or De La Rue (2nd, 1st, 68p). Perf 15x14. One phosphor band (2nd), two phosphor bands (others).

2nd (June 8, 1999, Walsall)	1.00	1.00
2nd (August 4, 2000, Questa)	1.00	1.00
2nd (June 5, 2002, De La Rue)	1.00	1.00
1st (June 8, 1999, Walsall)	1.20	1.20
1st (October 22, 2001, Questa)	1.35	1.25
1st (June 5, 2002, De La Rue)	1.25	1.25
E (June 8, 1999, Walsall)	1.75	1.75
E (October 22, 2001, Questa)	1.75	1.75
64p (June 8, 1999)	5.00	5.00
65p (April 25, 2000, Walsall)	2.00	2.00
65p (August 4, 2000, Questa)	2.00	2.00
68p (July 4, 2002)	2.20	2.20

(*The 2nd, 1st, E and 65p printed by Questa come from the 2000 Queen Mother and 2001 Unseen and Unheard prestige stamp books.)

First day cover (2nd, 1st E, 64p)	–	4.00
First day cover (65p)	–	2.50
First day cover (68p)	–	2.00
Stamp cards	5.00	14.00

PICTORIAL ISSUES WITH WHITE BORDERS

Scottish flag (2nd)

Scottish lion (1st)

Thistle (E, 40p, 42p, 44p, 48p, 50p, 56p, 60p, 87p, 88p, 97p, £1.00, £1.05)

Tartan (68p, 72p, 78p, 81p, 90p, 97p, £1.10, £1.28, £1.33)

■ 2003–2016
Des: A. Morris (2nd), F. Pottinger and T. Chalk (1st, E), Tayburn (68p), all adapted by Tayburn. Printed in gravure by De La Rue (2nd, 1st, E, 40p, 42p, 44p, 48p, 50p, 56p, 60p, 68p, 72p, 78p, 81p, 90p, 97p), in gravure by Walsall (42p), in gravure by Enschedé (2nd, 1st, 50p, 81p), in litho by De La Rue (1st, 78p, 81p), in litho by Enschedé (1st, in prestige stamp books only) or in litho by Cartor (2nd, 1st, 68p, 87p, 88p, £1.00, £1.05, £1.10, £1.28, £1.33). Perf 15x14. One phosphor band (2nd) or two phosphor bands (others).

2nd (October 14, 2003, De La Rue)	1.00	1.00
2nd (January 3, 2013, Cartor), silver head	1.00	1.00
2nd (2016, Cartor), grey head	1.50	1.50
1st (October 14, 2003, De La Rue)	1.20	1.20
1st (January 3, 2013, Cartor)	1.20	1.20
E (October 14, 2003)	1.75	1.75
40p (May 11, 2004)	1.00	1.00
42p (April 5, 2005, Walsall)	1.50	1.50
42p (May 10, 2005, De La Rue)	1.40	1.40
44p (March 28, 2006)	1.25	1.20
48p (March 27, 2007)	0.80	0.80
50p (April 1, 2008)	1.00	1.00
56p (March 31, 2009)	1.00	1.00
60p (March 30, 2010)	1.20	1.20
68p (October 14, 2003, De La Rue)	1.30	1.30
68p (March 29, 2011, Cartor)	1.40	1.40
72p (March 28, 2006)	1.70	1.70
78p (March 27, 2007)	1.50	1.50
81p (April 1, 2008)	1.80	1.80
87p (April 25, 2012)	2.00	2.00
88p (March 27, 2013)	1.90	1.90
90p (March 31, 2009)	2.00	2.00
97p (March 30, 2010)	2.00	2.00
97p (March 26, 2014)	2.00	2.00
£1.00 (March 24, 2015)	2.00	2.00
£1.05 (March 22, 2016)	2.25	2.25
£1.10 (March 29, 2011)	2.00	2.00
£1.28 (April 25, 2012)	2.25	2.25
£1.33 (March 24, 2015)	2.25	2.25

(*Various values have also appeared in miniature sheets and prestige stamp books. The 1st class also exists, self-adhesive, in Smilers sheets. Although January 3, 2013, was the official date of issue of the 1st class and 2nd class printed by Cartor, both stamps were available earlier from post offices.)

First day cover (2nd, 1st, E, 68p)	–	3.50
First day cover (40p)	–	2.00
First day cover (42p)	–	2.00
First day cover (44p, 72p)	–	2.50
First day cover (48p, 78p)	–	2.50
First day cover (50p, 81p)	–	3.50
First day cover (56p, 90p)	–	3.50
First day cover (60p, 97p)	–	3.50
First day cover (68p, £1.10)	–	3.50
First day cover (87p, £1.28)	–	5.00
First day cover (88p)	–	2.00
First day cover (97p)	–	2.25
First day cover (£1.00, £1.33)	–	4.00
First day cover (£1.05)	–	2.25
Stamp cards	5.00	11.00

Scottish flag (2nd)

Scottish lion (1st)

Thistle (£1.17, £1.25, £1.35)

Tartan (£1.40, £1.45, £1.55)

■ 2017 to date
As previous issue but with revised typeface for denomination. Printed in litho by Cartor. Perf 15 x 14. One phosphor band (2nd) or two phosphor bands (others).

2nd (March 20, 2018)	1.75	1.75
1st (March 20, 2018)	1.80	1.80
£1.17 (March 21, 2017)	2.20	2.20
£1.25 (March 20, 2018)	2.50	2.50
£1.35 (March 19, 2019)	2.50	2.50
£1.40 (March 21, 2017)	2.50	2.50
£1.45 (March 20, 2018)	2.75	2.75
£1.55 (March 19, 2019)	2.75	2.75

First day cover (£1.17, £1.40)	–	5.00
First day cover (2nd, 1st, £1.25, £1.45)	–	7.00
First day cover (£1.35, £1.55)	–	5.00

WALES DEFINITIVES

Prices in this section are quoted in two columns: mint (left) and fine used (right).

PRE-DECIMAL WILDING ISSUES

3d lilac, 4d blue, 5d blue   6d purple, 9d green

1/3 green, 1/6 grey-blue

◼ 1958–1969
Des: Reynolds Stone. Printed in gravure by Harrisons. Perf 15x14.

Wmk: Multiple St. Edward's Crown. Non-phosphor except where stated

3d lilac (August 18, 1958)	0.15	0.15
3d lilac, one phos band	0.15	0.20
4d blue (February 7, 1966)	0.20	0.15
4d blue, two phos bands	0.15	0.15
6d purple (September 29, 1958)	0.30	0.25
9d green (March 1, 1967), two phos bands	0.35	0.30
1/3 green (September 29, 1958)	0.45	0.40
1/6 grey-blue (March 1, 1967), two bands	0.40	0.30
First day cover (3d)	–	10.00
First day cover (6d, 1/3)	–	20.00
First day cover (4d)	–	7.50
First day cover (9d, 1/6)	–	2.75

No watermark. Two phosphor bands except where stated. PVA gum except where stated

3d lilac (June 6, 1967), one band, gum Arabic	0.20	0.20
4d blue (June 21, 1968)	0.20	0.30

4d sepia (September 4, 1968), one band	0.15	0.15
4d red (February 26, 1969), one band	0.40	0.15
5d blue (September 4, 1968)	0.30	0.25
1/6 grey-blue (December 12, 1968)	2.00	2.00
First day cover (4d sepia, 5d)	–	2.50
First day cover (4d red)	–	1.00

DECIMAL MACHIN ISSUES WITHOUT ELLIPTICAL PERFORATIONS

3p blue

Des: J. Matthews. Type I has the eye on the dragon symbol appearing as a circle, while the tongue, claws and tail are thin; type II (1983) has a solid eye, and thicker tongue, claws and tail.

◼ 1971–1980. Printed in gravure by Harrisons
Perf 15x14. Two phosphor bands except where stated.

Original coated paper. PVA gum

2½p pink (July 7, 1971), one phos band	0.25	0.25
3p blue (July 7, 1971)	0.15	0.15
5p violet (July 7, 1971)	0.50	0.50
7½p brown (July 7, 1971)	0.65	0.65

Fluorescent coated paper. Gum Arabic

2½p pink (September 22, 1972), one band	0.35	–
3p blue (June 6, 1973)	0.35	–

Fluorescent coated paper. PVA gum

2½p pink (1973), one phos band	2.25	2.00
3p blue (February 1973)	9.00	7.00
3p blue (January 1, 1974), one phos band	0.35	0.30
5p violet (June 1973)	18.00	18.00

Fluorescent coated paper. PVAD gum

3½p green (January 23, 1974)	0.15	0.25
3½p green, one phos band	0.15	0.25
4½p grey-blue (November 6, 1974)	0.15	0.30
5½p deep violet (January 23, 1974)	0.15	0.25
5½p deep violet, one phos band	0.20	0.30
6½p green-blue (January 14, 1976), one band	0.20	0.35
7p red-brown (January 18, 1978), one band	0.20	0.30
8p red (January 23, 1974)	0.20	0.35
8½p green (January 14, 1976)	0.20	0.35

9p violet–blue (January 18, 1978) 0.20 0.20
10p orange (October 20, 1976) 0.25 0.25
10p orange, one phos band 0.25 0.25
10¹/₂p grey–blue (January 18, 1978) 0.30 0.30
11p red (October 20, 1976) 0.30 0.30

Phosphor coated paper. PVAD gum
12p yellow–green (July 23, 1980) 0.30 0.30
13¹/₂p red–brown (July 23, 1980) 0.40 0.40
15p blue (July 23, 1980) 0.45 0.45

First day cover (2¹/₂p, 3p, 5p, 7¹/₂p) – 1.70
First day cover (3¹/₂p, 5¹/₂p, 8p) – 1.00
First day cover (4¹/₂p) – 1.25
First day cover (6¹/₂p, 8¹/₂p) – 1.00
First day cover (10p, 11p) – 1.00
First day cover (7p, 9p, 10¹/₂p) – 1.00
First day cover (12p 13¹/₂p, 15p) – 1.00

■ **1981–1991. Printed in litho by Questa**
*Perf 13¹/₂x14. Phosphor coated paper, except 11¹/₂p and 12¹/₂p (left
side band). PVA gum (11¹/₂p, 14p, 18p, 22p), PVAD gum (others)*
11¹/₂p mushroom (April 8, 1981) 0.40 0.40
12¹/₂p light green (February 24, 1982) 0.25 0.35
14p steel–blue (April 8, 1981) 0.35 0.35
15¹/₂p pale–violet (February 24, 1982) 0.40 0.40
16p light mushroom (April 27, 1983) 0.75 0.75
18p mauve (April 8, 1981) 0.70 0.75
19¹/₂p grey–green (February 24, 1982) 0.90 0.90
20¹/₂p bright blue (April 27, 1983) 1.50 1.50
22p deep blue (April 8, 1981) 0.50 0.50
26p red (February 24, 1982), type I 0.50 0.50
28p blue (April 27, 1983), type I 0.60 0.60

*Perf 15x14. One side phosphor band (12p, 12¹/₂p, 13p), phosphor
coated paper (16p, 17p, 19p, 20p, 22p, 23p, 24p, 26p, 28p, 31p, 32p,
34p, 37p, 39p), or as indicated. PVAD gum*
12p emerald–green (January 7, 1986) 0.50 0.50
12¹/₂p light green (January 10, 1984) 2.50 2.50
13p reddish–brown (Oct 23, 1984), type I 1.00 1.00
13p deep brown, type II 1.00 1.00
14p deep blue (November 8, 1988) 0.50 0.50
15p bright blue (November 28, 1989) 0.65 0.65
16p light mushroom (January 10, 1984) 1.00 1.00
17p steel–blue (October 23, 1984), type I 0.75 0.75
17p steel–blue, type I, advanced coated paper 1.00 1.00
17p steel–blue, type II 40.00 40.00
17p deep blue (December 4, 1990), one band 0.60 0.90
18p deep green (January 6, 1987) 0.60 0.60
18p bright green (December 3, 1991) 1.00 1.00
18p bright green, centre band 0.50 0.50
18p bright green, left band 1.50 1.50
18p bright green, right band 1.25 1.25
18p bright green, perf 14 5.50 5.50
19p orange–red (November 8, 1988) 0.50 0.75
20p brownish–black (November 28, 1989) 0.50 0.60
22p green (Oct 23, 1984), advanced paper 0.60 0.60
22p orange–red (December 4, 1990) 0.60 0.65
23p bright green (November 8, 1988) 0.60 0.60
24p deep red (November 28, 1989) 0.65 0.90

24p chestnut (December 3, 1991) 0.70 0.80
24p chestnut, two bands 1.00 1.00
24p chestnut, perf 14 5.00 5.00
26p red (Jan 27, 1987), type II, advanced paper 0.60 0.60
26p drab (December 4, 1990) 0.75 0.75
28p blue (Jan 27, 1987), type II, advanced paper 1.00 1.00
28p bluish grey (December 3, 1991) 0.60 0.60
31p purple (October 23, 1984) 0.90 0.90
31p purple, advanced coated paper 1.00 1.00
32p greenish blue (November 8, 1988) 1.00 1.20
34p bluish grey (November 28, 1989) 1.20 1.20
37p rosine (December 4, 1990) 1.20 1.20
39p mauve (December 3, 1991) 1.20 1.20
(*The 18p with one band at left or right comes from prestige
stamp books. The 13p also exists printed on paper supplied by
Coated Papers Ltd, with PVA gum, in 1987)

First day cover (11¹/₂p, 14p, 18p, 22p) – 1.00
First day cover (12¹/₂p, 15¹/₂p. 19¹/₂p, 26p) – 1.00
First day cover (16p, 20¹/₂p, 28p) – 1.50
First day cover (12p, 17p, 22p, 31p) – 1.50
First day cover (12p) – 1.00
First day cover (18p) – 1.00
First day cover (14p, 19p, 23p, 32p) – 2.00
First day cover (15p, 20p, 24p, 34p) – 2.00
First day cover (17p, 22p, 26p, 37p) – 2.00
First day cover (18p, 24p, 28p, 39p) – 2.00

DECIMAL MACHIN ISSUES WITH ELLIPTICAL PERFORATIONS

30p olive–grey

■ **1993–1996. Printed in litho by Questa**
Perf 15x14. One phosphor band (19p and 20p), two phosphor
bands (others).
19p bistre (December 7, 1993) 0.60 0.70
19p bistre, right band 1.25 1.25
20p bright green (July 23, 1996) 0.70 0.70
25p red (December 7, 1993) 0.85 0.80
26p red–brown (July 23, 1996) 0.90 1.25
30p olive–grey (December 7, 1993) 1.00 0.95
37p mauve (July 23, 1996) 1.30 2.50
41p grey–brown (December 7, 1993) 1.30 1.80
63p emerald (July 23, 1996) 2.75 2.75
(*The 19p with phosphor band to right comes from the 1995
National Trust prestige stamp book.)

26p chestnut

1997–2000. Printed in gravure by Walsall

Perf 15x14. One phosphor band (19p and 20p), two phosphor bands (others)

20p bright green (July 1, 1997)	1.00	1.00
26p chestnut (July 1, 1997)	1.00	1.00
37p mauve (July 1, 1997)	1.50	1.50
63p emerald (July 1, 1997)	3.00	3.00

(*The 20p with right phosphor band, the 26p perf 15x14 and perf 14, and the 37p also exist printed by Harrisons, from prestige stamp books.)

Perf 15x14. One phosphor band

1st orange–red (February 15, 2000)	2.00	2.00

(*This stamp was issued only in the Special By Design prestige stamp book.)

First day cover (19p, 25p, 30p, 41p)	–	2.50
First day cover (20p, 26p, 37p, 63p)	–	3.00

PICTORIAL ISSUES WITHOUT WHITE BORDERS

Leek (2nd)

Welsh dragon (1st)

Daffodil (E)

Prince of Wales' feathers (64p, 65p, 68p)

1999–2002

Des: D. Petersen (2nd), T. and G. Petersen (1st), I. Rees (E), R. Evans (64p), all adapted by Tutssels. Printed in gravure by Walsall (2nd, 1st, E, 64p, 65p) or De La Rue (2nd, 1st, 68p). Perf 15x14. One phosphor band (2nd), two phosphor bands (others).

2nd (June 8, 1999, Walsall)	1.00	1.00
2nd (September 18, 2000, Walsall), right band	1.75	1.75
2nd (May 28, 2003, De La Rue)	1.00	1.00
1st (June 8, 1999, Walsall)	1.20	0.95
1st (March 4, 2003, De La Rue)	1.60	1.60
E (June 8, 1999)	1.75	1.75
64p (June 8, 1999)	5.00	5.00
65p (April 25, 2000)	2.00	2.00
68p (July 4, 2002)	1.20	1.20

(*The 2nd class with band at right comes from the 2000 Treasury of Trees prestige stamp book.)

First day cover (2nd, 1st, E, 64p)	–	2.00
First day cover (65p)	–	2.00
First day cover (68p)	–	2.00
Stamp cards	5.00	15.00

PICTORIAL ISSUES WITH WHITE BORDERS

Leek (2nd)

Welsh dragon (1st)

Daffodil (E, 40p, 42p, 44p, 48p, 50p, 56p, 60p, 87p, 88p, 97p, £1.00, £1.05)

Prince of Wales' feathers (68p, 72p, 78p, 81p, 90p, 97p, £1.10, £1.28, £1.33)

2003–2016

Des: D. Petersen (2nd), T. and G. Petersen (1st), I. Rees (E), R. Evans (68p), all adapted by Tutssels. Printed in gravure by De La Rue (2nd, 1st, E, 40p, 42p, 44p, 48p, 50p, 56p, 60p, 68p, 72p, 78p,

81p, 90p, 97p), in gravure by Walsall (42p), in litho by De La Rue (1st, 78p, 81p), in litho by Enschedé (1st, in prestige stamp books only) or in litho by Cartor (2nd, 1st, 68p, 87p, 88p, £1.00, £1.05, £1.10, £1.28, £1.33). Perf 15x14. One phosphor band (2nd) or two phosphor bands (others).

2nd (October 14, 2003, De La Rue)	1.00	1.00
2nd (January 3, 2013, Cartor)	1.00	1.00
1st (October 14, 2003, De La Rue)	1.20	1.20
1st (January 3, 2013, Cartor)	1.20	1.20
E (October 14, 2003)	1.75	1.75
40p (May 11, 2004)	1.20	1.20
42p (April 5, 2005, Walsall)	1.60	1.60
42p (May 10, 2005, De La Rue)	1.60	1.60
44p (March 28, 2006)	1.20	1.20
48p (March 27, 2007)	0.80	0.80
50p (April 1, 2008)	0.90	0.90
56p (March 31, 2009)	0.90	0.90
60p (March 30, 2010)	1.20	1.20
68p (October 14, 2003, De La Rue)	1.20	1.20
68p (March 29, 2011, Cartor)	1.30	1.10
72p (March 28, 2006)	1.20	1.20
78p (March 27, 2007)	1.20	1.20
81p (April 1, 2008)	1.90	1.90
87p (April 25, 2012)	1.90	1.90
88p (March 27, 2013)	1.90	1.90
90p (March 31, 2009)	1.80	1.80
97p (March 30, 2010)	2.00	1.75
97p (March 26, 2014)	2.00	2.00
£1.00 (March 24, 2015)	2.00	2.00
£1.05 (March 22, 2016)	2.25	2.25
£1.10 (March 29, 2011)	2.00	1.50
£1.28 (April 25, 2012)	2.30	2.30
£1.33 (March 24, 2015)	2.50	2.50

(*Various values have also appeared in miniature sheets and prestige stamp books. The 1st class also exists, self-adhesive, in Smilers sheets. Although January 3, 2013, was the official date of issue of the 1st class and 2nd class printed by Cartor, both stamps were available earlier from post offices.)

First day cover (2nd, 1st, E, 68p)	–	3.00
First day cover (40p)	–	2.00
First day cover (42p)	–	2.00
First day cover (44p, 72p)	–	2.50
First day cover (48p, 78p)	–	3.00
First day cover (50p, 81p)	–	3.00
First day cover (56p, 90p)	–	3.00
First day cover (60p, 97p)	–	3.00
First day cover (68p, £1.10)	–	3.00
First day cover (87p, £1.28)	–	4.00
First day cover (88p)	–	2.00
First day cover (97p)	–	2.25

First day cover (£1.00, £1.33)	–	4.00
First day cover (£1.05)	–	2.25
Stamp cards	5.00	11.00

Leek (2nd)

Welsh dragon (1st)

Daffodil (£1.17, £1.25, £1.35)

Prince of Wales' feathers (£1.40, £1.45, £1.55)

2017 to date

As previous issue but with revised typeface for denomination. Printed in litho by Cartor. Perf 15 x 14. One phosphor band (2nd) or two phosphor bands (others).

2nd (March 20, 2018)	1.00	1.00
1st (March 20, 2018)	1.25	1.25
£1.17 (March 21, 2017)	2.20	2.20
£1.25 (March 20, 2018)	2.50	2.50
£1.35 (March 19, 2019)	2.50	2.50
£1.40 (March 21, 2017)	2.75	2.75
£1.45 (March 20, 2018)	2.75	2.75
£1.55 (March 19, 2019)	2.75	2.75

First day cover (£1.17, £1.40)	–	5.00
First day cover (2nd, 1st, £1.25, £1.45)	–	7.00
First day cover (£1.35, £1.55)	–	5.00

ENGLAND DEFINITIVES

Prices in this section are quoted in two columns: mint (left) and fine used (right).

PICTORIAL ISSUES WITHOUT WHITE BORDERS

Three lions (2nd)   Crowned lion and shield (1st)

Oak tree (E)   Tudor rose (65p, 68p)

■ 2001–2002

Des: Sedley Place, after sculptures by D. Dathan. Printed in gravure by De La Rue. Perf 15x14. One phosphor band (2nd), two phosphor bands (others).

2nd (April 23, 2001)	1.00	1.00
1st (April 23, 2001)	1.20	1.20
E (April 23, 2001)	1.90	1.90
65p (April 23, 2001)	1.75	1.75
68p (July 4, 2002)	1.75	1.60

(*The 2nd and 1st class also exist printed in gravure by Questa, from the 2002 Across The Universe prestige stamp book.)

First day cover (2nd, 1st, E, 65p)	–	3.00
First day cover (68p)	–	2.50
Stamp cards	6.00	14.00

Keep up with all the latest new issues in the pages of Stamp Magazine

PICTORIAL ISSUES WITH WHITE BORDERS

Three lions (2nd)   Crowned lion and shield (1st)

Oak tree (E, 40p, 42p, 44p, 48p, 50p, 56p, 60p, 87p, 88p, 97p, £1.00, £1.05)

Tudor rose (68p, 72p, 78p, 81p, 90p, 97p, £1.10, £1.28, £1.33)

■ 2003–2016

Des: Sedley Place, after sculptures by D. Dathan. Printed in gravure by De La Rue (2nd, 1st, E, 40p, 42p, 44p, 48p, 50p, 56p, 60p, 68p, 72p, 78p, 81p, 90p, 97p), in gravure by Walsall (2nd, 42p), in litho by De La Rue (1st, 78p, 81p), in litho by Enschedé (1st, in prestige stamp books only) or in litho by Cartor (2nd, 1st, 68p, 87p, 88p, £1.00, £1.05, £1.10, £1.28, £1.33). Perf 15x14. One phosphor band (2nd) or two phosphor bands (others).

2nd (October 14, 2003, De La Rue)	1.00	1.00
2nd (January 3, 2013, Cartor)	1.00	1.00
1st (October 14, 2003, De La Rue)	1.20	1.20
1st (January 3, 2013, Cartor)	1.20	1.20
E (October 14, 2003)	1.90	1.90
40p (May 11, 2004)	1.10	1.25
42p (April 5, 2005, Walsall)	1.50	1.50
42p (May 10, 2005, De La Rue)	1.75	1.75
44p (May 28, 2006)	1.00	1.00
48p (Mar 27, 2007)	0.90	0.90
50p (April 1, 2008)	0.90	0.90
56p (March 31, 2009)	0.90	0.90
60p (March 30, 2010)	1.25	1.00
68p (October 14, 2003, De La Rue)	1.50	1.50
68p (March 29, 2011, Cartor)	1.40	1.40
72p (March 28, 2006)	1.50	1.50
78p (March 27, 2007)	1.60	1.60
81p (April 1, 2008)	1.70	1.70

87p (April 25, 2012)	1.90	1.90
88p (March 27, 2013)	1.90	1.90
90p (March 31, 2009)	1.80	1.80
97p (March 30, 2010)	1.90	1.90
97p (March 26, 2014)	1.90	1.90
£1.00 (March 24, 2015)	1.90	1.90
£1.05 (March 22, 2016)	2.25	2.25
£1.10 (March 29, 2011)	2.00	1.50
£1.28 (April 25, 2012)	2.50	2.50
£1.33 (March 24, 2015)	2.60	2.60

(*Various values have also appeared in miniature sheets and prestige stamp books. The 1st class also exists, self–adhesive, from Smilers sheets. Although January 3, 2013, was the official date of issue of the 1st class and 2nd class printed by Cartor, both stamps were available earlier from post offices.)

First day cover (2nd, 1st, E, 68p)	–	4.50
First day cover (40p)	–	2.50
First day cover (42p)	–	2.00
First day cover (44p, 72p)	–	2.50
First day cover (48p, 78p)	–	3.00
First day cover (50p, 81p)	–	3.00
First day cover (56p, 90p)	–	3.50
First day cover (60p, 97p)	–	3.00
First day cover (68p, £1.10)	–	3.50
First day cover (87p, £1.28)	–	5.00
First day cover (88p)	–	2.00
First day cover (97p)	–	2.25
First day cover (£1.00, £1.33)	–	4.00
First day cover (£1.05)	–	2.25
Stamp cards	5.00	11.00

■ **2017 to date**

As previous issue but with revised typeface for denomination. Printed in litho by Cartor. Perf 15 x 14. One phosphor band (2nd) or two phosphor bands (others).

2nd (March 20, 2018)	1.00	1.00
1st (March 20, 2018)	1.20	1.20
£1.17 (March 21, 2017)	2.20	2.20
£1.25 (March 20, 2018)	2.50	2.50
£1.35 (March 19, 2019)	2.50	2.50
£1.40 (March 21, 2017)	2.75	2.75
£1.45 (March 20, 2018)	2.75	2.75
£1.55 (March 19, 2019)	2.75	2.75

First day cover (£1.17, £1.40)	–	5.00
First day cover (2nd, 1st, £1.25, £1.45)	–	7.00
First day cover (£1.35, £1.55)	–	5.00

Three lions (2nd)

Crowned lion and shield (1st)

Oak tree (£1.17, £1.25, £1.35)

Tudor rose (£1.40, £1.45, £1.55)

STITCHED OR STAPLED BOOKLETS

In this section, items are priced in very fine mint condition only.

EDWARD VII, 1904–10

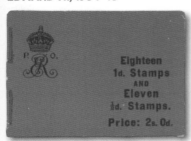

■ 2/– booklets

24 x 1d (sold at 2s ½d). Printed by De La Rue, 1904	£300
12 x 1d, 23 x ½d. Printed by De La Rue, 1906	£1,200
18 x 1d, 11 x ½d. Printed by De La Rue, 1907–09	£1,300
18 x 1d, 11 x ½d. Printed by Harrison, 1911	£1,500

GEORGE V, 1910–35

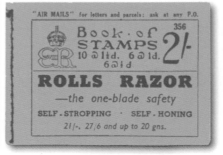

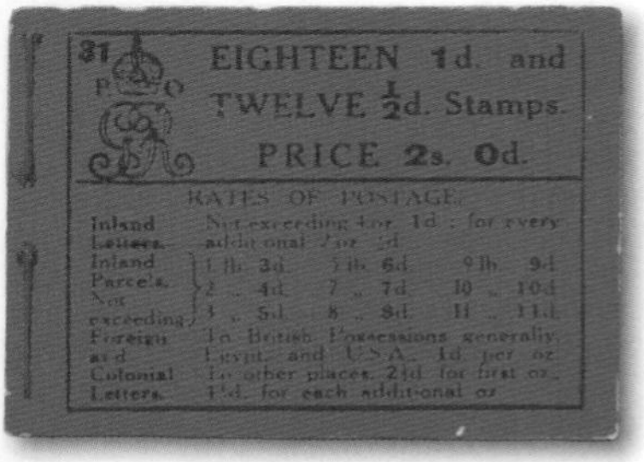

■ 2/– booklets, Downey head

18 x 1d, 12 x ½d. Wmk: Imperial Crown printed by Harrison, 1911	£900
18 x 1d, 12 x ½d. Wmk: Simple Royal Cypher printed by Harrison, 1912	£850

■ 2/– booklets, Mackennal head

18 x 1d, 12 x ½d. Wmk: Simple Royal Cypher printed by Harrison, 1913–17	£700
10 x 1½d, 6 x 1d, 6 x ½d. Wmk: Simple Royal Cypher printed by Harrison, 1924	£1,500
10 x 1½d, 6 x 1d, 6 x ½d. Wmk: Block GVR printed by Waterlow, 1924–33	£550
10 x 1½d, 6 x 1d, 6 x ½d. printed by Waterlow, 1929; PUC stamps	£425
10 x 1½d, 6 x 1d, 6 x ½d. Wmk: Block GVR printed by Harrison, 1934	£750
10 x 1½d, 6 x 1d, 6 x ½d. Wmk: Block GVR printed by Harrison, 1935; photogravure, intermediate	£2,000
10 x 1½d, 6 x 1d, 6 x ½d. Wmk: Block GVR	

printed by Harrison, 1935; photogravure, small format 12 x 1½d, 4 x 1d, 4 x ½d	£525
printed by Harrison, 1935; Silver Jubilee stamps	80.00

■ 3/– booklets

12 x 1½d, 12 x 1d, 12 x ½d. Wmk: Simple Royal Cypher printed by Harrison, 1918	£1,100
18 x 1½d, 6 x 1d, 6 x ½d. Wmk: Simple Royal Cypher printed by Harrison, 1919	£1,100
18 x 2d printed by Harrison, 1921	£1,600
24 x 1½d printed by Harrison, 1922	£1,600
18 x 1½d, 6 x 1d, 6 x ½d. Wmk: Block GVR printed by Waterlow, 1924–33	£400
18 x 1½d, 6 x 1d, 6 x ½d printed by Waterlow, 1929; PUC stamps	£325
18 x 1½d, 6 x 1d, 6 x ½d. Wmk: Block GVR printed by Harrison, 1934	£600
18 x 1½d, 6 x 1d, 6 x ½d. Wmk: Block GVR printed by Harrison, 1935; photogravure, intermediate	£1,600
18 x 1½d, 6 x 1d, 6 x ½d. Wmk: Block GVR printed by Harrison, 1935; photogravure, small format 20 x 1½d, 4 x 1d, 4 x ½d	£350
printed by Harrison, 1935; Silver Jubilee stamps	55.00

■ 3/6 booklets

18 x 2d, 6 x 1d printed by Harrison, 1920	£1,350
12 x 2d, 6 x 1½d, 6 x 1d, 6 x ½d printed by Harrison, 1921	£1,350

■ 5/– booklets

34 x 1½d, 6 x 1d, 6 x ½d. Green cover printed by Waterlow, 1931	£4,000
34 x 1½d, 6 x 1d, 6 x ½d. Buff cover printed by Waterlow, 1932	£3,600
34 x 1½d, 6 x 1d, 6 x ½d printed by Harrison, 1934	£1,500
34 x 1½d, 6 x 1d, 6 x ½d printed by Harrison, 1935; photogravure, intermediate	£4,500
34 x 1½d, 6 x 1d, 6 x ½d printed by Harrison, 1935; photogravure, small format	£400

EDWARD VIII, 1936

6d booklets
4 x 1½d (plain cover). Printed by Harrison, 1937 — 30.00

2/– booklets
10 x 1½d, 6 x 1d, 6 x ½d. Printed by Harrison, 1936 — 95.00

3/– booklets
18 x 1½d, 6 x 1d, 6 x ½d. Printed by Harrison, 1936 — 95.00

5/– booklets
34 x 1½d, 6 x 1d, 6 x ½d. Printed by Harrison, 1937 — £200

GEORGE VI, 1937–52

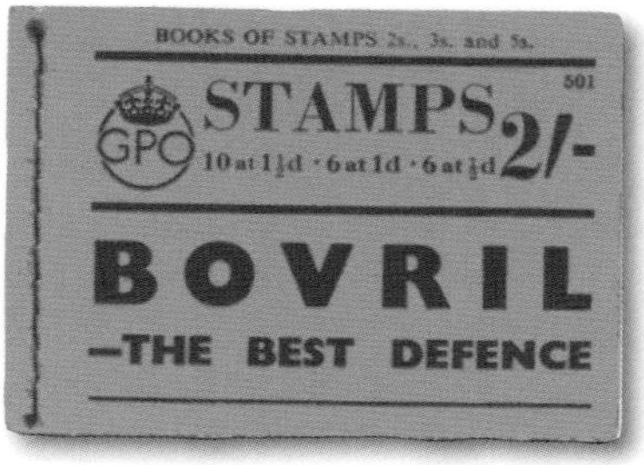

6d booklets
4 x 1½d (plain buff cover)
printed by Harrison, 1938 — 55.00
2 x 1½d, 2 x 1d, 2 x ½d (plain pink cover)
printed by Harrison, 1938 — £220
4 x 1d, 4 x ½d (plain green cover)
printed by Harrison, 1940 — 95.00

1/– booklets
4 x 1½d, 4 x 1d, 4 x ½d (in panes of two)
printed by Harrison, 1947; stamps in pale shades — 11.00
4 x 1½d, 4 x 1d, 4 x ½d (in panes of four)
printed by Harrison, 1948; stamps in pale shades — £5,000
4 x 1½d, 4 x 1d, 4 x ½d (in panes of two)
printed by Harrison, 1951; stamps in changed colours — 20.00
4 x 1½d, 4 x 1d, 4 x ½d (in panes of four)
printed by Harrison, 1951; stamps in changed colours — 15.00

2/– booklets
10 x 1½d, 6 x 1d, 6 x ½d (royal cypher on cover)
printed by Harrison, 1937 — £600
10 x 1½d, 6 x 1d, 6 x ½d (GPO cypher on cover)
printed by Harrison, 1938 — £600

2/6 booklets
6 x 2½d, 6 x 2d, 6 x ½d (red cover)
printed by Harrison, 1940 — £850
6 x 2½d, 6 x 2d, 6 x ½d (blue cover)
printed by Harrison, 1940 — £850
6 x 2½d, 6 x 2d, 6 x ½d (green cover)
printed by Harrison, 1940 — £550
6 x 2½d, 6 x 2d, 6 x ½d (green cover)
printed by Harrison, 1942; stamps in pale shades — £550

6 x 2½d, 6 x 2d, 6 x ½d (green cover, no advertising)
printed by Harrison, 1943; stamps in pale shades — £110
6 x 2½d, 6 x 2d, 6 x ½d (green cover, no advertising)
printed by Harrison, 1951; stamps in changed colours — 40.00
6 x 2½d, 6 x 1½d, 3 x 1d, 6 x ½d
printed by Harrison, 1952 — 30.00

3/– booklets
18 x 1½d, 6 x 1d, 6 x ½d (royal cypher on cover)
printed by Harrison, 1937 — £1,050
18 x 1½d, 6 x 1d, 6 x ½d (GPO cypher on cover)
printed by Harrison, 1938 — £1,050

5/– booklets
34 x 1½d, 6 x 1d, 6 x ½d (royal cypher on cover)
printed by Harrison, 1937 — £1,100
34 x 1½d, 6 x 1d, 6 x ½d (GPO cypher on cover)
printed by Harrison, 1938 — £1,100
18 x 2½d, 6 x 2d, 6 x ½d (GPO cypher on cover)
printed by Harrison, 1940 — £1,100
18 x 2½d, 6 x 2d, 6 x ½d (GPO cypher on cover)
printed by Harrison, 1942; stamps in pale shades — £1,100
18 x 2½d, 6 x 2d, 6 x ½d (GPO cypher, no advertising)
printed by Harrison, 1943; stamps in pale shades — £120
18 x 2½d, 6 x 2d, 6 x ½d (GPO cypher, no advertising)
printed by Harrison, 1951; stamps in changed colours — 50.00
18 x 2½d, 6 x 1½d, 3 x 1d, 6 x ½d
printed by Harrison, 1952 — 35.00
12 x 2½d, 6 x 2d, 6 x 1½d, 6 x 1d, 6 x ½d
printed by Harrison, 1953 — 50.00

ELIZABETH II WILDINGS, 1953–68

1/– booklets
4 x 1½d, 4 x 1d, 4 x ½d (panes of 2). Wmk: Tudor Crown
printed by Harrison, 1953 — 3.00
4 x 1½d, 4 x 1d, 4 x ½d (panes of 4). Wmk: Tudor Crown
printed by Harrison, 1954 — 6.00
4 x 1½d, 4 x 1d, 4 x ½d (panes of 2). Wmk: St. Edward's Crown
printed by Harrison, 1957 — 35.00
4 x 1½d, 4 x 1d, 4 x ½d (panes of 4). Wmk: St. Edward's Crown
printed by Harrison, 1956 — 4.00
4 x 1½d, 4 x 1d, 4 x ½d (panes of 4). Wmk: Multiple Crowns
printed by Harrison, 1959 — 3.00

2/– booklets
4 x 3d, 4 x 1½d, 4 x 1d, 4 x ½d. Wmk: St. Edward's Crown
printed by Harrison, 1959; pink cover — 5.00
4 x 3d, 4 x 1½d, 4 x 1d, 4 x ½d. Wmk: Multiple Crowns (upright)
printed by Harrison, 1960; pink cover — 5.00

4 x 3d, 4 x 1½d, 4 x 1d, 4 x ½d. Wmk: Multiple Crowns (upright)
printed by Harrison, 1961; yellow cover 4.00
4 x 3d, 4 x 1½d, 4 x 1d, 4 x ½d. Wmk: Multiple Crowns (sideways)
printed by Harrison, 1961–65; yellow cover 25.00
4 x 3d, 4 x 1½d, 4 x 1d, 4 x ½d. Wmk: Multiple Crowns (sideways)
printed by Harrison, 1961–65; yellow cover; phos bands 45.00
4 x 4d, 2 x 1d se-tenant with 2 x 3d. Wmk: Multiple Crowns
printed by Harrison, 1965–67; 3d with no phos bands 4.00
4 x 4d, 2 x 1d se-tenant with 2 x 3d. Wmk: Multiple Crowns
printed by Harrison, 1965–67; 3d with one phos band 8.00
4 x 4d, 2 x 1d se-tenant with 2 x 3d. Wmk: Multiple Crowns
printed by Harrison, 1968; 3d with two phos bands 3.00
8 x 2½d, 3 x ½d se-tenant with 1 x 2½d. Wmk: Multiple Crowns
printed by Harrison, 1963 3.00
8 x ½d, 8 x 2½d (se-tenant in panes). Wmk: Multiple Crowns
printed by Harrison, 1964 3.00
8 x 3d. Wmk: Multiple Crowns (sideways)
printed by Harrison, 1965 1.00

■ 2/6 booklets

6 x 2½d, 6 x 1½d (QEII), 3 x 1d, 6 x ½d (KGVI)
printed by Harrison, 1953–54 25.00
6 x 2½d, 6 x 1½d, 6 x ½d (QEII), 3 x 1d (KGVI)
printed by Harrison, 1954 £400
6 x 2½d, 6 x 1½d, 3x 1d, 6 x ½d. Wmk: Tudor Crown
printed by Harrison, 1954–55 35.00
6 x 2½d, 6 x 1½d, 3x 1d, 6 x ½d. Wmk: St Edward's Crown
printed by Harrison, 1955–57 22.00
6 x 2½d, 6 x 2d, 6 x ½d, Wmk: St Edward's Crown
printed by Harrison, 1957 20.00

■ 3/- booklets

6 x 3d, 6 x 1½d, 6 x 1d, 6 x ½d. Wmk: St Edward's Crown
printed by Harrison, 1958 18.00
6 x 3d, 6 x 1½d, 6 x 1d, 6 x ½d. Wmk: Multiple Crowns
printed by Harrison, 1959–65 30.00
6 x 3d, 6 x 1½d, 6 x 1d, 6 x ½d. Wmk: Multiple Crowns
printed by Harrison, 1959–60; stamps with graphite lines £150
6 x 3d, 6 x 1½d, 6 x 1d, 6 x ½d. Wmk: Multiple Crowns
printed by Harrison, 1960–65; stamps with phos bands 50.00

■ 3/9 booklets

18 x 2½d. Wmk: Tudor Crown
printed by Harrison, 1953–55 20.00
18 x 2½d. Wmk: St Edward's Crown
printed by Harrison, 1956–57 18.00

■ 4/6 booklets

18 x 3d. Wmk: St Edward's Crown
printed by Harrison, 1957–58 18.00
18 x 3d. Wmk: Multiple Crowns
printed by Harrison, 1959 18.00
18 x 3d. Wmk: Multiple Crowns
printed by Harrison, 1959–60; stamps with graphite lines 15.00
18 x 3d. Wmk: Multiple Crowns
printed by Harrison, 1960–65; stamps with phos bands 30.00
12 x 4d, 6 x 1d.Wmk: Multiple Crowns
printed by Harrison, 1965–67 18.00
12 x 4d, 6 x 1d.Wmk: Multiple Crowns
printed by Harrison, 1965–68; stamps with phos bands 7.00

■ 5/- booklets

12 x 2½d, 6 x 1½d (QEII), 6 x 2d, 6 x 1d, 6 x ½d (KGVI)
printed by Harrison, 1953–54 30.00
12 x 2½d, 6 x 1½d, 6 x ½d (QEII), 6 x 2d, 6 x 1d (KGVI)
printed by Harrison, 1954 £500
12 x 2½d, 6 x 1½d, 6 x ½d, 6 x 1d (QEII), 6 x 2d (KGVI)
printed by Harrison, 1954 £200
12 x 2½d, 6 x 1½d, 6 x ½d, 6 x 1d, 6 x 2d. Wmk: Tudor Crown
printed by Harrison, 1954–55 65.00
12 x 2½d, 6 x 1½d, 6 x ½d, 6 x 1d, 6 x 2d. Wmk: St Edward's
printed by Harrison, 1955–57 30.00
12 x 3d, 6 x 2½d, 6 x 1½d, 6 x ½d.Wmk: St Edward's Crown
printed by Harrison, 1958 20.00
12 x 3d, 6 x 2½d, 6 x 1½d, 6 x ½d. Wmk: Multiple Crowns
printed by Harrison, 1959–65 25.00
12 x 3d, 6 x 2½d, 6 x 1½d, 6 x ½d. Wmk: Multiple Crowns
printed by Harrison, 1959–60; stamps with graphite lines 80.00
12 x 3d, 6 x 2½d, 6 x 1½d, 6 x ½d. Wmk: Multiple Crowns
printed by Harrison, 1960–62; 2½d with two phos bands £150
12 x 3d, 6 x 2½d, 6 x 1½d, 6 x ½d. Wmk: Multiple Crowns
printed by Harrison, 1962–65; 2½d with one phos band £150

■ 6/- booklets

18 x 4d.Wmk: Multiple Crowns
printed by Harrison, 1965–67 30.00
18 x 4d.Wmk: Multiple Crowns
printed by Harrison, 1965–67; stamps with phos bands 35.00

■ 10/- booklets

30 x 3d, 6 x 2d, 6 x 1½d, 6 x 1d, 6 x ½d
printed by Harrison, 1961 80.00
30 x 3d, 6 x 2½d, 6 x 1½d, 6 x 1d
printed by Harrison, 1962–64 90.00
24 x 4d, 6 x 3d, 6 x 1d
printed by Harrison, 1965–66 25.00
24 x 4d, 6 x 3d, 6 x 1d
printed by Harrison, 1967; 3d with side phos band 8.00
24 x 4d, 6 x 3d, 6 x 1d
printed by Harrison, 1967–68; 3d with centre phos band 5.00

ELIZABETH II PRE–DECIMAL MACHINS, 1968–70

■ 2/- booklets

4 x 4d sepia (two phos bands), 2 x 1d se-tenant with 2 x 3d
(two phos bands)
printed by Harrison, 1968; yellow cover 0.80
4 x 4d sepia (two phos bands), plus 2 x 4d sepia (centre

phos band) se-tenant with two labels
printed by Harrison, 1968-70; grey cover 0.65
4 x 4d sepia (centre phos band), plus 2 x 4d sepia (centre
phos band) se-tenant with two labels
printed by Harrison, 1968-69; grey cover 1.00
4 x 4d red (centre phos band) plus 2 x 4d red (centre
phos band) se-tenant with two labels
printed by Harrison, 1969-70; grey cover 1.50

■ 4/6 booklets. Ships series
6 x 4d sepia, 6 x 4d sepia (two phos bands), 6 x 1d
printed by Harrison, 1968; blue plain cover 4.00
6 x 4d sepia, 6 x 4d sepia (two phos bands), 6 x 1d
printed by Harrison, 1968; Cutty Sark cover 1.00
6 x 4d sepia, 6 x 4d sepia (centre phos band), 6 x 1d
printed by Harrison, 1968; Golden Hind cover 1.00
6 x 4d sepia, 6 x 4d sepia (centre phos band), 6 x 1d
printed by Harrison, 1968; Discovery cover 1.00
6 x 4d red, 6 x 4d red (centre phos band), 6 x 1d
printed by Harrison, 1969; Queen Elizabeth 2 cover 1.25
6 x 4d red, 6 x 4d red (centre phos band), 6 x 1d
printed by Harrison, 1969; Sirius cover 2.50
6 x 4d red, 6 x 4d red (centre phos band), 6 x 1d
printed by Harrison, 1969; Dreadnought cover 1.50
6 x 4d red, 6 x 4d red (centre phos band), 6 x 1d
printed by Harrison, 1969-70; Mauretania cover 2.00
6 x 4d red, 6 x 4d red (centre phos band), 6 x 1d
printed by Harrison, 1970; Victory cover 2.00
6 x 4d red, 6 x 4d red (centre phos band), 6 x 1d
printed by Harrison, 1970; Sovereign on the Seas cover 4.00

■ 5/- booklets. English Homes series
6 x 5d, 6 x 5d
printed by Harrison, 1968; Ightham Mote cover 2.00
6 x 5d, 6 x 5d
printed by Harrison, 1969; Little Moreton Hall cover 2.00
6 x 5d, 6 x 5d
printed by Harrison, 1969; Long Melford Hall cover 2.50
6 x 5d, 6 x 5d
printed by Harrison, 1969; Mompesson House cover 2.00
6 x 5d, 6 x 5d
printed by Harrison, 1970; Cumberland Terrace cover 2.00
6 x 5d, 6 x 5d
printed by Harrison, 1970; Vineyard, Saffron Walden cover 2.50
6 x 5d, 6 x 5d
printed by Harrison, 1970; Mereworth Castle cover 3.25
6 x 5d, 6 x 5d
printed by Harrison, 1970; Philympia 1970 cover 2.00

■ 6/- booklets. Birds series
6 x 4d sepia, 6 x 4d sepia, 6 x 4d sepia (phos bands), gum arabic
printed by Harrison, 1967-68; plain purple cover 45.00
6 x 4d sepia, 6 x 4d sepia, 6 x 4d sepia (phos bands), PVA gum
printed by Harrison, 1970; plain purple cover £475
6 x 4d sepia, 6 x 4d sepia, 6 x 4d sepia (two phos bands)
printed by Harrison, 1968; Kingfisher cover 2.00
6 x 4d sepia, 6 x 4d sepia, 6 x 4d sepia (two phos bands)
printed by Harrison, 1968; Peregrine Falcon cover 1.80
6 x 4d sepia, 6 x 4d sepia, 6 x 4d sepia (centre phos band)
printed by Harrison, 1968; Peregrine Falcon cover 2.00

6 x 4d sepia, 6 x 4d sepia, 6 x 4d sepia (centre phos band)
printed by Harrison, 1968; Pied Woodpecker cover 2.00
6 x 4d sepia, 6 x 4d sepia, 6 x 4d sepia (centre phos band)
printed by Harrison, 1968; Great Crested Grebe cover 2.00
6 x 4d sepia, 6 x 4d sepia, 6 x 4d sepia (centre phos band)
printed by Harrison, 1969; Barn Owl cover 3.00
6 x 4d red, 6 x 4d red, 6 x 4d red (centre phos band)
printed by Harrison, 1969; Barn Owl cover 3.50
6 x 4d red, 6 x 4d red, 6 x 4d red (centre phos band)
printed by Harrison, 1969; Jay cover 3.00
6 x 4d red, 6 x 4d red, 6 x 4d red (centre phos band)
printed by Harrison, 1969; Puffin cover 3.00
6 x 4d red, 6 x 4d red, 6 x 4d red (centre phos band)
printed by Harrison, 1969-70; Cormorant cover 3.50
6 x 4d red, 6 x 4d red, 6 x 4d red (centre phos band)
printed by Harrison, 1970; Wren cover 3.50
6 x 4d red, 6 x 4d red, 6 x 4d red (centre phos band)
printed by Harrison, 1970; Golden Eagle cover 3.50

■ 10/- booklets. Explorers series
6 x 4d sepia, 6 x 4d sepia, 6 x 4d sepia (two
phos bands), 6 x 3d, 6 x 1d
printed by Harrison, 1968; Livingstone cover 4.50
6 x 5d, 6 x 5d, 6 x 4d sepia, 6 x 4d sepia (centre phos band),
4 x 1d se-tenant with 2 x 4d sepia (one phos band)
printed by Harrison, 1968; Scott cover 3.50
6 x 5d, 6 x 5d, 6 x 4d red, 6 x 4d red (centre phos band),
4 x 1d se-tenant with 2 x 4d red (one phos band)
printed by Harrison, 1969; Kingsley cover 3.50
6 x 5d, 6 x 5d, 6 x 4d red, 6 x 4d red (centre phos band),
4 x 1d se-tenant with 2 x 4d red (one phos band)
printed by Harrison, 1969; Shackleton cover 4.00
6 x 5d, 6 x 5d, 6 x 4d red, 6 x 4d red (centre phos band),
4 x 1d se-tenant with 2 x 4d red (one phos band)
printed by Harrison, 1970; Frobisher cover 5.50
6 x 5d, 6 x 5d, 6 x 4d red, 6 x 4d red (centre phos band),
4 x 1d se-tenant with 2 x 4d red (one phos band)
printed by Harrison, 1970; Cook cover 6.00

ELIZABETH II DECIMAL MACHINS, 1971-76

■ 10p booklets. Pillar box series
2 x ½p, 2 x 1p, 2 x 1½p, 2 x 2p
printed by Harrison, 1971; London's first box 1855 cover 1.50
2 x ½p, 2 x 1p, 2 x 1½p, 2 x 2p
printed by Harrison, 1971; Pillar box 1856 cover 1.50
2 x ½p, 2 x 1p, 2 x 1½p, 2 x 2p
printed by Harrison, 1971; Urban pillar box 1857 cover 2.00

2 x ½p, 2 x 1p, 2 x 1½p, 2 x 2p
printed by Harrison, 1971–72; Penfold box 1866 cover   2.50
2 x ½p, 2 x 1p, 2 x 1½p, 2 x 2p
printed by Harrison, 1972; Double–aperture 1899 cover   2.00
2 x ½p, 2 x 1p, 2 x 1½p, 2 x 2p
printed by Harrison, 1972; Mellor type 1968 cover   2.00
2 x ½p, 2 x 1p, 2 x 1½p, 2 x 2p
printed by Harrison, 1973; KEVIII type 1936 cover   2.50
2 x ½p, 2 x 1p, 2 x 1½p, 2 x 2p
printed by Harrison, 1973; QEII type 1952 cover   2.50
2 x ½p, 2 x 1p, 2 x 1½p, 2 x 2p
printed by Harrison, 1973; Double–aperture 1973 cover   2.00
2 x ½p, 2 x 1p, 2 x 1½p, 2 x 2p
printed by Harrison, 1974; Philatelic box 1974 cover   2.00

■ 10p booklets. Postal Uniforms series
2 x ½p, 2 x 1p, 2 x 1½p, 2 x 2p
printed by Harrison, 1974; Letter carrier 1793 cover   1.00
2 x ½p, 2 x 1p, 2 x 1½p, 2 x 2p
printed by Harrison, 1974; Letter carrier 1837 cover   1.00
2 x ½p, 2 x 1p, 2 x 1½p, 2 x 2p
printed by Harrison, 1975–76; Letter carrier 1855 cover   0.75

■ 25p booklets. Veteran Transport series
5 x ½p, 9 x 2½p
printed by Harrison, 1971; Knifeboard omnibus cover   3.50
5 x ½p, 9 x 2½p
printed by Harrison, 1971; B–type Omnibus cover   8.00
5 x ½p, 9 x 2½p
printed by Harrison, 1971; Showman's Engine cover   8.00
5 x ½p, 9 x 2½p
printed by Harrison, 1972; Royal Mail Van 1913 cover   5.00
5 x ½p, 9 x 2½p
printed by Harrison, 1972; Motor Wagonette 1901 cover   4.50
5 x ½p, 9 x 2½p
printed by Harrison, 1972; London Taxi Cab 1931 cover   5.00
5 x ½p, 9 x 2½p
printed by Harrison, 1973; Electric Tramcar cover   6.00

■ 25p booklets. 80 Years of British Stamp Books
5 x ½p, 9 x 2½p
printed by Harrison, 1971; 80 Years of Stamp Books cover   4.00

■ 25p booklets. Save The Children Fund
5 x ½p, 9 x 2½p
printed by Harrison, 1973; Help Children cover   6.00

■ 30p booklets. British Birds series
10 x 3p
printed by Harrison, 1971; Curlew cover   3.00
10 x 3p
printed by Harrison, 1971; Lapwing cover   4.00
10 x 3p
printed by Harrison, 1971; Robin cover   4.50
10 x 3p
printed by Harrison, 1971–72; Pied Wagtail cover   4.00
10 x 3p
printed by Harrison, 1972; Kestrel cover   4.50
10 x 3p
printed by Harrison, 1972; Black Grouse cover   4.50

10 x 3p
printed by Harrison, 1973; Skylark cover   4.50
10 x 3p
printed by Harrison, 1973; Oystercatcher cover (purple)   5.00
10 x 3p
printed by Harrison, 1973; Oystercatcher cover (bistre)   5.50

■ 30p booklets. 80 Years of British Stamp Books
10 x 3p
printed by Harrison, 1971; 80 Years of Stamp Books cover   4.00

■ 30p booklets. Save The Children Fund
10 x 3p
printed by Harrison, 1974; Help Children cover   3.50

■ 30p booklets. Canada Life Assurance
10 x 3p
printed by Harrison, 1974; Canada Life cover   4.00

■ 35p booklets. British Coins series
10 x 3½p
printed by Harrison, 1973–74; Cuthred Penny cover   3.00
10 x 3½p
printed by Harrison, 1974; Edward I Silver Groat cover   3.00

■ 35p booklets. Canada Life Assurance
10 x 3½p
printed by Harrison, 1974; Canada Life cover   3.00

■ 45p booklets. British Coins series
10 x 4½p
printed by Harrison, 1974; Elizabeth Gold Crown cover   3.50

■ 50p booklets. British Flowers series
5 x ½p, 7 x 2½p, 10 x 3p
printed by Harrison, 1971; Large Bindweed cover   5.00
5 x ½p, 7 x 2½p, 10 x 3p
printed by Harrison, 1971; Primrose cover   6.00
5 x ½p, 7 x 2½p, 10 x 3p
printed by Harrison, 1971; Honeysuckle cover   6.00
5 x ½p, 7 x 2½p, 10 x 3p
printed by Harrison, 1971; Hop cover   6.50
5 x ½p, 7 x 2½p, 10 x 3p
printed by Harrison, 1971; Common Violet cover   6.50
5 x ½p, 7 x 2½p, 10 x 3p
printed by Harrison, 1972; Lords–and–Ladies cover   6.50
5 x ½p, 7 x 2½p, 10 x 3p
printed by Harrison, 1972; Wood Anemone cover   6.50
5 x ½p, 7 x 2½p, 10 x 3p
printed by Harrison, 1972; Deadly Nightshade cover   6.00

■ 50p booklets. Canada Life Assurance
5 x ½p, 7 x 2½p, 10 x 3p
printed by Harrison, 1973; Canada Life cover (blue–green)   5.00
5 x 3p, 10 x 3½p
printed by Harrison, 1973; Canada Life cover (deep green)   4.50

■ 85p booklets. Canada Life Assurance
5 x 3½p, 15 x 4½p
printed by Harrison, 1973; Canada Life cover   6.50

FOLDED BOOKLETS

In this section, items are priced in mint condition only.

MACHINE–VENDED BOOKLETS OF MACHIN DEFINITIVES, 1976–2000

These booklets were sold from vending machines. They contain panes attached to covers by their top selvedge, so the Queen's portrait is face–down. In most cases, panes are folded along their perforations.

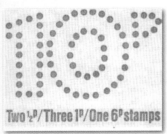

■ 10p booklet
2 x ½p, 3 x 1p, 1 x 6p
printed by Harrison, 1976–77; dotted '10p' cover — 0.60

■ 10p booklets. Farm Buildings series
2 x ½p, 2 x 1p, 1x 7p
printed by Harrison, 1978; Kent buildings cover — 0.50
2 x ½p, 2 x 1p, 1x 7p
printed by Harrison, 1978; N Ireland buildings cover — 0.60
2 x ½p, 2 x 1p, 1x 7p
printed by Harrison, 1978; Yorkshire buildings cover — 0.50
2 x ½p, 2 x 1p, 1x 7p
printed by Harrison, 1978; Wales buildings cover — 0.50
2 x ½p, 2 x 1p, 1x 7p
printed by Harrison, 1979; Scotland buildings cover — 0.50
2 x ½p, 2 x 1p, 1x 7p
printed by Harrison, 1979; Sussex buildings cover — 0.50

■ 10p booklet. London 1980 Exhibition
2 x 1p, 1 x 8p
printed by Harrison, 1979–80; London 1980 cover — 0.45
(*This booklet exists with differing postal rates quoted on its inside covers.)

■ 50p booklets
2 x ½p, 2 x 1p, 2 x 6½p (phos band at left), 4 x 8½p
printed by Harrison, 1977; bold '50p' cover — 1.40
2 x ½p, 2 x 1p, 2 x 6½p (phos band at right), 4 x 8½p
printed by Harrison, 1977; bold '50p' cover — 1.40
2 x 1p, 3 x 7p (phos band at left), 3 x 9p
printed by Harrison, 1977; bold '50p' cover — 2.00
2 x 1p, 3 x 7p (phos band at right), 3 x 9p
printed by Harrison, 1977; bold '50p' cover — 3.00

■ 50p booklets. Commercial Vehicles series
2 x 1p, 3 x 7p (phos band at left), 3 x 9p
printed by Harrison, 1978; Clement Talbot Van cover — 2.00
2 x 1p, 3 x 7p (phos band at right), 3 x 9p
printed by Harrison, 1978; Clement Talbot Van cover — 3.00
2 x 1p, 3 x 7p (phos band at left), 3 x 9p
printed by Harrison, 1978; Austin Cape Taxi cover — 2.00
2 x 1p, 3 x 7p (phos band at right), 3 x 9p
printed by Harrison, 1978; Austin Cape Taxi cover — 3.00
2 x 1p, 3 x 7p (phos band at left), 3 x 9p
printed by Harrison, 1978; Morris Royal Mail Van cover — 2.00
2 x 1p, 3 x 7p (phos band at right), 3 x 9p
printed by Harrison, 1978; Morris Royal Mail Van cover — 3.50
2 x 1p, 3 x 7p (phos band at left), 3 x 9p
printed by Harrison, 1978; Guy Electric Dustcart cover — 2.00
2 x 1p, 3 x 7p (phos band at right), 3 x 9p
printed by Harrison, 1978; Guy Electric Dustcart cover — 4.50
2 x 1p, 3 x 7p (phos band at left), 3 x 9p
printed by Harrison, 1979; Albion Van cover — 4.00
2 x 1p, 3 x 7p (phos band at right), 3 x 9p
printed by Harrison, 1979; Albion Van cover — 5.00
2 x 1p, 3 x 7p (phos band at left), 3 x 9p
printed by Harrison, 1979; Leyland Fire Engine cover — 3.00
2 x 1p, 3 x 7p (phos band at right), 3 x 9p

printed by Harrison, 1979; Leyland Fire Engine cover — 4.00
2 x 2p, 2 x 8p (phos band at left or right), 3 x 10p
printed by Harrison, 1979; Leyland Fire Engine — 2.00

■ 50p booklets. Veteran Cars series
2 x 2p, 2 x 8p (phos band left or right), 3 x 10p
printed by Harrison, 1979; Rolls Royce Silver Ghost cover — 1.50
3 x 2p, 2 x 10p (phos band left or right), 2 x 12p
printed by Harrison, 1980; Grand Prix Austin cover — 1.75
3 x 2p, 2 x 10p (phos band left or right), 2 x 12p
printed by Harrison, 1980; Vauxhall cover — 1.50
3 x 2p, 2 x 10p (phos band left or right), 2 x 12p
printed by Harrison, 1980; Daimler cover — 1.50
1 x ½p, 1 x 1p, 1 x 14p, 3 x 11½p (phos band left or right)
printed by Harrison, 1981; Lanchester cover — 1.50
1 x ½p, 1 x 1p, 1 x 14p, 3 x 11½p (phos band left or right)
printed by Harrison, 1981; Bullnose Morris cover — 1.75

■ 50p booklets. Follies series
1 x ½p, 1 x 1p, 1 x 14p, 3 x 11½p (phos band left or right)
printed by Harrison, 1981; Mugdock Castle cover — 1.50
3 x 2½p, 2 x 4p, 3 x 11½p (phos band at left)
printed by Harrison, 1981; Mugdock Castle cover — 7.00
3 x 2½p, 2 x 4p, 3 x 11½p (phos band at right)
printed by Harrison, 1981; Mugdock Castle cover — 5.50
3 x 2½p, 2 x 4p, 3 x 11½p (phos band at left)
printed by Harrison, 1981; Mow Cop Castle cover — 5.00
3 x 2½p, 2 x 4p, 3 x 11½p (phos band at right)
printed by Harrison, 1981; Mow Cop Castle cover — 3.50
1 x ½p, 4 x 3p pink, 3 x 12½p (phos band left or right)
printed by Harrison, 1982; Paxton's Tower cover — 2.00
1 x ½p, 4 x 3p pink, 3 x 12½p (phos band left or right)
printed by Harrison, 1982; Temple of the Winds cover — 2.00
1 x ½p, 4 x 3p pink, 3 x 12½p (phos band left or right)
printed by Harrison, 1982; Temple of the Sun cover — 2.00
1 x ½p, 4 x 3p pink, 3 x 12½p (phos band left or right)
printed by Harrison, 1982; Water Garden cover — 2.00

■ 50p booklets. Rare Farm Animals series
1 x ½p, 4 x 3p pink, 3 x 12½p (phos band left or right)
printed by Harrison, 1983; Bagot Goat cover — 2.00
2 x 1p, 3 x 3½p, 3 x 12½p (all with centre phos band)
printed by Harrison, 1983; Gloucester Old Spot Pig cover — 3.50
2 x 1p, 3 x 3½p, 3 x 12½p (all with centre phos band)
printed by Harrison, 1983; Gloucester Old Spot Pig cover
with postal rate information corrected — 12.00
2 x 1p, 3 x 3½p, 3 x 12½p (all with centre phos band)
printed by Harrison, 1983; Toulouse Goose cover — 3.50
2 x 1p, 3 x 3½p, 3 x 12½p (all with centre phos band)
printed by Harrison, 1983; Orkney Sheep cover — 3.50

■ 50p booklets. Orchids series
3 x 1p, 2 x 4p, 3 x 13p (all with centre phos band)
printed by Harrison, 1984; Dendrobium Nobile cover — 2.50
3 x 1p, 2 x 4p, 3 x 13p (all with centre phos band)
printed by Harrison, 1985; Cyripedium and Ophrys cover — 2.50
3 x 1p, 2 x 4p, 3 x 13p (all with centre phos band)
printed by Harrison, 1985; Bifienasia and Vandatricolour — 2.50
3 x 1p, 2 x 4p, 3 x 13p (all with centre phos band)
printed by Harrison, 1985; Cymbidium and Arpophyllum — 2.50

■ 50p booklet
3 x 17p (two phos bands, stars printed on gummed side)
printed by Harrison, 1985; Pillar box cover — 2.50

■ 50p booklets. Pond Life series
3 x 17p (two phos bands, stars printed on gummed side)
printed by Harrison, 1986; Emperor Dragonfly cover — 2.00
3 x 17p (two phos bands, stars printed on gummed side)
printed by Harrison, 1986; Common Frog cover — 2.30
3 x 17p (two phos bands, without stars on gummed side)
printed by Harrison, 1986; Common Frog cover — 2.50
1 x 1p, 2 x 5p, 3 x 13p (all with centre phos band)
printed by Harrison, 1986; Moorhen and Dabchicks cover — 3.50
1 x 1p, 2 x 5p, 3 x 13p (all with centre phos band)
printed by Harrison, 1987; Giant Pond Snail cover — 3.00

■ 50p booklets. Roman Britain series
2 x 1p, 4 x 12p emerald–green (all with centre phos band)
printed by Harrison, 1986; Hadrian's Wall cover — 5.50
1 x 1p (right band), 1 x 13p (left band), 2 x 18p (two bands)
printed by Harrison, 1986; Roman Theatre cover — 2.50
1 x 1p (right band), 1 x 13p (left band), 2 x 18p (two bands)
printed by Harrison, 1987; Portchester Castle cover — 2.50

■ 50p booklets. Marylebone Cricket Club series
1 x 1p (right band), 1 x 13p (left band), 2 x 18p (two bands)
printed by Harrison, 1987; Weather Vane at Lord's cover — 1.75
1 x 1p (right band), 1 x 13p (left band), 2 x 18p (two bands)
printed by Harrison, 1987; Ashes Urn cover — 1.75
1 x 1p (right band), 1 x 13p (left band), 2 x 18p (two bands)
printed by Harrison, 1987; Lord's pavilion cover — 1.75
1 x 1p (right band), 1 x 13p (left band), 2 x 18p (two bands)
printed by Harrison, 1988; Lord's New Stand cover — 1.75

■ 50p booklets. Botanical Gardens series
1 x 1p, 2 x 5p, 3 x 13p (all with centre phos band)
printed by Harrison, 1987; Bodnant Gardens cover — 3.00
1 x 1p, 2 x 5p, 3 x 13p (all with centre phos band)
printed by Harrison, 1987; Edinburgh Gardens cover — 3.00
1 x 1p, 2 x 5p, 3 x 13p (centre phos bands, side edges imperf)
printed by Harrison, 1987; Mount Stuart cover — 2.00
1 x 1p, 2 x 5p, 3 x 13p (all with centre phos band)
printed by Harrison, 1987; Mount Stewart (corrected) — 2.00
1 x 1p, 2 x 5p, 3 x 13p (all with centre phos band)
printed by Harrison, 1988; Kew Gardens cover — 2.00

■ 50p booklets. London Zoo series
1 x 1p, 1 x 13p, 2 x 18p
printed by Harrison, 1988; Pigs cover — 2.00
1 x 1p, 1 x 13p, 2 x 18p
printed by Harrison, 1988; Birds cover — 2.00
1 x 1p, 1 x 13p, 2 x 18p
printed by Harrison, 1988; Elephants cover — 2.00

■ 50p booklets. Marine Life series
1 x 1p, 2 x 5p, 3 x 13p (all with centre phos band)
printed by Harrison, 1988; Anenome, Whelk, Jellyfish cover — 2.00
1 x 14p, 2 x 19p
printed by Harrison, 1989; Crab, Bladderwrack cover — 5.00

■ **50p booklets. Gilbert & Sullivan Operas series**
1 x 14p, 2 x 19p
printed by Harrison, 1988; Yeomen of the Guard cover ... 4.50
1 x 14p, 2 x 19p
printed by Harrison, 1989; Pirates of Penzance cover ... 4.50
1 x 14p, 2 x 19p
printed by Harrison, 1989; Mikado cover ... 4.50

■ **50p booklets. Aircraft series**
2 x 15p, 1 x 20p
printed by Harrison, 1989; AW Atalanta & DH Dragon ... 7.00
2 x 15p, 1 x 20p (Penny Black Anniversary stamps)
printed by Harrison, 1990; AW Atalanta & DH Dragon ... 5.50
2 x 15p, 1 x 20p
printed by Harrison, 1990; BAC 1–11 & VC10 ... 10.00
2 x 15p, 1 x 20p
printed by Harrison, 1991; BAe ATP, 146 & Concorde ... 10.00

■ **50p booklets. Archaeology series**
2 x 1p, 2 x 24p
printed by Harrison, 1991; Sir Arthur Evans at Crete ... 2.00
2 x 1p, 2 x 24p
printed by Harrison, 1992; Howard Carter, Tutankhamun ... 2.00
2 x 1p, 2 x 24p
printed by Harrison, 1992; Sir Austen Layard in Assyria ... 1.50
2 x 1p, 2 x 24p
printed by Harrison, 1992; Sir Flinders Petrie at Giza ... 1.60

■ **50p booklet. Sheriff's Millennium**
2 x 1p, 2 x 24p
printed by Harrison, 1992; Sheriff's millennium cover ... 1.50

■ **50p booklets. Postal History series**
2 x 1p, 2 x 24p
printed by Harrison, 1993; Airmail markings cover ... 1.50
2 x 1p, 2 x 24p
printed by Harrison, 1993; Ship mail markings cover ... 1.50
2 x 1p, 2 x 24p
printed by Harrison, 1993; Registered mail cover ... 1.50
2 x 25p
printed by Harrison, 1993; 'Paid' marking cover ... 1.50

■ **50p booklets. Coaching Inns series**
2 x 25p
printed by Harrison, 1994; Swan With Two Necks cover ... 1.50
2 x 25p
printed by Harrison, 1994; Bull & Mouth cover ... 1.50
2 x 25p
printed by Harrison, 1994; Golden Cross cover ... 1.50
2 x 25p
printed by Harrison, 1994; Pheasant Inn cover ... 1.50

■ **50p booklets. Sea Charts series**
2 x 25p
printed by Harrison, 1995; John O'Groats cover ... 1.50
2 x 25p
printed by Harrison, 1995; Land's End cover ... 1.50
2 x 25p
printed by Harrison, 1995; St. David's Head cover ... 2.00
2 x 25p
printed by Harrison, 1995; Giant's Causeway cover ... 2.00

■ **£1 booklets. Musical Instruments series**
6 x 17p (advanced coated paper)
printed by Harrison, 1986; Violin cover ... 3.00
1 x 13p (phos band at right), 5 x 18p (two phos bands)
printed by Harrison, 1986; French Horn cover ... 3.00
1 x 13p (phos band at right), 5 x 18p (two phos bands)
printed by Harrison, 1987; Bass Clarinet cover ... 3.00

■ **£1 booklets. Sherlock Holmes series**
1 x 13p (phos band at right), 5 x 18p (two phos bands)
printed by Harrison, 1987; A Study in Scarlet cover ... 3.00
1 x 13p (phos band at right), 5 x 18p (two phos bands)
printed by Harrison, 1987; Hound of the Baskervilles cover ... 3.00
1 x 13p (band at right), 5 x 18p (two bands), edges imperf
printed by Harrison, 1987; Adventure of the Speckled Band ... 3.00
1 x 13p (band at right), 5 x 18p (two bands), edges imperf
printed by Harrison, 1988; The Final Problem cover ... 3.00

■ **£1 booklet. London Zoo series**
1 x 13p (phos band at right), 5 x 18p (two phos bands)
printed by Harrison, 1988; Bears ... 3.00

■ **£1 booklets. Charles Dickens series**
1 x 13p (phos band at right), 5 x 18p (two phos bands)
printed by Harrison, 1988; Oliver Twist cover ... 4.00
2 x 14p (phos band at right), 4 x 19p (two phos bands)
printed by Harrison, 1988; Nicholas Nickleby cover ... 4.00
2 x 14p (phos band at right), 4 x 19p (two phos bands)
printed by Harrison, 1989; David Copperfield cover ... 4.00
2 x 14p (phos band at right), 4 x 19p (two phos bands)
printed by Walsall, 1989; Great Expectations cover ... 7.50

■ **£1 booklet. Marine Life series**
2 x 14p (phos band at right), 4 x 19p (two phos bands)
printed by Harrison, 1989; Sea urchin, starfish, crab ... 4.00

■ **£1 booklets. Mills series**
5 x 20p
printed by Harrison, 1989; Wicken Fen cover (matt) ... 4.00
5 x 20p (Penny Black Anniversary stamps)
printed by Walsall, 1990; Wicken Fen cover (glossy) ... 9.00
5 x 20p (Penny Black Anniversary stamps)
printed by Harrison, 1990; Click Mill cover ... 6.00

2 x 17p, 3 x 22p
printed by Harrison, 1990; Jack & Jill Mills cover 2.95
2 x 17p, 3 x 22p
printed by Harrison, 1991 Howell Mill cover 2.95

■ £1 booklets. Punch Magazine series
2 x 2p, 4 x 24p
printed by Harrison, 1991; illustrations by Doyle, Hoffnung 2.00
2 x 2p, 4 x 24p
printed by Harrison, 1992; illustrations by Tenniel, Burgin 2.00
2 x 2p, 4 x 24p
printed by Harrison, 1992; illustrations by Tenniel, Anton 2.00
2 x 2p, 4 x 24p
printed by Harrison, 1992; illustrations by Tenniel, Hewison 2.00

■ £1 booklet. Sheriff's Millennium
2 x 2p, 4 x 24p
printed by Harrison, 1992; Sheriff's Millennium cover 2.00

■ £1 booklets. Educational Institutions series
2 x 2p, 4 x 24p
printed by Walsall, 1993; University of Wales cover 3.50
2 x 2p, 4 x 24p
printed by Walsall, 1993; St. Hilda's College, Oxford 3.50
2 x 2p, 4 x 24p
printed by Walsall, 1993; Marlborough College cover 3.50
4 x 25p
printed by Walsall, 1993; Free Church of Scotland College 3.50

■ £1 booklets. Prime Ministers series
4 x 25p
printed by Walsall, 1994; Herbert Asquith cover 2.00
4 x 25p
printed by Harrison, 1994; David Lloyd-George cover 2.00
4 x 25p
printed by Harrison, 1994; Winston Churchill cover 2.00
4 x 25p
printed by Harrison, 1994; Clement Attlee cover 2.00

■ £1 booklets. Second World War series
4 x 25p
printed by Harrison, 1995; Violette Szabo cover 2.00
4 x 25p
printed by Harrison, 1995; Dame Vera Lynn cover 2.00
4 x 25p
printed by Harrison, 1995; R. J. Mitchell cover 2.00
4 x 25p
printed by Harrison, 1995; Archibald McIndoe cover 2.00

■ £1 booklets. Red cover series
4 x 25p (litho)
printed by Questa, 1996; Royal Mail cruciform cover 3.50
2 x 1p, 1 x 20p, 3 x 26p (litho)
printed by Questa, 1996–97; Royal Mail cruciform cover 3.50
2 x 1p, 1 x 20p, 3 x 26p (gravure)
printed by Questa, 1998; Royal Mail cruciform cover 18.00
1 x 1p, 1 x 2p, 1 x 19p, 3 x 26p (gravure)
printed by Questa, 1999; Royal Mail cruciform cover 6.00
1 x 2nd, 3 x 1st (gravure)
printed by Questa, 2000–01; Royal Mail cruciform cover 7.00

■ £2 booklets. Postal Vehicles series
8 x 25p
printed by Harrison, 1993; Motorised Cycle cover 3.50
8 x 25p
printed by Harrison, 1994; Motor Mail Van cover 4.00
8 x 25p
printed by Harrison, 1994; Electric Mail Van cover 4.00

■ £2 booklets. Sir Rowland Hill series
8 x 25p
printed by Harrison, 1995; London & Brighton Railway 3.50
8 x 25p
printed by Harrison, 1995; Hazlewood School 3.50
8 x 25p
printed by Harrison, 1995; Secretary to the Post Office 3.50
8 x 25p
printed by Harrison, 1995; Uniform Penny Postage 3.50

■ £2 booklets. Red cover series
8 x 25p
printed by Questa, 1996; Royal Mail cruciform cover 4.00
1 x 20p, 7 x 26p (litho)
printed by Questa, 1996; Royal Mail cruciform cover 4.50
1 x 20p, 7 x 26p (gravure)
printed by Questa, 1998; Royal Mail cruciform cover 19.50
1 x 19p, 7 x 26p
printed by Questa, 1999; Royal Mail cruciform cover 6.50
2 x 2nd, 6 x 1st
printed by Questa, 2000; Royal Mail cruciform cover 6.50

COUNTER BOOKLETS OF MACHIN DEFINITIVES, 1976–89

These booklets were sold over post office counters. They contain panes attached to covers by their side selvedge, so the Queen's portrait appears upright. Panes can have a margin to the left or right; prices are the same for both, except where stated.

65p booklets
10 x 6½p (right margin)
printed by Harrison, 1976; bold '65p' cover — 5.50
10 x 6½p (left margin)
printed by Harrison, 1976; bold '65p' cover — 10.00

70p booklets
10 x 7p
printed by Harrison, 1977; bold '70p' cover — 3.50

70p booklets. Country Crafts series
10 x 7p (right margin)
printed by Harrison, 1978; Horse–Shoeing cover — 3.00
10 x 7p (left margin)
printed by Harrison, 1978; Horse–Shoeing cover — 33.00
10 x 7p (right margin)
printed by Harrison, 1978; Thatching cover — 3.00
10 x 7p (left margin)
printed by Harrison, 1978; Thatching cover — £180
10 x 7p (right margin)
printed by Harrison, 1978; Dry–Stone Walling cover — 3.00
10 x 7p (left margin)
printed by Harrison, 1978; Dry–Stone Walling cover — £150
10 x 7p (right margin)
printed by Harrison, 1978; Wheel–Making cover — 4.50
10 x 7p (left margin)
printed by Harrison, 1978; Wheel–Making cover — 5.75
10 x 7p (right margin)
printed by Harrison, 1979; Wattle Fence–Making cover — 3.50
10 x 7p (left margin)
printed by Harrison, 1979; Wattle Fence–Making cover — 11.00
10 x 7p (right margin)
printed by Harrison, 1979; Basket–Making cover — 3.00
10 x 7p (left margin)
printed by Harrison, 1979; Basket–Making cover — 6.00

70p booklet. Derby Letter Office series
10 x 7p
printed by Harrison, 1979; Kedleston Hall cover — 5.00

80p booklets. Military Aircraft series
10 x 8p
printed by Harrison, 1979; Vickers Gun Bus cover — 2.00

85p booklets
10 x 8½p (right margin)
printed by Harrison, 1976; bold '85p' cover — 7.00
10 x 8½p (left margin)
printed by Harrison, 1976; bold '85p' cover — 6.00

90p booklets
10 x 9p (left margin)
printed by Harrison, 1977; bold '90p' cover — 3.00
10 x 9p (right margin)
printed by Harrison, 1977; bold '90p' cover — 4.50

90p booklets. British Canals series
10 x 9p (right margin)
printed by Harrison, 1978; Grand Union Canal cover — 4.00
10 x 9p (left margin)
printed by Harrison, 1978; Grand Union Canal cover — 20.00
10 x 9p (right margin)
printed by Harrison, 1978; Llangollen Canal cover — £300
10 x 9p (left margin)
printed by Harrison, 1978; Llangollen Canal cover — 4.00
10 x 9p (right margin)
printed by Harrison, 1978; Kennet & Avon Canal cover — 8.00
10 x 9p (left margin)
printed by Harrison, 1978; Kennet & Avon Canal cover — 10.00
10 x 9p (right margin)
printed by Harrison, 1978; Caledonian Canal cover — 5.00
10 x 9p (left margin)
printed by Harrison, 1978; Caledonian Canal cover — 6.00
10 x 9p (right margin)
printed by Harrison, 1979; Regent's Canal cover — 6.00
10 x 9p (left margin)
printed by Harrison, 1979; Regent's Canal cover — 10.00
10 x 9p
printed by Harrison, 1979; Leeds & Liverpool Canal cover — 4.00

90p booklets. Derby Letter Office series
10 x 9p
printed by Harrison, 1979; Tramway Museum, Crich, cover — 6.50

£1 booklets. Industrial Archaeology series
10 x 10p (all–over phosphor)
printed by Harrison, 1979; Ironbridge, Telford, cover — 3.00

£1 booklets. Military Aircraft series
10 x 10p (one centre phos band)
printed by Harrison, 1980; Sopwith Camel, Vickers Vimy — 2.50
10 x 10p (one centre phos band)
printed by Harrison, 1980; Hawker Fury, HP Heyford — 3.50
10 x 10p (one centre phos band)
printed by Harrison, 1980; Wellington, Hurricane — 2.50

£1.15 booklets. Military Aircraft series
10 x 11½p (one centre phos band)
printed by Harrison, 1981; Spitfire, Lancaster — 3.50
10 x 11½p (one centre phos band)
printed by Harrison, 1981; Lightning, Vulcan — 3.50

£1.15 booklets. Museums series
10 x 11½p (one centre phos band)
printed by Harrison, 1981; Natural History Museum — 3.50
10 x 11½p (one centre phos band)
printed by Harrison, 1981; National Museum of Antiquities — 3.50

■ £1.20 booklets. Industrial Archaeology series
10 x 12p yellow–green
printed by Harrison, 1980; Beetle Mill cover   3.50
10 x 12p yellow–green
printed by Harrison, 1980; Tin Mines cover   3.50
10 x 12p yellow–green
printed by Harrison, 1980; Bottle Kilns cover   3.50

■ £1.20 booklets
10 x 12p emerald–green (one centre phos band)
printed by Harrison, 1986; Pillar Box   4.50
10 x 12p emerald–green (one centre phos band)
printed by Harrison, 1986; National Gallery cover   4.25
10 x 12p emerald–green (one centre phos band)
printed by Harrison, 1986; 'Maybe' cover   4.25

■ £1.25 booklets. Museums series
10 x 12½p (one centre phos band)
printed by Harrison, 1982; Ashmolean Museum cover   3.50
10 x 12½p (one centre phos band)
printed by Harrison, 1982; National Museum of Wales   3.50
10 x 12½p (one centre phos band)
printed by Harrison, 1982; Ulster Museum, Belfast   3.50
10 x 12½p (one centre phos band)
printed by Harrison, 1982; Castle Museum, York   3.50

■ £1.25 booklets. Railway Engines series
10 x 12½p (one centre phos band)
printed by Harrison, 1983; GWR IK Brunel cover   4.00
10 x 12½p (one centre phos band)
printed by Harrison, 1983; LMS Class 4P cover   4.50
10 x 12½p (one centre phos band)
printed by Harrison, 1983; LNER Mallard cover   4.00
10 x 12½p (one centre phos band)
printed by Harrison, 1983; SR/BR Clan Line cover   4.00

■ £1.30 booklets. Postal History series
6 x 14p (two phos bands), 2 x 11½p (left phos band),
2 x 11½p (right phos band) (right margin)
printed by Harrison, 1981; Penny Black cover   3.50
6 x 14p (two phos bands), 2 x 11½p (left phos band),
2 x 11½p (right phos band) (left margin)
printed by Harrison, 1981; Penny Black cover   3.50
6 x 14p (two phos bands), 2 x 11½p (left phos band),
2 x 11½p (right phos band) (left margin)
printed by Harrison, 1981; Downey Head cover   5.00
6 x 14p (two phos bands), 2 x 11½p (left phos band),
2 x 11½p (right phos band) (right margin)
printed by Harrison, 1981; Downey Head cover   14.00

■ £1.30 booklets. Trams series
10 x 13p (one centre band)
printed by Harrison, 1984; Swansea Car cover   3.25
10 x 13p (one centre band)
printed by Harrison, 1985; Glasgow Car cover   3.25
10 x 13p (one centre band)
printed by Harrison, 1985; Blackpool Car cover   3.25
10 x 13p (one centre band)
printed by Harrison, 1985; London Car cover   3.25

■ £1.30 booklets. Special Offers series
10 x 13p (one centre band)
printed by Harrison, 1986; Books For Children offer   3.00
10 x 13p (one centre band)
printed by Harrison, 1987; 'Keep In Touch' Pack offer   3.00
10 x 13p (one centre band)
printed by Harrison, 1987; 'Ideas For Your Garden' offer   3.00
10 x 13p (one centre band)
printed by Harrison, 1987; 'Brighter Writer' Pack offer   3.00
10 x 13p (one centre band)
printed by Harrison, 1987; 'Jolly Postman' Pack offer   3.00
10 x 13p (one centre band)
printed by Harrison, 1988; Natural History Postcards offer   3.50
10 x 13p (one centre band)
printed by Harrison, 1988; Recipe Cards offer   3.00
10 x 13p (one centre band)
printed by Harrison, 1988; Children's Party Pack offer   3.00

■ £1.40 booklets. Industrial Archaeology series
10 x 14p (phos–coated paper)
printed by Harrison, 1981; Preston Mill cover   3.00
10 x 14p (phos–coated paper)
printed by Harrison, 1981; Talyllyn Railway cover   3.00

■ £1.40 booklets. Women's Costumes series
10 x 14p (phos–coated paper)
printed by Harrison, 1981; Costumes of 1800–1815   3.00
10 x 14p (phos–coated paper)
printed by Harrison, 1981; Costumes of 1815–1830   3.00

■ £1.40 booklet. Special Offers series
10 x 14p (phos–coated paper)
printed by Harrison, 1988; Pocket Planner offer   3.00

■ £1.40 booklet. Fox Talbot Photography
10 x 14p (phos–coated paper)
printed by Harrison, 1989; photography equipment cover   3.50

■ £1.43 booklets. Postal History series
6 x 15½p (two bands), 2 x 12½p (left band), 2 x 12½p (right band)
printed by Harrison, 1982; James Chalmers cover   3.75
6 x 15½p (two bands), 2 x 12½p (left band), 2 x 12½p (right band)
printed by Harrison, 1982; Edmund Dulac cover   3.75
6 x 15½p (two bands), 2 x 12½p (left band), 2 x 12½p (right band)
printed by Harrison, 1982; Forces Postal Service cover   3.75
6 x 15½p (two bands), 2 x 12½p (left band), 2 x 12½p (right band)
printed by Harrison, 1982; £5 Orange cover   3.75
6 x 15½p (two bands), 2 x 12½p (left band), 2 x 12½p (right band)
printed by Harrison, 1983; Postmark History cover   3.75

■ £1.43 booklets. Holiday Postcard Stamp Book
6 x 15½p (two bands), 2 x 12½p (left band),
2 x 12½p (right band)
printed by Harrison, 1982; Golden Hinde cover   3.75

■ £1.45 booklet. Britain's Countryside
10 x 16p (phos–coated paper, 'D' printed on the gummed
side) printed by Harrison, 1983; Lyme Regis cover   3.75
(*This booklet was sold at a discount of 15p off face value.)

■ £1.46 booklets. Postal History series
6 x 16p (two bands), 2 x 12¹/₂p (left band), 2 x 12¹/₂p (right band)
printed by Harrison, 1983; Seahorses cover   5.00
6 x 16p (two bands), 2 x 12¹/₂p (left band), 2 x 12¹/₂p (right band)
printed by Harrison, 1983; Parcel Post cover   5.00
6 x 16p (two bands), 2 x 12¹/₂p (left band), 2 x 12¹/₂p (right band)
printed by Harrison, 1983; Regional Stamps cover   5.00
(*Panes have either four 12¹/₂p followed by one 16p on the bottom row, or one 16p followed by four 12¹/₂p.)

■ £1.50 booklets. Special Offer series
6 x 17p (two bands), 2 x 12p (left band), 2 x 12p (right band)
printed by Harrison, 1986; 'Write Now' letter pack offer   4.20
6 x 17p (two bands), 2 x 12p (left band), 2 x 12p (right band)
printed by Harrison, 1986; National Gallery offer   4.20
6 x 17p (two bands), 2 x 12p (left band), 2 x 12p (right band)
printed by Harrison, 1986; 'No' Graphology offer   4.20
(*Panes have either four 12p followed by one 17p on the bottom row, or one 17p followed by four 12p.)

■ £1.54 booklets. Postal History series
6 x 17p (two bands), 2 x 13p (left band), 2 x 13p (right band)
printed by Harrison, 1984; To Pay Labels cover   3.00
6 x 17p (two bands), 2 x 13p (left band), 2 x 13p (right band)
printed by Harrison, 1985; Embossed Stamps cover   3.00
6 x 17p (two bands), 2 x 13p (left band), 2 x 13p (right band)
printed by Harrison, 1985; Surface–Printed Stamps cover   3.00
6 x 17p (two bands), 2 x 13p (left band), 2 x 13p (right band)
printed by Harrison, 1985; 350 Years of Service cover   3.00
(*Panes have either four 13p followed by one 17p on the bottom row, or one 17p followed by four 13p.)

■ £1.55 booklets. Women's Costumes series
10 x 15¹/₂p (phos–coated paper)
printed by Harrison, 1982; Costumes of 1830–1850   3.00
10 x 15¹/₂p (phos–coated paper)
printed by Harrison, 1982; Costumes of 1850–1860   3.00
10 x 15¹/₂p (phos–coated paper)
printed by Harrison, 1982; Costumes of 1860–1880   3.00
10 x 15¹/₂p (phos–coated paper)
printed by Harrison, 1982; Costumes of 1880–1900   3.00

■ £1.55 booklet. Social Letter Writing series
10 x 17p (phos–coated paper, 'D' printed on gummed side)
printed by Harrison, 1985; Paper Boat and Plane cover   6.00
(*This booklet was sold at a discount of 15p off face value.)

■ £1.60 booklets. Special Offers series
10 x 16p (phos–coated paper)
printed by Harrison, 1983; Birthday Box offer   4.00
10 x 16p (phos–coated paper)
printed by Harrison, 1984; 'Write It' wallet offer   4.00

■ £1.60 booklet. Britain's Countryside series
10 x 16p (phos–coated paper)
printed by Harrison, 1983; Weavers' Cottages cover   4.00

■ £1.70 booklets. Social Letter Writing series
10 x 17p (phos–coated paper)
printed by Harrison, 1984; Love Letters cover   4.00

10 x 17p (phos–coated paper)
printed by Harrison, 1984; Fan Letters cover   4.00

■ £1.70 booklets. Special Offers series
10 x 17p (phos–coated paper)
printed by Harrison, 1985; 'Write Now' pack offer   4.00
10 x 17p (phos–coated paper)
printed by Harrison, 1986; National Gallery offer   4.00
10 x 17p (phos–coated paper)
printed by Harrison, 1986; 'Yes' Graphology offer   4.00

■ £1.80 booklets. Special Offers series
10 x 18p (phos–coated paper)
printed by Harrison, 1986; Books For Children offer   4.25
10 x 18p (phos–coated paper)
printed by Harrison, 1987; 'Keep In Touch' Pack offer   4.25
10 x 18p (phos–coated paper)
printed by Harrison, 1987; 'Ideas For Your Garden' offer   4.25
10 x 18p (phos–coated paper)
printed by Harrison, 1987; 'Brighter Writer' Pack offer   4.25
10 x 18p (phos–coated paper)
printed by Harrison, 1987; 'Jolly Postman' Pack offer   4.25
10 x 18p (phos–coated paper)
printed by Harrison, 1988; Natural History Postcards offer   4.25
10 x 18p (phos–coated paper)
printed by Harrison, 1988; Recipe Cards offer   4.25
10 x 18p (phos–coated paper)
printed by Harrison, 1988; Children's Party Pack offer   4.25

■ £1.90 booklet. Special Offer series
10 x 19p
printed by Harrison, 1988; Pocket Planner offer   4.50

■ £1.90 booklet. Fox Talbot Photography
10 x 19p
printed by Harrison, 1989; Fox Talbot with camera cover   4.50

COUNTER BOOKLETS OF ROYAL MAIL COMMEMORATIVES, 1985

■ £1.53 booklet. 350th Anniversary of Royal Mail Service to the Public
10 x 17p 350th Anniversary stamp ('D' pattern on gummed side)
printed by Harrison, 1985; van, plane, Concorde cover   4.00
(*This booklet was sold at a discount of 17p off face value.)

5 **Why is that?** Because, as the world revolved **the Stamp Market, imperceptibly** *Changed*, **and incrementally – Massively**

So, although few will tell you this, it's clearly evident that the problem for most Sellers of Stamps today is no longer absent stock – but **absent collectors in the place they choose to sell their stamps in.** Simply put, other Dealers, Auctions, Stamp Fairs have not invested in marketing to have a strong Customer-core. To be fair, this is not true of all – but it is true of most – so that our nearest competitor 'Apex' had 800 bidders in a recent auction. In my most recent 20,000+ lot UPA 68th Auction we had 2,184 different bidders from 58 different countries, 95% of whom were Collectors. Some other well-advertised auctions only have 200 bidders (a high percentage of whom are dealers – so that, essentially they are Dealer-dominated auctions) – so that when you sell through them – you're paying up to 18% (including VAT) seller's commission and the buyer is paying up to 25% **and** more in Buyer's Premium, credit card fees, on-line bidding fee, delivery and insurance etc… **AND all of that so that your stamps may be sold,** wait for it – **TO DEALERS (and some collectors),** but Dealers, that naturally must make a profit to survive…

6 Now, let's examine the cost implications **– Example:** Your stamp collection sells in public auction for £800. Upon a 25% buyer's premium, the dealer pays £1,000 and it could be more. He breaks it into £2,000+ selling price (much lower and he'll go out of business). The auction charges you a seller's commission of up to 18% (VAT included) upon the £800 sale price. This is GBP£144. Therefore you receive approaching £656 – which is approximately 33% of the dealer's £2,000+/- retail selling price - **BUT… now that we have identified the problem…**

Isn't the Solution Staring us Right in The Face ?

7 Why Pay an Auction to Sell to Dealers: **Sell to Collectors instead ?** In our example with buyer's premium, sellers commission, lotting fees, extra credit card charges, VAT and even insurance - you're already being charged in different ways up to 40% of the selling price to sell, possibly or probably, **to the wrong person**.

Why not direct that 40% cost you're paying to sell to Collectors instead? Sounds good, so why hasn't this been done before ?

8 Truth is, it *Has* been done before…Sometimes the 'old' ways are the best ways aren't they? But in today's enthusiasm to obscure the obvious so that money may be taken, almost surreptitiously, in numerous different ways, (without us apparently noticing until we see the cheque in our pocket) – the transparent 'seller pays' has been deliberately 'obscured' – so much so that, **amazingly,** the latest 2017 European Auction Selling Legislation just introduced – now requires auctions that charge 'buyer's premiums' **to warn the buyer in advance.** Just imagine going into the petrol station, and being warned that the price you're paying to put fuel in you tank is not the real price, you have to pay a premium! Obviously, there would be an uproar…

9 How can you cut out the middleman and sell to Collectors instead? Well, I can think of two ways. 1). **DIY** - Do It Yourself selling on eBay. That may be fine for lower grade material – but, would you risk auctioning relatively unprotected rare material on eBay ? We don't and we're professionals, so we should know what we're doing. Or 2). Cut out the extra middle-man. **Use my company UPA, which reaches collectors instead.** Here's how it works: Continuing from our previous **Example:**

The auction sold your stamps to a dealer for £1,000 – but You received circa £656

UPA sells them to collectors for you for up to £2,000 – even after 40% commission you receive up to £1,200. Up to £544 more. Now that's amazing, isn't it? 🏆

10 Sounds Good Andrew, but Can You 'Deliver'? Obviously, nothing is as simple as that, and as we auction stamps to collectors some collections may 'break' to the example £2,000+/- but others may be sold for more or less – especially as we reserve all lots at 20% below, (Estimate £2,000 = £1,600 reserve) and not everything sells first or even 2nd time so prices may come down… Naturally, it's not that straightforward for a dealer either – he may sell at a discount to 'move' stock **OR,** like many dealers he may be sitting on the same unsold stamps, that you see time and time again, in dealer's stocks years later and still at the same unattractive prices…

So, I think it is more reasonable for you to expect up to 36% to 50% more, indirectly or directly via my **Collector's Secret Weapon:** Universal Philatelic Auctions, which moves material more quickly, by incrementally reducing estimate (and reserve) price in a structured selling system…

11 *Q.)* What is the Collector's 'Secret Weapon'?

A.) **It's called the Unique UPA Reducing Estimate System…** ★★

This is a rather long explanation, I don't want to bore you, but 18 years ago, when my wife and I set up Universal Philatelic Auctions I detected that the stamp trade's biggest problem then was not what sold – *but what didn't sell…* So, because I didn't want to try to keep on offering the same either unsaleable or overpriced stock I created the unique UPA Reducing Estimate (and reserve) Selling System. Simply put, if a lot doesn't sell in the 1st auction we reduce the estimate (and reserve) by 11% and unlike other dealers and auctions **WE TELL YOU** – 'US' = once unsold. If unsold after the following auction we **reduce by a further 12%** and **WE TELL YOU 'US2'**, if unsold after a 3rd UPA auction we reduce by a further 13% and **WE TELL YOU 'US3'** and so on till the lot finds its price, is sold or virtually given away…

12 Any Scientist will tell you that combinations of ingredients can produce powerful results. So we created the unique combination of my UPA Reducing Estimate System, married (in stone), with UPA's fair 'NO BUYER'S Premium' policy, PLUS each lot carries my total 'no quibble' guarantee – this formula is the reason why within the span of 4 auctions (one year)… 90%-95% of lots broken from a collection have sold. This Unique Philatelic Selling System **Formula** is the reason why we are the largest stamp auction in the UK today with 2,184 different bidders in my recent auction. 🐝

In Hindsight Dealers warned me 18 years ago that my idea wouldn't work. 18 years later I think I've proven that it does. (Reader: Please Request a complimentary UPA catalogue – using the contact details further below)

13 OK, Cut to the Chase Andrew, what's the offer? All of my Selling Systems are based upon **selling to Collectors Globally,** so that 95% of stamps sold by UPA are

RETAIL STAMP BOOKS

In this section, items are priced in mint condition only. These booklets were intended to be sold not only over post office counters, but also through alternative retail outlets. All have a barcode on the outside back cover.

BOOKLETS OF DEFINITIVES WITHOUT ELLIPTICAL PERFORATIONS, 1987–93

Booklets with a 'window' in the cover, through which one of the stamps can be seen, and with the panes surrounded by a white margin.

◾ 4 x 13p
August 4, 1987. Printed by Harrison — 2.75

◾ 10 x 13p
August 4, 1987. Printed by Harrison — 3.75

◾ 4 x 14p
August 23, 1988. Printed by Harrison — 4.00
October 11, 1988. Stamps by Harrison; cover by Walsall — 4.50

◾ 10 x 14p
August 23, 1988. Printed by Harrison — 9.50
October 11, 1988. Printed by Questa — 11.00

◾ 4 x 18p
August 4, 1987. Printed by Harrison — 3.00

◾ 10 x 18p
August 4, 1987. Printed by Harrison — 5.00

◾ 4 x 19p
August 23, 1988. Printed by Harrison — 4.25
October 11, 1988. Stamps by Harrison; cover by Walsall — 4.50

◾ 10 x 19p
August 23, 1988. Printed by Harrison — 7.00

October 11, 1988. Printed by Questa — 12.50

◾ 4 x 26p
August 4, 1987. Printed by Harrison — 10.00

◾ 4 x 27p
August 23, 1988. Printed by Harrison — 8.00

Booklets with an illustration of the contents in place of the 'window' on the cover, containing panes with no margin, and with either the top and bottom or all three edges imperforate.

◾ 4 x 14p
October 11, 1988. Printed by Harrison — 4.50
January 24, 1989. Stamps by printed Harrison, cover printed by Walsall — 19.00

◾ 10 x 14p
October 11, 1988. Printed by Harrison — 9.00
October 11, 1988. Printed by Questa — 11.00

◾ 4 x 19p
October 11, 1988. Printed by Harrison — 6.00
January 24, 1989. Stamps by printed Harrison, cover printed by Walsalll — 4.50

◾ 10 x 19p
October 11, 1988. Printed by Harrison — 7.00
October 11, 1988. Printed by Questa — 12.50

◾ 4 x 27p
October 11, 1988. Printed by Harrison — 8.00

◾ 4 x 29p
October 2, 1989. Printed by Walsall (two phos bands) — 8.50
April 17, 1990. Printed by Walsall (phos paper) — 10.00

◾ 4 x 31p
September 17, 1990. Printed by Walsall — 4.00

◾ 4 x 33p
September 16, 1991. Printed by Walsall — 4.00
September 8, 1992. Printed by Walsall (yellow strip at right is inscribed 'For Worldwide Postcards') — 7.00

2 x 39p
July 28, 1992. Printed by Harrison   3.95

4 x 39p
September 16, 1991. Printed by Walsall   4.50

Booklets with an illustration of the contents on the cover, containing non–value indicator stamps in panes with no margin, and with either the top and bottom edges or all three edges imperforate.

4 x 2nd bright blue
August 22, 1989. Printed by Walsall   4.00
November 28, 1989. Stamps printed by Harrison;
cover by Walsall   22.00
August 6, 1991. Printed by Walsall
Cover features Royal Mail cruciform   3.50
January 21, 1992. Printed by Walsall
Cover features logos of Olympic and Paralympic Games   3.50

10 x 2nd bright blue
August 22, 1989. Printed by Harrison   9.00
September 19, 1989. Printed by Questa   9.00
August 6, 1991. Printed by Walsall
Cover features Royal Mail cruciform   8.00
August 6, 1991. Printed by Questa
Cover features Royal Mail cruciform   9.00
January 21, 1992. Printed by Walsall
Cover features logos of Olympic and Paralympic Games   8.00
March 31, 1992. Printed by Questa
Cover features logos of Olympic and Paralympic Games   9.00
September 22, 1992. Printed by Harrison
Cover features Royal Mail cruciform   9.00

4 x 2nd deep blue
August 7, 1990. Printed by Walsall   4.00

10 x 2nd deep blue
August 7, 1990. Printed by Harrison   9.00
August 7, 1990. Printed by Questa   7.00
August 7, 1990. Printed by Walsall   7.00

4 x 1st brownish–black
August 22, 1989. Printed by Walsall   7.75
December 5, 1989. Stamps by Harrison; cover by Walsall   25.00

10 x 1st brownish–black
August 22, 1989. Printed by Harrison   10.00
September 19, 1989. Printed by Questa   13.00

4 x 1st orange–red
August 7, 1990. Printed by Walsall   4.25
August 7, 1990. Printed by Walsall. Perf: 13   7.00
January 21, 1992. Printed by Walsall
Cover features logos of Olympic and Paralympic Games   4.25

10 x 1st orange–red
August 7, 1990. Printed by Harrison   10.00
August 7, 1990. Printed by Questa   10.00
August 7, 1990. Printed by Walsall   10.00
January 21, 1992. Printed by Harrison
Cover features logos of Olympic and Paralympic Games   10.00
January 21, 1992. Printed by Walsall
Cover features logos of Olympic and Paralympic Games   10.00
February 9, 1993. Printed by Walsall
Cover features Royal Mail cruciform; back cover has
advertisement for Greetings stamps   10.00

BOOKLETS OF PENNY BLACK ANNIVERSARY DEFINITIVES, 1990

Booklets with an illustration of the contents on the cover, containing denominated stamps in panes with all four edges perforated, or with either two or three edges imperforate.

4 x 15p
January 30, 1990. Printed by Walsall   4.50

10 x 15p
January 30, 1990. Printed by Harrison   5.50
April 17, 1990. Printed by Questa   11.00
June 12, 1990. Printed by Walsall   6.00

4 x 20p
January 30, 1990. Printed by Walsall   5.00
April 17, 1990. Stamps by Harrison; cover by Walsall   6.00

5 x 20p
January 30, 1990.
Cover shows Wicken Fen, printed on glossy card   10.00
January 30, 1990.
Cover shows Click Mill   6.00

■ **10 x 20p**

January 30, 1990. Printed by Harrison	6.00
April 17, 1990. Printed by Questa	12.00
June 12, 1990. Printed by Walsall	10.00

■ **2 x 15p, 1 x 20p se–tenant**

January 30, 1990.

Cover shows Vickers Viscount and De Havilland Comet	10.00

BOOKLETS OF DEFINITIVES WITH ELLIPTICAL PERFORATIONS, 1993–2000

Booklets of denominated stamps in panes with all four edges perforated.

■ **4 x 30p**

May 5, 1998. Printed by Walsall	
Cover shows a block of stamps	3.00
August 3, 1998. Printed by Walsall	
Cover inscribed 'Make their post memorable'	3.00

■ **4 x 35p**

November 1, 1993. Printed by Walsall	
Cover shows a single stamp	4.25
May 16, 1995. Printed by Walsall	
Cover shows a block of stamps	4.00
March 19, 1996. Printed by Walsall	
Back cover features Olympic symbols	4.00

■ **4 x 37p**

July 8, 1996. Printed by Walsall	
Back cover features Olympic symbols	5.00
February 4, 1997. Printed by Walsall	
Back cover features no Olympic symbols	4.00
August 26, 1997. Printed by Walsall	
Cover shows street names in London	4.00
August 3, 1998. Printed by Walsall	
Cover inscribed 'Make their post memorable'	4.00

■ **4 x 38p**

April 26, 1999. Printed by Walsall	
Cover shows a block of stamps	4.00

■ **4 x 40p**

April 27, 2000. Printed by Walsall	
Cover shows a block of stamps	4.00

■ **4 x 41p**

November 1, 1993. Printed by Walsall	
Cover shows a single stamp	4.00
May 16, 1995. Printed by Walsall	
Cover shows a block of stamps	4.00
March 19, 1996. Printed by Walsall	
Back cover features Olympic symbols	4.00

■ **4 x 60p**

August 9, 1994. Printed by Walsall	
Cover shows a single stamp	5.50
October 4, 1994. Printed by Walsall	
Cover inscribed 'Worldwide Airmail Stamps'	5.00
May 16, 1995. Printed by Walsall	
Cover shows a block of stamps	5.00
March 19, 1996. Printed by Walsall	
Back cover features Olympic symbols	5.00

■ **4 x 63p**

July 8, 1996. Printed by Walsall	
Back cover features Olympic symbols	8.00
February 4, 1997. Printed by Walsall (litho)	
Cover shows a block of stamps	8.00
August 26, 1997. Printed by Walsall (gravure)	
Cover shows a block of stamps	5.00
May 5, 1998. Printed by Walsall	
Cover shows airmail label below block of stamps	5.00

■ **4 x 64p**

April 26, 1999. Printed by Walsall	
Cover shows a block of stamps	6.00

■ **4 x 65p**

April 27, 2000. Printed by Walsall	
Cover shows a block of stamps	6.00

Booklets of non–value indicator stamps in panes with all four edges perforated.

■ **4 x 2nd bright blue**

April 6, 1993. Printed by Walsall	
Cover shows a single stamp	4.25
September 7, 1993. Printed by Harrison	
Cover shows a single stamp	4.75
January 10, 1995. Printed by Harrison	
Cover has white lines through block of stamps	4.00

December 12, 1995. Printed by Walsall
Cover shows block of stamps   4.50
February 6, 1996. Printed by Walsall
Back cover features Olympic symbols   4.00
February 4, 1997. Printed by Walsall (litho)
Cover has no line through block of stamps   4.00
August 26, 1997. Printed by Walsall (gravure)
Cover has no line through block of stamps   4.75

■ 10 x 2nd bright blue
April 6, 1993. Printed by Questa
Cover shows a single stamp   8.00
November 1, 1993. Printed by Walsall
Cover shows a single stamp   8.00
January 10, 1995. Printed by Questa
Cover has white lines through block of stamps   8.00
December 12, 1995. Printed by Harrison
Cover shows block of stamps   8.00
February 6, 1996. Printed by Harrison
Back cover features Olympic symbols   8.00
February 6, 1996. Printed by Questa
Back cover features Olympic symbols   8.00
August 6, 1996. Printed by Harrison
Cover has no white line through block of stamps
Back cover features Olympic symbols   8.00
August 6, 1996. Printed by Questa
Cover has no white line through block of stamps
Back cover features Olympic symbols   8.00
February 4, 1997. Printed by Harrison
Cover has no white line through block of stamps   9.00
February 4, 1997. Printed by Questa
Cover has no white line through block of stamps   8.00
May 5, 1998. Printed by De La Rue
Cover has no white line through block of stamps   9.00
December 1, 1998. Printed by Questa (gravure)
Cover has no white line through block of stamps   10.00

■ 4 x 1st orange–red
April 6, 1993. Printed by Harrison
Cover shows a single stamp   4.50
August 17, 1993. Printed by Walsall
Cover shows a single stamp   4.50
January 10, 1995. Printed by Walsall
Cover has white lines through block of stamps   4.50
February 6, 1996. Printed by Walsall
Back cover features Olympic symbols   4.50
February 4, 1997. Printed by Walsall (litho)
Cover has no white line through block of stamps   4.50
August 26, 1997. Printed by Walsall (gravure)
Cover has no white line through block of stamps   5.50

■ 4 x 1st orange–red with commemorative label
July 27, 1994. Printed by Questa
Label marks 300th anniversary of Bank of England   6.00
May 16, 1995. Printed by Walsall
Label marks centenary of birth of R. J. Mitchell   5.00
April 16, 1996. Printed by Walsall
Label marks 70th birthday of Queen Elizabeth II   5.00
February 12, 1997. Printed by Walsall
Label marks Hong Kong '97 stamp exhibition   5.00

October 21, 1997. Printed by Walsall
Label marks Commonwealth Heads of Government Meeting 6.00
November 14, 1998. Printed by Walsall
Label marks 50th birthday of the Prince of Wales   5.00
May 12, 1999. Printed by Walsall
Label marks 50th anniversary of the Berlin Airlift   5.50
October 1, 1999. Printed by Walsall
Label marks the Rugby World Cup   5.00
(*Stamp cards were produced illustrating the Bank of England,
R. J. Mitchell, Elizabeth II, Berlin Airlift and Rugby World Cup
labels; price £10–£16 each mint, £35 postally used.)

■ 4 x 1st olive–brown with commemorative label
March 21, 2000. Printed by Walsall
Label shows Postman Pat   5.00
April 4, 2000. Printed by Walsall
Label shows National Botanic Garden of Wales   5.00
(*Stamp cards were produced illustrating the Postman Pat and
National Botanic Garden of Wales labels; price £13–£16 mint,
£30–£35 postally used.)

■ 10 x 1st orange–red
April 6, 1993. Printed by Harrison
Cover shows a single stamp   10.00
April 6, 1993. Printed by Walsall
Cover shows a single stamp   10.00
November 1, 1993. Printed by Questa
Cover shows a single stamp   10.00
November 1, 1993. Printed by Walsall
Back cover has advertisement for Greetings stamps   10.50
February 22, 1994. Printed by Walsall
Yellow strip has 'Free postcards'   10.00
July 1, 1994. Printed by Walsall
Yellow strip has 'Open now, chance to win a kite',
and inside back cover has 'Better luck next time'   10.00
July 1, 1994. Printed by Walsall
Yellow strip has 'Open now, chance to win a kite',
and inside back cover has 'You've won'   10.00
September 20, 1994. Printed by Walsall
Cover has 'Stampers' and 'Do not open until'   10.00
September 20, 1994. Printed by Walsall
Cover has 'Stampers' and 'Keep in touch'   10.00
September 20, 1994. Printed by Walsall
Cover has 'Stampers' and 'Happy birthday'   10.00
September 20, 1994. Printed by Walsall
Cover has 'Stampers' and 'What's happenin'?'   10.00
January 10, 1995. Printed by Harrison
Cover has white lines through block of stamps   10.00
January 10, 1995. Printed by Questa
Cover has white lines through block of stamps   10.00
January 10, 1995. Printed by Walsall
Cover has white lines through block of stamps   10.00
February 14, 1995. Printed by Walsall
Cover has 'Brighten up someone's day'   10.00
April 4, 1995. Printed by Harrison
Stamps have two phosphor bands   10.00
April 24, 1995. Printed by Walsall
Yellow strip has 'W H Smith Special Offer'   10.00
June 26, 1995. Printed by Questa
Yellow strip has 'Sainsbury's Promotion'   10.00

September 4, 1995. Printed by Harrison
Cover shows Benjy Bear and Harry Hedgehog | 10.50
February 6, 1996. Printed by Walsall
Back cover features Olympic symbols | 10.50
February 19, 1996. Printed by Harrison
Cover shows Walt Disney World | 10.50
March 19, 1996. Printed by Harrison
Back cover features Olympic symbols | 10.50
May 13, 1996. Printed by Harrison
Cover has 'Will you be at the Olympics?'
Back cover shows shot put | 10.00
May 13, 1996. Printed by Harrison
Cover has 'Will you be at the Olympics?'
Back cover shows hurdling | 10.00
May 13, 1996. Printed by Harrison
Cover has 'Will you be at the Olympics?'
Back cover shows archery | 10.00
July 15, 1996. Printed by Walsall
Yellow strip has 'W H Smith Offer Inside' | 10.00
August 16, 1996. Printed by Harrison
Cover has no white line through block of stamps
Back cover features Olympic symbols | 10.00
August 16, 1996. Printed by Walsall
Cover has no white line through block of stamps
Back cover features Olympic symbols | 10.50
September 9, 1996. Printed by Walsall
Cover shows iced cakes | 10.00
October 7, 1996. Printed by Walsall
Yellow strip has 'Offer Inside' | 10.00
February 4, 1997. Printed by Harrison
Cover has no white line through block of stamps | 10.00
February 4, 1997. Printed by Walsall (litho)
Cover has no white line through block of stamps | 10.00
November 8, 1997. Printed by Walsall (gravure)
Cover has no white line through block of stamps | 10.50
February 2, 1998. Printed by De La Rue
Cover has 'Win an adventure holiday' | 10.00
April 27, 1998. Printed by De La Rue
Cover has 'Stick one of these on your drive' | 10.00
May 5, 1998. Printed by De La Rue
Cover has no white line through block of stamps | 10.00
July 1, 1998. Printed by De La Rue
Cover has 'Zoom out with one of these' | 10.00
August 3, 1998. Printed by De La Rue
Cover inscribed 'Make their post memorable' | 10.00
September 7, 1998. Printed by Questa (litho)
Cover has no white line through block of stamps | 10.00
December 1, 1998. Printed by Questa (gravure)
Cover has no white line through block of stamps | 10.00

■ 10 x 1st gold
April 21, 1997. Printed by Harrison
Cover shows a block of stamps | 10.00
April 21, 1997. Printed by Walsall
Cover shows a block of stamps | 10.00
September 15, 1997. Printed by Harrison
Cover shows a beach, and 'First class travel' | 10.00

■ 10 x 1st olive–brown
January 6, 2000. Printed by Questa

Cover shows a block of stamps | 10.00
January 6, 2000. Printed by Walsall
Cover shows a block of stamps | 10.00

■ 4 x E dark blue
January 19, 1999. Printed by Walsall
Cover shows a block of stamps and 'By Air Mail' label | 6.25

BOOKLETS OF DEFINITIVES & MILLENNIUM COMMEMORATIVES, 1999–2000

■ 8 x 1st orange–red, 1 x 26p Settlers' Tale, 1 x 26p Workers' Tale
May 12, 1999. Printed by Walsall | 11.00

■ 8 x 1st orange–red, 2 x 26p Farmers' Tale
September 21, 1999. Printed by Walsall | 12.00

■ 8 x 1st olive–brown, 1 x 1st Above & Beyond, 1 x 1st Life & Earth
May 26, 2000. Printed by Walsall | 11.00

■ 8 x 1st olive–brown, 1 x 1st Stone & Soil, 1 x 1st Tree & Leaf
September 5, 2000. Printed by Walsall | 11.00

Keep up with the latest news of Great Britain stamp issues

BOOKLETS OF SELF-ADHESIVE DEFINITIVES, 1993–2010

Booklets with experimental format.

■ **20 x 1st orange-red**
October 19, 1993. Printed by Walsall — 14.00

Booklets with a mainly red cover, and an illustration of the contents.

■ **6 x 2nd bright blue**
January 29, 2001. Printed by Walsall — 5.00

■ **10 x 2nd bright blue**
January 29, 2001. Printed by Questa — 7.50

■ **12 x 2nd bright blue**
January 29, 2001. Printed by Questa — 8.00

■ **6 x 1st orange-red and commemorative label**
January 29, 2001. Printed by Walsall
Label marks centenary of the death of Queen Victoria — 10.00

■ **6 x 1st orange-red**
January 29, 2001. Printed by Walsall — 6.00
July 4, 2002. Printed by Questa — 6.00

■ **10 x 1st orange-red**
January 29, 2001. Printed by Questa — 10.00

■ **12 x 1st orange-red**
January 29, 2001. Printed by Questa — 10.00
January 29, 2001. Printed by Walsall — 10.00

Booklets in the colour of the stamps, and with one (1st class), two (2nd class) or no notches (other values) along the right hand edge.

■ **12 x 2nd bright blue**
July 4, 2002. Printed by Questa — 10.50
March 27, 2003. Printed by Walsall
Inscription 'The Real Network' under Royal Mail cruciform — 10.50
June 15, 2004. Printed by Walsall
No 'The Real Network' inscription — 10.50
June 5, 2007. Printed by Walsall
Includes PiP information — 10.50

■ **6 x 1st gold**
June 5, 2002. Printed by Questa — 6.00
June 5, 2002. Printed by Walsall — 6.00
March 27, 2003. Printed by Walsall
Inscription 'The Real Network' under Royal Mail cruciform — 6.00
June 15, 2004. Printed by Walsall
Inscription 'Supporting London 2012' — 6.50
March 22, 2005. Printed by Walsall
Advertisement for Smilers on inside front cover — 6.50
June 5, 2007. Printed by Walsall
Includes PiP information — 7.00
June 5, 2007. Printed by Walsall
Includes facsimile of Arnold Machin's signature — 6.00
August 28, 2007. Printed by Walsall
Advertisement for Harry Potter stamps — 6.00
September 29, 2007. Printed by Walsall
Improved postcode information — 6.00
June 10, 2008. Printed by Walsall
Advertisement for Classic Carry On & Hammer stamps — 6.00

■ **12 x 1st gold**
June 5, 2002. Printed by Walsall — 12.00
March 27, 2003. Printed by Walsall
Inscription 'The Real Network' under Royal Mail cruciform — 12.00
June 5, 2007. Printed by Walsall
Includes PiP information — 12.00

■ 6 x E
July 4, 2002. Printed by Walsall — 10.00
May 28, 2003. Printed by Walsall
Inscription 'The Real Network' under Royal Mail cruciform — 10.00

■ 6 x 42p
July 4, 2002. Printed by Walsall — 25.00
May 28, 2003. Printed by Walsall
Inscription 'The Real Network' under Royal Mail cruciform — 25.00

■ 6 x 68p
July 4, 2002. Printed by Walsall — 26.00
May 28, 2003. Printed by Walsall
Inscription 'The Real Network' under Royal Mail cruciform — 26.00

■ 4 x Europe up to 20g
March 30, 2010. Printed by Walsall — 2.00

■ 4 x Europe up to 40g
March 27, 2003. Printed by Walsall
Inscription 'The Real Network' under Royal Mail cruciform — 10.00
June 15, 2004. Printed by Walsall
No 'The Real Network' inscription — 10.00

■ 4 x Worldwide up to 20g
April 1, 2004. Printed by Walsall — 8.50
March 30, 2010. Printed by Walsall — 8.50

■ 4 x Worldwide up to 40g
March 27, 2003. Printed by Walsall
Inscription 'The Real Network' under Royal Mail cruciform — 11.50
June 15, 2004. Printed by Walsall
No 'The Real Network' inscription — 11.50

BOOKLETS OF SELF–ADHESIVE DEFINITIVES & COMMEMORATIVES, 2001–2008

Booklets with a cover illustrating the special stamps inside (except Cats & Dogs).

■ 2 x 1st orange–red, 10 x 1st Cats & Dogs
February 13, 2001. Printed by Walsall — 25.00

■ 4 x 1st orange–red, 2 x 1st Submarines
April 17, 2001. Printed by Questa — 67.50

■ 4 x 1st orange–red, 2 x 1st Punch & Judy
September 4, 2001. Printed by Questa — 15.00

■ 4 x 1st orange–red, 2 x 1st Flags & Ensigns
October 22, 2001. Printed by Questa — 15.00

■ 4 x 1st orange–red, 2 x 1st Airliners
May 2, 2002. Printed by Questa — 7.00

■ 4 x 1st orange–red, 2 x 1st Football World Cup
May 21, 2002. Printed by Questa — 7.00

■ 4 x 1st gold, 2 x 1st Bridges of London
September 10, 2002. Printed by Questa — 7.50

■ 4 x 1st gold, 2 x 1st Hello!
March 4, 2003. Printed by Questa — 7.50

■ 4 x 1st gold, 2 x 1st Extreme Endeavours
April 29, 2003. Printed by De La Rue — 7.50

■ 4 x 1st gold, 2 x 1st British Journey: Scotland
July 15, 2003. Printed by De La Rue — 7.00

■ 4 x 1st gold, 2 x 1st Toys
September 18, 2003. Printed by De La Rue — 7.00

■ 4 x 1st gold, 2 x 1st British Journey: Northern Ireland
March 16, 2004. Printed by De La Rue — 7.00

■ 4 x 1st gold, 2 x 1st Ocean Liners
April 13, 2004. Printed by De La Rue — 7.00

■ 4 x 1st gold, 2 x 1st British Journey: Wales
June 15, 2004. Printed by De La Rue — 7.00

■ 4 x 1st gold, 2 x 1st Beside The Seaside
March 13, 2008. Printed by Walsall — 6.50

BOOKLETS OF SELF–ADHESIVE SMILERS STAMPS, 2005–15

■ **6 x 1st Smilers stamps of October 4, 2005**
October 4, 2005. Printed by Walsall   10.00
July 17, 2006. Printed by Walsall. With PiP information.   10.00

■ **6 x 1st Smilers stamps of October 17, 2006**
October 17, 2006. Printed by Walsall   8.00

■ **1 x 1st 'Love', 5 x 1st gold**
January 16, 2007. Printed by Walsall   18.00

■ **2 x 1st 'Love', 4 x 1st gold**
January 15, 2008. Printed by Walsall   7.00

■ **6 x 1st Smilers stamps of 2005 and 2006**
February 28, 2008. Printed by Walsall   32.00

■ **12 x 1st Smilers stamps of 2015**
January 6, 2015. Printed by ISP   18.00

BOOKLETS OF SELF–ADHESIVE PRICING–IN–PROPORTION DEFINITIVES, 2006–07

■ **12 x 2nd bright blue**
September 12, 2006. Printed by Walsall   9.00

■ **4 x 2nd Large bright blue**
August 15, 2006. Printed by Walsall   5.00

■ **6 x 1st gold**
September 12, 2006. Printed by Walsall   7.00
February 1, 2007. Printed by Walsall
With postcode advertisement inside front cover   7.00

■ **12 x 1st gold**
September 12, 2006. Printed by Walsall   12.00

■ **4 x 1st Large gold**
August 15, 2006. Printed by Walsall   6.00

BOOKLETS OF SELF–ADHESIVE SECURITY DEFINITIVES, 2009 to date

■ **12 x 2nd blue**
March 31, 2009. Printed by Walsall
Back cover includes printer's name   12.00
August 19, 2010. Printed by Walsall
Back cover has printer's name removed   13.00
October 25, 2011. Printed by Walsall
Back cover includes FSC logo   13.00
2015. Printed by ISP
Security backing paper   15.00
October 20, 2016. Printed by ISP
Cover has revised typeface. Security backing paper   12.00

■ **4 x 2nd Large blue**
March 31, 2009. Printed by Walsall
Back cover includes printer's name   7.50
March 22, 2011. Printed by Walsall
Back cover has printer's name removed   6.00
October 25, 2011. Printed by Walsall
Back cover includes FSC logo   6.00
2016. Printed by ISP
Security backing paper   20.00
October 20, 2016. Printed by ISP
Cover has revised typeface. Security backing paper   11.00

■ **6 x 1st gold**
March 31, 2009. Printed by Walsall
Inside front cover has web address 'Postcodes4free'   9.75
December 15, 2009. Printed by Walsall
Back cover has printer's name removed   7.00
January 26, 2010. Printed by Walsall
Inside front cover has web address 'postcodes4free'   10.00
March 30, 2010. Printed by Walsall
Inside front cover has publicity for Festival of Stamps 9.00
October 25, 2011. Printed by Walsall
Back cover includes FSC logo   12.00

■ **12 x 1st gold**
March 31, 2009. Printed by Walsall
Back cover includes printer's name   12.00
December 15, 2009. Printed by Walsall
Back cover has printer's name removed   14.00

October 25, 2011. Printed by Walsall
Back cover includes FSC logo — 14.00

■ 4 x 1st Large gold
March 31, 2009. Printed by Walsall
Back cover includes printer's name — 11.00
March 22, 2011. Printed by Walsall
Back cover has printer's name removed — 8.00
October 25, 2011. Printed by Walsall
Back cover includes FSC logo — 8.00

■ 6 x 1st diamond blue
October 1, 2012. Printed by Walsall — 6.25
(*This booklet was available from some post offices before its official release date.)

■ 12 x 1st diamond blue
February 6, 2012. Printed by Walsall — 11.50

■ 4 x 1st Large diamond blue
April 25, 2012. Printed by Walsall — 8.00

■ 6 x 1st red
January 3, 2013. Printed by Walsall — 7.00
July 28, 2016. Printed by ISP
Front cover has padlock motif — 7.00
2016. Printed by ISP
Front cover has padlock motif. Security backing paper — 6.00

■ 12 x 1st red
January 3, 2013. Printed by Walsall — 12.00
2015. Printed by ISP
Security backing paper — 12.00

■ 4 x 1st Large red
January 3, 2013. Printed by Walsall — 13.00
2016. Printed by ISP
Security backing paper — 13.00

■ 6 x 1st amethyst purple
September 9, 2015. Printed by ISP
Label portraying the Queen — 7.00
2015. Printed by ISP
Security backing paper. Label portraying the Queen — 15.00

■ 6 x 1st deep red
October 20, 2016. Printed by ISP.
Front cover has padlock motif and revised typeface.
Security backing paper — 7.00
June 5, 2017. Printed by ISP.
Inside front cover notes Machin Anniversary. Security backing paper — 7.00

■ 12 x 1st deep red
October 20, 2016. Printed by ISP.
Cover has revised typeface. Security backing paper — 15.00

■ 4 x 1st Large deep red
October 20, 2016. Printed by ISP.
Cover has revised typeface. Security backing paper — 15.00

BOOKLETS OF SELF–ADHESIVE SECURITY DEFINITIVES & COMMEMORATIVES, 2009 to date

■ 6 x 1st. British Design Classics
4 x 1st gold, 1 x 1st Telephone Kiosk, 1 x 1st Routemaster
March 10, 2009. Printed by Walsall — 6.00
4 x 1st gold, 2 x 1st Mini
April 21, 2009. Printed by Walsall — 6.00
4 x 1st gold, 2 x 1st Concorde
August 18, 2009. Printed by Walsall — 6.00
4 x 1st gold, 2 x 1st Mini Skirt
September 17, 2009. Printed by Walsall — 6.00
4 x 1st gold, 2 x 1st Spitfire
September 15, 2010. Printed by Walsall — 6.00

■ 6 x 1st. National Association of Flower Arrangement Societies
4 x 1st, gold 1 x 1st Iris latifolia, 1 x 1st Tulipa
May 21, 2009. Printed by Walsall — 10.00

■ 6 x 1st. Olympic and Paralympic Games
4 x 1st gold, 1 x 1st Paralympic Archery, 1 x 1st Judo
January 7, 2010. Printed by Walsall — 6.00
4 x 1st gold, 1 x 1st Track Athletics, 1 x 1st Basketball
February 25, 2010. Printed by Walsall — 6.00
4 x 1st gold, 1 x 1st Paralympic Rowing, 1 x 1st Table Tennis
July 27, 2010. Printed by Walsall — 6.00
4 x 1st gold, 1 x 1st Football, 1 x 1st Cycling
October 12, 2010. Printed by Walsall — 6.00
4 x 1st gold, 1 x 1st Wheelchair Rugby, 1 x 1st Paralympic Sailing
July 27, 2011. Printed by Walsall — 6.00
4 x 1st gold, 1 x 1st Gymnastics, 1 x 1st Fencing
September 15, 2011. Printed by Walsall — 6.00

■ 6 x 1st. Mammals
4 x 1st gold, 1 x 1st Otter, 1 x 1st Hedgehog
June 15, 2010. Printed by Walsall — 11.00

■ 6 x 1st. Thunderbirds
4 x 1st gold, 2 x 1st Thunderbirds
January 11, 2011. Printed by Walsall — 6.00

■ **6 x 1st. Medical Breakthroughs**
4 x 1st gold, 2 x 1st Beta-Blockers
February 24, 2011. Printed by Walsall   6.00

■ **6 x 1st. Thomas the Tank Engine**
4 x 1st gold, 2 x 1st Goodbye Bertie
June 14, 2011. Printed by Walsall   6.00

■ **6 x 1st. Classic Locomotives of England**
4 x 1st gold, 2 x 1st BR Dean Goods locomotive
August 23, 2011. Printed by Walsall   6.00

■ **6 x 1st. Diamond Jubilee**
4 x 1st diamond blue, 2 x 1st Golden Jubilee 2002
May 31, 2012. Printed by Walsall   6.00

■ **6 x 1st. Classic Locomotives of Scotland**
4 x 1st diamond blue, 2 x 1st Class D34 locomotive
September 27, 2012. Printed by Walsall   6.00

■ **6 x 1st. London Underground**
4 x 1st red, 2 x 1st Boston Manor Station
January 9, 2013. Printed by Walsall   7.00

■ **6 x 1st. Football Heroes (first issue)**
4 x 1st red, 1 x 1st George Best, 1 x 1st Bobby Moore
May 9, 2013. Printed by Walsall   9.00

■ **6 x 1st. Classic Locomotives of Northern Ireland**
4 x 1st red, 2 x 1st UTA W No.103 locomotive
June 18, 2013. Printed by Walsall   6.50

■ **6 x 1st. Butterflies**
4 x 1st red, 1 x 1st Chalkhill Blue, 1 x 1st Comma
July 11, 2013. Printed by Walsall   6.00

■ **6 x 1st. Royal Mail Transport**
4 x 1st red, 1 x 1st Morris Minor van, 1 x 1st RMS
'Britannia'
September 19, 2013. Printed by Walsall   16.00

■ **6 x 1st. Football Heroes (second issue)**
4 x 1st red, 1 x 1st John Charles, 1 x 1st Dave Mackay
February 20, 2014. Printed by Walsall   10.00

■ **6 x 1st. Buckingham Palace**
4 x 1st red, 1 x 1st Grand Staircase, 1 x 1st Throne Room
April 15, 2014. Printed by Walsall   6.00

■ **6 x 1st. Glasgow 2014 Commonwealth Games**
4 x 1st red, 2 x 1st Swimming
July 17, 2014. Printed by Walsall   6.00

■ **6 x 1st. Sustainable Fish**
4 x 1st red, 1 x 1st Common Skate, 1 x 1st Cornish Herring
August 18, 2014. Printed by Walsall   10.00

■ **6 x 1st. Classic Locomotives of Wales**
4 x 1st red, 2 x 1st LMS 2F No.7720 locomotive
September 18, 2014. Printed by Walsall   6.00

■ **6 x 1st. Alice in Wonderland**
4 x 1st red, 1 x 1st Drink Me, 1 x 1st White Rabbit's House
January 6, 2015. Printed by ISP   12.00

■ **6 x 1st. Comedy Greats**
4 x 1st red, 1 x 1st Norman Wisdom, 1 x 1st Morecambe & Wise
April 1, 2015. Printed by ISP   9.00

■ **6 x 1st. Bees**
4 x 1st red, 2 x 1st Great Yellow Bumblebee
August 18, 2015. Printed by ISP   6.00

■ **6 x 1st. Rugby World Cup**
4 x 1st amethyst, 1 x 1st Try, 1 x 1st Conversion
September 18, 2015. Printed by ISP   7.00

■ **6 x 1st. The Queen's 90th Birthday (issue 1)**
4 x 1st amethyst, 1 x 1st Prince Charles, 1 x 1st Queen
Elizabeth II
April 21, 2016. Printed by ISP   9.00

■ **6 x 1st. The Queen's 90th Birthday (issue 2)**
4 x 1st amethyst, 1 x 1st Prince George, 1 x 1st Prince William
June 9, 2016. Printed by ISP   6.00

■ **6 x 1st. Beatrix Potter**
4 x 1st amethyst, 1 x 1st Peter Rabbit, 1 x 1st Mrs Tiggy-Winkle
July 28, 2016. Printed by ISP   10.00

■ **6 x 1st. Landscape Gardens**
4 x 1st amethyst, 1 x 1st Compton Verney, 1 x 1st Highclere Castle
August 16, 2016. Printed by ISP   8.00

■ **6 x 1st. Mr. Men and Little Miss**
4 x 1st deep red, 1 x 1st Mr. Happy, 1 x 1st Mr. Tickle
October 20, 2016. Printed by ISP   6.00

■ **6 x 1st. St. George's Chapel**
4 x 1st deep red, 1 x 1st Bray roof boss, 1 x 1st Fan-vaulted roof
February 15, 2017. Printed by ISP   6.00

■ **6 x 1st. David Bowie**
4 x 1st deep red, 1 x 1st Aladdin Sane, 1 x 1st Heroes
March 14, 2017. Printed by ISP   6.00

■ **6 x 1st. Star Wars: Droids**
4 x 1st deep red, 1 x 1st BB–8, 1 x 1st R2–D2
October 12, 2017. Printed by ISP   6.50

■ **6 x 1st. Star Wars: Aliens and Creatures**
4 x 1st deep red, 1 x 1st Maz Kanata, 1 x 1st Chewbacca
October 12, 2017. Printed by ISP   6.50

■ **6 x 1st. RAF Centenary**
4 x 1st deep red, 1 x 1st Lightning F6, 1 x 1st Hurricane Mk1
March 20, 2018. Printed by ISP   6.50

■ **6 x 1st. RAF Centenary: Red Arrows**
4 x 1st deep red, 1 x 1st Flypast, 1 x 1st Swan
May 11, 2018. Printed by ISP   6.50

■ **6 x 1st. Dad's Army**
4 x 1st deep red, 1 x 1st Capt Mainwaring, 1 x 1st Lance Corp Jones
June 26, 2018. Printed by ISP   6.50

■ **6 x 1st. Hampton Court Palace**
4 x 1st deep red, 1 x 1st Great Hall, 1 x 1st King's Great Bedchamber
July 31, 2018. Printed by ISP   6.50

■ **6 x 1st. First World War**
4 x 1st deep red, 1 x 1st Poppy by Fiona Strickland,
1 x 1st 100 Poppies by Zafer and Barbara Baran
September 13, 2018. Printed by ISP   6.00

■ **6 x 1st. Harry Potter**
4 x 1st deep red, 1 x 1st Hermione Granger, 1 x 1st Harry Potter
October 16, 2018. Printed by ISP   6.00

■ **6 x 1st. Marvel**
4 x 1st deep red, 1 x 1st Spider–Man, 1 x 1st Hulk
March 14, 2019. Printed by ISP   6.00

■ **6 x 1st. Birds of Prey**
4 x 1st deep red, 1 x 1st Buzzard, 1 x 1st Hobby
April 4, 2019. Printed by ISP   6.00

■ **6 x 1st. D–Day**
4 x 1st deep red, 1 x 1st Gold, 1 x 1st Sword
June 6, 2019. Printed by ISP   6.00

BOOKLETS OF SELF–ADHESIVE OLYMPIC GAMES DEFINITIVES, 2012

■ **6 x 1st. Olympic and Paralympic Games**
3 x 1st Olympic Games logo, 3 x 1st Paralympic Games logo
Cover: Union flag. Inside front cover: quote from Lord Coe
January 5, 2012. Printed by Walsall   6.50

■ **6 x 1st. Olympic and Paralympic Games**
3 x 1st Olympic Games logo, 3 x 1st Paralympic Games logo
Cover: Union flag. Inside front cover: timetable of events
January 5, 2012. Printed by Walsall   6.50
(*The cover design and the arrangement of the stamps varies
between these two booklets.)

BOOKLETS OF SELF–ADHESIVE COMMEMORATIVES, 2013 to date

■ **6 x 1st. Doctor Who**
4 x 1st Tardis, 1 x 1st Matt Smith, 1 x 1st William Hartnell
March 26, 2013. Printed by Walsall   14.00

■ **6 x 1st. 175th Anniversary of the Penny Black**
6 x 1st Penny Black
May 6, 2015. Printed by ISP   10.00

■ **6 x 1st. 175th Anniversary of the Penny Red**
6 x 1st Penny Red
February 18, 2016. Printed by ISP   6.50

■ **6 x 1st. Game of Thrones**
6 x 1st The Iron Throne
January 23, 2018. Printed by ISP   7.00

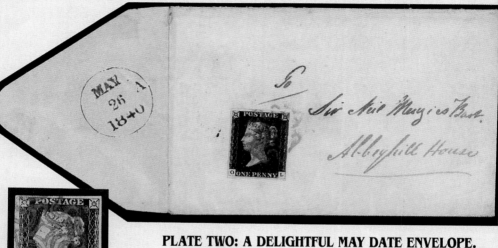

CHRISTMAS BOOKLETS

In this section, prices are quoted for mint condition only. These booklets contain definitive stamps or Christmas special issues.

COUNTER BOOKLETS, 1978–86

■ **1978, November 15**
£1.60 (10 x 7p, 10 x 9p definitives).
Decoration of holly cover, 'Christmas 1978'   3.00

■ **1979, November 14**
£1.80 (10 x 8p, 10 x 10p definitives).
Christmas cracker cover, 'Christmas 1979'   3.75

■ **1980, November 12**
£2.20 (10 x 10p, 10 x 12p definitives).
Nativity scene cover, 'Christmas 1980'   4.00

■ **1981, November 11**
£2.55 (10 x 14p, 10 x 11½p definitives).
Skating scene cover, 'Christmas Greetings 1981'   5.00

■ **1982, November 10**
£2.50 (10 x 15½p, 10 x 12½p definitives).
Christmas mummers cover, 'Christmas Special Offer'   5.50
(* Sold at a discount of 30p off face value; stamps
have a blue star printed on the gummed side)

■ **1983, November 9**
£2.20 (20 x 12½p definitives).
Pantomime scene cover, 'Christmas Special Offer'   5.00
(* Sold at a discount of 30p off face value; stamps
have a blue star printed on the gummed side.)

■ **1984, November 20**
£2.30 (20 x 13p Christmas stamps).
Manger scene cover, 'Christmas Special Offer'   5.50
(* Sold at a discount of 30p off face value; stamps
have a blue star printed on the gummed side)

■ **1985, November 19**
£2.40 (20 x 12p Christmas stamps).
Cinderella's slipper cover   5.00

■ **1986, December 2**
£1.20 (10 x 13p definitives).

Cooking Shetland yule cakes cover, 'Special Offer'   5.50
(*Sold at a discount of 10p off face value; stamps
have a blue star printed on the gummed side.)

RETAIL BOOKLETS, 1990–2000

■ **1990, November 13**
20 x 17p Christmas stamps   6.00

■ **1991, November 12**
20 x 18p Christmas stamps   6.00

■ **1992, November 10**
20 x 18p Christmas stamps   7.00

■ **1993, November 9**
20 x 19p Christmas stamps   6.50
10 x 25p Christmas stamps   5.50

■ **1994, November 1**
20 x 19p Christmas stamps   6.75
10 x 25p Christmas stamps   5.00

■ **1995, October 30**
20 x 19p Christmas stamps   6.50
10 x 25p Christmas stamps   4.00
4 x 60p Christmas stamps   4.50

■ **1996, October 28**
20 x 2nd Christmas stamps   13.50
10 x 1st Christmas stamps   8.50

■ **1997, October 27**
20 x 2nd Christmas stamps   12.00
10 x 1st Christmas stamps   8.50

■ **1998, November 2**
20 x 20p Christmas stamps   6.50
10 x 26p Christmas stamps   4.50

■ **1999, November 2**
20 x 19p The Christians' Tale stamps   7.00
10 x 26p The Christians' Tale stamps   5.00

■ **2000, November 7**
20 x 2nd Spirit and Faith stamps   13.00
10 x 1st Spirit and Faith stamps   9.50

SELF–ADHESIVE FOLDERS, 2001–05

■ **2001, November 6**
24 x 2nd Christmas stamps	16.50
12 x 1st Christmas stamps	11.00

■ **2002, November 5**
24 x 2nd Christmas stamps	16.50
12 x 1st Christmas stamps	11.00

■ **2003, November 4**
24 x 2nd Christmas stamps	17.00
12 x 1st Christmas stamps	11.00

■ **2004, November 2**
24 x 2nd Christmas stamps	17.00
12 x 1st Christmas stamps	12.50

■ **2005, November 1**
24 x 2nd Christmas stamps	17.00
12 x 1st Christmas stamps	11.00

SELF–ADHESIVE BOOKLETS, 2006–15

■ **2006, November 7**
12 x 2nd Christmas stamps	9.50
12 x 1st Christmas stamps	11.50

■ **2007, November 6**
12 x 2nd Christmas stamps	9.50
12 x 1st Christmas stamps	11.50

■ **2008, November 4**
12 x 2nd Christmas stamps. Pane inscribed 'Oh yes it is'	9.50
12 x 2nd Christmas stamps. Pane inscribed 'Oh no it isn't'	9.50

12 x 1st Christmas stamps. Pane inscribed 'It's behind you'	11.00
12 x 2nd Christmas stamps. Pane inscribed 'Abracadabra'	11.00

■ **2009, November 3**
12 x 2nd Christmas stamps	10.00
12 x 1st Christmas stamps	11.00

■ **2010, November 2**
12 x 2nd Christmas stamps	10.00
12 x 1st Christmas stamps	11.00

■ **2011, November 8**
12 x 2nd Christmas stamps	10.00
12 x 1st Christmas stamps	11.00

■ **2012, November 6**
12 x 2nd Christmas stamps	10.00
12 x 1st Christmas stamps	11.00

■ **2013, November 5**
12 x 2nd Christmas stamps	10.00
12 x 1st Christmas stamps	11.00

■ **2014, November 4**
12 x 2nd Christmas stamps	12.00
12 x 1st Christmas stamps	13.50

■ **2015, November 3**
12 x 2nd Christmas stamps	10.00
12 x 1st Christmas stamps	11.00

SELF–ADHESIVE BOOKLETS, 2016 to date

■ **2016, November 8**
12 x 2nd Christmas stamps	10.00
12 x 1st Christmas stamps	11.00

■ **2017, November 7**
12 x 2nd Christmas stamps (Madonna and Child)	10.00
12 x 2nd Christmas stamps (six of each design)	10.00
12 x 1st Christmas stamps (Madonna and Child)	11.00
12 x 1st Christmas stamps (six of each design)	11.00

■ **2018, November 1**
12 x 2nd Christmas stamps	11.00
12 x 1st Christmas stamps	12.00

GREETINGS BOOKLETS

In this section, prices are quoted for mint condition only.
These booklets contain Greetings stamps, which are listed
individually in the Queen Elizabeth II Decimal section. Normally
the panes comprise one of each design, with additional
greetings labels.

■ 1989, January 31. Greetings
Two of each of the five 19p designs as January 31, 1989,
plus 12 labels. Cover designs differ 25.00

■ 1990, February 6. Smiles
One each of ten 20p designs as February 6, 1990,
plus 12 labels. Cover shows smiling mouth 14.00

■ 1991, February 5. Good Luck
One each of ten 1st class designs as February 5, 1991,
plus 12 labels. Cover shows lucky charms 10.00

■ 1991, March 26. Smiles
One each of ten 1st class designs as March 26, 1991,
plus 12 labels. Cover shows laughing pillar box 9.00

■ 1992, January 28. Memories
One each of ten 1st class designs as January 28, 1992,
plus 12 labels. Cover shows label and pressed flowers 9.00

■ 1993, February 2. Gift Giving
One each of ten 1st class designs as February 2, 1993,
plus 20 labels. Cover shows Rupert and Wilfrid 9.00

■ 1994, February 1. Messages
One each of ten 1st class designs as February 1, 1994,
plus 20 labels. Cover shows Rupert and Paddington 9.00

■ 1995, March 21. Art
One each of ten 1st class designs as March 21, 1995,
plus 20 labels. Cover shows clown
Yellow strip has 'Pull Open' 9.00
Yellow strip has no inscription 9.00

■ 1996, February 26. Cartoons
One each of ten 1st class designs as February 26, 1996,
plus 20 labels. Cover shows figure holding bowl
Inside cover has 1996 dates 9.00

■ 1996, November 11. Cartoons
One each of ten 1st class designs as November 11, 1996,
plus 20 labels. Figure holding bowl cover.
Inside cover omits 1996 dates 25.00

■ 1997, January 6. Flower Paintings
One each of ten 1st class designs as January 6, 1997,
plus 20 labels. Cover shows gentiana flower 9.00

■ 1997, February 3. Flower Paintings
One each of ten 1st class designs as January 6, 1997, plus
20 labels. Cover shows gentiana flower and 'Win a
beautiful bouquet instantly' 9.00

■ 1998, January 5. Flower Paintings
One each of ten 1st class designs as January 6, 1997, plus
20 labels. Cover shows box of chocolates 9.00

■ 1998, August 3. Flower Paintings
One each of ten 1st class designs as January 6, 1997, plus
20 labels. Cover shows Christmas cards 9.00

PRESTIGE STAMP BOOKS

In this section, prices are quoted for mint condition only.

Stamps for Cooks, 1969

■ **1969, December 1. £1.00 Stamps for Cooks**

Pane of six 1d, three 4d, three 4d, three 5d (recipe label)	6.00
Pane of fifteen 4d (label 'Stuffed Cucumber')	2.00
Pane of fifteen 4d (label 'Method')	2.00
Pane of fifteen 5d (recipe label)	2.00
Complete book	7.50

(*A stapled version of this stitched book exists that is much rarer. Price: £350.)

The Story of Wedgwood, 1972

■ **1972, May 24. £1.00 The Story of Wedgwood**

Pane of twelve 3p	3.00
Pane of six 2½p, six 3p	6.00
Pane of nine 2½p, one ½p	7.50
Pane of four ½p, two 2½p	40.00
Complete book	45.00

The Story of Wedgwood, 1980

■ **1980, April 16. £3.00 The Story of Wedgwood**

Pane of six 2p	0.50
Pane of nine 10p	2.00
Pane of nine 12p	2.00
Pane of one 2p, four 10p, four 12p	2.00
Complete book	5.00

■ **1982, May 19. £4.00 The Story of Stanley Gibbons**

Pane of six 12½p	1.75
Pane of six 15½p	1.75
Pane of nine 15½p	2.50
Pane of one 2p, one 3p, seven 12½p	3.00
Complete book	6.00

■ **1983, September 14. £4.00 The Story of the Royal Mint**

Pane of six 12½p (label 'The Royal Mint & America')	1.75
Pane of six 12½p (label 'Maundy Money')	1.75
Pane of nine 16p	2.50
Pane of one 3p, two 3½p, six 16p	3.00
Complete book	6.00

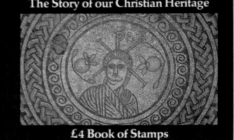

The Story of our Christian Heritage, 1984

■ **1984, September 4. £4.00 The Story of Our Christian Heritage**

Pane of six 17p	2.25
Pane of six 13p (label 'William Wilberforce')	2.00
Pane of six 13p (label 'Lillian Bayliss')	2.00
Pane of one 10p, one 13p, seven 17p	13.00
Complete book	15.00

■ **1985, January 8. £5.00 The Story of The Times**

Pane of six 17p	2.50
Pane of nine 13p	2.50
Pane of nine 17p	3.00
Pane of two 4p, four 13p, two 17p, one 34p	8.00
Complete book	10.00

■ **1986, March 18. £5.00 The Story of British Rail**

Pane of six 17p	2.50
Pane of nine 12p	3.00
Pane of nine 17p	3.00
Pane of six 12p, two 17p, one 31p	9.00
Complete book	10.00

1987, March 3. £5.00 The Story of P&O

Pane of six 13p	2.25
Pane of nine 13p	2.75
Pane of nine 18p	3.00
Pane of one 1p, two 13p, five 18p, one 26p	8.00
Complete book	10.00

1988, March 3. £5.00 FT100 (Financial Times)

Pane of nine 18p	4.50
Pane of six 13p	2.50
Pane of six 13p, one 18p, one 22p, one 34p	14.00
Pane of six 18p	2.50
Complete book	17.50

1989, March 21. £5.00 The Scots Connection

Pane of nine 19p Scotland	2.75
Pane of six 14p Scotland	2.50
Pane of five 14p, two 19p, one 23p, all Scotland	10.00
Pane of six 19p Scotland	2.50
Complete book	11.00

1990, March 20. £5.00 London Life

Pane of four 20p Alexandra Palace	2.50
Pane of six 20p Penny Black Anniversary (label 'Eros')	2.50
Pane of six 20p Penny Black Anniversary (label 'Street Signs')	2.50
Pane of one 15p, one 20p, one 29p all Penny Black Anniversary, plus one 2nd, one 1st, one 15p, one 20p, one 50p	11.00
Complete book	14.00

1991, March 19. £6.00 Alias Agatha Christie

Pane of six 17p (label 'Styles')	2.25
Pane of six 17p (label 'Mousetrap')	2.25
Pane of nine 22p	4.50
Pane of six 22p, two 33p	5.50
Complete book	10.00

1992, February 25. £6.00 Cymru Wales

Pane of four 39p Wintertime	2.50
Pane of six 18p Wales	2.25
Pane of two 18p, two 24p, all Wales, plus one 2nd, one 1st, two 33p	7.50
Pane of six 24p Wales	2.25
Complete book	9.50

Tolkien: The Centenary, 1992

1992, October 27. £6.00 Tolkien: The Centenary

Pane of six 24p (label 'Runes')	2.50
Pane of six 24p (label 'Hobbit')	2.50
Pane of six 18p	2.00
Pane of one 2nd, one 1st, two 18p, two 24p, two 39p	7.50
Complete book	10.00

The Story of Beatrix Potter, 1992

1993, August 10. £5.64 The Story of Beatrix Potter

Pane of four 1st Beatrix Potter	3.00
Pane of one 24p of each of Scotland, Wales and Northern Ireland, one 18p of each of Scotland, Wales and Northern Ireland	7.50
Pane of three 1st, three 2nd	6.50
Pane of two 2nd, two 18p, two 33p, two 39p	7.50
Complete book	12.50

1994, July 26. £6.04 Northern Ireland

Pane of four 30p Prince of Wales Paintings	2.50
Pane of one 6p, one 19p, four 25p	7.50
Pane of two 19p, four 25p, one 30p, one 41p, all Northern Ireland	5.00
Pane of one 19p, one 25p, one 30p, one 41p, all Northern Ireland	5.00
Complete book	11.50

1995, April 25. £6.00 The National Trust

Pane of six 25p National Trust	2.00
Pane of two 19p, two 25p, one 10p, one 30p, one 35p, one 41p	9.00
Pane of one 19p of each of Scotland, Wales and Northern Ireland, plus one 25p of each of Scotland, Wales and Northern Ireland	5.50
Pane of six 19p	7.50
Complete book	11.00

1996, May 14. £6.48 European Football Championships

Pane of four 19p Football Legends	1.75
Pane of four 25p Football Legends	2.00
Pane of two 35p, two 41p, two 60p Football Legends	4.50
Pane of two 25p, two 25p Scotland, two 25p Wales, two 25p Northern Ireland	3.50
Complete book	9.00

■ 1997, September 23. £6.15 Celebrating 75 Years of the BBC

Pane of one 26p, one 37p Scotland, one 26p, one 37p Wales, one 26p, one 37p Northern Ireland	4.00
Pane of four 26p gold, four 1st gold	4.50
Pane of three 20p, three 26p	4.00
Pane of four 20p Children's Television	4.50
Complete book	11.00

■ 1998, March 10. £7.49 The Definitive Portrait

Pane of nine 26p Wilding	4.50
Pane of six 20p Wilding	3.00
Pane of four 20p, two 26p, two 37p Wilding	5.50
Pane of three 26p, three 37p Wilding	5.50
Complete book	13.00

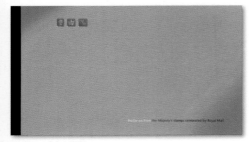

Breaking Barriers, 1998

■ 1998, October 13. £6.16 Breaking Barriers

Pane of four 20p Land Speed Records	4.00
Pane of one 20p Scotland, one 20p Wales, one 20p Northern Ireland, three 43p	6.00
Pane of three 2nd, one 26p Scotland, one 26p Wales, one 26p Northern Ireland	5.00
Pane of three 43p, two 10p, three 2nd	6.50
Complete book	19.00

Profile on Print, 1999

■ 1999, February 16. £7.54 Profile on Print

Pane of eight 1st orange-red	7.00
Pane of four 1st Machin large format embossed	7.00
Pane of four Machin large format intaglio	7.00
Pane of four Machin large format typographed	7.00
Pane of nine 1st orange-red	9.00
Complete book	22.00

■ 1999, September 21. £6.99 World Changers

Pane of four 20p Millennium Jenner's vaccination	2.00
Pane of four 44p Millennium Faraday's electricity	6.00
Pane of four 26p Millennium Darwin's theory	6.50
Pane of four 63p Millennium Computers in brain	8.00
Pane of four 1p, three 19p, one 26p	3.00
Complete book	15.00

Special by Design, 2000

■ 2000, February 15. £7.50 Special by Design

Pane of eight 1st Millennium definitive	5.50
Pane of three 1st Scotland, three 1st Wales, three 1st Northern Ireland	7.00
Pane of four 19p, olive-green, two 38p	10.00
Pane of six 1st Penny Black Anniversary	6.50
Complete book	21.00

■ 2000, August 4. £7.03 HM Queen Elizabeth, The Queen Mother

Pane of six 2nd Scotland, two 65p Scotland	5.00
Pane of nine 1st olive brown	5.00
Queen Mother's Century miniature sheet	7.00
Pane of four 27p Queen Mother	6.00
Complete book	16.00

■ 2000, September 18. £7.00 A Treasury of Trees

Pane of two 65p Millennium Doire Dach forest	3.50
Pane of four 45p Millennium Sycamore seeds,	4.00
Pane of two 65p Millennium Bluebell wood	3.50
Pane of four 1st Millennium definitives, four 2nd Wales	8.00
Pane of four 2nd Millennium Roots of trees	2.50
Complete book	18.00

■ 2001, October 21. £6.76 Unseen and Unheard

Pane of two 1st, two 65p Submarines	7.00
Pane of two 2nd, two 45p Submarines	7.00
Pane of four Flags and Ensigns	5.50
Pane of four 1st Scotland, four E Scotland	5.50
Complete book	19.00

■ 2002, February 6. £7.29 A Gracious Accession

Pane of four 2nd, four E	6.50
Pane of one 2nd, one 1st, one E, one 45p Golden Jubilee	8.00
Pane of one 1st, one E, one 45p, one 65p Golden Jubilee	8.00
Pane of four 1st Wilding, five 2nd Wilding (one tilted)	9.00
Complete book	21.00

2002, September 24. £6.83 Across the Universe
Pane of four 1st England, four 2nd England, one 1st Scotland	5.50
Pane of four 1st Millennium National Space Centre	8.50
Pane of four 1st gold, four E	6.00
Astronomy miniature sheet	4.00
Complete book	19.50

2003, February 25. £6.99 Microcosmos
Pane of four 1st Northern Ireland, five 2nd Northern Ireland	7.00
Pane of four 1st gold, four E	7.00
Pane of two 1st and two 2nd Discovery of DNA	3.00
Pane of four E Discovery of DNA	7.00
Complete book	21.00

2003, June 2. £7.46 A Perfect Coronation
Pane of four 1st gold, four 2nd	4.75
Pane of four 1st 50th Anniversary of Coronation	2.75
Pane of four (different) 1st 50th Anniversary of Coronation	2.75
Pane of two 47p Wilding, two 68p Wilding, one £1 Coronation	30.00
Complete book	35.00

Letters by Night, 2004

2004, March 16. £7.44 Letters by Night
Pane of three 2nd Scotland, three 68p Scotland	5.00
Pane of one 28p, one E, one 42p Classic Locomotives	5.00
Pane of four 1st Pub Signs	4.00
Pane of four 1st gold, four 37p	6.00
Complete book	16.00

The Glory of the Garden, 2004

2004, May 25. £7.23 The Glory of the Garden
Pane of four 1st gold, two 42p, two 47p	5.50
Pane of one 2nd, one E, one 68p, one 42p RHS	5.50
Pane of one 1st Iris latifolia, two 1st Tulipa, one 1st Gentiana acaulis	6.50
Pane of two 1st, two 47p RHS	6.50
Complete book	20.00

2005, February 24. £7.43 The Brontë Sisters
Pane of four 2nd, two 39p, two 42p	4.50
Pane of two 2nd England, two 40p England	3.00
Pane of two 1st Brontë, two 1st Brontë	4.00
Pane of one 40p, one 57p, one 68p, one £1.12 Brontë	5.50
Complete book	15.00

2005, October 4. £7.26 Bicentenary of the Battle of Trafalgar
Pane of four 1st, two 50p, two 68p	6.00
Pane of three 1st White Ensign	5.50
Pane of one 1st, one 42p, one 68p Trafalgar (first designs)	3.00
Pane of one 1st, one 42p, one 68p Trafalgar (second designs)	3.00
Complete book	15.00

2006, February 23. £7.40 Brunel
Pane of one 40p, one 60p, one 47p all Brunel	3.50
Pane of one 1st, one 42p, one 68p all Brunel	3.00
Pane of four 1st, two 35p, two 40p	5.50
Pane of two 68p Ocean Liners, one 47p Brunel	10.00
Complete book	15.00

Victoria Cross, 2006

2006, September 21. £7.41 Victoria Cross
Pane of first 1st, 64p and 72p Victoria Cross	3.50
Pane of second 1st, 64p and 72p Victoria Cross	3.50
Pane of four 20p Gallantry Awards	9.00
Pane of four 1st, four 50p	6.00
Complete book	15.00

2007, March 1. £7.68 World of Invention
Pane of three 2nd Scotland and three 44p Wales	5.00
Pane of four 1st revised style and four 5p definitives	3.25
Pane of two 1st and two 64p World of Invention	6.50
Pane of two 1st and two 72p World of Invention	6.00
Complete book	16.00

■ 2007, June 5. £7.66 The Machin: The Making of a Masterpiece

Pane of four 2p, two 46p, two 48p definitives	4.50
Pane of two £1 ruby definitives	5.00
Pane of two 1st Arnold Machin and two 1st 4d deep olive-sepia definitives	5.00
Pane of one 2nd and one 1st revised style, and two 2nd and two 1st Large definitives	5.50
Complete book	16.00

■ 2007, September 20. £7.49 British Army Uniforms

Pane of one each of 1st definitives of England, Northern Ireland, Scotland and Wales	5.00
Pane of three (different) 1st British Army Uniforms	4.00
Pane of three (different) 78p British Army Uniforms	5.00
Pane of two 1p, four 46p and two 54p definitives	5.50
Complete book	15.00

Ian Fleming's James Bond, 2008

■ 2008, January 8. £7.40 Ian Fleming's James Bond

Pane of one 1st Casino Royale, one 54p Goldfinger, one 78p For Your Eyes Only	3.75
Pane of one 1st Dr No, one 54p Diamonds Are Forever, one 78p From Russia With Love	3.75
Pane of eight 1st class gold	6.50
Pane of two 1st White Ensign and two 1st Union Jack, as of October 22, 2001	5.50
Complete book	17.50

■ 2008, September 18. £7.15 Pilot to Plane: RAF Uniforms

Pane of three (different) 1st RAF Uniforms	3.50
Pane of three (different) 81p RAF Uniforms	4.50
Pane of four 1st gold and four 2nd definitives	3.50
Pane of two 1st Air Displays design of July 17, 2008, and two 20p Spitfire design of June 10, 1997	6.00
Complete book	16.00

■ 2008, September 29. £9.72 The Regional Definitives: Heraldry and Symbol

Pane of the 1958 3d, 6d and 1s 3d designs of Northern Ireland, Scotland and Wales re-denominated as 1st	7.50
Pane of the 1958 3d, 6d and 1s 3d designs of Northern Ireland, re-denominated as 1st, and three 1st class Northern Ireland of October 14, 2003	5.50
Pane of the 1958 3d, 6d and 1s 3d designs of Scotland, re-denominated as 1st, and three 1st class Scotland of October 14, 2003	5.50

Pane of the 1958 3d, 6d and 1s 3d designs of Wales, re-denominated as 1st, and three 1st class Wales of October 14, 2003	5.50
Complete book	21.00

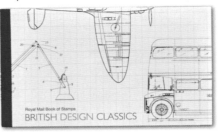

British Design Classics, 2009

■ 2009, January 13. £7.68 British Design Classics

Pane of four 16p and four 50p definitives	5.50
Pane of one 1st Spitfire, two 1st Routemaster, one 1st Mini	4.50
Pane of one 1st London Underground Map, one 1st Telephone Kiosk, one 1st Penguin Books, one 1st Anglepoise Lamp, one 1st Polypropylene Chair, one 1st Mini Skirt	7.00
Pane of two 1st Concorde, and two 1st Concorde design of May 2, 2002	4.50
Complete book	21.00

■ 2009, February 12. £7.75 Charles Darwin

Pane of the 48p, 50p and 56p Charles Darwin	11.00
Pane comprising the Charles Darwin miniature sheet	5.50
Pane of the 1st, 72p and 81p Charles Darwin	11.00
Pane of two 1st, two 5p, two 10p and two 48p definitives	6.00
Complete book	36.00

Treasures of the Archive, 2009

■ 2009, August 18. £8.18 Treasures of the Archive

Pane of four 1st Penny Black Anniversary and four 20p Penny Black Anniversary	6.50
Pane of four 20p Royal Mail coach design of October 17, 1989	4.00
Pane of four (different) 1st Post Boxes	6.00
Pane of four 17p, two 22p and two 62p definitives	7.00
Complete book	15.00

2009, September 17. £7.93 Royal Navy Uniforms

Pane of the three (different) 90p Naval Uniforms	4.50
Pane of the three (different) 1st Naval Uniforms	3.50
Pane of two 1st White Ensign and two 1st Jolly Roger designs of October 22, 2001	6.00
Pane of two 1p, four 17p, and two 90p definitives	10.50
Complete book	15.00

2010, January 7. £8.06 Classic Album Covers

Pane of four 20p, two 54p (wrong font), two 62p definitives	6.00
Pane of six (different) 1st Classic Album Covers	9.00
Pane of four (different) 1st Classic Album Covers	8.50
Pane of two 5p (wrong font), five 10p, two 22p definitives	6.00
Complete book	28.00

2010, February 25. £7.72 The Royal Society

Pane of four (different) 1st Royal Society	4.00
Pane of four 22p and four 54p definitives (the 54p stamps with wrong font in error)	6.50
Pane of four (different) 1st Royal Society	4.00
Pane of four (different) 1st Royal Society	4.00
Complete book	16.00

2010, May 8. £11.15 King George V

Pane of three 1st, three £1 Centenary of Accession	8.00
Pane of two (different) £1 Seahorses	6.00
Pane of four 1st British Empire Exhibition	6.00
Pane of four 1st, two 2nd, two 50p definitives, self-adhesive	8.00
Complete book	26.00

Britain Alone, 2010

2010, May 13. £9.76 Britain Alone

Pane of four 5p, two 10p, two 60p definitives	4.00
Pane of four (different) Britain Alone	5.00
Pane of four (different) Britain Alone	5.50
Pane of four (different) Dunkirk	7.00
Complete book	16.00

2011, March 11. £9.05 WWF

Pane of six (different) 1st WWF	8.00
Pane of four (different) 1st WWF	5.00
Pane of WWF miniature sheet	5.00
Pane of three 5p, three 10p, one 67p and one 97p definitives	9.00
Complete book	25.00

Morris & Co, 2011

2011, May 5. £9.99 Morris & Co

Pane of two 1st, two £1.10 Morris & Co	6.00
Pane of one 1st, two 76p, one £1.10 Morris & Co	8.00
Pane of four 2nd Christmas designs of 2009	4.00
Pane of four 5p, two 10p, two 50p definitives, self-adhesive	6.00
Complete book	17.00

2011, September 9. £9.97 First UK Aerial Post

Pane of one £1.10 Aerial Post and two 1st Aerial Post	8.00
Pane of one £1 Aerial Post and two 68p Aerial Post	6.50
Pane of four 50p Windsor Castle designs of 2005	11.00
Pane of four 5p, two 1st, two 76p definitives	20.00
Complete book	42.00

Roald Dahl, 2012

2012, January 10. £11.47 Roald Dahl: Master Storyteller

Pane of two 2p, two 10p and four 68p definitives	8.00
Pane of 1st, 68p and 76p Roald Dahl	5.00
Pane of 66p, £1 and £1.10 Roald Dahl	6.50
Pane of 1st, 68p, 76p, £1 from Roald Dahl miniature sheet	5.00
Complete book	16.00

2012, May 31. £12.77 Diamond Jubilee

Pane of four 1st Wilding, four 1st diamond blue definitives	10.00
Pane of 1st Trooping the Colour and 77p Royal Welsh	3.00
Pane of 1st Golden Jubilee, £1.26 United Nations Address, 87p Silver Jubilee and 87p Garter Ceremony	8.50
Pane of 77p First Christmas TV Broadcast and £1.28 Commonwealth Games	4.50
Complete book	19.00

■ **2012, July 27. £10.71 Keeping The Flame Alive**

Pane of three 1st Olympics, three 1st Paralympics, one Worldwide Olympics and one Worldwide Paralympics definitives	32.00
Pane of 1st Aquatics, 1st Field Athletics	3.00
Pane of 1st Paralympic Archery, 1st Equestrian	3.00
Pane of 1st Football, 1st Track athletics	3.00
Complete book	36.00

■ **2013, March 26. £13.77 50 Years of Doctor Who**

Pane of four 1st Tardis, one 5p, one 10p, one 20p and one 87p definitives	10.50
Pane of four (different) 1st Doctor Who	5.50
Pane of four (different) 1st Doctor Who	5.50
Pane of three (different) 1st Doctor Who	5.50
Pane of Doctor Who miniature sheet	5.50
Complete book	24.00

(*This book was designed with one half upside–down, so it can be read from either end.)

Football Heroes, 2013

■ **2013, May 9. £11.85 Football Heroes**

Pane of five (different) 1st Football Heroes	14.00
Pane of six (different) 1st Football Heroes	14.00
Pane of two 2p, two 5p and two 10p definitives	2.50
Pane of two 1st red, two 1p definitives, one 1st England flag, one 1st Northern Ireland, one 1st Scotland flag and one 1st Wales flag	9.00
Complete book	28.00

(*This book was issued in a sealed plastic wrapper.)

■ **2013, September 19. £11.19 Merchant Navy**

Pane of three (different) 1st Merchant Navy	3.50
Pane of three (different) £1.28 Merchant Navy	5.00
Pane of four (different) 1st Atlantic and Arctic Convoys	5.00
Pane of four 5p, four 50p definitives	7.00
Complete book	18.00

■ **2014, February 20. £13.97 Locomotives of the United Kingdom**

Pane of two 1st and two 60p Classic Locos of England	7.00
Pane of two 1st and two 68p Classic Locos of Scotland	8.00
Pane of two 1st and two 78p Classic Locos of Northern Ireland	9.00
Pane of two 1st and two 78p Classic Locos of Wales	9.00
Pane of two 2p, two 5p, 1st Northern Ireland, 1st English flag, 1st Scottish flag and 1st Welsh flag	6.00
Complete book	35.00

Buckingham Palace, 2014

■ **2014, April 15. £11.39 Buckingham Palace**

Pane of four 1st Buckingham Palace (exterior)	6.00
Pane of two 1st Buckingham Palace (exterior)	4.00
Pane of four 1st Buckingham Palace (interior)	6.00
Pane of two 10p, four 20p and two £1 definitives	7.00
Complete book	17.50

■ **2014, July 28. £11.30 The Great War, 1914**

Pane of three (different) 1st First World War	4.50
Pane of three (different) £1.47 First World War	10.00
Pane of two 10p, two 20p, 1st England, 1st Northern Ireland, 1st Scotland and 1st Wales	6.50
Pane of one £1 definitive	2.00
Complete book	20.00

■ **2015, February 19. £14.65 Inventive Britain**

Pane of two 1p, two 2p, one 81p and two 97p definitives	12.00
Pane of one 1st Station X, (2012) two 1st Bombe (2012) and one 1st Colossus	5.50
Pane of two (different) 81p, one £1.28 and one £1.47 Inventive Britain	8.00
Pane of two (different) 1st, one £1.28 and one £1.47 Inventive Britain	7.50
Complete book	20.00

■ **2015, May 14. £13.96 The Great War, 1915**

Pane of four 1st Observer Royal Field Artillery (2007)	5.00
Pane of three (different) 1st First World War 2015	4.00
Pane of three (different) £1.52 First World War 2015	7.50
Pane of two 1p, two 5p and two £1.33 definitives, and two 1st Poppies	6.00
Complete book	20.00

Battle of Waterloo, 2015

■ 2015, June 18. £14.47 Battle of Waterloo

Pane of Battle of Waterloo miniature sheet	8.50
Pane of one 1st, two (different) £1.00, one £1.52 Battle of Waterloo	8.50
Pane of one 1st, one £1.52 Battle of Waterloo	6.50
Pane of two 5p, two 10p, two 50p, two £1 definitives	7.50
Complete book	28.00

The Making of Star Wars, 2015

■ 2015, December 17. £16.99 The Making of Star Wars

Pane of six (different) 1st Star Wars	6.00
Pane of six (different) 1st Star Wars	6.00
Double pane of Star Wars miniature sheet. Self-adhesive	8.00
Pane of four 1st Union Flag, two 1st red , two 2nd blue definitives	8.00
Complete book	26.00

(*A limited edition of this book was produced with silver–foil printing, sold at £127.)

■ 2016, February 24. £16.36 Royal Mail 500

Pane of two (different) 1st, one £1.52 Royal Mail 500	5.00
Pane of one 1st, two (different) £1.52 Royal Mail 500	8.50
Pane of two (different) 1st, two (different) £1.33 Classic GPO Posters	8.50
Pane of two 1st Penny Black, three 1st Twopenny Blue, three 1st Penny Red	8.50
Complete book	24.00

The Queen's 90th Birthday, 2016

■ 2016, April 21. £15.11 The Queen's 90th Birthday

Pane of two (different) £1.52 Queen's Birthday	5.50
Pane of three (different) 1st, one £1.52 Queen's Birthday	6.00

Pane of Queen's Birthday miniature sheet	5.00
Pane of 1st England, 1st Northern Ireland, 1st Wales, 1st Scotland, two 1st red and two 1st amethyst definitives	7.50
Complete book	35.00

(*A limited edition of this book was produced with gold–foil printing, sold at £59.95.)

■ 2016, June 21. £16.49 The Great War, 1916

Pane of three 1st First World War 2016	3.00
Pane of three £1.52 First World War 2016	7.00
Pane of two 1st, two £1.33 Post Office at War	6.00
Pane of four 1st Poppy, one 1st Northern Ireland, one 1st English flag, one 1st Scottish flag, one 1st Welsh flag	7.50
Complete book	23.00

The Tale of Beatrix Potter, 2016

■ 2016, July 28. £15.37 The Tale of Beatrix Potter

Pane of 1st, £1.33, £1.52 Beatrix Potter	5.50
Pane of 1st, £1.33, £1.52 Beatrix Potter (different)	5.50
Pane of two 1st, two £1.33 Tale of Peter Rabbit	6.50
Pane of three 5p, two 10p, three £1.05 definitives	6.00
Complete book	23.00

(*A limited edition of this book was produced with extra pages, sold at £59.99.)

■ 2017, February 15. £14.58 Windsor Castle

Pane of two 1st, two £1.52 Windsor Castle	6.50
Pane of one 1st, one £1.52 Windsor Castle (different)	4.00
Pane of three 1st deep red, two 2p, two 10p and one £1.05 definitives	4.50
Pane of two 1st, two £1.33 St George's Chapel	6.50
Complete book	22.00

■ 2017, June 5. £15.59 The Machin Definitive: 50th Anniversary

Pane of three 1st Machin Definitive Design Icon	3.50
Pane of three 1st Machin Definitive Design Icon	3.50
Pane of one 1p, one 2p, one 5p, one 10p, one 20p, one 50p, one 2nd, one £1 definitives	4.50
Pane of one 1st brownish black, two 20p Penny Black Anniversary, two 1st orange–red, one 1st gold, one 1st Millennium, one 1st PiP definitives	7.00
Pane of four £1 gold	12.00
Complete book	30.00

(*A limited edition of this book was produced wth silver–foil printing and a silver medallion, sold at £99.95.)

The Great War 1917, 2017

■ 2017, July 31. £15.41 The Great War, 1917

Pane of four (different) 1st Poppies	5.00
Pane of three 1st First World War 1917	4.00
Pane of three £1.57 First World War 1917	7.00
Pane of eight 1st Poppies	8.00
Complete book	24.00

■ 2017, December 14. £15.99 Star Wars: The Making of the Droids, Aliens and Creatures

Pane of four 1st deep red, two 2p, two £1.40 definitives	7.50
Pane of four (different) 1st Star Wars	6.00
Pane of four (different) 1st Star Wars	6.00
Pane of four (different) 1st Star Wars	6.00
Complete book	24.00

(*A limited edition of this book was produced, with silver-foil printing and an embossed metal case, sold at £75.)

■ 2018, January 23. £13.95 Game of Thrones

Pane of six (different) 1st Game of Thrones	7.50
Pane of four (different) 1st Game of Thrones	6.00
Pane of four 1st Game of Thrones from miniature sheet	6.00
Pane of two 5p, one 20p, one £1.17 definitives, two 2nd Northern Ireland, two 1st Iron Throne	5.00
Complete book	22.00

(*A limited edition of this book was produced, with a leather folder, sold at £75.)

The RAF Centenary, 2018

■ 2018, March 20. £18.69 The RAF Centenary

Pane of two 1st Lightning F6, two £1.40 Typhoon FGR4	7.00
Pane of 1st Hurricane Mk1, £1.40 Vulcan B2, £1.57 Sopwith Camel F1, £1.57 Nimrod MR2	7.00

Pane of four 1st 75th Anniversary of the Battle of Britain	6.00
Pane of two 1st, two £1.40 Red Arrows	6.00
Pane of three 2p, three 5p, two £1.17 definitives	4.50
Complete book	28.00

(*A limited edition of this book was produced, with an insert illustrating enlarged stamp artwork, sold at £45.)

■ 2018, September 13. £15.65 The Great War, 1918

Pane of four 1st Poetry (First World War 2014–2017)	4.50
Pane of three 1st First World War 2018	3.50
Pane of three £1.55 First World War 2018	7.00
Pane of four 1st Poppies (2006), four 1st deep red definitives	8.00
Complete book	23.00

■ 2018, December 4. £15.50 Harry Potter

Pane of five 1st (different) Harry Potter	5.00
Pane of five 1st (different) Harry Potter	5.00
Pane of two 1p, two 20p, two 50p, two £1.25 definitives	6.00
Panes comprising Harry Potter miniature sheet	7.00
Complete book	23.00

(*A limited edition of this book was produced, with different covers and a card case, sold at £75.)

Leonardo da Vinci: 500 years, 2019

■ 2019, February 13. £13.10 Leonardo da Vinci: 500 Years

Pane of four (different) 1st Leonardo da Vinci	4.00
Pane of four (different) 1st Leonardo da Vinci	4.00
Pane of four (different) 1st Leonardo da Vinci	4.00
Pane of two 5p, four 10p, two £1.55 definitives	6.00
Complete book	18.00

■ 2019, March 14. £17.45 Make Mine Marvel

Pane of four (different) 1st Marvel	4.00
Pane of six (different) 1st Marvel	6.00
Panes comprising Marvel miniature sheet	7.00
Pane of two 1p, three 20p, two £1.25, one £1.45 definitives	8.00
Complete book	24.00

(*A limited edition of this book was produced with a retro-style cover and a tin presentation case, sold at £64.99.)

■ 2019, May 24. £17.20 Victoria: A Long and Glorious Reign

Pane of three (different) Queen Victoria Bicentenary	6.00
Pane of two 2p, two 50p definitives, two 1st Penny Black, one 1st Penny Red, one 1st Twopenny Blue	5.00
Pane comprising Legacy of Prince Albert miniature sheet	7.00
Pane of three (different) Queen Victoria Bicentenary	5.00
Complete book	23.00

JERWOOD PHILATELICS

(Established 2010)

Great Britain dealer specialising in:

* Stitched Booklets
* Folded Booklets
* Window Booklets
* Prestige Booklets
* Greetings & Christmas Booklets
* Machins, including Cylinder, Date Blocks etc.
* Smilers™ Sheets, inc. Business Customised Sheets
* Post & Go™ stamps
* Modern commemoratives, inc. errors & varieties
* Royal Mail Year Books & Year Packs
* Accessories, including stockcards, mounts etc.
* Selected material from earlier reigns

Collections & quality single items bought
Detailed booklet listings using both the
Stanley Gibbons and Modern British Philatelic Circle catalogues.

1103A Bristol Road South, Birmingham, B31 2QP
Website: www.jerwoodphilatelics.co.uk
Email: dave@jerwoodphilatelics.co.uk
Telephone: (0121) 249 5277

**Insert bsmv20 at checkout to receive a 10% discount
on any order over £25. Free P&P on all UK orders.**

BUSINESS SHEETS

Sheets of self-adhesive stamps comprising either 100 stamps (1st class, 2nd class) or 50 stamps (1st Large, 2nd Large), supplied folded in concertina style. In early sheets the matrix was not removed; in later sheets it has been removed.

The date of printing has appeared within the stamps' security overlay since 2010, but separate dates are not listed here.

In this section, prices are given for what is typically collected: the top section of the sheet only, giving details of the contents and bearing four (1st, 2nd) or 5 (1st Large, 2nd Large) stamps, unmounted mint.

■ 1998–2000
Printed in gravure by Walsall. Matrix intact.

2nd bright blue (June 22, 1998)	75.00
1st orange–red (June 22, 1998)	75.00

■ 2000–2002
Printed in gravure by Walsall. (2nd) or Questa (1st). Matrix intact. Telephone number included.

2nd bright blue (September 4, 2000)	30.00
1st orange–red (September 4, 2000)	30.00

■ 2002
Printed in gravure by Enschedé. Matrix intact. Telephone number removed.

2nd bright blue (May 9, 2002)	25.00
1st orange–red (May 9, 2002)	25.00

■ 2002
Printed in gravure by Enschedé. Matrix intact.

2nd bright blue (July 4, 2002)	20.00
1st gold (July 4, 2002)	20.00

■ 2003–2015
Printed in gravure by Walsall except where stated. Matrix removed.

2nd bright blue

(March 18, 2003) 'The Real Network' added	17.00
(June 15, 2004) 'The Real Network' removed	15.00
(May 16, 2006) tariff change information added	15.00
(September 12, 2006) Pricing in Proportion stamps	15.00
(June 5, 2007) standard stamps with PiP information	15.00
(March 31, 2009) stamps with security overlay 'To find the correct postcode...' added	15.00
(2013) FSC number added, fax number 08456 000606	10.00
(2014) FSC number added, fax number 03456 000606	10.00
(2015) stamps and backing paper with security overlay	10.00

2nd Large bright blue

(March 27, 2007) with PiP information	15.00
(March 31, 2009) stamps with security overlay	14.00
(2013) FSC number added, fax number 08456 000606	17.00
(2014) FSC number added, fax number 03456 000606	17.00
(2016) stamps and backing paper with security overlay	17.00

1st gold

(March 18, 2003) 'The Real Network' added	18.00
(June 15, 2004) 'The Real Network' removed	15.00
(May 16, 2006) tariff change information added	15.00
(September 12, 2006) Pricing in Proportion stamps	15.00
(June 5, 2007) standard stamps with PiP information	15.00
(March 31, 2009) stamps with security overlay; 'To find the correct postcode...' added	15.00

1st diamond blue

(2012) FSC number C020244 (De La Rue)	35.00
(2012) FSC number C023216 (Walsall)	12.00

1st red

(2013) FSC number added, fax number 08456 000606	10.00
(2014) FSC number added, fax number 03456 000606	10.00
(2015) stamps and backing paper with security overlay	10.00

1st Large gold

(March 27, 2007) with PiP information	16.00
(March 31, 2009) stamps with security overlay	14.00

1st Large diamond blue

(2012) stamps with 'Diamond Jubilee' overlay	15.00

1st Large red

(2013) FSC number added, fax number 08456 000606	17.00
(2014) FSC number added, fax number 03456 000606	17.00
(2015) stamps and backing paper with security overlay	17.00

■ 2016
Printed in gravure by Walsall. Matrix removed. Revised font. Security backing paper, with text upright (SBP) or in alternate pairs of rows upright and inverted (SBP2).

2nd bright blue (October 20, 2016)	14.00
2nd Large bright blue (October 20, 2016)	16.00
1st dark red (October 20, 2016)	14.00
1st Large dark red (October 20, 2016)	19.00

OFFICIAL STAMPS

During the reigns of Queen Victoria and King Edward VII stamps were overprinted for use by Government Departments. The prices in this section are quoted in two columns: mint (left) and fine used (right).

QUEEN VICTORIA, 1840–1901

■ Penny Black 'VR'

Printed by Perkins Bacon. Design as the standard stamp but with the stars in the top corners replaced by the letters 'V' and 'R'. Not officially issued.

1d black (1840 issue) with gum	£30,000	–
1d black (1840 issue) without gum	£16,000	–
1d black (1840 issue) with trial cancel	–	£40,000

■ Overprinted 'I.R. OFFICIAL' for use by the Inland Revenue

Printed by De La Rue.

½d green (1880 issue)	80.00	15.00
½d blue (1884 issue)	45.00	13.00
½d orange (1887 issue)	6.00	1.00
½d green (1900 issue)	8.00	3.50
1d lilac (1881 issue)	2.75	1.40
2½d lilac (1884 issue)	£350	50.00
2½d purple on blue paper (1887 issue)	£100	6.00
6d grey (1881 issue)	£350	50.00
6d purple on red paper (1887 issue)	£300	45.00
1/– green (1884 issue)	£6,000	£1,600
1/– green (1887 issue)	£900	95.00
1/– green, red (1900 issue)	£4,000	£1,100
5/– red (1884 issue)	£9,000	£2,000

10/– blue (1884 issue)	£10,000	£3,000
£1 brown (1884 issue)	£55,000	£24,000
£1 brown (1888 issue)	£75,000	£30,000
£1 green (1891 issue)	£10,000	£2,200

■ Overprinted 'O.W. OFFICIAL' for use by the Office of Works

Printed by De La Rue.

½d orange (1887 issue)	£200	£100
½d green (1900 issue)	£300	£150
1d lilac (1881 issue)	£350	£100
5d purple and blue (1887 issue)	£3,000	£900
10d purple and red (1887 issue)	£6,500	£2,000

■ Overprinted 'ARMY OFFICIAL'

Printed by De La Rue.

½d orange (1887 issue)	2.75	1.25
½d green (1900 issue)	3.00	5.00
1d lilac (1881 issue)	2.50	2.00
2½d purple on blue paper (1887 issue)	25.00	10.00
6d purple on red paper (1887 issue)	60.00	30.00

■ Overprinted 'GOVT PARCELS' for use by the Government

Printed by De La Rue.

1d lilac (1881 issue)	70.00	10.00
1½d lilac (1884 issue)	£300	40.00
1½d purple and green (1887 issue)	£100	4.00
2d green and red (1887 issue)	£150	14.00
4½d green and red (1887 issue)	£260	£110
6d green (1884 issue)	£2,400	£900
6d purple on red paper (1887 issue)	£200	40.00
9d green (1884 issue)	£2,000	£700
9d purple and blue (1887 issue)	£275	60.00
1/– brown (1881 issue)	£1,200	£200
1/– green (1887 issue)	£500	£110
1/– green, red (1887 issue)	£500	£125

■ **Overprinted 'BOARD OF EDUCATION'**
Printed by De La Rue.

5d purple and blue (1887 issue)	£4,500	£800
1/– green and red (1887 issue)	£10,000	£5,000

KING EDWARD VII, 1902–1904

■ **Overprinted 'I.R OFFICIAL' for use by the Inland Revenue**
Printed by De La Rue.

½d blue–green	20.00	2.00
1d red	15.00	1.25
2½d blue	£900	£200
6d purple	–	£300,000
1/– green and red	£3,500	£600
5/– red	£40,000	£9,000
10/– blue	£80,000	£40,000
£1 green	£50,000	£18,000

■ **Overprinted 'O.W. OFFICIAL' for use by the Office of Works**
Printed by De La Rue.

½d blue–green	£400	£110
1d red	£400	£100
2d green and red	£1,500	£400
2½d blue	£2,500	£500
10d purple and red	£35,000	£6,000

■ **Overprinted 'ARMY OFFICIAL'**
Printed by De La Rue.

½d blue-green	4.00	1.25
1d red	4.00	1.25
6d purple	£130	45.00

■ **Overprinted 'GOVT PARCELS' for use by the Government**
Printed by De La Rue.

1d red	30.00	10.00
2d green and red	£150	25.00
6d purple	£240	20.00
9d purple and blue	£550	85.00
1/– green and red	£1,200	£250

■ **Overprinted 'BOARD OF EDUCATION'**
Printed by De La Rue.

½d blue-green	£150	20.00
1d red	£150	20.00
2½d blue	£4,000	£275
5d purple and blue	£32,000	£9,000
1/– green and red	£150,000	–

■ **Overprinted 'R.H. OFFICIAL' for use by the Royal Household**
Printed by De La Rue.

½d blue-green	£300	£200
1d red	£275	£150

■ **Overprinted 'ADMIRALTY OFFICIAL' for use by the Royal Navy**
Printed by De La Rue.

½d blue-green	20.00	10.00
1d red	12.00	4.00
1½d purple and green	£275	70.00
2d green and red	£300	80.00
2½d blue	£425	75.00
3d purple on yellow paper	£375	70.00

POSTAGE DUES

From 1914 until they were withdrawn from service in 2000, postage dues were affixed to covers by the postal service to denote postage unpaid or underpaid.

Up to 1936, prices are quoted in three columns: unmounted mint (left), mounted mint (centre) and used (right). After 1936, they are quoted for mint (left) and fine used (right).

PRE–DECIMAL ISSUES 1914–70

½d to 1/–

2/6 to £1

■ 1914–1923

Des: G. Eve. Printed in typography by Harrison (all values except 1/–) or Somerset House (½d, 1d, 5d, 1/–). Wmk: Simple Royal Cypher GVR. Perf 14x15.

Wmk sideways, with crown facing left when viewed from front

½d green	1.25	0.40	0.35
1d red on ordinary paper	1.25	0.50	0.25
1d red on chalky paper	7.50	4.00	4.00
1½d brown	95.00	35.00	13.00
2d black	1.25	0.80	0.30
3d violet	25.00	4.00	0.60
4d green	£300	£150	40.00
5d brown	11.00	4.00	2.00
1/– blue	90.00	19.00	3.00
Set	£400	95.00	22.00

Wmk inverted, with crown facing right

½d green	1.50	1.00	1.00
1d red	2.00	1.00	1.00
1½d brown	£120	50.00	15.00
2d black	3.00	1.00	1.00
3d violet	25.00	6.50	2.50
4d green	£110	35.00	5.00
5d brown	32.00	12.00	4.00
1/– blue	90.00	20.00	15.00

■ 1924–1935

Printed in typography by Waterlow and (from 1934) Harrison. Wmk: Multiple Crowns and Block GVR. Perf 14x15.

Wmk sideways, with crown facing left when viewed from front

½d green	1.25	0.50	0.30
1d red	1.25	0.50	0.10
1½d brown	90.00	27.00	9.00
2d black	6.00	1.25	0.20
3d violet	6.00	1.75	0.20
4d green	40.00	5.00	0.85
5d brown	110.00	35.00	17.00
1/– blue	25.00	4.00	0.25
2/6 purple (yellow paper)	190.00	50.00	0.80
Set	£450	£120	24.50

Wmk inverted, with crown facing right

½d green	4.50	2.00	1.50
1d red	–	–	8.50
1½d brown	–	–	25.00
2d black	–	–	8.50
3d violet	60.00	20.00	20.00
4d green	£125	40.00	40.00
1/– blue	–	–	–
2/6 purple (yellow paper)	–	–	–

■ 1936–1937

Printed in typography by Harrison. Wmk: Multiple Crowns and E8R, sideways. Perf 14x15.

½d green	7.00	6.50
1d red	1.00	1.50
2d black	6.00	6.00
3d violet	1.50	1.50
4d green	60.00	22.00
5d brown	40.00	18.00
1/– blue	20.00	6.50
2/6 purple on yellow paper	£300	10.00
Set	£425	65.00

■ 1937–1938

Printed in typography by Harrison. Wmk: Multiple Crowns and GVIR. Perf 14x15.

Wmk sideways, with crown facing left when viewed from front

½d green	8.50	4.50
1d red	2.00	0.20
2d black	1.25	0.30
3d violet	7.00	0.30
4d green	60.00	7.00
5d brown	7.00	0.80
1/– blue	45.00	0.90
2/6 purple on yellow paper	50.00	2.00
Set	£160	12.00

Wmk inverted, with crown facing right

1d red	£170	–
2d black	£170	–
3d violet	£170	–
4d green	£300	–
5d brown	£170	–
1/– blue	£170	–

■ 1951–1952

Printed in typography by Harrison. Wmk: Multiple Crowns and

GVIR. Perf 14x15.

Wmk sideways, with crown facing left when viewed from front

½d orange	3.50	3.50
1d blue	1.25	0.50
1½d green	1.25	1.50
4d blue	30.00	12.00
1/– brown	22.00	4.00
Set	45.00	18.00

Wmk inverted, with crown facing right

1d blue	–	–
1½d green	£110	–
1/– brown	£2,000	–

■ 1954–1955

Printed in typography by Harrison. Wmk: Tudor Crown and E2R. Perf 14x15.

Wmk sideways, with crown facing left when viewed from front

½d orange	8.00	8.50
2d black	25.00	16.00
3d violet	70.00	30.00
4d blue	20.00	16.00
5d brown	15.00	10.00
2/6 purple on yellow paper	£150	8.00
Set	£220	85.00

Wmk inverted, with crown facing right

½d orange	£150	–

■ 1955–1957

Printed in typography by Harrison. Wmk: St Edward's Crown and E2R. Perf 14x15.

Wmk sideways, with crown facing left when viewed from front

½d orange	4.00	4.00
1d blue	3.00	1.25
1½d green	7.00	4.50
2d black	25.00	5.25
3d violet	3.50	1.25
4d blue	16.00	2.00
5d brown	20.00	1.75
1/– brown	40.00	2.00
2/6 purple on yellow paper	£115	10.00
5/– red on yellow paper	60.00	18.00
Set	£240	40.00

Wmk inverted, with crown facing right

½d orange	60.00	–
1½d green	60.00	–
3d violet	90.00	–
4d blue	£125	–
1/– brown	–	–
2/6 purple on yellow paper	–	–
5/– red on yellow paper	–	£300

■ 1959–1963

Printed in typography by Harrison. Wmk: Multiple St Edward's Crown. Perf 14x15.

Wmk sideways, with crown facing left when viewed from front

½d orange	0.15	0.25
1d blue	0.15	0.10
1½d green	1.50	2.00
2d black	1.00	0.30
3d violet	0.35	0.15

4d blue	0.35	0.15
5d brown	0.35	0.30
6d purple	0.50	0.15
1/– brown	1.00	0.15
2/6 purple on yellow paper	1.50	0.20
5/– red on yellow paper	4.00	0.50
10/– blue on yellow paper	10.00	3.00
£1 black on yellow paper	30.00	4.50
Set	45.00	9.50

Wmk inverted, with crown facing right

½d orange	1.25	–
1d blue	90.00	–
2d black	£150	–
3d violet	60.00	–
4d blue	£225	–
5d brown	4.00	–
6d purple	£225	–
1/– brown	75.00	–
2/6 purple on yellow paper	15.00	–
5/– red on yellow paper	25.00	–
10/– blue on yellow paper	50.00	–

■ 1968–1969

Printed in typography by Harrison. No watermark. Perf 14x15. Chalky paper.

Gum Arabic

2d black	0.50	0.50
4d blue	0.40	0.20

PVA gum

2d black	1.50	1.00
3d violet	0.50	0.50
5d brown	5.00	5.00
6d purple	1.00	1.25
1/– brown	3.00	2.00

■ 1968–1969

Printed in gravure by Harrison. No watermark. Perf 14x15. Chalky paper. PVA gum.

4d blue	4.50	5.00
8d red	0.50	1.00

DECIMAL ISSUES 1970–2000

½p to 7p

10p to £5

1p to 5p

10p to £5

■ 1970–1975

Des: J. Matthews. Printed in gravure by Harrison. No watermark. Chalky paper. Perf: 14x15.

PVA gum. Original coated paper

½p turquoise	0.10	0.25
1p purple	0.50	0.10
2p green	0.25	0.10
3p blue	0.75	0.20
4p sepia	0.25	0.10
5p violet	1.00	0.30
10p carmine	0.80	0.30
20p deep green	1.10	0.50
50p blue	2.25	1.00
£1 black	4.00	0.25

PVA gum. Fluorescent coated paper

1p purple	0.50	–
3p blue	1.75	–
5p violet	2.25	–
10p carmine	45.00	–
20p deep green	45.00	–
£5 orange and black	15.00	1.00

PVAD gum, blue–tinged

1p purple	0.10	–
2p green	0.10	–
3p blue	0.15	–
4p sepia	0.15	–
5p violet	0.15	–
7p red–brown	0.25	0.25
10p carmine	0.25	–
11p green	0.40	0.35
20p deep green	0.50	–
50p blue	1.00	–
£1 black	2.00	–
£5 orange and black	18.00	1.00
Set (one of each value)	20.00	10.00

PVAD gum. Phosphor coated paper

10p carmine	0.70	0.50
20p deep green	1.00	0.75

■ 1982, June 9

Des: Sedley Place. Printed in gravure by Harrisons. No watermark. Perf: 14x15.

1p crimson	0.15	0.10
2p bright blue	0.15	0.10
3p purple	0.15	0.15
4p blue	0.15	0.10
5p brown	0.15	0.10
10p light brown	0.20	0.10
20p sage green	0.40	0.30
25p blue–grey	0.60	0.60
50p charcoal	1.00	1.50
£1 red	1.50	0.50
£2 turquoise	3.00	2.50
£5 dull orange	6.00	1.25
Set	11.00	5.00
Gutter pairs	30.00	–

1p to £5

■ 1994, February 15

Des: Sedley Place. Printed in lithography by Questa. No watermark. Perf: 15x14.

1p yellow, orange–red and black	0.15	0.30
2p magenta, purple and black	0.15	0.30
5p yellow, brown and black	0.20	0.30
10p yellow, green and black	0.30	0.40
20p violet, emerald–green and black	1.00	1.00
25p magenta, claret and black	1.50	1.50
£1 pink, violet and black	6.00	6.00
£1.20 green, blue and black	7.50	7.50
£5 green, charcoal and black	17.50	17.50
Set	27.00	28.00
First day cover	–	35.00

FRAMA LABELS

In this section, prices are quoted in two columns: mint (left) and
fine used (right).

From May 1984 until April 1985, Frama machines were
installed at five locations, printing labels to order for any value
from ½p (until withdrawn in January 1985) to 16p (17p from
August 28, 1984).

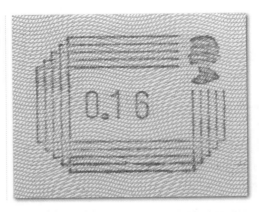

■ **1984, May 1**
Machine–printed in red on phosphor–coated security paper with
a grey–green background pattern. Gummed and imperforate.

Set (½p to 17p)	12.50	15.00
Pack (all values from ½p to 16p)	25.00	–
Pack (16½p, 17p)	4.00	–
Pack (3½p, 12½p, 16p)	4.00	–
First day cover (3½p, 12½p, 16p)	–	2.50

POST & GO STAMPS

In most of this section, prices are quoted in two columns: mint on backing paper (left) and fine used (right). Where there is only one column, this is for mint stamps on backing paper, except in the case of first day covers.

This listing is limited to labels dispensed from self-service machines, with the value printed at point of sale and no restrictions on date of use.

Post office machines

Since October 2008, automated kiosks have been installed at an increasing number of post offices, vending self-adhesive stamps to order.

Besides a 'Post It Now' service with labels meeting a wide range of postage rates (which are outside the scope of this publication), they offer a 'Buy A Stamp' service in which a pre-printed base design is overprinted at the time of the transaction with details of one of a limited selection of postage rates, along with a code which identifies the post office and machine number.

The machines installed in post offices from 2008 were manufactured by Wincor Nixdorf, and could print the stamps in strips of up to five. Between February 2014 and March 2015, these were gradually replaced by machines manufactured by NCR, which can print in strips of up to six.

Royal Mail machines

Since 2011, Royal Mail has also had its own range of machines, initially referred to as Hytech but upgraded to Series B in 2014. Overprints from these have a slightly different typeface from the machines installed in post offices.

Royal Mail machines have been used to print the strips and packs which are available from the philatelic service. They have also been temporarily installed at various philatelic events in Britain and abroad, in 'pop up' post shops, and permanently installed at a growing range of museums, in many cases dispensing stamps with an additional commemorative or location-identifying inscription. They have also been available at Royal Mail enquiry offices, initially with location-identifiers in 2014–15 although this practice was then discontinued.

Some machines, such as those at the Royal Mail Engineering Department at Wheatstone House, Swindon, and at RAF Northolt, are accessible only to people working on the premises.

As the use of Post & Go has extended to other stamp-issuing countries, machines installed at Broad Street in Jersey, Envoy House in Guernsey and Gibraltar House in London have also dispensed stamps with UK postage rates and location-identifying overprints.

When machines are installed at exhibitions beyond Europe, strips with the same event inscription are also made available from Tallents House in Edinburgh.

Postage rates

From 2008, the five rates available were 1st class, 1st Large, Europe up to 20g, Worldwide up to 10g and Worldwide up to 20g. Towards the end of 2011, Worldwide up to 40g was added to offer a sixth option.

From 2011, vending machines have offered a 'collector's strip' comprising one of each of the six standard rates (although in

the case of Wincor Nixdorf machines these were vended as two strips of three).

A 2nd class rate was introduced in 2013, although it was not made widely available until 2014 and is not included in standard collector's strips.

With tariff changes in 2014, the Worldwide up to 10g and Worldwide up to 20g rates were replaced by Europe up to 60g and Worldwide up to 60g, and after a short delay the Europe up to 20g rate was changed to Europe up to 20g/Worldwide up to 10g (expressed on the stamps as 'Euro 20g/World 10g'). In 2015, both 60g rates were uprated to 100g.

Although pictorial sets are regularly superseded by new designs, none has formally been withdrawn from use, with the result that new rates have been reported machine-printed on old designs. Examples have also been found of the 2nd class design printed with 1st class rates, and vice versa.

Printing

It is possible to distinguish the type of machine used to print a stamp from its typeface. In most cases the differences are slight, but two exceptions are '60g' and 'Euro 20g/World 10g', where there are clear differences between different machines.

Starting in September 2015, some rolls of stamps required in limited quantities were printed digitally. These have a shinier appearance than gravure printings.

Stamps printed in corrupted typefaces, with misplaced inscriptions and with incorrect values also exist, especially from the 2010–12 period, but they are are outside the scope of this publication.

Phosphor

All the stamps have two phosphor bands, except the 2nd class Machin, which has one phosphor band.

DEFINITIVE ISSUES

Machin portrait (1st, 1st L, E20g, W10g, W20g)

■ 2008, October 8. Machin Portrait
Printed in gravure by Walsall. Self-adhesive. Olive-brown security overlay with no year code. Machine-printed in black.

Strip of five (one of each value)	35.00
Philatelic pack (one of each value)	90.00

Machin portrait (1st, 1st L, E20g, E20/W10, E60g, E100g, W10g, W20g, W40g, W60g, W100g)

■ 2010, September. Machin Portrait
Printed in gravure by Walsall. Self-adhesive. Olive-brown security overlay with no year code, or year code from '13' onwards. Machine-printed in black, in a new typeface suitable for use with pictorial designs.

Collector's strips

1st, 1st L, E20, W10, W20, W40	20.00
1st, 1st L, E20, E60, W40, W60 (Wincor)	14.00
1st, 1st L, E20, E60, W40, W60 (NCR)	30.00
1st, 1st L, E20/W10, E60, W40, W60 (NCR)	18.00
1st, 1st L, E20/W10, E60, W40, W60 (RM)	25.00
1st, 1st L, E20/W10, E60, W20, W60 (Wincor)	45.00
1st, 1st L, E20/W10, E100, W20, W100 (NCR)	17.00
1st, 1st L, E20/W10, E100, W20, W100 (RM)	17.00
'The B.P.M.A.' (1st, 1st L, E20, W10, W20, W40)	25.00
'The B.P.M.A.' (1st, 1st L, E20/W10, E60, W40, W60)	25.00
'The B.P.M.A.' (1st, 1st L, E20/W10, E100, W20, W100)	25.00
'Arnold Machin/1911–1999' (Autumn Stampex 2011)	20.00
'Diamond Jubilee/1952–2012' (Spring Stampex 2012)	20.00
'Perth 2012/19–22 October' (ABPS Exhibition 2012)	80.00
'The Coronation/60th Anniversary' (Spring Stampex 2013)	20.00
'84th Scottish/Congress 2013' (ASPS Congress 2013)	24.00
'Australia 2013/Stamp Expo' (Australia 2013)	30.00
'Australia 2013/World Stamp Expo' (Tallents House 2013)	20.00
'Stampex 2014/19–22 February' (Spring Stampex 2014)	24.00
'Stampex Spring/19–22 February' (Spring Stampex 2014)	30.00
'The B.P.M.A./Postage Due 1914' (BPMA 2014)	

(1st, 1st L, E20, W10, W20, W40)	32.00
(1st , 1st L, E20, E60, W40, W60)	20.00
'85th Scottish/Congress 2014' (ASPS Congress 2014)	30.00
'The B.P.M.A./Inland Airmail 1934' (BPMA 2014)	25.00
'The NMRN' (National Museum of the Royal Navy 2014)	
(1st, 1st L, E20/W10, E60, W20, W60)	25.00
(1st, 1st L, E20/W10, E100, W20, W100)	22.00
'PhilaKorea 2014/World Stamp Expo' (PhilaKorea 2014)	20.00
'The RMM' (Royal Marines Museum 2014)	
(1st, 1st L, E20/W10, E60, W20, W60)	21.00
(1st, 1st L, E20/W10, E100, W20, W100)	22.00
'Crewe' (Royal Mail Enquiry Office 2014)	27.00
'Bradford N' (Royal Mail Enquiry Office 2014)	27.00
'The B.P.M.A./Trollope 200' (BPMA 2015)	
(1st, 1st L, E20/W10, E60, W20, W60)	22.00
(1st, 1st L, E20/W10, E100, W20, W100)	22.00
'The FAAM' (Fleet Air Arm Museum 2015)	21.00
'86th Scottish Congress' (ASPS Congress 2015)	40.00
'86th Scottish Congress 2015' (ASPS Congress 2015)	25.00
'Messe Essen/7–9 May 2015' (Essen Stamp Fair 2015)	27.00
'The B.P.M.A./Penny Black 175' (BPMA 2015)	20.00
'Europhilex London/Penny Black 175' (London 2015)	17.00
'Wheatstone House' (Royal Mail Engineering Dept 2015)	–
'Steam GWR' (Museum of the Great Western Railway 2015)	22.00
'The RNSM' (Royal Navy Submarine Museum 2015)	21.00
'Singpex 2015 World Stamp Expo' (Singpex 2015)	20.00
'Queen Elizabeth II Longest Reign' (Autumn Stampex 2015)	17.00
'Sindelfingen October 2015' (Sindelfingen Stamp Fair 2015)	20.00
'Paris November 2015' (Paris Autumn Stamp Fair 2015)	19.00
'RN Submarine' (Royal Navy Submarine Museum 2015)	20.00
'Royal Navy' (National Museum of the Royal Navy 2015)	20.00
'Royal Marines' (Royal Marines Museum 2015)	20.00
'Fleet Air Arm' (Fleet Air Arm Museum 2015)	20.00
'The Postal Museum' (The Postal Museum 2016)	20.00
'500 Years of Royal Mail' (Spring Stampex 2016)	17.00
'500 Years of Royal Mail' (Guildhall June 2016)	17.00
'87th Scottish Congress' (ASPS Congress 2016)	25.00
'RN Submarine/Battle of Jutland' (RNSM 2016)	20.00
'Royal Navy/Battle of Jutland' (RNM 2016)	20.00
'Royal Marines/Battle of Jutland' (RMM 2016)	20.00
'Fleet Air Arm/Battle of Jutland' (FAAM 2016)	20.00
'King Edward VIII 1936' (The Postal Museum 2016)	20.00
'Liverpool 2016' (Labour Party Conference 2016)	45.00
'Glasgow 2016' (Scottish Nationalists Conference 2016)	35.00
'Birmingham 2016' (Conservative Party Conference 2016)	35.00
'Shakespeare Birthplace Trust' (Shakespeare Gift Shop 2016)	20.00
'Royal Corps of Signals' (Royal Signals Museum 2016)	20.00
'Fleet Air Arm L2551/G 1st Jet Carrier Landing' (FAAM 2016)	20.00
'Season's Greetings from all at BFPO' (RAF Northolt 2016)	35.00
'Machin Anniversary 1967–2017' (Spring Stampex 2017)	20.00
'65th Anniversary of Accession' (Spring Stampex 2017)	20.00
'Ministry of Defence' (MOD Abbey Wood 2017)	20.00
'Steam GWR King George V 90th' (Museum of GWR 2017)	20.00
'Shakespeare Week' (Shakespeare Gift Shop 2017)	20.00
'Steam GWR' (Museum of Great Western Railway 2017)	20.00
'EARM' (East Anglia Railway Museum 2017)	20.00
'88th Scottish Congress' (ASPS Congress 2017)	20.00
'Heligoland Big Bang 1947' (Explosion Museum 2017)	20.00
'HMS Alliance 14th May 1947' (Submarine Museum 2017)	20.00
'HMS Trincomalee 200 Years' (HMS Trincomalee 2017)	20.00

'Royal Mail HQ' (Unilever House 2017)	40.00
'Fleet Air Arm Sea King ZA298 Junglie' (FAAM 2017)	16.00
'Royal Navy Queen Elizabeth II Carrier' (NMRN 2017)	20.00
'Royal Navy Queen Elizabeth Carrier 2017' (NMRN 2017)	16.00
'Brighton 2017' (Labour Party Conference 2017)	30.00
'Glasgow 2017' (Scottish Nationalists Conference 2017)	30.00
'Manchester 2017' (Conservative Party Conference 2017)	30.00
'Royal Navy' with small logo (NMRN 2017)	16.00
'HMS Trincomalee 12th Oct 1817' (HMS Trincomalee 2017)	16.00
'HMS Trincomalee 19th Oct 1817' (HMS Trincomalee 2017)	16.00
'HMS Trincomalee' (HMS Trincomalee 2018)	16.00
'The Postal Museum' with no logo (Postal Museum 2018)	16.00
'The Postal Museum'/'F' box 50' (Postal Museum 2018)	16.00

Union flag (1st, 1st L, E20g, E20/W10, E60g, E100g, W10g, W20g, W40g, W60g, W100g)

■ **2012, May 21. Union Flag**

Des: Dick Davis, from illustration by Anton Morris. Printed in gravure by Walsall. Self-adhesive. Blue security overlay with no year code or year code '13'. Machine-printed in black.

Single (1st)	1.70
Philatelic pack (1st only)	3.25
First day cover	3.00

Collector's strips

1st, 1st L, E20, W10, W20, W40	17.50
1st, 1st L, E20, E60, W40, W60 (Wincor)	20.00
1st, 1st L, E20/W10, E60, W40, W60 (RM)	30.00
1st, 1st L, E20/W10, E100, W20, W100 (RM)	25.00
1st, 1st L, E20/W10, E100, W20, W100 (NCR)	20.00
'The B.P.M.A.' (1st, 1st L, E20, W10, W20, W40)	20.00
'The B.P.M.A.' (1st, 1st L, E20/W10, E60, W40, W60)	25.00
'Diamond Jubilee'/1952–2012 (Autumn Stampex 2012)	20.00
'Perth 2012/19–22 October' (ABPS Exhibition 2012)	50.00
'84th Scottish/Congress 2013' (ASPS Congress 2013)	22.00
'Australia 2013/Stamp Expo' (Australia 2013)	32.00
'Australia 2013/World Stamp Expo' (Tallents House 2013)	20.00
'The Coronation/60th Anniversary' (Autumn Stampex 2013)	17.00
'The B.P.M.A./Postage Due 1914' (BPMA 2014)	
(1st, 1st L, E20, W10, W20, W40)	25.00
(1st, 1st L, E20, E60, W40, W60)	27.00
'85th Scottish/Congress 2014' (ASPS Congress 2014)	30.00
'The NMRN' (National Museum of the Royal Navy 2014)	
(1st, 1st L, E20/W10, E60, W20, W60)	22.00
(1st, 1st L, E20/W10, E100, W20, W100)	22.00
'The NMRN/Trafalgar Day' (NMRN October 2014)	35.00
'The NMRN/V.E. Day 70' (NMRN May 2015)	22.00
'PhilaKorea 2014/World Stamp Expo' (Philakorea 2014)	22.00
'The RMM' (Royal Marines Museum 2014)	
(1st, 1st L, E20/W10, E60, W20, W60)	22.00
(1st, 1st L, E20/W10, E100, W20, W100)	22.00

'The RMM/V.E. Day 70' (RMM May 2015)	22.00
'Broad Street' (Jersey 2015)	27.00
'Spring Stampex/February 2015' (Spring Stampex 2015)	17.00
'The FAAM' (Fleet Air Arm Museum 2015)	22.00
'The FAAM/V.E. Day 70' (FAAM May 2015)	22.00
'86th Scottish Congress' (ASPS Congress 2015)	40.00
'86th Scottish Congress 2015' (ASPS Congress 2015)	22.00
'Messe Essen/7–9 May 2015' (Essen Stamp Fair 2015)	27.00
'Gibraltar House' (Gibraltar Embassy, London 2015)	32.00
'Steam GWR' (Museum of the Great Western Railway 2015)	22.00
'The RNSM' (Royal Navy Submarine Museum 2015)	22.00
'Singpex 2015 World Stamp Expo' (Singpex 2015)	20.00
'Envoy House' (Guernsey 2015)	20.00
'Sindelfingen October 2015' (Sindelfingen Stamp Fair 2015)	20.00
'Hong Kong/November 2015' (Hong Kong 2015)	18.00
'RN Submarine' (RNSM 2015)	20.00
'Royal Navy' (NMRN 2015)	20.00
'Royal Navy/Trafalgar Day' (NMRN October 2015)	22.00
'Royal Marines' (RMM 2015)	20.00
'Royal Marines/Trafalgar Day' (RMM October 2015)	22.00
'Fleet Air Arm' (FAAM 2015)	20.00
'The Postal Museum' (The Postal Museum 2016)	20.00
'Steam GWR/Swindon 175' (GWR Museum 2016)	25.00
'87th Scottish Congress 2016' (ASPS Congress 2016)	22.00
'Royal Navy/Battle of Jutland' (NMRN June 2016)	21.00
'RN Submarine/Battle of Jutland' (RNSM June 2016)	21.00
'Royal Marines/Battle of Jutland' (RMM June 2016)	21.00
'Fleet Air Arm/Battle of Jutland' (FAAM June 2016)	21.00
'World Stamp Show NY2016' (New York 2016)	18.00
'Steam GWR Swindon 175' (Museum of GWR 2016)	20.00
'Shakespeare Birthplace Trust' (Shakespeare Gift Shop 2016)	20.00
'Royal Corps of Signals' (Royal Signals Museum 2016)	20.00
'Headquarters BFPO' (RAF Northolt 2016)	35.00
'Fleet Air Arm L2551/G 03 Dec 45' (FAAM 2016)	20.00
'Shakespeare Week' (Shakespeare Gift Shop 2017)	20.00
'Ministry of Defence' (MOD Abbey Wood 2017)	20.00
'Heligoland Big Bang 1947' (Explosion Museum 2017)	20.00
'HMS Alliance 14th May 1947' (Submarine Museum 2017)	20.00
'Royal Signals White Helmets' (Royal Signals Museum 2017)	20.00
'HMS Trincomalee 200 Years' (HMS Trincomalee 2017)	20.00
'The Postal Museum Official Opening' (Postal Museum 2017)	16.00
'Fleet Air Arm GR9A Harrier ZD433' (FAAM 2017)	16.00
'Royal Navy QE II Carrier' (NMRN 2017)	20.00
'Royal Navy QE Carrier 2017' (NMRN 2017)	16.00
'HMS Trincomalee 12th Oct 1817' (HMS Trincomalee 2017)	16.00
'HMS Trincomalee' (HMS Trincomalee, January 2018)	16.00
'The Postal Museum' (Postal Museum 2018)	16.00

Machin portrait (2nd, 2nd Large)

■ **2013, February 20. Machin Portrait**
Printed in gravure by Walsall. Self-adhesive. Blue security overlay with year code from '12' onwards. Machine-printed in black.

Pair (2nd, 2nd L)	5.00
Philatelic pack (2nd, 2nd L)	3.50
First day cover	4.00
Collector's strips	
'The B.P.M.A.'	7.50
'The B.P.M.A./Inland Airmail 1934' (BPMA 2014)	12.00
'The B.P.M.A./Trollope 200' (BPMA 2015)	7.50
'The B.P.M.A./Penny Black 175' (BPMA 2015)	7.50
'Crewe' (Royal Mail enquiry office)	14.00
'Bradford N' (Royal Mail enquiry office)	14.00
'Wheatstone House' (Royal Mail Engineering Dept 2015)	–
'The Postal Museum' (The Postal Museum 2016)	6.00
statue motif (RAF Northolt 2016)	32.00
'King Edward VIII 1936' (The Postal Museum 2016)	5.00
'Headquarters BFPO' (RAF Northolt 2016)	30.00
'Royal Mail HQ' (Unilever House 2017)	12.00
'The Postal Museum Official Opening' (Postal Museum 2017)	7.00
'The Postal Museum' with no logo (Postal Museum 2017)	5.00
'Brighton 2017' (Labour Party Conference 2017)	10.00
'Glasgow 2017' (Scottish Nationalists Conference 2017)	10.00
'Manchester 2017' (Conservative Party Conference 2017)	10.00
'The Postal Museum/'F' box 50' (Postal Museum 2018)	5.00

Machin portrait (wide range of values available)

■ **2014, February 28. Machin Portrait. New Service Indicia**
Printed in gravure by Walsall. Self-adhesive. Olive-brown or blue security overlay with year code '12', '13' or '14'. Machine-printed in black with new service indicia of NCR machines.

Collector's pack (2L, 1L, 2LG, 1LG, A)	25.00

(*The collector's pack was issued on July 7.)

PICTORIAL ISSUES

The values noted for each design are those which appertained when they were first issued, and should be expected in collector's strips. They may also exist with values which were introduced later.

Blue tit (1st, 1st L, E20g, W10g, W20g)
Goldfinch (1st, 1st L, E20g, W10g, W20g)
House sparrow (1st, 1st L, E20g, W10g, W20g)
Robin (1st, 1st L, E20g, W10g, W20g)
Starling (1st, 1st L, E20g, W10g, W20g)
Wood pigeon (1st, 1st L, E20g, W10g, W20g)

■ **2010, September 17. Birds of Britain, series 1**
Des: Kate Stephens, from illustrations by Robert Gillmor. Printed in gravure by Walsall. Self-adhesive. Machine-printed in black.

Set of 6 (all 1st class)	20.00	–
Collector's strip (one of each value)	75.00	–
Philatelic pack (all 1st class)	25.00	–
First day cover	–	25.00

Blackbird (1st, 1st L, E20g, W10g, W20g)
Chaffinch (1st, 1st L, E20g, W10g, W20g)
Collared dove (1st, 1st L, E20g, W10g, W20g)
Greenfinch (1st, 1st L, E20g, W10g, W20g)
Long-tailed tit (1st, 1st L, E20g, W10g, W20g)
Magpie (1st, 1st L, E20g, W10g, W20g)

■ **2011, January 24. Birds of Britain, series 2**
Des: Kate Stephens, from illustrations by Robert Gillmor. Printed in gravure by Walsall. Self-adhesive. Machine-printed in black.

Set of 6 (all 1st class)	32.00	–
Collector's strip (one of each value)	40.00	–
Philatelic pack (all 1st class)	35.00	–
First day cover	–	37.00

002011 5 51840 03

Great crested grebe (1st, 1st L, E20g, W10g, W20g)
Greylag goose (1st, 1st L, E20g, W10g, W20g)
Kingfisher (1st, 1st L, E20g, W10g, W20g)
Mallard (1st, 1st L, E20g, W10g, W20g)
Moorhen (1st, 1st L, E20g, W10g, W20g)
Mute swan (1st, 1st L, E20g, W10g, W20g)

■ 2011, May 19. Birds of Britain, series 3
Des: Kate Stephens, from illustrations by Robert Gillmor. Printed in gravure by Walsall. Self-adhesive. Machine-printed in black.

Set of 6 (all 1st class)	7.00	–
Collector's strip (one of each value)	20.00	–
Philatelic pack (all 1st class)	8.00	–
First day cover	–	15.00

002011 9 51840 04

Arctic tern (1st, 1st L, E20g, W10g, W20g, W40g)
Cormorant (1st, 1st L, E20g, W10g, W20g, W40g)
Gannet (1st, 1st L, E20g, W10g, W20g, W40g)
Oystercatcher (1st, 1st L, E20g, W10g, W20g, W40g)
Puffin (1st, 1st L, E20g, W10g, W20g, W40g)
Ringed plover (1st, 1st L, E20g, W10g, W20g, W40g)

■ 2011, September 16. Birds of Britain, series 4
Des: Kate Stephens, from illustrations by Robert Gillmor. Printed in gravure by Walsall. Self-adhesive. Machine-printed in black.

Set of 6 (all 1st class)	7.00	–
Collector's strip (one of each value)	18.00	–
Philatelic pack (all 1st class)	8.00	–
First day cover	–	16.00

Dalesbred (1st, 1st L, E20g, W10g, W20g, W40g)
Jacob (1st, 1st L, E20g, W10g, W20g, W40g)
Leicester longwool (1st, 1st L, E20g, W10g, W20g, W40g)

Soay (1st, 1st L, E20g, W10g, W20g, W40g)
Suffolk (1st, 1st L, E20g, W10g, W20g, W40g)
Welsh mountain badger face (1st, 1st L, E20g, W10g, W20g, W40g)

■ 2012, February 24. Sheep
Des: Kate Stephens, from illustrations by Robert Gillmor. Printed in gravure by Walsall. Self-adhesive. Machine-printed in black.

Set of 6 (all 1st class)	7.00	–
Collector's strip (one of each value)	15.00	–
Philatelic pack (all 1st class)	7.00	–
First day cover	–	16.00

Berkshire (1st, 1st L, E20g, W10g, W20g, W40g)
British saddleback (1st, 1st L, E20g, W10g, W20g, W40g)
Gloucestershire old spots (1st, 1st L, E20g, W10g, W20g, W40g)
Oxford sandy and black (1st, 1st L, E20g, W10g, W20g, W40g)
Tamworth (1st, 1st L, E20g, W10g, W20g, W40g)
Welsh (1st, 1st L, E20g, W10g, W20g, W40g)

■ 2012, April 24. Pigs
Des: Kate Stephens, from illustrations by Robert Gillmor. Printed in gravure by Walsall. Self-adhesive. Machine-printed in black.

Set of 6 (all 1st class)	10.00	–
Collector's strip (one of each value)	15.00	–
Philatelic pack (all 1st class)	8.00	–
First day cover	–	15.00

Aberdeen Angus (1st, 1st L, E20g, W10g, W20g, W40g)
Highland (1st, 1st L, E20g, W10g, W20g, W40g)
Irish moiled (1st, 1st L, E20g, W10g, W20g, W40g)
Red poll (1st, 1st L, E20g, W10g, W20g, W40g)
Welsh black (1st, 1st L, E20g, W10g, W20g, W40g)
White park (1st, 1st L, E20g, W10g, W20g, W40g)

■ 2012, September 28. Cattle
Des: Kate Stephens, from illustrations by Robert Gillmor. Printed in gravure by Walsall. Self-adhesive. Machine-printed in black.

Set of 6 (all 1st class)	9.00	–
Collector's strip (one of each value)	20.00	–
Philatelic pack (all 1st class)	7.00	–
First day cover	–	16.00

1st Class
up to 100g

002010 9 51840 01

Robin (1st, 1st L, E20g, W10g, W20g, W40g)

■ **2012, November 6. Christmas Robin**
Des: Kate Stephens, from illustration by Robert Gillmor (as the Robin design from Birds of Britain series I, but with year code). Printed in gravure by Walsall. Self-adhesive. Year code '12' or '13' in security overlay. Machine-printed in black.

Single (1st)	2.50	–
Collector's strip (up to W40)	40.00	–
Collector's strip ('The B.P.M.A.')	20.00	–
First day cover	–	3.00

(*Denominations quoted are those initially available.)

1st Class
up to 100g

Emperor dragonfly (1st, 1st L, E20g, W10g, W20g, W40g)
Fairy shrimp (1st, 1st L, E20g, W10g, W20g, W40g)
Glutinous snail (1st, 1st L, E20g, W10g, W20g, W40g)
Lesser silver water beetle (1st, 1st L, E20g, W10g, W20g, W40g)
Smooth newt (1st, 1st L, E20g, W10g, W20g, W40g)
Three-spined stickleback (1st, 1st L, E20g, W10g, W20g, W40g)

■ **2013, February 22. Pond Life**
Des: Kate Stephens, from illustrations by Chris Wormell. Printed in gravure by Walsall. Self-adhesive. Machine-printed in black.

Set of 6 (all 1st class)	8.00	–
Collector's strip (one of each value)	18.00	–
Philatelic pack (all 1st class)	8.00	–
First day cover	–	10.00

1st Class
up to 100g

Arctic char (1st, 1st L, E20g, W10g, W20g, W40g)
Caddis fly larvae (1st, 1st L, E20g, W10g, W20g, W40g)
Common toad (1st, 1st L, E20g, W10g, W20g, W40g)
Crucian carp (1st, 1st L, E20g, W10g, W20g, W40g)

European eel (1st, 1st L, E20g, W10g, W20g, W40g)
Perch (1st, 1st L, E20g, W10g, W20g, W40g)

■ **2013, June 25. Lake Life**
Des: Kate Stephens, from illustrations by Chris Wormell. Printed in gravure by Walsall. Self-adhesive. Machine-printed in black.

Set of 6 (all 1st class)	8.00	–
Collector's strip (one of each value)	20.00	–
Philatelic pack (all 1st class)	8.00	–
First day cover	–	10.00

1st Class
up to 100g

Atlantic salmon (1st, 1st L, E20g, W10g, W20,g W40g)
Blue-winged olive mayfly larva (1st, 1st L, E20g, W10g, W20g, W40g)
Brown trout (1st, 1st L, E20g, W10g, W20g, W40g)
Minnow (1st, 1st L, E20g, W10g, W20g, W40g)
River lamprey (1st, 1st L, E20g, W10g, W20g, W40g)
White-clawed crayfish (1st, 1st L, E20g, W10g, W20g, W40g)

■ **2013, September 20. River Life**
Des: Kate Stephens, from illustrations by Chris Wormell. Printed in gravure by Walsall. Self-adhesive. Machine-printed in black.

Set of 6 (all 1st class)	8.00	–
Collector's strip (one of each value)	18.00	–
Philatelic pack (all 1st class)	8.00	–
First day cover	–	10.00

1st Class
up to 100g

Blackthorn (1st, 1st L, E20g, W10g, W20g, W40g)
Dog violet (1st, 1st L, E20g, W10g, W20g, W40g)
Lesser celandine (1st, 1st L, E20g, W10g, W20g, W40g)
Primrose (1st, 1st L, E20g, W10g, W20g, W40g)
Snowdrop (1st, 1st L, E20g, W10g, W20g, W40g)
Wild daffodil (1st, 1st L, E20g, W10g, W20g, W40g)

■ **2014, February, 19. Spring Blooms**
Des: Kate Stephens, from illustrations by Julia Trickey. Printed in gravure by ISP. Self-adhesive. Year code '14' in security overlay. Machine-printed in black.

Set of 6 (all 1st class)	8.00	–
Collector's strip (up to W40)	20.00	–
Philatelic pack (all 1st class)	8.00	–
First day cover	–	10.00

1st Class
up to 100g

Forget-me-not (1st, 1st L, E20/W10, E60g, W20g, W60g)
Common poppy (1st, 1st L, E20/W10, E60g, W20g, W60g)
Dog rose (1st, 1st L, E20/W10, E60g, W20g, W60g)
Spear thistle (1st, 1st L, E20/W10, E60g, W20g, W60g)
Heather (1st, 1st L, E20/W10, E60g, W20g, W60g)
Cultivated flax (1st, 1st L, E20/W10, E60g, W20g, W60g)

■ 2014, September 17. Symbolic Flowers
Des: Kate Stevens, from illustrations by Julia Trickey. Printed in gravure by ISP. Self-adhesive. Year code '14' in security overlay. Machine-printed in black.

Set of 6 (all 1st class)	10.00	–
Collector's strip (one of each value)	16.00	–
Collector's strip (Shakespeare Birthplace Trust)	20.00	–
Philatelic pack (all 1st class)	10.00	–
First day cover	–	10.00

Common Poppy collector's strips

1st, 1st L, E20/W10, E60, W20, W60 (2014)	30.00	–
1st, 1st L, E20/W10, E100, W20, W100 (2015)	20.00	–
'First World War/Centenary' (Sep 2014)	23.00	–
'The B.P.M.A.' (Oct 2014)	23.00	–
'The NMRM/Remembrance' (Oct 2014)	35.00	–
'The B.P.M.A.' (Oct 2015)	22.00	–
'Sindelfingen October 2015' (Oct 2015)	20.00	–
'Paris November 2015' (Nov 2015)	19.00	–
'RN Submarine' (Nov 2015)	21.00	–
'Royal Navy' (Nov 2015)	21.00	–
'Royal Marines' (Nov 2015)	21.00	–
'Fleet Air Arm' (Nov 2015)	21.00	–
'The Battle of the Somme' (Sep 2016)	20.00	–
'Royal Marines' (Oct 2016)	20.00	–
'Headquarters BFPO Lest We Forget' (Oct 2016)	35.00	–
'The Postal Museum' (Oct 2016)	20.00	–
'WWI Battle of Passchendaele' (Sep 2017)	16.00	–
'The Postal Museum' with no logo (Oct 2017)	16.00	–
'RN Submarine' (Oct 2017)	16.00	–
'HMS Trincomalee 12th Oct 1817' (Nov 2017)	35.00	–
'Postal Museum/WWI 1918–2018' (Oct 2018)	16.00	–

Spear Thistle collector's strips

'88th Scottish Congress' (Apr 2017)	20.00	–
'88th Scottish Congress 2017' (Apr 2017)	50.00	–

1st Large
up to 100g

Common ivy (2nd, 2nd L)
Mistletoe (2nd, 2nd L)
Butcher's broom (1st, 1st L, E20/W10, E60g, W20g, W60g)
Holly (1st, 1st L, E20/W10, E60g, W20g, W60g)

■ 2014, November 13. Winter Greenery
Des: Kate Stevens, from illustrations by Julia Trickey. Printed in gravure by ISP. Self-adhesive. One phosphor band (2nd), two phosphor bands (1st). Year code '14' or '17' in security overlay. Machine-printed in black.

Set of 4 (2nd, 2ndL, 1st, 1st L)	6.00	–
Collector's strip (2nd, 2nd L)	4.00	–
Collector's strip (higher values)	15.00	–
Collector's strip (2nd, 2nd L, BPMA)	5.00	–
Collector's strip (higher values, BPMA)	20.00	–
Collector's strip (2nd, 2nd L, Postal Museum)	20.00	–
Collector's strip (higher values, Postal Museum)	20.00	–
Philatelic pack (2nd, 2nd,1st, 1st L)	7.00	–
First day cover	–	7.00

(*Denominations quoted are those initially available.)

1st Class
up to 100g

'Falcon' (1st, 1st L, E20/W10, E60g, W20g, W60g)
'Briar' (1st, 1st L, E20/W10, E60g, W20g, W60g)
'Harry' (1st, 1st L, E20/W10, E60g, W20g, W60g)
'Margaret' (1st, 1st L, E20/W10, E60g, W20g, W60g)
'Stag' (1st, 1st L, E20/W10, E60g, W20g, W60g)
'Nell Morgan' (1st, 1st L, E20/W10, E60g, W20g, W60g)

■ 2015, February 18. Working Sail
Des: Osborne Ross. Printed in gravure by ISP. Self-adhesive. Year code '15' in security overlay. Machine-printed in black.

Set of 6 (all 1st class)	8.00	–
Collector's strip (one of each value)	20.00	–
Philatelic pack (all 1st class)	8.00	–
First day cover	–	10.00

1st Class
up to 100g

Lion (1st, 1st L, E20/W10, E100g, W20g, W100g)
Unicorn (1st, 1st L, E20/W10, E100g, W20g, W100g)
Yale (1st, 1st L, E20/W10, E100g, W20g, W100g)
Dragon (1st, 1st L, E20/W10, E100g, W20g, W100g)
Falcon (1st, 1st L, E20/W10, E100g, W20g, W100g)
Griffin (1st, 1st L, E20/W10, E100g, W20g, W100g)

■ **2015, May 13. Heraldic Beasts**
Des: Osborne Ross. Printed in gravure by ISP. Self-adhesive. Year code '15' in security overlay. Machine-printed in black.

Set of 6 (all 1st class)	8.00	–
Collector's strip (one of each value)	20.00	–
Philatelic pack (all 1st class)	8.00	–
First day cover	–	10.00

Heraldic Lion collector's strips

'BPMA' (Sep 2015)	22.00	–
'Sindelfingen' (Oct 2015)	20.00	–
'Paris' (Nov 2015)	19.00	–
'The Postal Museum' (Feb 2016)	13.00	–
'87th Scottish Congress' (Apr 2016)	22.00	–
'88th Scottish Congress' (Apr 2017)	20.00	–
'88th Scottish Congress 2017' (Apr 2017)	50.00	–

White Cliffs of Dover (1st, 1st L, E20/W10, E100g, W20g, W100g)
Hong Kong Harbour (1st, 1st L, E20/W10, E100g, W20g, W100g)
Sydney Opera House (1st, 1st L, E20/W10, E100g, W20g, W100g)
Ha Long Bay (1st, 1st L, E20/W10, E100g, W20g, W100g)
New York Harbour (1st, 1st L, E20/W10, E100g, W20g, W100g)
Venice (1st, 1st L, E20/W10, E100g, W20g, W100g)

■ **2015, September 16. Sea Travel**
Des: Osborne Ross, from illustrations by Andy Tuohy. Printed in gravure by ISP. Self-adhesive. Year code '15' in security overlay. Machine-printed in black.

Set of 6 (all 1st class)	8.00	–
Collector's strip (one of each value)	20.00	–
Philatelic pack (all 1st class)	8.00	–
First day cover	–	10.00

Hong Kong collector's strips

'Hong Kong November 2015' (Nov 2015)	18.00	

New York collector's strips

'World Stamp Show NY 2016' (May 2016)	18.00	–

(*The Hong Kong strip was digitally printed.)

Mountain hare (2nd, 2nd L)
Redwing (2nd, 2nd L)
Red fox (1st, 1st L, E20/W10, E100g, W20g, W100g)
Red squirrel (1st, 1st L, E20/W10, E100g, W20g, W100g)

■ **2015, November 16. Winter Fur and Feathers**
Des: Osborne Ross, from illustrations by Robert Gillmor. Printed in gravure by ISP. Self-adhesive. One phosphor band (2nd), two phosphor bands (1st). Year code '15' in security overlay. Machine-printed in black.

Set of 4 (2nd, 2nd L, 1st, 1st L)	8.00	–
Collector's strip (2nd, 2nd L)	4.00	–
Collector's strip (higher values)	16.00	–
Collector's strip (2nd, 2nd L, BPMA)	6.00	–
Collector's strip (higher values, BPMA)	20.00	–
Philatelic pack (2nd, 2nd L, 1st, 1st L)	8.00	–
First day cover	–	7.00

Post boy 1640s (1st, 1st L, E20/W10, E100g, W20g, W100g)
Mail coach 1790s (1st, 1st L, E20/W10, E100g, W20g, W100g)
Falmouth packet ship 1820s (1st, 1st L, E20/W10, E100g, W20, W100)
Travelling Post Office 1890s (1st, 1st L, E20/W10, E100, W20, W100)
Airmail 1930s (1st, 1st L, E20/W10, E100g, W20g, W100g)
Minivan 1970s (1st, 1st L, E20/W10, E100g, W20g, W100g)

■ **2016, February 17. Royal Mail Heritage: Transport**
Des: Howard Brown, from illustrations by Andrew Davidson. Printed in gravure by ISP. Self-adhesive. Year code '16' in security overlay. Machine-printed in black.

Set of 6 (all 1st class)	7.00	–
Collector's strip (one of each value)	17.50	–
Collector's strip (Postal Museum)	9.00	–
Collector's strip ('Liverpool 2016')	30.00	–
Collector's strip ('Glasgow 2016')	25.00	–
Collector's strip ('Birmingham 2016')	25.00	–
Philatelic pack (all 1st class)	7.00	–
First day cover	–	10.00

Mail Coach collector's strips

'The Postal Museum' (2016)	20.00	–
'The Postal Museum Official Opening' (2017)	20.00	–
'The Postal Museum' with no logo (Sep 2017)	16.00	–
'The Post Museum/NPM 50' (Feb 2019)	16.00	–

Travelling Post Office collector's strips

'Spring Stampex 2016' (Feb 2016)	20.00	–
'Steam GWR Swindon 175' (Feb 2016)	25.00	–
'Steam GWR [logo] Swindon 175' (Sep 2016)	20.00	–
'Steam GWR' (Feb 2017)	20.00	–
'Steam GWR King George V 90th' (Mar 2017)	20.00	–
'EARM' (Mar 2017)	20.00	–

Seven–spot ladybird (1st, 1st L, E20/W10, E100, W20, W100)
Fourteen–spot ladybird (1st, 1st L, E20/W10, E100, W20, W100)
Orange ladybird (1st, 1st L, E20/W10, E100, W20, W100)
Heather ladybird (1st, 1st L, E20/W10, E100, W20, W100)
Striped ladybird (1st, 1st L, E20/W10, E100, W20, W100)
Water ladybird (1st, 1st L, E20/W10, E100, W20, W100)

■ 2016, September 14. Ladybirds
Des: Osborne Ross, from illustrations by Chris Wormell. Printed in gravure by ISP. Self-adhesive. Year code '16' in security overlay. Machine–printed in black.

Set of 6 (all 1st class)	7.00	–
Collector's strip (one of each value)	18.00	–
Philatelic pack (all 1st class)	7.00	–
First day cover	–	10.00

Hedgehog (2nd, 2nd L)
Grass snake (2nd, 2nd L)
Dormouse (1st, 1st L, E20/W10, E100, W20, W100)
Brown long-eared bat (1st, 1st L, E20/W10, E100, W20, W100)

■ 2016, November 14. Hibernating Animals
Des: Osborne Ross from illustrations by Chris Wormell. Printed in gravure by ISP. Self-adhesive. One phosphor band (2nd) or two phosphor bands (1st). Year code '16' in security overlay. Machine–printed in black.

Set of 4 (2nd, 2nd L, 1st, 1st L)	6.00	–
Collector's strip (2nd, 2nd L)	4.50	–
Collector's strip (higher values)	19.00	–
Collector's strip (2nd, 2nd L, Postal Museum)	4.00	–
Collector's strip (high values, Postal Museum)	18.00	–
Philatelic pack (2nd, 2nd L, 1st, 1st L)	6.00	–
First day cover	–	7.00

TPO: bag exchange (1st, 1st L, E20/W10, E100, W20, W100)
Post Office Railway (1st, 1st L, E20/W10, E100, W20, W100)
Night Mail (1st, 1st L, E20/W10, E100, W20, W100)
TPO: loading (1st, 1st L, E20/W10, E100, W20, W100)
TPO: sorting (1st, 1st L, E20/W10, E100, W20, W100)
TPO: on the move (1st, 1st L, E20/W10, E100, W20, W100)

■ 2017, February 15. Royal Mail Heritage: Mail by Rail
Des: Osborne Ross, from illustrations by Andrew Davidson. Printed in gravure by ISP. Self-adhesive. Year code '17' in security overlay. Machine–printed in black.

Set of 6 (all 1st class)	7.00	–
Collector's strip (one of each value)	18.00	–
Collector's strip (Postal Museum)	7.00	–
Collector's strip (Steam GWR)	7.00	–
Philatelic pack (all 1st class)	10.00	–
First day cover	–	10.00

Post Office Railway collector's strips

'The Postal Museum' (Feb 2017)	18.00	–
'The Postal Museum Official Opening' (2017)	20.00	–
'The Postal Museum', no logo (Sept 2017)	16.00	–

Commemorative head, orange (1st, 1st L, E20/W10, E100, W20, W100)
Commemorative head, gold (1st, 1st L, E20/W10, E100, W20, W100)
Commemorative head, violet (1st, 1st L, E20/W10, E100, W20, W100)
Commemorative head, olive (1st, 1st L, E20/W10, E100, W20, W100)
Commemorative head, green (1st, 1st L, E20/W10, E100, W20, W100)
Commemorative head, olive–brown (1st, 1st L, E20/W10, E100, W20, W100)

■ 2017, June 5. Machin Anniversary 1967–2017
Des: Royal Mail Group. Printed in gravure by ISP. Self-adhesive. 'Machin Anniversary 1967–2017' security overlay. Machine-printed in black.

Set of 6 (all 1st class)	8.00	–
Collector's strip (one of each value)	19.00	–
Collector's strip (Postal Museum)	10.00	–
Collector's strip (Postal Museum Opening)	8.00	–
Collector's strip (Autumn Stampex 2017)	8.00	–
Collector's strip (Postal Museum)	8.00	–
Collector's strip (NPM 50, 2019)	7.00	–
Philatelic pack (all 1st class)	8.00	–
First day cover	–	10.00

(*A collector's strip comprising one stamp of each value, with the overprint '88th Scottish Congress 2017', was produced in error by the philatelic service, and sent out to subscribers in advance of the event in April. Price £150.)

1st Class
up to 100g

First UK aerial mail, 1911

First UK aerial mail, 1911 (1st, 1st L, E20/W10, E100, W20, W100)
Military mail flight, 1919 (1st, 1st L, E20/W10, E100, W20, W100)
International airmail, 1933 (1st, 1st L, E20/W10, E100, W20, W100)
Domestic airmail, 1934 (1st, 1st L, E20/W10, E100, W20, W100)
Flying boat airmail 1937 (1st, 1st L, E20/W10, E100, W20, W100)
Datapost service, 1980s (1st, 1st L, E20/W10, E100, W20, W100)

■ **2017, September 13. Royal Mail Heritage: Mail by Air**
Des: Osborne Ross, from illustrations by Andrew Davidson. Printed in gravure by ISP. Self-adhesive. Year code '17' in security overlay. Machine-printed in black.

Set of 6 (all 1st class)	7.00	–
Collector's strip (one of each value)	20.00	–
Collector's strip (Postal Museum)	7.00	–
Philatelic pack (all 1st class)	7.00	–
First day cover	–	10.00

1st Class
up to 100g

THE IRON THRONE

The Iron Throne (2nd, 2nd L)
The Iron Throne (1st, 1st L, E20/W10, E100, W20, W100)

■ **2018, January 3. Game of Thrones**
Des: Robert Ball. Printed in gravure by ISP. Self-adhesive. Year code '18' in security overlay. Machine-printed in black.

Set of 2 (2nd, 1st)	3.00	–
Collector's strip (2nd, 2nd L)	4.00	–
Collector's strip (higher values)	18.00	–
Collector's strip (2nd, 2nd L, Postal Museum)	4.00	–
Collector's strip (higher values, Postal Museum)	18.00	–
Philatelic pack (2nd, 1st)	3.00	–
First day cover	–	50.00

1st Class
up to 100g

RMS *Olympic*, 1911

Packet 'Antelope', 1780 (1st, 1st L, E20/W10, E100, W20, W100)
SS 'Great Western', 1838 (1st, 1st L, E20/W10, E100, W20, W100)
SS 'Britannia', 1887 (1st, 1st L, E20/W10, E100, W20, W100)
RMS 'Olympic', 1911 (1st, 1st L, E20/W10, E100, W20, W100)
RMS 'Queen Mary', 1936 (1st, 1st L, E20/W10, E100, W20, W100)
RMS 'St Helena', 1990 (1st, 1st L, E20/W10, E100, W20, W100)

■ **2018, February 14. Royal Mail Heritage: Mail by Sea**
Des: Royal Mail Group Ltd, from illustrations by Andrew Davidson. Printed in gravure by ISP. Self-adhesive. Year code '18' in security overlay. Machine-printed in black.

Set of 6 (all 1st class)	7.00	–
Collector's strip (one of each value)	20.00	–
Collector's strip (Postal Museum)	7.00	–
Collector's strip (Voices from the Deep/TPM)	7.00	–
Philatelic pack (all 1st class)	7.50	–
First day cover	–	10.00

1st Class
up to 100g

Pentacycle, 1882

Pentacycle, 1882 (1st, 1st L, E20/W10, E100, W20, W100)
Motorcycle and trailer, 1902 (1st, 1st L, E20/W10, E100, W20, W100)
Tricycle and basket, 1920 (1st, 1st L, E20/W10, E100, W20, W100)
Bicycle, 1949 (1st, 1st L, E20/W10, E100, W20, W100)
Motorcycle, 1965 (1st, 1st L, E20/W10, E100, W20, W100)
Quad bike, 2002 (1st, 1st L, E20/W10, E100, W20, W100)

■ **2018, September 12. Royal Mail Heritage: Mail by Bike**
Des: Royal Mail Group Ltd, from illustrations by Andrew Davidson. Printed in gravure by ISP. Self-adhesive. Year code '18' in security overlay. Machine-printed in black.

Set of 6 (all 1st class)	7.00	–
Collector's strip (one of each value)	18.00	–
Collector's strip (Postal Museum)	7.00	–
Philatelic pack (all 1st class)	7.00	–
First day cover	–	10.00

SMILERS GENERIC SHEETS

Smilers sheets are personalisable, by way of having a photograph or other supplied image printed on labels alongside conventional stamps. Listed here are Royal Mail's generic sheets for each available issue, which have decorative labels instead of customers' photographs.

Smilers

THE STAMP SHOW 2000

The Stamp Show, 2000

■ **2000, May 22. The Stamp Show 2000**
Sheet of 10 1st class Smiles as March 26, 1991   23.00

■ **2000, October 3. Christmas: Robin in Letterbox**
Sheet of 20 19p Robin in pillar box as October 30,
1995, inscribed copyright 'Post Office 2000'   £125

■ **2000, October 3. Christmas: Father Christmas**
Sheet of 10 1st class Father Christmas as October 27,
1997, inscribed copyright 'Post Office 2000'   £125

■ **2001, June 5. Occasions: Hallmarks**
Sheets of 20 1st class as February 6, 2001   £120

■ **2001, July 3. Smiles**
Sheet of 10 1st class Smiles as May 22, 2000,
but with revised labels and border   £170

■ **2001, October 9. Christmas: Robin in Letterbox**
Sheet of 20 19p Robin in pillar box as
October 30, 1995, inscribed copyright 'Consignia 2001'   £600

■ **2001, October 9. Christmas: Father Christmas**
Sheet of 10 1st class Father Christmas as October 27,
1997, inscribed copyright 'Consignia 2001'   £600

■ **2001, December 18. Cartoons**
Sheet of 10 1st class as February 26, 1996   30.00

■ **2002, April 23. Occasions: Pictorial Messages**
Sheet of 20 1st class as March 5, 2002   60.00

■ **2002, May 21. Football World Cup**
Sheet of 20 1st class Flag as May 21, 2002   25.00

■ **2002, October 1. Smiles**
Sheet of 10 1st class Teddy Bear and 10 1st class
Dennis the Menace as March 26, 1991   27.00

■ **2002, October 1. Christmas: Father Christmas**
Sheet of 20 1st class as October 27, 1997   30.00

■ **2003, January 21. Flowers**
Sheet of 20 1st class Flower Paintings as January 6, 1997   30.00

Occasions, 2003

■ **2003, February 4. Occasions: Multiple Choice**
Sheet of 20 1st class as February 4, 2003   20.00

■ **2003, July 29. Cartoons Crossword**
Sheet of 20 1st class as February 26, 1996   18.00

■ **2003, September 30. Christmas: Winter Robins**
Sheet of 20 1st class as November 6, 2001. Self–adhesive   18.00

■ **2003, November 4. Christmas: Ice Sculptures**
Sheet of 20 2nd class Ice Sculptures as November 4,
2003. Self–adhesive   20.00
Sheet of 20 1st class Ice Sculptures as November 4,
2003. Self–adhesive   20.00

■ **2004, January 30. Hong Kong Stamp Exhibition**
Sheet of 20 1st class Hello as March 5, 2002   17.50

■ **2004, February 3. Occasions: Entertaining Envelopes**
Sheet of 20 1st class as February 3, 2004   19.00

■ **2004, May 25. Royal Horticultural Society**
Sheet of 20 1st class as May 25, 2004   19.00

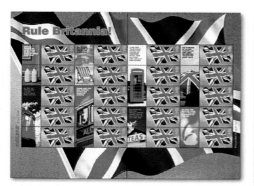

Rule Britannia, 2004

■ **2004, July 27. Rule Britannia**
Sheet of 20 1st class Union Flag as October 22, 2001   19.00

■ **2004, November 2. Christmas: Father Christmas**
Sheet of 10 1st class and 10 2nd class. Self–adhesive   17.50

■ **2005, January 11. Farm Animals**
Sheet of 20 1st class as January 11, 2005   20.00

■ **2005, March 15. Magic**
Sheet of 20 1st class as March 15, 2005   17.50

■ **2005, April 21. Pacific Explorer Stamp Exhibition**
Sheet of 20 1st class Hello as March 5, 2002   19.00

■ **2005, June 21. White Ensign**
Sheet of 20 1st class White Ensign as October 22, 2001   18.00

■ **2005, September 15. Classic ITV**
Sheet of 20 1st class as September 15, 2005   18.00

■ **2005, November 1. Christmas: Winter Robins**
Sheet of 10 1st class and 10 2nd class as November 6, 2001. Self–adhesive   18.00

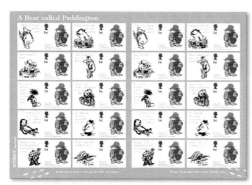

A Bear Called Paddington, 2006

■ **2006, January 10. A Bear Called Paddington**
Sheet of 20 1st class Paddington Bear as January 10, 2006. Self–adhesive   18.00

■ **2006, March 7. Fun Fruit and Veg**
Sheet of 20 1st class as March 7, 2006. Self–adhesive   20.00

■ **2006, May 25. Washington Stamp Exhibition**
Sheet of 20 1st class Hello as March 5, 2002   18.00

■ **2006, June 6. World Cup Winners**
Sheets of 20 1st class as June 6, 2006   18.00

■ **2006, July 4. For Life's Special Moments**
Sheet of 20 1st class as October 4, 2005. Self–adhesive   18.00

■ **2006, October 17. For Life's Extra Special Moments**
Sheet of 20 1st class as October 17, 2006 Self–adhesive   18.00

■ **2006, November 7. Christmas**
Sheet of 10 1st class and 10 2nd class as November 7, 2006 Self–adhesive   18.00

■ **2006, November 9. We Will Remember Them, issue 1**
Sheet of 20 1st class Poppies as November 6, 2006   18.00

■ **2006, November 14. Belgica Stamp Exhibition**
Sheet of 20 1st class Hello as March 5, 2002   18.00

Glorious Wales, 2007

■ **2007, March 1. Glorious Wales**
Sheet of 20 1st class Wales as October 14, 2003.
Self–adhesive   18.00

■ **2007, April 23. Glorious England**
Sheet of 20 1st class England as October 14, 2003.
Self–adhesive   18.00

■ **2007, May 17. Wembley Stadium**
Sheet of 20 1st class Lion & Shield of St George
as May 17, 2007   18.00

■ **2007, June 5. 40th Anniversary of the Machin Definitive**
Sheet of 20 1st class Arnold Machin as June 5, 2007   19.00

■ 2007, July 17. Harry Potter
Sheet of 20 1st class Crest of Hogwarts School as
July 17, 2007. Self–adhesive   18.00

Christmas, 2007

■ 2007, November 6. Christmas
Sheet of 20 2nd class, 1st class and 78p as
November 6, 2007. Self-adhesive   18.00

■ 2007, November 8. We Will Remember Them, issue 2
Sheet of 20 1st class Poppy as November 8, 2007   18.00

■ 2007, November 30. Glorious Scotland
Sheet of 20 1st class Scotland as October 14, 2003.
Self–adhesive   18.00

■ 2008, January 15. I Wrote To Say ...
Sheet of 20 1st class as October 4, 2005, with
circular labels. Self-adhesive   19.00

■ 2008, March 11. Glorious Northern Ireland
Sheet of 20 1st class Northern Ireland as October
14, 2003. Self-adhesive   18.00

■ 2008, July 17. 100 Years of Aviation
Sheet of 20 1st class as July 17, 2008   18.00

■ 2008, August 5. Beijing 2008 Olympic Expo
Sheet of 20 1st class Hello as March 5, 2002   18.00

■ 2008, September 29. Glorious United Kingdom
Sheet of 20 1st class England, Northern Ireland, Scotland
and Wales as as October 14, 2003. Self-adhesive   20.00

■ 2008, November 4. Christmas
Sheet of 20 2nd class, 1st class and 81p as
November 4, 2008. Self-adhesive   19.00

■ 2008, November 6. We Will Remember Them, issue 3
Sheet of 20 1st class Poppy as November 6, 2008   18.00

■ 2009, January 13. The Mini
Sheet of 20 1st class Mini as January 13, 2009   18.00

Concorde, 2009

■ 2009, March 2. Concorde
Sheet of 20 1st class Concorde as January 13, 2009   17.00

■ 2009, March 17. Castles of Northern Ireland
Sheet of 20 1st class Northern Ireland as
October 14, 2003. Self-adhesive   18.00

■ 2009, April 23. Castles of England
Sheet of 20 1st class English flag as April 23, 2007.
Self-adhesive   20.00

■ 2009, August 3. Thaipex 2009 Exhibition
Sheet of 20 1st class Hello as March 5, 2002   18.00
(*Panes of 10 were sold separately at the exhibition.)

Post Boxes, 2009

■ 2009, August 18. Post Boxes
Sheet of 20 1st class as August 18, 2009   18.00

■ 2009, October 21. Italia 2009 Exhibition
Sheet of 20 1st class Hello as March 5, 2002   19.00

■ 2009, November 3. Christmas
Sheet of 20 2nd class, 1st class, 56p and 90p
as November 3, 2009. Self-adhesive   20.00

■ **2009, November 30. Castles of Scotland**
Sheet of 20 1st class Scotland as October 14, 2003.
Self–adhesive   20.00

■ **2009, December 4. MonacoPhil 2009 Exhibition**
Sheet of 20 1st class Hello as March 5, 2002   18.00

■ **2010, January 26. For All Occasions**
Sheet of 20 1st class, Europe and Worldwide
as January 26, 2010. Self–adhesive   32.00

■ **2010, March 1. Castles of Wales**
Sheet of 20 1st class Wales as October 14, 2003.
Self–adhesive   20.00

■ **2010, May 8. 10th Anniversary of Smilers**
Sheet of 20 1st class, Europe and Worldwide
as January 26, 2010. Self–adhesive   52.00

■ **2010, May 8. London 2010 Exhibition**
Sheet of 20 1st class Hello as October 4, 2005.
Self–adhesive   18.00

■ **2010, September 15. Battle of Britain**
Sheet of 20 1st class Spitfire as January 13, 2009   19.00

■ **2010, November 2. Christmas**
Sheet of 20 2nd class, 1st class, 60p and 97p
as November 2, 2010. Self–adhesive   20.00

Indipex, 2011

■ **2011, February 12. Indipex 2011 Exhibition**
Sheet of 20 1st class Union Flag as October 4, 2005.
Self–adhesive   20.00

■ **2011, July 28. Philanippon 2011 Exhibition**
Sheet of 20 1st class Union Flag as October 4, 2005.
Self–adhesive   20.00

■ **2011, September 15. 350 Years of Postmarks**
Sheet of 20 1st class Seal as January 26, 2010   18.00

■ **2011, November 8. Christmas**
Sheet of 20 1st class, 2nd class, 68p, £1.10 as
November 8, 2011. Self–adhesive   32.00

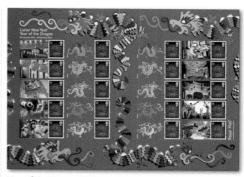

Year of the Dragon, 2012

■ **2012, January 20. Year of the Dragon**
Sheet of 20 1st class Firework as October 17, 2006.
Self–adhesive   23.00

■ **2012, June 18. Indonesia 2012 Exhibition**
Sheet of 20 1st class Hello as October 4, 2005.
Self–adhesive   18.00

■ **2012, June 27. Olympic and Paralympic Games Venues**
Sheet of 20 1st class and Worldwide Olympic Games and
Paralympic Games as January 5, 2012. Self–adhesive   95.00

■ **2012, November 6. Christmas**
Sheet of 20 1st class, 2nd class, 87p and £1.28
as November 6, 2012. Self–adhesive   20.00

■ **2013, February 2. Year of the Snake**
Sheet of 20 1st class Firework as October 17, 2006.
Self–adhesive   21.00

Doctor Who, 2013

■ **2013, March 26. Doctor Who**
Sheet of 20 1st class Tardis as March 26, 2013.
Self–adhesive   21.00

■ **2013, May 10. Australia 2013 Exhibition**
Sheet of 20 1st class Hello as October 4, 2005.
Self–adhesive   21.00

■ 2013, August 2. Thailand 2013 Exhibition
Sheet of 20 1st class Hello as October 4, 2005.
Self–adhesive   21.00

■ 2013, November 5. Christmas
Sheet of 20 1st class, 2nd class, 88p, £1.28 and £1.88
as November 5, 2013. Self-adhesive   35.00

■ 2013, December 10. Year of the Horse
Sheet of 20 1st class Firework as October 17, 2006.
Self–adhesive   21.00

■ 2014, November 4. Christmas
Sheet of 20 1st class, 2nd class, £1.28 and £1.47 as
November 4, 2014. Self-adhesive   22.00

■ 2014, November 19. Year of the Sheep
Sheet of 20 1st class Firework as October 17, 2006.
Self–adhesive   21.00

■ 2014, December 1. Malaysia 2014 Exhibition
Sheet of 20 1st class Hello as October 4, 2005.
Self–adhesive.   21.00

Smilers 2015

■ 2015, January 20. Smilers 2015
Sheet of 20 1st class Smilers as January 20, 2015.
Self–adhesive   £200

■ 2015, May 6. 175th Anniversary of the Penny Black
Sheet of 20 1st class Penny Black and 1st class
Twopenny Blue as May 6, 2015. Self-adhesive 65.00

■ 2015, May 13. London 2015 Exhibition
Sheet of 20 1st class Hello as October 4, 2005.
Self–adhesive   20.00

■ 2015, October 20. Star Wars: Heroes and Villains
Sheet of 10 1st class Yoda, Han Solo, Darth Vader and
Stormtrooper as October 20, 2015. Self-adhesive 11.00

■ 2015, November 3. Christmas
Sheet of 20 1st class, 2nd class, £1, £1.33, £1.52 and £2.25
as November 3, 2015. Self-adhesive   30.00

■ 2015, November 9. Year of the Monkey
Sheet of 20 1st class Firework as October 17, 2006.
Self–adhesive   21.00

175th Anniversary of the Penny Red, 2016

■ 2016, February 18. 175th Anniversary of the Penny Red
Sheet of 20 1st class Penny Red as February 18, 2016.
Self–adhesive   21.00

■ 2016, May 26. New York 2016 Exhibition
Sheet of 20 1st class Hello as October 4, 2005.
Self–adhesive   21.00

■ 2016, October 20. Mr. Men and Little Miss
Sheet of 10 1st class Mr Men and Little Miss as
October 20, 2016. Self-adhesive   12.00

■ 2016, November 8. Christmas
Sheet of 20 1st class, 2nd class, £1.05, £1.33, £1.52 and £2.25
as November 8, 2016. Self-adhesive   25.00

50 Years of Christmas Stamps, 2016

■ 2016, November 8. 50 Years of Christmas stamps
Sheet of 10 1st class and 10 2nd class as November 8,
2016. Self-adhesive   17.50

■ 2016, November 15. Year of the Rooster
Sheet of 20 1st class Firework as October 17, 2006.
Self–adhesive   21.00

Finlandia, 2017

SMILERS FOR KIDS

Peter Rabbit, 2008

■ **2017, May 24. Finlandia 2017 Exhibition**
Sheet of 20 1st class Hello as October 4, 2005.
Self-adhesive   21.00

■ **2017, October 12. Star Wars**
Sheet of 10 1st class Star Wars as October 12. 2017.
Self-adhesive   11.00

■ **2017, November 7. Christmas**
Sheet of 20 1st class, 2nd class, £1.17, £1.40, £1.57 and £2.27
Madonna and Child as November 8, 2016. Self-adhesive   24.00

■ **2017, November 7. Christmas**
Sheet of 20 1st class, 2nd class Children's designs as
November 8, 2016. Self-adhesive   18.00

■ **2017, November 16. The Year of the Dog**
Sheet of 20 1st class Firework as October 17, 2006.
Self-adhesive   20.00

■ **2018, January 23. Game of Thrones**
Sheet of 10 1st class Game of Thrones as January 23, 2018.
Self-adhesive   11.00

■ **2018, June 26. Dad's Army**
Sheet of 10 1st class Dad's Army as June 26, 2018.
Self-adhesive   11.00

■ **2018, October 16. Harry Potter**
Sheet of 10 1st class Harry Potter as October 16, 2018.
Self-adhesive   13.00

■ **2018, November 1. Christmas**
Sheet of 20 1st class, 2nd class, £1.25, £1.45, £1.55, £2.25
Madonna and Child as November 8, 2016. Self-adhesive   27.00

■ **2018, November 15. The Year of the Pig**
Sheet of 20 1st class Firework as October 17, 2006.
Self-adhesive   22.00

■ **2019, March 14. Marvel**
Sheet of 10 1st class Marvel as March 14, 2019.
Self-adhesive   13.00

■ **2019, May 29. Stockholmia 2019 Exhibition**
Sheet of 20 1st class Hello as October 4, 2005.
Self-adhesive   22.00

■ **2008, October 28. Mr Happy**
Sheet of 20 1st class Balloons. Self-adhesive   £100
Sheet of 10 1st class Balloons, and writing pack   60.00

■ **2008, October 28. Almond Blossom**
Sheet of 20 1st class Flower. Self-adhesive   £100
Sheet of 10 1st class Flower, and writing pack   60.00

■ **2008, October 28. Peter Rabbit**
Sheet of 20 1st class New Baby. Self-adhesive   £100
Sheet of 10 1st class New Baby, and writing pack   60.00

■ **2008, October 28. Noddy**
Sheets of 20 1st class Balloons. Self-adhesive   £100
Sheets of 10 1st class Balloons, and writing pack   60.00

■ **2009, April 30. Little Miss Sunshine**
Sheet of 20 1st class Balloons. Self-adhesive   £100
Sheet of 10 1st class Balloons, and writing pack   60.00

■ **2009, April 30. Wild Cherry**
Sheet of 20 1st class Flower. Self-adhesive   £100
Sheet of 10 1st class Flower, and writing pack   60.00

■ **2009, April 30. Jeremy Fisher**
Sheet of 20 1st class Hello. Self-adhesive   £100
Sheet of 10 1st class Hello, and writing pack   60.00

■ **2009, April 30. Big Ears**
Sheets of 20 1st class Balloons. Self-adhesive   £100
Sheets of 10 1st class Balloons, and writing pack   60.00

COMMEMORATIVE SHEETS

In this section, prices are quoted for complete mint sheets only.

Commemorative sheets are an evolution of Smilers sheets. They are not personalisable but are customised as a souvenir product by Royal Mail.

Early issues had normal gum, but most subsequent issues have been self–adhesive.

GUMMED SHEETS

Centenary of the Territorial Army, 2008

■ **2008, April 1. Centenary of the Territorial Army**
Sheet of 10 1st class Union Flag as October 22, 2001   20.00

■ **2008, July 24. London 1908 Olympic Games**
Sheet of 10 1st class Union Flag as October 22, 2001   20.00

■ **2009, October 22. Olympic and Paralympic Games**
Sheet of 10 1st class as October 22, 2009   20.00

■ **2010, July 27. Olympic and Paralympic Games**
Sheet of 10 1st class as July 27, 2010   20.00

■ **2011, July 27. Olympic and Paralympic Games**
Sheet of 10 1st class as July 27, 2011   20.00

SELF–ADHESIVE SHEETS

■ **2008, November 14. 60th Birthday of Prince Charles**
Sheet of 10 1st class Wales   20.00

■ **2009, July 21. 40th Anniversary of the First Moon Landing**
Sheet of 10 1st class Union Flag as February 28, 2008   20.00

■ **2009, September 18. 150th Anniversary of Big Ben**
Sheet of 10 1st class Union Flag as February 28, 2008   20.00

■ **2009, October 7. 800th Anniversary of the University of Cambridge**
Sheet of 10 1st class Firework as February 28, 2008   20.00

■ **2010, May 18. Halley's Comet**
Sheet of 10 1st class Union Flag as February 28, 2008   20.00

■ **2010, July 8. British World Champion Grand Prix Drivers**
Sheet of 10 1st class Union Flag as February 28, 2008   20.00

■ **2010, August 10. 10th Anniversary of the London Eye**
Sheet of 10 1st class Union Flag as February 28, 2008   20.00

■ **2010, October 28. National Memorial Arboretum**
Sheet of 10 1st class Poppies as January 26, 2010   20.00

50th Anniversary of the Jaguar E–Type, 2011

■ **2011, March 30. 50th Anniversary of the Jaguar E–Type**
Sheet of 10 1st class Union Flag as February 28, 2008   20.00

90th Birthday of Prince Philip, 2011

■ **2011, June 10. 90th Birthday of Prince Philip, Duke of Edinburgh**
Sheet of 10 1st class Union Flag as February 28, 2008   20.00

■ **2012, April 10. 100th Anniversary of the RMS Titanic**
Sheet of 10 1st class Seal as January 26, 2010   20.00

■ **2012, May 1. 50th Anniversary of James Bond**
Sheet of 10 1st class Union Flag as February 28, 2008   20.00

■ **2012, October 5. 40th Anniversary of the Last Goon Show**
Sheet of 10 1st class Union Flag as February 28, 2008   20.00

■ **2012, November 8. 150th Anniversary of Notts County Football Club**
Sheet of 10 1st class Firework as February 28, 2008   20.00

■ **2013, April 16. 60th Anniversary of the Launch of HMY Britannia**
Sheet of 10 1st class Union Flag as February 28, 2008   20.00

■ **2013, May 1. Bicentenary of the Birth of David Livingstone**
Sheet of 10 1st class Scottish Flag as November 30, 2006   20.00

■ **2013, September 19. 150th Anniversary of the Birth of Bertram Mackennel**
Sheet of 10 1st class Seal as January 26, 2010   22.00

■ **2014, February 25. 150th Anniversary of Middlesex County Cricket Club**
Sheet of 10 1st class Firework as February 28, 2008   22.00

■ **2014, March 26. 350th Anniversary of the Royal Marines**
Sheet of 10 1st class Union Flag as February 28, 2008   22.00

■ **2014, October 16. Donald Campbell**
Sheet of 10 1st class Union Flag as February 28, 2008   20.00

■ **2014, November 11. 100th Anniversary of the Christmas Truce**
Sheet of 10 1st class Poppies as January 26, 2010   20.00

■ **2015, March 18. The Post Office Rifles**
Sheet of 10 1st class Union Flag as February 28, 2008   20.00

■ **2015, April 24. Bicentenary of the Birth of Anthony Trollope**
Sheet of 10 1st class Union Flag as February 28, 2008   20.00

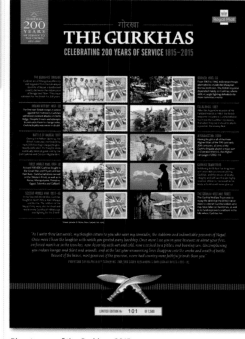

Bicentenary of the Gurkhas, 2015

■ **2015, August 20. Bicentenary of the Gurkhas' Service to the Crown**
Sheet of 10 1st class Union Flag as February 28, 2008   20.00

■ **2015, September 17. Animals of the First World War**
Sheet of 10 1st class Union Flag as February 28, 2008   20.00

■ 2015, September 25. 3oth Anniversary of Danger Mouse
Sheet of 10 1st class Union Flag as February 28, 2008   26.00

■ 2016, January 12. 6oth Anniversary of The Duke of Edinburgh's Award
Sheet of 10 1st class Union Flag as February 28, 2008   20.00

■ 2016, March 8. 8oth Anniversary of Oor Wullie
Sheet of 10 1st class Scottish Flag as November 30, 2006 20.00

■ 2016, March 8. 8oth Anniversary of The Broons
Sheet of 10 1st class Scottish Flag as November 30, 2006 20.00

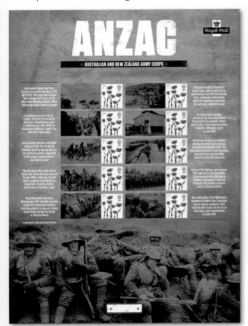

ANZAC, 2016

■ 2016, April 25. Australian and New Zealand Army Corps (ANZAC)
Sheet of 10 1st class Poppies as January 26, 2010   20.00

■ 2016, May 18. Farewell Boleyn (West Ham United FC)
Sheet of 10 1st class Union Flag as February 28, 2008   20.00

■ 2016, August 30. Eddie Stobart
Sheet of 10 1st class Union Flag as October 22, 2001   26.00

■ 2016, October 14. 950th Anniversary of the Battle of Hastings
Sheet of 10 1st class English Flag as April 23, 2007   20.00

■ 2017, May 25. 50th Anniversary of the Lisbon Lions
Sheet of 10 1st class Scottish Flag as November 30, 2006 20.00

■ 2017, June 13. 30th Anniversary of The Princess Royal
Sheet of 10 1st class Union Flag as October 22, 2001   20.00

■ 2017, June 30. Celebrating Canada
Sheet of 10 1st class Firework as October 17, 2006   20.00

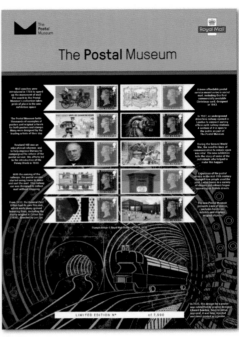

The Postal Museum, 2017

■ 2017, September 13. Opening of The Postal Museum
Sheet of 10 1st class Penny Black, Penny Red and Twopenny Blue as May 6, 2015, and February 18, 2016   22.00

■ 2018, June 1. 150th Anniversary of the Trades Union Congress
Sheet of 10 1st class Seal as January 26, 2010   22.00

■ 2018, October 10. United for Wildlife
Sheet of 10 1st Seal as January 26, 2010   22.00

PRESENTATION PACKS

In this section, prices are quoted for packs in mint condition only.

   Presentation packs have been issued regularly for special stamp issues since 1964, and definitives since 1967, but many collectors regard the packs sold in 1960 (which were also marketed in the USA and therefore also found priced in US dollars) as the forerunners of these collectables.

   Packs issued by Royal Mail in foreign language and other special versions are listed in this section, but those produced privately, commercially sponsored or not placed on general sale are outside the scope of this publication.

'FORERUNNERS'

Wilding definitives 'forerunner' pack, 1960

■ 1960
Wilding definitives (priced in Sterling)	£200
Wilding definitives (priced in Dollars)	£325
Phosphor–graphite definitives (priced in Sterling)	£200
Phosphor–graphite definitives (priced in Dollars)	£325
Regional definitives (priced in Sterling)	£200
Regional definitives (priced in Dollars)	£325
Castle high values (priced in Sterling)	£1,500
Castle high values (priced in Dollars)	£2,000
Castle high values (unpriced)	£1,750

SPECIAL ISSUES

Shakespeare Festival, 1964

■ 1964
Shakespeare Festival	17.00
Geographical Congress	£110
Botanical Congress	£125
Forth Road Bridge	£350

■ 1965
Churchill Commemoration	40.00
700th Anniversary of Parliament	65.00
Battle of Britain	45.00
Post Office Tower	13.00

World Cup, 1966

■ 1966
Robert Burns	42.00
Westminster Abbey	40.00
World Cup	32.00
British Birds	16.00
British Technology	20.00
Battle of Hastings	12.00
Christmas	18.00

■ 1967
EFTA	50.00
British Wild Flowers	22.00
British Paintings	22.00
British Discovery and Invention	10.00

■ 1968
British Bridges	6.00
Anniversaries	5.50
British Paintings	5.00
British Paintings (German version)	30.00
Christmas	10.00
Christmas (German version)	30.00

■ 1969
British Ships	5.00
British Ships (German version)	40.00
British Ships (Cunard version)*	20.00
Concorde	8.00
Concorde (German version)	75.00
Anniversaries	4.50
Anniversaries (German version)	55.00
British Cathedrals	6.00
British Cathedrals (German version)	40.00

Investiture of the Prince of Wales	3.50
Investiture of the Prince of Wales (German version)	40.00
Investiture of the Prince of Wales (Welsh version)	25.00
Post Office Technology	5.00
Christmas	4.00

(*A version of the British Ships pack with slightly amended text was sold exclusively on the Cunard ocean liner QE2.)

General Anniversaries, 1970

■ 1970
Rural Architecture	3.50
General Anniversaries	4.50
Literary Anniversaries	5.00
Commonwealth Games	3.50
Philympia Exhibition	3.50
Christmas	5.00

■ 1971
Ulster Paintings	3.50
Literary Anniversaries	3.50
General Anniversaries	3.50
Modern University Buildings	5.50
Christmas	3.00

■ 1972
Polar Explorers	5.50
General Anniversaries	3.00
Village Churches	5.50
Village Churches (Belgica version)	7.00
BBC*	4.00
Christmas	3.00
Royal Silver Wedding	3.00
Royal Silver Wedding (Japanese version)	5.00

(*The BBC produced a souvenir pack in a similar format to the Royal Mail pack, titled '50th Anniversary of the BBC', as a gift to its staff; price £15.00)

■ 1973
European Communities	4.50
British Trees: Oak	2.00
British Explorers	3.00
County Cricket	4.00
British Painters	2.50
Inigo Jones	2.00
Parliamentary Conference	2.50

| Royal Wedding | 2.00 |
| Christmas | 3.00 |

British Trees: Horse Chestnut, 1974

■ 1974
British Trees: Horse Chestnut	2.00
Fire Service	2.25
UPU	2.75
Medieval Warriorss	2.25
Winston Churchill	2.75
Christmas	2.25

■ 1975
J. M. W. Turner	2.25
Architectural Heritage Year	2.25
Sailing	2.00
Public Railways	3.00
Inter–Parliamentary Union Conference	1.50
Jane Austen	9.00
Christmas	2.00

Bicentennial of American Independence, 1976

■ 1976
Telephones	2.00
Social Reformers	2.00
Bicentennial of American Independence	1.25
Cultural Traditions	2.00
Royal National Rose Society	2.00
British Printing	2.00
Christmas	2.00

1977

Racket Sports	2.00
Royal Institute of Chemistry	2.00
Silver Jubilee	2.00
Commonwealth Heads of Government	1.25
British Wildlife	2.50
Christmas	1.50

Energy Resources, 1978

1978

Energy Resources	1.50
Historic Buildings	1.50
25th anniversary of Coronation	1.50
Horses	1.50
Cycling	1.50
Christmas	1.50

1979

British Dogs	1.00
Spring Wild Flowers	1.00
Elections to European Assembly	1.00
Horse Racing Paintings	1.00
Year of the Child	2.50
Rowland Hill	1.00
Metropolitan Police	1.00
Christmas	1.00

1980

Water Birds	1.00
Liverpool & Manchester Railway	1.00
London 1980 Exhibition	1.00
London Landmarks	1.00
Famous Authoresses	1.00
British Conductors	1.00
Sports Centenaries	1.00
Christmas	1.00

1981

Folklore	1.50
Year of the Disabled	1.50
British Butterflies	1.50
British Landscapes	1.50
Royal Wedding	1.50
Duke of Edinburgh Awards	1.50
Fishing Industry	1.50
Christmas	1.50

Charles Darwin, 1982

1982

Charles Darwin	1.50
Youth Organisations	1.50
British Theatre	1.50
Maritime Heritage	2.00
British Textiles	1.50
Information Technology Year	1.50
British Motor Cars	1.50
Christmas	2.00

1983

British River Fish	1.50
Commonwealth Day	1.50
Engineering Achievements	1.50
British Army Uniforms	2.00
British Gardens	1.50
British Fairs	1.50
Christmas	2.00

1984

College of Arms	2.00
British Cattle	2.00
Urban Renewal	2.00
CEPT/Elections to European Parliament	2.00
Greenwich Meridian	2.00
Mail Coaches	2.00
British Council	2.00
Christmas	2.50

1985

Famous Trains	3.00
Insects	2.00
British Composers	2.00
Safety at Sea	2.00
350th Anniversary of Royal Mail	2.00
Arthurian Legend	2.00
British Film Year	2.50
Christmas	2.00

1986

Industry Year	2.00
Halley's Comet	2.00
Queen's 60th Birthday	2.50
Nature Conservation	2.00

Domesday Book	2.00
Commonwealth Games/World Hockey Cup	2.50
Royal Wedding	1.00
Royal Air Force	2.50
Christmas	2.00

1987
Flowers	2.00
Sir Isaac Newton	2.50
British Architects in Europe	2.00
St John Ambulance	2.00
Order of the Thistle	2.00
150th Anniversary of Accession of Queen Victoria	2.00
Studio Pottery	2.00
Christmas	2.00

1988
Linnean Society	2.00
Welsh Bible	2.00
Sports Organisations	2.00
Transport and Mail Services	2.00
Bicentennary of Australian Settlement	2.00
Spanish Armada	2.00
Edward Lear	2.00
Christmas	2.00

Industrial Archaeology, 1989

1989
Royal Society for the Protection of Birds	2.00
Food and Farming Year	2.00
Anniversaries and Events	2.50
Games and Toys	2.00
Industrial Archaeology	2.00
Royal Microscopical Society	2.00
Lord Mayor's Show	2.00
Christmas	2.00

1990
Penny Black Anniversary	4.00
RSPCA	2.50
Stamp World Exhibition and Glasgow	2.25
Queen's Awards for Export and Technology	2.50
Kew Gardens	2.00
Thomas Hardy	1.00
90th Birthday of the Queen Mother	3.50

Gallantry Awards	2.00
Astronomy	2.50
Christmas	2.50

1991
Dog Paintings	2.50
Scientific Achievements	2.25
Europe in Space	2.50
World Student Games/Rugby World Cup	2.25
World Congress of Roses	3.00
Identification of Dinosaurs	3.75
Ordnance Survey	2.75
Christmas	2.75

Four Seasons: Wintertime, 1992

1992
Four Seasons: Wintertime	2.40
40th Anniversary of Accession	3.50
Alfred, Lord Tennyson	2.50
International Events	2.75
Civil War	2.40
Gilbert and Sullivan Operas	3.00
Protection of the Environment	2.40
Single European Market	1.25
Christmas	2.50

1993
Abbotsbury Swannery	4.50
John Harrison	2.50
World Orchid Conference	2.50
Contemporary Art	2.50
Roman Britain	2.40
Inland Waterways	2.50
Four Seasons: Autumn	2.75
Sherlock Holmes	3.50
Christmas	3.50

1994
Age of Steam	4.00
25th Anniversary of Investiture of the Prince of Wales	3.00
Picture Postcards	3.00
Channel Tunnel	3.00
D–Day	3.00
Scottish Golf Courses	3.00
Four Seasons: Summertime	3.00
Medical Discoveries	3.00
Christmas	3.00

Cats, 1995

■ 1995
Cats	3.00
Four Seasons: Springtime	3.00
National Trust	3.00
Peace and Freedom	3.00
Novels of H. G. Wells	3.00
Shakespeare' Globe Theatre	3.00
Pioneers of Communications	3.00
Rugby League	3.00
Christmas	3.00

■ 1996
Robert Burns	3.00
Wildfowl and Wetlands Trust	3.00
Cinema	3.00
European Football Championship	3.50
Olympic and Paralympic Games, Atlanta	3.25
Famous Women	3.50
Children's Television	3.50
Classic Sports Cars	3.50
Christmas	3.50

■ 1997
King Henry VIII	6.00
Religious Anniversaries	4.00
Tales of Horror	3.50
British Aircraft Designers	4.00
All The Queen's Horses	3.50
Sub Post Offices	3.50
Enid Blyton	4.00
Christmas	4.25
Royal Golden Wedding Anniversary	4.50

Diana, Princess of Wales, 1998 (Welsh version)

■ 1998
Endangered Species	4.75
Diana, Princess of Wales	8.50
Diana, Princess of Wales (Welsh version)	60.00
The Queen's Beasts	3.00
Lighthouses	4.00
Comedians	4.25
National Health Service	3.00
Children's Fantasy Novels	4.00
Notting Hill Carnival	3.00
British Land Speed Records	4.00
Christmas	4.00

(*A limited–edition Welsh language version of the Princess of Wales pack was available only at post offices in Wales.)

Inventors' Tale, 1999

■ 1999
Inventors' Tale	3.50
Travellers' Tale	3.50
Patients' Tale	3.50
Settlers' Tale	3.50
Workers' Tale	3.50
Entertainers' Tale	3.50
Royal Wedding	2.50
Citizens' Tale	3.50
Scientists' Tale	3.50
Farmers' Tale	3.50
Soldiers' Tale	3.50
Christians' Tale	3.50
Artists' Tale	3.50
Millennium Timekeeper	12.00

■ 2000
Above and Beyond	4.00
Fire and Light	4.00
Water and Coast	4.00
Life and Earth	4.00
Art and Craft	4.00
Her Majesty's Stamps	45.00
People and Places	4.00
Stone and Soil	4.00
Tree and Leaf	4.00
Queen Mother's 100th Birthday	12.00
Mind and Matter	4.00
Body and Bone	4.00
Spirit and Faith	4.00
Sound and Vision	4.00

Punch and Judy, 2001

2001

Rights of the Child	4.50
Occasions	8.50
Cats and Dogs	11.00
The Weather	10.00
Submarine Service	17.00
Double–Decker Buses	10.00
Fashion Hats	4.50
Pond Life	5.50
Punch and Judy Puppets	7.00
Nobel Prizes	16.00
Flags and Ensigns	16.00
Christmas	6.00

2002

Just So Stories	11.00
Golden Jubilee	7.50
Occasions	5.25
British Coastlines	5.00
Circus	5.50
Queen Mother Memorial	4.75
Airliners	7.00
Football World Cup	6.50
Commonwealth Games	5.50
Peter Pan	6.50
Bridges of London	32.00
Astronomy	12.00
Pillar Boxes	5.50
Wilding Definitives, part I	27.00
Christmas	5.50

Rugby World Cup, 2003

2003

Birds of Prey	11.00
Occasions	6.50
Discovery of DNA	6.00
Fun Fruit and Veg	12.50
Extreme Endeavours	6.50
Wilding Definitives, part II	10.00
50th Anniversary of Coronation	11.00
21st Birthday of Prince William	8.50
British Journey: Scotland	6.50
Pub Signs	5.50
Classic Transport Toys	5.50
British Museum	6.50
Christmas	7.50
Rugby World Cup	22.00

Classic Locomotives (miniature sheet version), 2004

2004

Classic Locomotives	11.00
Classic Locomotives (miniature sheet version)	12.00
Occasions	6.50
Lord of the Rings	12.00
British Journey: Northern Ireland	5.50
Entente Cordiale	9.00
Ocean Liners	6.00
Royal Horticultural Society	6.50
British Journey: Wales	5.00
Royal Society of Arts	6.50
Woodland Animals	11.00
Crimean War	7.00
Christmas	6.00

2005

Farm Animals	10.00
British Journey: South–West England	6.00
Jane Eyre	7.00
Magic Circle	9.00
50th Anniversary of the Castles Definitives	7.00
Royal Wedding	9.00
World Heritage Sites	8.00
Trooping the Colour	6.50
Motorcycles	6.00
London 2012 Host City	6.00
Changing Tastes in Britain	5.50
Classic ITV Programmes	5.50
The Ashes	4.75
Battle of Trafalgar	6.50
Christmas	6.50

Modern Architecture, 2006

2006

Animal Tales	7.75
British Journey: England	11.00
Isambard Kingdom Brunel	6.50
Ice Age Animals	6.00
Queen's 80th Birthday	7.50
World Cup Winners	6.50
Modern Architecture	6.00
National Portrait Gallery	11.00
Victoria Cross	7.00
Sounds of Britain	6.50
Smilers	11.00
Christmas	8.00
Lest We Forget, issue I	8.00
Celebrating Scotland	6.00

Beside The Seaside, 2007

2007

The Beatles	12.00
Sea Life	11.00
The Sky at Night	7.50
World of Invention	7.00
Abolition of the Slave Trade	6.50
Celebrating England	5.50
Beside the Seaside	6.75
40th Anniversary of Machin Definitives	6.00
Grand Prix	6.50
Harry Potter	14.00
Scouting	6.50
Endangered Species: Birds	11.00
British Army Uniforms	7.50
Royal Diamond Wedding Anniversary	13.00
Christmas	10.50
Lest We Forget, issue II	7.00

2008

Ian Fleming's James Bond	7.50
Working Dogs	7.00
Houses of Lancaster and York	11.50
Celebrating Northern Ireland	5.00
Rescue at Sea	6.50
Endangered Species: Insects	11.00
Cathedrals	11.50
Classic Carry On & Hammer Films	7.00
Air Displays	7.00
Handover of Olympic Flag	32.00
RAF Uniforms	7.50
50th Anniversary of Country Definitives	11.00
Women of Distinction	6.50
Christmas	7.00
Lest We Forget, issue III	7.00

Olympic and Paralympic Games, 2009

2009

British Design Classics	11.00
Robert Burns	6.50
Charles Darwin	11.50
Celebrating Wales	5.50
Industrial Revolution	8.00
House of Tudor	12.50
Endangered Species: Plants	16.00
Mythical Creatures	8.00
Post Boxes	5.50
Fire and Rescue Services	7.50
Royal Navy Uniforms	8.00
Eminent Britons	11.00
Olympic and Paralympic Games, issue I	11.00
Christmas	10.00

2010

Classic Album Covers	12.00
Business Customised and Smilers Stamps	12.00
Girlguiding	7.00
Royal Society	11.50
Battersea Dogs & Cats Home	11.50
House of Stewart	11.00
Endangered Species: Mammals	11.50
Accession of George V/The King's Stamps	9.00
Britain Alone	14.00
House of Stuart	11.00
Olympic and Paralympic Games, issue II	11.50
Great British Railways	7.50

Medical Breakthroughs	8.00
Winnie-the-Pooh	12.50
Christmas	11.50

2011

FAB. The Genius of Gerry Anderson	13.00
Classic Locomotives of England	5.75
Musicals	10.50
Magical Realms	9.50
WWF	16.00
Royal Shakespeare Company	14.00
Royal Wedding	14.00
Morris & Co	8.50
Thomas the Tank Engine	13.00
Olympic and Paralympic Games, issue III	11.00
Crown Jewels	10.50
First UK Aerial Post	5.75
House of Hanover	13.00
UK A–Z, part 1	12.50
Christmas	10.50

House of Windsor and Saxe–Coburg Gotha, 2012

2012

Roald Dahl	14.00
House of Windsor and Saxe–Coburg Gotha	12.50
Diamond Jubilee (miniature sheet)	8.00
Britons of Distinction	10.50
Classic Locomotives of Scotland	5.75
Comics	11.00
UK A–Z, part 2	15.00
Great British Fashion	10.50
Diamond Jubilee (set)	18.00
Charles Dickens	15.00
Welcome to the Olympic Games	22.00
Welcome to the Paralympic Games	10.00
Memories of London 2012	20.00
Space Science	9.50
Christmas	13.00

2013

London Underground	15.00
Jane Austen	9.50
Doctor Who	16.00
Great Britons	11.00
Football Heroes	11.75
Royal Portraits	10.50
Classic Locomotives of Northern Ireland	7.00
Butterflies	11.00

Andy Murray	7.00
British Auto Legends	14.00
Merchant Navy	14.00
Dinosaurs	10.75
Christmas	12.00
Children's Christmas	11.00

Classic Children's TV, 2014

2014

Classic Children's TV	13.50
Working Horses	10.50
Classic Locomotives of Wales	7.50
Remarkable Lives	10.50
Buckingham Palace	11.00
Great British Film	14.50
Sustainable Fish	11.00
Commonwealth Games	12.50
First World War 1914	11.00
Seaside Architecture	16.50
Prime Ministers	11.50
Christmas	13.50

Battle of Waterloo, 2015

2015

Alice's Adventures in Wonderland	26.00
Smilers	9.50
Inventive Britain	15.00
Bridges	11.50
Comedy Greats	11.50
175th anniversary of the Penny Black	11.50
First World War 1915	11.50
Magna Carta	12.00
Battle of Waterloo	18.00
Battle of Britain	10.50
Bees	20.00
Long To Reign Over Us	10.00
Rugby World Cup	13.00

Star Wars	20.00
Christmas	16.00

Royal Mail 500, 2016

2016

Shackleton and the Endurance Expedition	15.50
Royal Mail 500	16.00
British Humanitarians	10.50
Shakespeare	14.00
The Queen's 90th Birthday	17.00
Animail	10.50
First World War 1916	18.00
Pink Floyd	19.00
Beatrix Potter	20.00
Landscape Gardens	13.50
The Great Fire of London	11.50
Agatha Christie	12.50
Mr. Men and Little Miss	11.50
Christmas	18.00

Racehorse Legends, 2017

2017

Ancient Britain	16.00
Windsor Castle	18.00
David Bowie	19.00
Racehorse Legends	16.00
Songbirds	11.50
50th Anniversary of the Machin	13.00
Windmills and Watermills	12.50
Landmark Buildings	11.50
First World War 1917	11.50
Classic Toys	11.00
Ladybird Books	15.00
Star Wars	9.00
Christmas	30.00
Royal Wedding: Platinum Anniversary	12.00

Reintroduced Species, 2018

2018

Game of Thrones	16.00
Votes for Women	15.00
RAF Centenary	20.00
Reintroduced Species	13.00
Owls	11.50
Royal Wedding	8.00
Royal Academy of Arts	12.00
Dad's Army	15.00
Hampton Court Palace	18.00
Captain Cook and Endeavour Voyage	16.00
The Old Vic	16.00
First World War 1918	11.00
Harry Potter	18.00
Christmas	16.50
Prince of Wales' 70th Birthday	11.00

Leonardo da Vinci, 2019

2019

Stamp Classics	11.00
Leonardo da Vinci	12.00
Marvel	18.00
Birds of Prey	11.00
British Engineering	19.00
Queen Victoria Bicentenary	18.00
75th Anniversary of D–Day	16.50
Curious Customs	14.00

Keep up with GB news in Stamp Magazine

LOW–VALUE DEFINITIVES

Low–value definitives, 1971

1967	½d to 1/9	7.50
1967	½d to 1/9 (German version)	£100
1971	½p to 9p	6.50
1971	½p to 9p (Scandinavia tour)	18.00
1971	½p to 10p	27.00
1977	½p to 50p	4.50
1981	2½p to 75p (pack No129a)	12.00
1983	½p to 75p (pack No1)	25.00
1984	½p to 75p	22.00
1987	1p to 75p	25.00
1988	14p to 35p	6.25
1989	15p to 37p	5.50
1990	Penny Black Anniversary issue	4.00
1990	10p to 33p	5.75
1991	1p to 75p	25.00
1991	6p to 39p	6.00
1993	self–adhesive booklet	20.00
1993	19p to 41p	5.00
1995	1p to £1	32.00
1996	20p to 63p	6.00
1997	2nd and 1st	4.00
1997	26p and 1st	4.50
1998	2nd, 1st, 1p to £1	14.00
1999	7p to 64p	10.00
2000	Millennium 1st	3.50
2000	Jeffery Matthews Colour Palette	80.00
2000	8p to 65p	7.00
2002	2nd, 1st, 1p to £1	15.00
2002	37p to 68p	4.25
2002	Wildings (issue 1)	27.00
2002	Definitives Collection folder, containing the low values pack (2002), high values pack (2002) and country packs (2001–02)	32.00
2003	Worldwide and Europe	5.50
2003	Wildings (issue 2)	10.00
2004	1st, Worldwide Postcard, 7p to 43p	10.00
2005	1p, 2p, 5p, 9p, 10p, 20p, 35p, 40p, 42p, 46p, 47p, 50p, 68p, £1, plus self–adhesive 2nd, 1st, Europe, Worldwide and postcard	50.00
2005	Definitives Collection folder, containing the low values pack (2005), high values pack (2003), country packs (2003) and country 42p values pack (2005)	32.00

2006	37p to 72p	10.00
2006	Pricing in Proportion	7.00
2007	16p to 78p	8.50
2007	1p to £1 ruby	37.50
2008	15p to 81p	4.00
2009	2nd to £1 with security features	7.50
2009	17p to 90p	7.00
2010	Definitives Collection folder, containing 1p to £1.46, plus Europe, Worldwide, Worldwide Postcard and 'Recorded Signed For'	50.00
2010	Low values in current use	23.00
2010	Special Delivery	23.00
2011	1p to £1.65	14.00
2012	Olympic and Paralympic Games	12.00
2012	1st, 1st Large, 87p, £1.28, £1.90	11.00
2013	1p to £1 in new colour palette	8.00
2013	78p to £1.88 and 'Royal Mail Signed For'	13.00
2014	81p to £2.15	10.00
2015	£1.33 to £3.30	21.00
2016	£1.05	3.25
2017	£1.17 to £2.55	16.00
2018	£1.25 to £2.65	12.50
2019	£1.35 to £3.60	14.00

HIGH–VALUE DEFINITIVES

£10 definitive, 1993

1969	2/6 to £1	13.00
1969	2/6 to £1 (German version)	60.00
1970	10p to 50p	7.00
1971	20p to £1	10.00
1977	£1 to £5 (pack no. 91)	13.50
1987	£1 to £5 (pack no. 13)	£125
1987	£1.60	19.00
1988	Castles £1 to £5	16.00
1992	Castles £1 to £5	16.00
1993	£10	30.00
1995	£3	14.00
1997	Castles £1.50 to £5	65.00
1999	£1.50 to £5 (Enschedé)	34.00
2000	£1.50 to £5 (De La Rue)	29.00
2003	£1.50 to £5 (gravure)	19.00
2009	£1.50 to £5 with security features	19.00
2017	£5 65th Anniversary of Accession	12.50

Visit www.stampmagazine.co.uk

COUNTRY DEFINITIVES

Scotland definitives, 1983

■ Northern Ireland

1970	3d, 4d sepia, 4d red, 5d, 9d, 1/3, 1/6	3.50
1971	2½p, 3p, 5p, 7½p	2.50
1974	3p, 3½p, 5½p, 8p	3.00
1974	3p, 3½p, 4½p, 5½p, 8p	3.00
1976	6½p, 8½p, 10p, 11p	2.00
1981	7p, 9p, 10½p, 11½p, 12p, 13½p, 14p, 15p, 18p, 22p	6.00
1983	10p, 12½p, 16p, 20½p, 26p, 28p	13.00
1984	10p, 13p, 16p, 17p, 22p, 26p, 28p, 31p	10.00
1987	12p, 13p, 17p, 18p, 22p, 26p, 28p, 31p	14.00
1999	19p, 26p, 38p, 64p	14.00
2000	1st, 40p, 65p	12.50
2001	2nd, 1st, E, 65p	5.00
2003	2nd, 1st, E, 68p	5.00

■ Scotland

1970	3d, 4d sepia, 4d red, 5d, 6d, 9d, 1/3, 1/6	7.50
1971	2½p, 3p, 5p, 7½p	2.50
1974	3p, 3½p, 5½p, 8p	3.00
1974	3p, 3½p, 4½p, 5½p, 8p	3.00
1976	6½p, 8½p, 10p, 11p	2.00
1981	7p, 9p, 10½p, 11½p, 12p, 13½p, 14p, 15p, 18p, 22p	6.00
1983	10p, 12½p, 16p, 20½p, 26p, 28p	13.00
1984	10p, 13p, 16p, 17p, 22p, 26p, 28p, 31p	10.00
1987	12p, 13p, 17p, 18p, 22p, 26p, 28p, 31p	14.00
1999	2nd, 1st, E, 64p	8.50
2000	65p	9.00
2002	2nd, 1st, E, 65p	15.00
2003	2nd, 1st, E, 68p	6.00

■ Wales

1970	3d, 4d sepia, 4d red, 5d, 9d, 1/6	5.50
1971	2½p, 3p, 5p, 7½p	2.50
1974	3p, 3½p, 5½p, 8p	3.00
1974	3p, 3½p, 4½p, 5½p, 8p	3.00
1976	6½p, 8½p, 10p, 11p	2.00
1981	7p, 9p, 10½p, 11½p, 12p, 13½p, 14p, 15p, 18p, 22p	6.00
1983	10p, 12½p, 16p, 20½p, 26p, 28p	13.00
1984	10p, 13p, 16p, 17p, 22p, 26p, 28p, 31p	10.00
1987	12p, 13p, 17p, 18p, 22p, 26p, 28p, 31p	12.00
1997	20p, 26p, 37p, 63p	10.50
1999	2nd, 1st, E, 64p	7.50
2000	65p	8.50
2002	2nd, 1st, E, 65p	14.00
2003	2nd, 1st, E, 68p	6.00

■ England

| 2001 | 2nd, 1st, E, 65p | 5.00 |
| 2003 | 2nd, 1st, E, 68p | 5.00 |

Country definitives, 2012

■ All Countries
(comprising the stamps of Northern Ireland, Scotland and Wales up to 1998, and additionally England from 2002)

1988	14p, 19p, 23p, 32p (three countries)	9.00
1989	15p, 20p, 24p, 34p (three countries)	9.00
1990	17p, 22p, 26p, 37p (three countries)	9.00
1991	18p, 24p, 28p, 39p (three countries)	9.00
1993	19p, 25p, 30p, 41p (three countries)	9.00
1996	20p, 26p, 37p, 63p (three countries)	14.00
1998	20p (centre band), 26p, 37p, 63p (three countries)	15.00
2002	68p (four countries)	5.00
2004	40p (four countries)	6.00
2005	42p (four countries)	6.00
2006	44p, 72p (four countries)	10.00
2007	48p, 78p (four countries)	8.50
2008	50p, 81p (four countries)	10.00
2008	2nd, 1st, 50p, 81p (four countries)	38.00
2008	50th anniversary of Country Definitives	10.00
2009	56p, 90p (four countries)	11.00
2010	60p, 97p (four countries)	15.00
2011	68p, £1.10 (four countries)	13.00
2012	87p, £1.28 (four countries)	17.00
2013	88p (four countries)	7.00
2014	97p (four countries)	7.50
2015	£1, £1.33 (four countries)	22.00
2016	£1.05 (four countries)	8.00
2017	£1.17, £1.40 (four countries)	19.00
2018	2nd to £1.45 (four countries)	28.00
2019	£1.35, £1.55 (four countries)	16.00

Isle of Man definitives, 1971

■ Isle of Man

| 1971 | 2½p, 3p, 5p, 7½p | 2.50 |

POSTAGE DUES

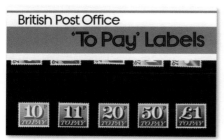

Postage dues, 1977

1971	½p to 5p, 10p, 20p, 50p, £1	28.00
1977	½p to £1	10.00
1982	1p to £5	26.00
1994	1p to £5	34.00

CHRISTMAS ISSUES

Christmas, 1985

1985	Christmas stamps (50 x 12p)	25.00
1986	Christmas stamps (36 x 13p)	7.00
1987	Christmas stamps (36 x 13p)	6.00

GREETINGS ISSUES

Memories, 1992

1992	Memories	11.00
1993	Gift giving	11.50
1994	Messages	11.00
1995	Art	11.00
1996	Cartoons	11.00
1997	Flowers	11.00

SPECIAL PACKS

British Films, 1985

1971	NABA Exhibition	
	(definitives ½p to £1 and postage dues)	85.00
1972	Belgica Exhibition	
	(1971 Christmas and 1972 Village Churches sets)	5.00
1972	Royal Silver Wedding	2.00
1973	County Cricket	4.00
1973	Palace of Westminster	
	(Parliamentary Conference set)	4.00
1974	Winston Churchill	2.50
1975	Railways	2.50
1977	Silver Jubilee	2.00
1978	25th Anniversary of Coronation	2.00
1981	Royal Wedding	2.00
1982	Electronic Post (Information Technology set)	£175
1984	Royal Mail (Mail Coaches set)	4.00
1985	British Films	5.00
1986	The Queen's Birthday	5.00
1988	Australian Bicentennary	7.50
1990	Penny Black Anniversary	
	(set of five stamps and miniature sheet)	10.50
1994	Channel Tunnel (joint issue with France)	35.00
1997	Royal Golden Wedding	
	(Queen's Horses and Golden Wedding sets)	20.00
2000	Stamp Show 2000	
	(mint and cancelled miniature sheets)	70.00
2000	Stamp Show 2000	
	(The Definitive Portrait, Profile On Print and	
	Special By Design prestige stamp books)	£100
2004	Entente Cordiale (joint issue with France)	12.00
2005	World Heritage (joint issue with Australia)	25.00
2008	Lest We Forget collection	
	(2006, 2007 and 2008 miniature sheets)	35.00
2009	Brilliant Britain collection	
	(2006 Celebrating Scotland, 2007 Celebrating	
	England, 2008 Celebrating Northern Ireland	
	and 2009 Celebrating Wales miniature sheets)	30.00
2009	Military Uniforms collection	
	(2007, 2008, and 2009 miniature sheets)	30.00
2011	Harry Potter Heroes and Villains	
	(Magical Realms block of 10)	12.00

FACSIMILE PACKS

Penny Black, 2000

2000	1840 Penny Black (Stamp Show 2000)	60.00
2010	1929 PUC £1 (London 2010)	17.50
2011	1841 Penny Red (170th anniversary)	9.00
2012	1948 Olympic Games set (London Olympics)	35.00
2013	1913 Seahorses set (100th anniversary)	15.00
2014	Festival of Britain 2½d	11.00

MINIATURE SHEET PACKS

Miniature Sheets, 2005

2005	Miniature Sheets collection	65.00
2006	Miniature Sheets collection	80.00
2007	Miniature Sheets collection	60.00
2008	Miniature Sheets collection	60.00
2009	Miniature Sheets collection	60.00
2010	Miniature Sheets collection	55.00
2011	Miniature Sheets collection	£130
2012	Miniature Sheets collection	60.00
2013	Miniature Sheets collection	70.00
2014	Miniature Sheets collection	40.00
2015	Miniature Sheets collection	70.00
2016	Miniature Sheets collection	70.00
2017	Miniature Sheets collection	85.00
2018	Miniature Sheets collection	85.00

sold directly to Collectors. If you wish to benefit by up to 50% or more, depending upon your circumstance and type of material, by cutting out the middleman – then this offer may be for you. Generally 'time' is the enemy in our lives, and for most dealers not being able to sell stock. Now is the time to let 'time' do the 'heavy-lifting' and consider making 'time' work for you, so that at UPA you can make time your friend. 👍

14 AND the SMALL PRINT? Some lots are too small in value for us to offer this system. Other lots may not be suited to selling in this manner (e.g. surplus mint British decimal stamps best used for postage) – especially if the market is heavily compromised by stock overhang in specific areas. Some Collectors will not wish to use time and systems to leverage price, others will want to agree a specific price and know that they are paid precisely this amount. No client is treated like a number and no client is forced like a square peg into a round hole. ☀

15 OK, What Do I Do Next?

a). You contact UPA to discuss with Andrew or a highly-qualified Auction Valuer/Describer what you have to dispose of and your options bearing in mind your specific interests / requirements

b). If you wish, get a 2nd opinion, but investigate what type of auction / dealer you are dealing with. Is it a Dealer's auction with relatively few collectors? Can you see where / how the Dealer sells? If you can't easily see any pricelists or high quality selling catalogues – that Dealer may sell your stamps to other dealers…

c). Finally you ask U P A to collect your stamps, insure in transit for an estimated replacement retail value…☎ 🖥 🚚

16 What Happens then? A member of my Team telephones/e-mails you to confirm safe receipt. 'Overnight' valuations, unless simple, are rare. Valuing stamp collections that have taken tens of years to create takes time. Depending upon your priorities / timescale I, or an experienced member of my Team will contact you to discuss your requirements and the options available to you for the sale

Contact UPA: 01451 861 111

of your collection. Provided only that you feel well-informed and comfortable do we agree strategy 📋 ✍

17 How Strong is the Stamp and Cover Market? Everybody knows that the strongest areas are GB and British Empire. Post-Independence / QEII material sells but if hinged at considerable discount. Mint hinged material pre 1952 is regarded as the

industry 'norm' and therefore desirable – but genuine never-hinged commands a premium. Europe sells but at reduced levels, Americas is good, as generally is Asia but the 'heat' has come off China which is still good – and Russia which can still be good. East Europe is weaker. Overall, Rarities throughout can command their own price levels and real Postal History has good demand.

18 What Should I Do Next? Discuss your collection with U P A. Contact Andrew or an experienced member of his Team now… 🖥 ☎

19 Guarantee: I want You to be absolutely Sure So If You're not sure we'll transport and return your stamps for FREE up to £200 in actual shipping cost at our expense. It sounds generous (and it is), but it's far less than the cost of driving 100+ miles each way and 3 to 6 hours in your home valuing your stamps 😊

20 My Double Cast Iron Guarantee: We can do a better job valuing your stamps in our office than in your home. If you don't agree I'll pay you an extra $50 for you to pay somebody trusted to open the boxes and put your albums back, in the same place, on the shelf they came from. 😊 😊

21 Act NOW: Contact Andrew or an experienced member of his Team using the on-line selling form at our website, by fax, telephone or by mail. We'll work harder for you not to regret the decision to sell all or part of your collection…☎ 🖥

Andrew McGavin, Philatelic Expert,
Author, Managing Director
Universal Philatelic Auctions UPA

Request Your Next FREE Catalogue NOW

UNIVERSAL PHILATELIC AUCTIONS (BSMV)
4 The Old Coalyard, West End, Northleach, Glos. GL54 3HE UK
Tel: 01451 861111 • Fax: 01451 861297

www.upastampauctions.co.uk • info@upastampauctions.co.uk

YEAR BOOKS & PACKS

In this section, prices are quoted for packs in mint condition only.

YEAR PACKS

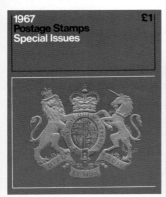

Year Pack, 1967

1967 year pack	3.50
1968 year pack (blue cover)	3.50
1968 year pack (red cover)	3.50
1968 year pack (German version)	£100
1969 year pack	10.00
1970 year pack	15.00
1971 year pack	22.00
1972 year pack	14.00
1973 year pack	12.50
1974 year pack	6.00
1975 year pack	5.00
1976 year pack	7.50
1977 year pack	5.00
1978 year pack	4.50
1979 year pack	6.00
1980 year pack	7.00
1981 year pack	9.50
1982 year pack	12.50
1983 year pack	15.00
1984 year pack	17.00
1985 year pack	17.00
1986 year pack	17.00
1987 year pack	17.00
1988 year pack	17.00
1989 year pack	17.00
1990 year pack	19.00
1991 year pack	20.00
1992 year pack	20.00
1993 year pack	22.00
1994 year pack	29.00
1995 year pack	27.00
1996 year pack	32.00
1997 year pack	34.00

1998 year pack	42.00
1999 year pack	65.00
2000 year pack	65.00
2001 year pack	70.00
2002 year pack	68.00
2003 year pack	76.00
2004 year pack	70.00
2005 year pack	70.00
2006 year pack	70.00
2007 year pack	£125
2008 year pack	90.00

Year Pack, 2009

2009 year pack	£110
2010 year pack	£140
2011 year pack	£150
2012 year pack	£180
2013 year pack	£150
2014 year pack	£140
2015 year pack	£160
2016 year pack	£165
2017 year pack	£160
2018 year pack	£180

YEAR BOOKS

Year Book, 1984

1984 year book	45.00
1985 year book	30.00
1986 year book	25.00
1987 year book	14.00
1988 year book	14.00
1989 year book	15.00
1990 year book	18.00
1991 year book	18.50
1992 year book	19.00
1993 year book	22.00
1994 year book	23.00
1995 year book	23.00
1996 year book	22.00
1997 year book	27.00
1998 year book	37.00
1999 year book	50.00
2000 year book	50.00
2001 year book	50.00
2002 year book	50.00
2003 year book	55.00
2004 year book	60.00
2005 year book	60.00
2006 year book	75.00
2007 year book	90.00
2008 year book	£100

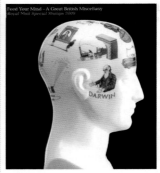

Year Book, 2009

2009 year book	£100
2010 year book	£120
2011 year book	£135
2012 year book	£325
2013 year book	£160
2014 year book	£165
2015 year book	£185
2016 year book	£185
2017 year book	£185
2018 year book	£195

KEY CONTACTS

To help you find your way around the hobby, here are contact details for the major players in British philately

ROYAL MAIL
■ **Philatelic Bureau**
Tallents House, 21 South Gyle Crescent,
Edinburgh EH12 9PB.
Tel: 08457 641641 (orders)
www.royalmail.com/stamps
■ **London Special Handstamp Centre**
Royal Mail, Mount Pleasant, Farringdon Road,
London EC1A 1BB.
■ **Northern Special Handstamp Centre**
Royal Mail, Tallents House, 21 South Gyle Crescent,
Edinburgh EH12 9PB.
■ **Wales & The West Special Handstamp Centre**
Royal Mail, 220–228 Penarth Road, Cardiff CF11 8TA.

PHILATELIC COLLECTIONS
■ **British Library**
96 Euston Road, London NW1 2DB.
Tel: 020 7412 7635
www.collectbritain.co.uk
■ **The Postal Museum**
Phoenix Place, London WC1X 0DA.
Tel: 020 7239 2570
www.postalmuseum.org
■ **Royal Philatelic Collection**
www.royal.gov.uk

SOCIETIES
■ **Royal Philatelic Society London**
15 Abchurch Lane, London EC4N 7BW.
www.rpsl.org.uk
■ **National Philatelic Society**
www.ukphilately.org.uk/nps
■ **Great Britain Philatelic Society**
www.gbps.org.uk
■ **Association of British Philatelic Societies**
www.abps.org.uk
■ **Machin Collectors Club**
www.machins.org
■ **Modern British Philatelic Circle**
www.mbp-circle.co.uk
■ **Association of Great Britain First Day Cover Collectors**
www.gbfdc.co.uk
■ **British Thematic Association**
www.brit-thematic-assoc.com
■ **Philatelic Traders Society**
PO Box 290, Lingfield, Surrey RH7 9AX.
www.thephilatelictraderssociety.co.uk

EXHIBITIONS
■ **Stampex**
www.thephilatelictraderssociety.co.uk

COLLECTIONS

(15) 2d BLUE COLLECTION
The complete 1858 2d Blue collection. SG45 plates 7-15 (7) all good - fine used examples (SG Cat £351)
OUR PRICE: £50

(16) QV, KEVII & KGV COLLECTION
Over 120 issues to include 1840 1d Black and 2d Blue plus a splendid range of Victorian, Edwardian & Georgian stamps, good to fine used to include a £1 Value (SG Cat £4800+)
EACH COLLECTION CONTAINS A QV 10/- VALUE & KEVII 5/-
OUR PRICE: £620.00

(17) GREAT BRITAIN Fiscal and Revenue
Issues 1855 - 1950
Includes Victoria £1
Issues x2
An inexpensive collection
25 types - **£5.95**
50 types - **£12.50**

(18) THE QV & KEVII COLLECTION
1d black up to 1910 & includes 1883 10/- A marvellous collection of 100 stamps which includes plate variations and Officials all good to fine used. (SG Cat £3800)
OUR PRICE: £395

(19) KGV CONTROLS
SG351 - 395.
½d - 1/-

Each stamp mint hinged with original marginal sheet Control numbers (only 1 printed on each sheet), Set of 14 (1x9d) £57
Do. SG 393a scarce 9d Olive (1 stamp) £85

(20). ANCIENT POSTALLY USED LETTERS
All with postal markings & hand surcharges showing amount of postage paid.

King George III, 1738-1820	Reigned 1760-1820	£10.50
King George IV, 1762-1830	Reigned 1820-1830	£7.50
King William IV, 1765-1837	Reigned 1830-1837	£5.50
Queen Victoria, 1819-1901	Reigned 1837-1901	£4.50
	Or ONE from each reign	£27

(23) QV-KEVII ISSUES ONLY!
1841-1911 A collection of over 30 different types. Includes QV to 1/- & KEVII to 2/6d. Collectable stamps with slight faults. (SG CAT £625)
OUR PRICE: £42.00

(24) GB PARCELS
For over 40 years we have pleased many thousands of customers with these mixed Lots of Great Britain stamps. We have previously offered these as either "Treasure Parcels" or "The GB Box". Our regular customers will confirm these Lots are ALWAYS EXCELLENT VALUE, to include stamps, covers, and part collections that we are currently breaking down. Don't be confused with other dealers catch penny offers, this is not kiloware or 'throw-outs'. Each Lot comes with a no quibble money-back guarantee.

GB Parcel A	Contains around 500 items	£50
GB Parcel B	A Double Lot	£95
GB Box	Around 6kg of stamps & covers in albums QV - QEII	£165
GB Double Box	A very large lot to keep you busy for ages	£300

(25) QV SURFACE PRINTED COLLECTION
1857 - 1880 all better or scarcer types, 3d - 5/- & includes the scarce 1867 5/-. 15 different types (no plate variations), good to fine used and arranged on a stock card (SG Cat £1900+)
OUR PRICE: £200

42 Fisherton Street, Salisbury SP2 7RB - Tel 01722 412100
sales@worldstamps.co.uk - www.worldstamps.co.uk

HAWID MOUNTS FOR GB STAMP COLLECTORS

CUT TO SIZE: GB stamps. Pack of 50   £2.75

		Black	Clear	£
21x24mm	Definitives			
41x24mm	Commems - horizontal			
24x41mm	Commems - vertical			
44x27mm	High values - 1955-1963			
30x35mm	High values - Machin			

CUT TO SIZE: GB stamps. Pack of 50   £3.95

41x30mm	Paintings etc			
30x41mm	Commems - from 1970			
35x37mm	New 'square' Commems			
37x35mm	New 'square' Commems			

STRIPS 210mm Pack of 25   £6.95

21mm	Very small stamps			
24mm	Definitive Commems			
26mm	USA & CANADA Commems			
27.5mm	1955-1963 High values			
29mm	Jersey - Guernsey			
30mm	Modern GB Commems			
31mm	Jersey High Value			
33mm	Misc. Foreign Issues			

All items listed are post-free!

STRIPS 210mm. Packs of 25   £8.75

Height		Black	Clear	£
36mm	GB Machin High values			
39mm	Various Forgeign Issues			
41mm	Modern GB Commems			
44mm	Various Foreign Issues			
48MM	Blocks of 4 GB Issues			
55mm	Blocks of 4			

(BLOCK SIZES - suitable for Blocks, Miniature sheets, Gutter Pairs etc)
(size quoted - height)   **£6.95**

210x66mm				
210x70mm	Pack of 10			
210x76mm	Pack of 10			
210x86mm	Pack of 10			
130x85mm	Pack of 10			
148x105mm	Pack of 10			
160x120mm	Pack of 10			
210x170mm	Pack of 5			
Mixed blocks	Pack of 9 different			

MIXED 'STARTER' PACKS   £3.95

13 Strips Various sizes		

EXTRA LARGE BLOCKS   £10.95

297x210mm	Pack of 5		

GB MINIATURE SHEET   £3.95

122x90mm	Pack of 5		

HAWID GLUE PEN £5.10	HAWID GLUE £2.25

Hawid - NEW PRODUCTS

GB mounts
Pack (black or clear)
350 mounts
7 different sizes
Ref: 6500
£12.95 post paid

Hawid

GB mounts
Pack
200 mounts in black only
4 different sizes
£8.95 post paid

ADVERTISING INDEX